# GENERAL METEOROLOGY

# GENERAL METEOROLOGY

## Horace Robert Byers, Sc.D.

PROFESSOR OF METEOROLOGY
THE UNIVERSITY OF CHICAGO

*THIRD EDITION*

McGRAW-HILL BOOK COMPANY, INC.

New York    Toronto    London

1959

# PREFACE

This book, written at about the level of some of the textbooks of general physics, is intended for the serious student of physical sciences and technology. It presupposes that the reader has taken elementary courses in mechanics and heat and that he has some familiarity with or is concurrently learning calculus. It can form the basis of a course in meteorology to be given as early as the sophomore year for those technical students who have seriously prepared for it, or it may be given as late as the senior year.

This third edition differs from the earlier ones in several aspects. Primarily, of course, it brings the material up to date in this rapidly changing field. Also, the book is now more fundamental in nature than previously. The emphasis on basic material is necessary in order to place the student in a position to branch out into areas of meteorology in which quantitative methods have only recently been used. Furthermore, the applications have become so specialized that a separate book is needed to treat each one, and such specialized books have been appearing in increasing numbers. The author of a book such as this has the satisfaction of knowing that the applications become outdated more rapidly than do the fundamentals.

A number of my colleagues deserve acknowledgment for their help in the task of preparing the manuscript. Dr. James E. McDonald of the University of Arizona and Dr. George W. Platzman of the University of Chicago read and suggested changes in some of the more technical chapters. The illustrations came from many sources and the author is grateful for the prompt and cheerful cooperation of all persons concerned.

*Horace Robert Byers*

# CONTENTS

Ceiling. Cloud Top. Cloud Classification. Meteors (Nonastronomical).
Hydrometeors. Lithometeors. Photometeors. Electrometeors.

The Gas Laws. The Laws of Boyle and Gay-Lussac. Avogadro's Law and
the Meaning of $C$. Equation of State in Different Forms. Effects of
Water Vapor—Virtual Temperature. The First Law of Thermodynamics.
The Concept of Internal Energy. Statement of the First Law. Work Done
by External Forces. The Internal Energy. Application to the Atmos-
phere. Adiabatic Process. Hydrostatic Equation. Adiabatic Tempera-
ture Changes in Terms of Height. Determination of Altitude. Geody-
namic Altitude. Altimeters. Potential Temperature and Stability of
Dry Air. Potential Temperature Defined. Constant $\theta$, Adiabatic and
Isentropic. Distribution of Potential Temperature. The Importance of
Vertical Motions. The Adiabatic Rate of Cooling and the Prevailing
Lapse Rate. Temperature Lapse Rate and Stability. Nature of Vertical
Accelerations. Auto-convective Lapse Rate: Homogeneous Atmosphere.
Layer Stability.

Vapor Pressure and Saturation. Absolute Humidity. Specific Humidity.
The Mixing Ratio. Relative Humidity. Temperature of the Dew Point.
Isentropic-condensation Temperature. Variability of Humidity Quanti-
ties. Water-vapor Content of an Air Column. Change of Phase. The
Adiabatic Process at Saturation. Conditional Instability. The Condensa-
tion Adiabatic Processes and Precipitation. Pseudoadiabatic Process.
Entrainment. The Adiabatic Chart and Thermodynamic Diagram.
Graphical Computations on the Diagrams. Wet-bulb Temperature.
Equivalent Temperature and Equivalent-potential Temperature. Prop-
erties Used in Tracing Air Parcels. Energy Diagrams. Layer Stability,
Convective Instability.

Angular Velocity. Angular-velocity Vector. Component sat a Point on
the Earth. Foucault's Pendulum Experiment. Centripetal Force.
Conservation of Angular Momentum. Apparent and True Gravity.
Motions in Accelerating Coordinate Systems. Inertial, Noninertial
Forces. Quantitative Determination in a Rotating Plane. Coriolis
Acceleration on the Spherical Earth. Pressure Gradient. Balance of
Forces. Geostrophic Balance. Cyclones and Anticyclones. Effects of
Friction. Motion in a Curved Path. Summary of Motions. Representa-
tion on Constant-pressure Surfaces. Other Properties on Constant-pres-
sure Surfaces. Change of the Geostrophic Wind with Height.

Vorticity. Streamline, Stream Function, and Velocity Potential. Circulation and Vorticity. Circulation and Solenoids. Barotropic and Baroclinic Atmospheres. Eulerian Expansion. Continuity and Divergence.
Continuity, Angular Momentum, and Vorticity. The Tendency Equation.
Comment.

Structure and Life Cycle of a Cell.  Thermodynamics of Entrainment and of the Downdraft.  Thunderstorm Weather near the Surface.  Dry Thunderstorms.  Night Thunderstorms.  Development of New Cells.  Hail.  Tornadoes.  Waterspouts.

Classification of Fogs.  Land- and Sea-breeze Fog.  Sea Fog.  Tropical-air Fog.  Steam Fogs.  Ground Fog.  High-inversion Fog.  Advection-radiation Fog.  Upslope Fog.  Prefrontal Fog.  Postfrontal Fog.  Front-passage Fog.  The Fogs of the United States.  Foggy Regions of the Earth.  Smog.  Ice Fog.  Fog Forecasting.

The Search for an Eddy Coefficient.  Eddy Viscosity, Shear, and Momentum Transport.  Wind in the Surface Boundary Layer.  Evaporation.  Reynolds Stresses and Fluxes.  Diffusion from Small Sources.

# CHAPTER 1

## THE SUN AND THE EARTH

That great nuclear reactor, the sun, is the original source of the energy of the atmosphere. When we burn coal in our homes and industrial plants we are using stored-up energy from the sun. Coal represents the fossilized remains of forests that grew thousands of years ago and, just like the forests of today, required sunlight for their growth. Other forms of heat and mechanical energy also are derived from the sun indirectly: oil and its refined products, natural gases, and many chemicals are produced by the sun acting on what once were live organisms. In fact, even our own existence depends on the sun; for without it there would be no plants for food, no fish in the sea, and no animals or other living creatures on the earth. Except as man has learned to duplicate on a relatively minute scale the approximate nuclear reactions of the sun, we owe to this one relatively small star practically all forms of energy available on our planet. The energy furnished us by other stars and celestial bodies is negligible by comparison, as is also the heat coming out from the hot interior of the earth. We shall learn in this book that the sun is of great importance in meteorology and that all natural meteorological phenomena can be traced to the manner in which the energy from the sun is received over different parts of the earth.

Because of the importance of the sun, every student of meteorology should be familiar with it, particularly in its relationship to the earth. For the purposes of this book, only a few outstanding facts will be considered. Elementary textbooks of astronomy usually contain a fairly complete chapter on the sun, and the student is referred to them.

Among other things, these books relate that the sun (at least the outer portion of it) is a mass of flaming gas having a temperature of about 6000°K or about 10,300°F. Most of its heat is wasted, as far as we are concerned, by passing out into endless space, only an infinitesimally small portion of the whole output being intercepted by the earth and other planets. Yet to us this *relatively* small amount of heat which we receive from the sun represents a huge store of energy.

1

**Motions of the Earth.**   The movement of the earth with which we are most familiar is its *rotation*.   Once every 24 hr with respect to the sun, it makes a complete rotation eastward about an axis through the poles. This rotation is the cause of the most obvious of all time periods, i.e., the alternation of day and night which comes about as the sun shines on the different parts of the earth exposed to it within the 24 hr.   Our 24-hr day is established and our timepieces are set in accordance with this rotational period of the earth.   For purposes of computations involving the motions of the earth it is convenient to use reference points fixed by the mean position of the stars instead of the sun.   In these terms the *sidereal day* of 23 hr 56 min 4.09 sec replaces the 24-hr *mean solar day*.   Discussions of this problem can be found in textbooks of astronomy.

Another movement of the earth is its *revolution*.   It revolves eastward around the sun once in approximately 365¼ days at a variable speed that averages 18½ miles per sec.   Its orbit is an ellipse of slight eccentricity having the sun as one focus.

An ellipse is a plane curve such that the sum of the distances of any point on the curve from two fixed points, called the *foci*, is constant.   An

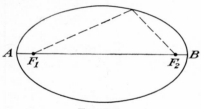

ellipse can be constructed as shown in Fig. 1–1 with a slack string tied to two nails $F_1$ and $F_2$ (the foci). The sum of the distances of the curve from the two foci is the length of the string, which is constant. The line $AB$ through the foci is called the *major axis*.   The *eccentricity* is the distance between the

Fig. 1–1.

two foci divided by the distance between $A$ and $B$.   As the eccentricity approaches zero, the form of the ellipse approaches that of a circle, i.e., the foci converge toward a single point.   The eccentricity of the orbit of the earth is very near zero.

Two other movements of the earth have been noted by astronomers, but they are of little consequence to meteorology.   One is the *precessional motion*, which is a slow conical movement of the earth's axis, like that of a spinning top, but making, at the present rate, a single complete turn in about 26,000 years.   Another is the *solar motion*, in which the whole solar system, including the earth, is flying through space at 12 miles a second in the general direction of the star Vega.

The rotation and revolution of the earth are the motions of most significance in meteorology.   The rotation indirectly accounts for the *diurnal* changes in the weather, such as the warming up during the daytime and the cooling off at night, diurnal changes in the wind velocity, cloudiness, and other phenomena, including land and sea breezes, air drainage, etc.

**The Earth's Revolution.** The revolution of the earth is associated with the *seasonal* changes. If the plane of the orbit were in the plane of the earth's equator, then there would be very little seasonal change. At *perihelion*, when the earth describing its ellipse in space reaches the major axis at the end nearest the sun, the greatest intensity of total solar radiation will be received; and, when the earth is at *aphelion*, which is the farthest end of the major axis, a minimum of solar heating will be experienced. This difference in amount of solar radiation received over

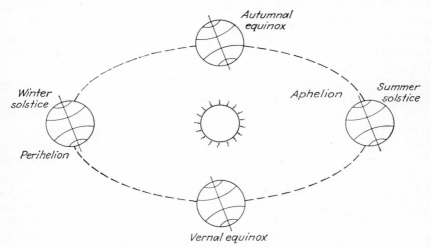

FIG. 1–2. The revolution of the earth and the seasons.

the earth as a whole is extremely small compared with the seasonal variations known to exist from another cause.

A study of Fig. 1–2 reveals the real explanation of the seasons. The plane of the equator is inclined at an angle of 23½° from the plane of the earth's orbit. This means that the axis of the earth is inclined at an angle of 23½° from the perpendicular to the plane of the orbit. The direction toward which the axis is inclined is very nearly in the major axis of the ellipse. Therefore, the *solstices*, the places where this inclination is toward the sun, are very near the points of perihelion and aphelion. The *winter solstice*, when the sun, with respect to the earth, is farthest south, occurs just a few days before perihelion. (Note that the earth is nearest the sun during the winter of the Northern Hemisphere.)[1]

---

[1] To illustrate the difference in energy received from the sun at perihelion and at aphelion, we may consider the amount received at the equator at about the time of the solstices when the altitude of the sun north of the equator in summer is the same as the

At that time the sun is directly overhead at noon in lat 23½°S. The *summer solstice*, when the sun, with respect to the earth, is farthest north, occurs just a few days before aphelion. At that time the sun is directly overhead at noon in lat 23½°N. At two points midway between the solstices, a line drawn from the sun to the earth is perpendicular to the plane of inclination of the earth's axis so that the sun shines equally in both hemispheres. These are the *equinoxes*, the *vernal equinox* occurring in the spring and the *autumnal equinox* in the fall. The approximate dates of these significant points or events are vernal equinox, Mar. 21; summer solstice, June 22; autumnal equinox, Sept. 23; and winter solstice, Dec. 22. The dates vary slightly on account of our system of leap years. The time from the vernal equinox to the summer solstice is sometimes denoted as spring; from then until the autumnal equinox as summer; autumn, from the autumnal equinox to the winter solstice; then winter until the next vernal equinox. An examination of weather records shows that these dates have only a very general meaning as far as meteorology is concerned.

In astronomy it has been found convenient for purposes of reference in making measurements and computations to assume that the earth is fixed in space and to speak of the "apparent motion" of the sun and stars. The plane in which the apparent motion of the sun takes place is called the *ecliptic plane*. It is obvious that this is the same as the plane of the earth's orbit. It is inclined at an angle of 23½° to the plane of the *celestial equator*, which is the extension into space of the earth's equatorial plane. The equinoxes are at the intersection of the two planes. The vernal equinox is found where the sun in its apparent motion in the ecliptic crosses the celestial equator going northward, and the autumnal equinox is at the intersection as the sun is going southward.

**The Tropics and Polar Circles.** The latitude circles of 23½° N and S are called the *Tropic of Cancer* and *Tropic of Capricorn*, respectively. They are the highest latitudes from the equator where the sun can be observed directly overhead, and then only one day each during the year. As a consequence of the inclination of the earth's axis, when the sun shines directly on lat 23½° in one hemisphere, the portion of the earth poleward from $90 - 23½ = 66½°$ in the other hemisphere

---

altitude in the south in winter. From Sir Napier Shaw's "Manual of Meteorology," vol. 2, Cambridge University Press, London, 1926, we obtain the value for Dec. 20 when the sun passes through the zenith 23°26′ south of the equator, a total of 977 kilowatthours of energy per 100 m² of horizontal surface received at the top of the atmosphere over the equator. On June 21 when the sun is at 23°27′N, 915 kilowatthours per 100 m² are received at the equator. The difference is less than 7 per cent. At 40°N lat, however, we receive more than three times as much energy at the summer solstice as at the winter solstice.

is without sunlight. For the Northern and Southern Hemispheres these latitude circles are called the *Arctic* and *Antarctic Circles*, respectively. Every point poleward from these circles has at least one day of darkness during the year. At the poles there are 6 months without sun and 6 months with continuous sunlight between the equinoxes.

In Fig. 1–2, where the earth is viewed from the side, the Arctic Circle and the two tropics are shown, the equator being omitted. If the rays from the sun are considered as coming in parallel lines, the darkening of the arctic regions during winter is apparent, as is also the pre-ponderance of daylight in these latitudes during summer. With a little imagination it is easy to see how these things occur in opposite phase in the antarctic regions. To try this experimentally, one may take an apple and revolve it around a light in a room with the stem of the apple (the north pole) always pointed toward one corner of the ceiling. When the apple is between the light and the corner, conditions representa-tive of the winter solstice will be noted, whereas, with the light between the apple and the corner, the conditions at the summer solstice will be noted. If, in addition, the apple is rotated around the axis while it revolves around the light source, the diurnal period will be shown, and some idea of the length of the day in different latitudes and between one season and another will be obtained.

**Duration and Intensity of Sunshine.** The lengthening or shortening of the period of daylight at a given latitude follows the increase or decrease in the meridian angle of the sun above the southern horizon in the Northern Hemisphere and above the northern horizon in the Southern Hemisphere. Thus, during summer the temperatures are higher in our latitudes, not only because the sun shines more directly and therefore more intensely on the surface of the earth, but also because it shines

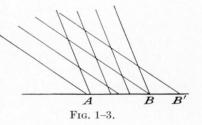

Fig. 1–3.

for a greater number of hours. These two effects are shown in Figs. 1–3 and 1–4. In Fig. 1–3, let the lines intersecting the ground represent a bundle of rays from the sun representing a given amount of energy. As these rays strike the ground obliquely, as in winter, the energy is distributed over an area whose width is the distance from $A$ to $B'$. In summer, with the sun nearly overhead, the same bundle of rays falls on the area whose width is $AB$, which, it will be noted, is considerably less than $AB'$. In other words, the energy is concentrated and there-fore received over a given surface with greater *intensity* in summer. Figure 1–4 illustrates the length of the day as dependent on the angular

size of the arc forming the apparent path of the sun across the sky.
In winter the arc inscribed by the apparent motion of the sun is smaller
than in summer.

In Fig. 1–5 the approximate values of the altitude angles of the noon
sun at Washington, D.C., are plotted for the twenty-first day of each

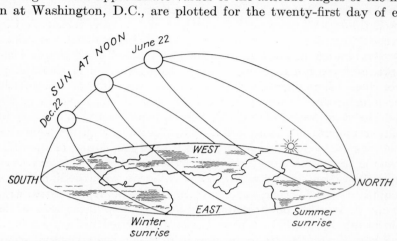

FIG. 1–4. Seasonal variations of the length of day as illustrated by the arc of the path
of the sun.

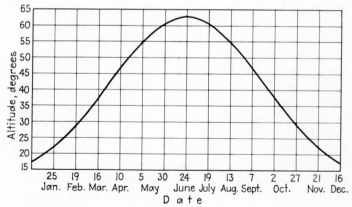

FIG. 1–5. Altitude angle of the noon sun at Washington, D.C., during the course of
the year.

month and joined with a smooth curve. A curve of this nature is useful
in showing the different rates at which the sun's noon altitude angle
increases. Near the time of the vernal equinox the sun is rapidly assuming a higher and higher noon position in the Northern Hemisphere, but as
summer approaches, it does not change its altitude so much from one day

to the next. The same thing in a reverse sense is noted in the fall. In midsummer and midwinter the changes are relatively slight, and the sun hovers awhile near its highest or lowest position before starting its apparent seasonal ascent or descent. This is meteorologically important in two ways. First, spring and autumn are then really transition seasons between the two more constant seasons, winter and summer. Second, the vernal warming and autumnal cooling are favored by the year's greatest rate of change of noon altitude of the sun.

**The Lag of the Seasons.** Curve 4 in Fig. 1–6 is constructed from a plot of the mean temperatures for each day of the year at Washington, D.C., as determined from 50 consecutive years of observations. It is reproduced here to show how the temperature trend lags behind the changes in the sun's altitude. If the temperature depended solely on the amount of radiation received from the sun at a given time, the temperature would be highest in June and lowest in December, or, to be more specific, May, June, and July would be the three warmest months and November, December, and January the three coldest. Actually, June, July, and August are the warmest months and December, January, and February the coldest.

This lag is accounted for on the basis of the time required for heating and cooling. One may have a roaring fire in a stove to heat a room in the early morning on a cold day, but the temperature in the room will not reach its highest point until later on, even though the fire may have died down by that time. Conditions in the heating of the earth by the sun are somewhat analogous. The same lag is also noticed in the diurnal period of solar heating. The highest temperatures occur not at noon when the sun is most intense but about three hours later. A discussion of the differences between land and sea surfaces with respect to heating and cooling will be found in a subsequent chapter.

An object in space, such as the earth, can give off heat as well as receive it. For a certain rate of gain of heat the object may undergo no change in temperature if it loses the heat as rapidly as it gains it. For the earth as a whole, there is no net gain or loss of heat, but through the year at a given latitude, e.g., in the Northern Hemisphere, outside the tropics, the heat received exceeds the heat lost until sometime in August, when the heat lost begins to exceed that received. Cooling then predominates until sometime in February, when the heat gained begins to exceed the heat lost. The process is complicated somewhat by the transport of heat and cold from various regions by the winds.

**Solar Radiation.** In Chap. 2 the nature of radiation will be discussed in some detail. It is assumed here that the reader is familiar with the fact that the energy of the sun is transmitted to us as radiant energy, a part of which is depleted in passing through the atmosphere.

*Solar-radiation Measurements.* Not all of the solar radiation measured in the atmosphere comes directly from the sun. If the measuring apparatus is pointed at a portion of the sky away from the sun, an appreciable amount of incoming energy recognizable as of solar origin is detected. This is called sky radiation. It is the downward-directed component of solar radiation that is scattered in all directions by the air molecules and by fine, dustlike particles that are suspended in the atmosphere.

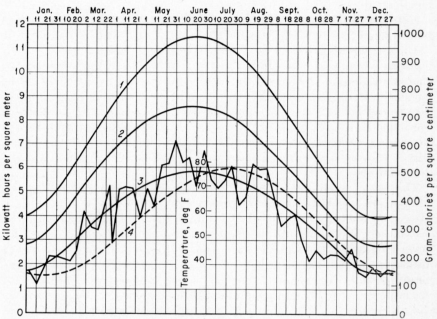

FIG. 1–6. Solar radiation and temperature. Curve 1, computed daily insolation outside the atmosphere at the latitude of Washington, D.C. Curve 2, insolation received at the ground at Washington, with cloudless sky. Curve 3, the same for average sky conditions. Curve 4, normal daily-temperature curve for Washington. The irregular solid line represents actually observed weekly values of daily total solar and sky radiation at Washington during a representative year—1925.

*Scattering* in the atmosphere will be treated in greater detail in Chap. 2. It is a phenomenon that exists because of the presence of the atmosphere and it would not be observed outside the atmosphere.

Most solar-radiation measurements are concerned with the total radiation—direct solar plus sky radiation. To establish standards and to study solar-terrestrial relationships, direct solar-radiation measurements are necessary. Most of the standards and other data used in this work were obtained by the Smithsonian Institution during several years of pioneering effort, mainly at its solar observatories at Mount Wilson and

Table Mountain, California. In particular the Smithsonian measurements have been directed toward obtaining the value of the solar constant. This is defined as the amount of solar radiant energy received per minute outside the atmosphere on a surface of 1 cm² normal to the incident radiation at the earth's mean distance from the sun. The technique of these measurements will not be discussed here but may be found in the various reports of the Smithsonian Institution.[1] The Smithsonian standard value of the solar constant, originally computed in 1913, is 1.94 g-cal cm$^{-2}$ min$^{-1}$. This value is frequently accepted as a standard even though it is thought to be in error by as much as 3 per cent.

Meteorologists are more concerned with what is usually called the *insolation*, which is the rate at which the total solar energy—direct plus sky radiation—is received on a *horizontal* surface. This would be the same as the solar constant only if the surface were at the outside of the atmosphere and the sun were directly overhead at its mean distance from the earth. The insolation received at the surface of the earth depends upon the solar constant, the distance from the sun, the inclination of the sun's rays, and the amount depleted while passing through the atmosphere.

The solar radiation is measured by instruments called *pyrheliometers*. They operate on the principle of an indirect measurement based upon temperature effects of the radiation falling upon an absorbing element. For direct solar-radiation measurements the Smithsonian silver-disk pyrheliometer or the Marvin pyrheliometer is used. In these instruments the rays of the sun are permitted to fall on a blackened surface for a period of one minute. The increase in temperature produced by the absorption of this radiation is an indication of the amount of energy received.

For obtaining records of total solar and sky radiation on a horizontal surface, the U.S. Weather Bureau uses the Eppley thermoelectrical pyrheliometer. This instrument consists of two concentric circular rings of equal area, one blackened and the other painted white. A thermocouple with one junction on the lower side of the black ring and the other on the white ring records the differential in temperature between the two rings. The electromotive force created between the hot (black) junction and the cold (white) junction is very nearly proportional to the amount of radiation received. For a description of thermocouples and their uses, the reader is referred to textbooks on physics.

A continuous curve or plot of the radiation values throughout the day is made by means of a recording potentiometer. Hourly radiation totals are obtained from the record sheet by a mechanical integration

---

[1] For recent data determined from high-altitude rockets, see Johnson, F. S., The Solar Constant, *J. Meteorol.*, vol. 11, p. 431, 1954.

of the curves with a planimeter, and the daily totals can be obtained
in a similar way.  The measurements are usually expressed in gram-
calories per square centimeter per minute.  Frequently the *langley* is
used as the unit equivalent to 1 g-cal per $cm^2$.  The unit is named in
honor of S. P. Langley (1834–1906), noted physicist and astronomer of
the Smithsonian Institution.

Figure 1–6, taken from papers by H. H. Kimball, shows the daily
totals of solar radiation on a horizontal surface at Washington, D.C.
under different sky conditions.  Also shown are the daily averages of air
temperatures.  Curve 1 represents the computed insolation outside the

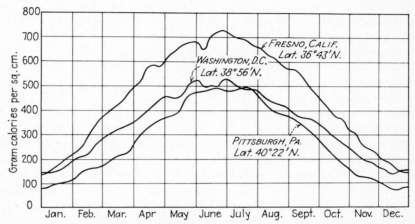

Fig. 1–7. Average daily insolation received through the year at selected United States
stations.  (*I. F. Hand.*)

atmosphere at the latitude of Washington, D.C., while curve 2 shows
the insolation received at the ground at Washington with cloudless sky,
and curve 3 is the same for average sky conditions.  It will be noted
that curve 1 is symmetrical with respect to the solstices, but that the
normal daily temperature curve for Washington (curve 4) shows the usual
seasonal lag.  The irregular solid line represents the actually observed
weekly averages at Washington during 1925, reproduced here to show the
many irregularities in the amount of radiation received from week to
week.  The other curves are smooth because they represent mean values.
Other curves showing the radiation received at other places are shown
in Fig. 1–7.  Since the three stations are in nearly the same latitude, the
differences can be ascribed to differences in the amount of cloudiness and
of city smoke.

# CHAPTER 2

# THE NATURE OF RADIATION

A fairly thorough knowledge of radiation processes in the atmosphere, particularly as they involve the exchange of heat between the earth's surface and its atmospheric envelope, is important in many phases of meteorological work. Such problems as the occurrence of fogs and low clouds, frost protection, prediction of cold waves, etc., involve radiation applications.

**Types of Heat Transfer.** Three types of heat transfer are recognized by physicists and meteorologists, viz., conduction, convection (horizontal as well as vertical), and radiation. Heat *conduction* is a form of heat transfer with which everyone is familiar through ordinary observation, such as when one holds an iron rod with one end in a hot flame and experiences a heating of the other end by conduction from the hot part. Most metals are good conductors of heat, whereas fluids and, particularly, gases are poor conductors. In most meteorological problems heat conduction need not be taken into consideration because in the atmosphere it is of extremely small magnitude in comparison with the other processes of heat transfer. It is important in considering the small details of heat transfer, especially under certain circumstances within centimeters of the surface.

*Convection* involves the transfer of heat by means of mass motions of the medium through which the heat is transferred. This is possible only in fluids or gases, because they alone have internal mass motions. In rigid bodies, of course, this type of transfer cannot occur. In convection, the moving masses carry with them heat acquired by conduction in their previous positions. The motion itself is sometimes referred to as convection, although properly convection should be only a measure of the rate of heat transfer by the mass motions. Since the atmosphere is a medium in which mass motions are easily started, convection is found to be one of the chief ways in which heat is transferred there. This transfer may be accomplished either by vertical or by horizontal motions. In ordinary meteorological parlance, however, the vertical motions are usually meant when speaking of convection. This is mainly because

11

the horizontal convection is on a much greater scale, involving the slow heat transfer from the equatorial to the polar regions, whereas vertical convection may cover an area about the size of a single cloud and proceeds at a fairly rapid rate.

Horizontal convection transport is called *advection*. For the earth as a whole, it is the most important means of heat transfer. The pronounced day-to-day changes in weather observed in most middle-latitude regions are due to the interplay of great advectional currents. Ordinarily the horizontal components of air motions are greater and more sustained than the vertical components.

Part of the convectional system of heat transport is the heat exchange involved in evaporation and condensation. When water is evaporated from the surface of the earth, heat is removed that is carried latent in the water vapor to be released again when the vapor condenses to form clouds or surface condensation products such as dew and frost. The heat transported to the clouds and released there by this process is quite appreciable.

Also included in the convective transport as we are now considering it is that type of vertical convection which is forced by wind action. This is usually called *mechanical turbulence*. It accounts for important heat exchanges next to the ground. For example, by transporting heat downward, it partly compensates for the net loss of heat by radiation during a windy night.

Both conduction and convection depend on the existence of a material medium that is solid, fluid, or gaseous. *Radiation* is the only means by which heat can be transferred through space without the aid of a material medium. In our everyday experience we meet with examples of radiation. The ordinary steam or hot-water radiator used in homes and buildings is really not a radiator at all, because it is so constructed that the heating of the room is accomplished mainly through convection, although some radiation heat also is involved. If we were to depend upon heating a room by radiation only, a fireplace would be in order. In this case, the convection currents rise up mainly through the chimney, and much of the heat carried by convection is lost. We can warm our bodies by standing in front of the fireplace, but considering the amount of fuel consumed, the temperature of the room is raised but little. The heating of the air in the room itself depends on the small amount of convective transport that may occur either from the fire directly into the room or from objects in the room that may themselves have been heated by the radiation from the fire. The air itself absorbs directly only a very small amount of this radiation.

In the interplanetary space between the sun and the earth where a relatively minute quantity of matter exists, radiation is the only important form of heat transfer. A material medium through which the radiation can pass is said to be *transparent* to that radiation.

**Radiant Energy and Light.** Radiant energy or radiated heat cannot be easily distinguished from light. As a matter of fact, the differentiation between the radiation of heat and the radiation of light is based only on the scope of our visual perceptions. Energy that comes to us as visible light represents only a certain portion of the radiation from a hot body such as the sun. A large quantity of it is invisible. Even cold bodies emit radiation, but none of it is visible.

Although our knowledge of the exact nature of all forms of radiation is still incomplete, physicists have learned that, with respect to many of its most important properties, radiant energy acts as if it were transmitted in the form of waves similar to radio waves but much shorter. Certain aspects of it are better considered as particle emanations, especially in radioactive substances, cosmic rays, etc., which, in the wave concept, correspond to extremely small wavelengths ($10^{-10}$ to $10^{-8}$ cm). In meteorology, the radiation usually is of such a form and the problems of such a nature that treatment from the wave point of view is preferable.

Some of the radiation is in what is called the *visible range*, i.e., it can be detected by the human eye. That of a wavelength too short to be observed may be classed as *ultraviolet radiation* and the long-wave type as *infrared radiation*. Just as in the case of light radiation, all radiant energy travels in straight paths through space and at all wavelengths the speed is the same, viz., that of light, which is known to be 186,000 miles per sec, or $3 \times 10^{10}$ cm per sec = 300,000 km per sec.

Wavelengths of radiation usually are given in microns (abbreviated $\mu$) or in angstrom units. A micron is $10^{-4}$ cm (0.0001 cm), and an angstrom (A) is $10^{-8}$ cm (0.00000001 cm).

The wavelengths of the visible range are those lying between 0.4 and 0.7 $\mu$, or 4000 and 7000 A. The sun radiates its maximum energy at wavelengths within the visible range. A perfectly radiating body at a temperature of 300° K radiates at maximum energy in wavelengths of 10 to 15 $\mu$, or 100,000 to 150,000 A, which would be in the infrared range. In meteorology, only those wavelengths between about 0.1 and 30 $\mu$ are of practical importance, although future discoveries may well show the importance of other wavelengths.

**The Spectrum.** When light or radiant energy is arranged or displayed in proper order in its component colors or wavelengths, we have the *spectrum* of the radiation. Students are usually introduced to the visible part of the solar spectrum through a classroom demonstration of sunlight dispersed by passing through a glass prism to display the different colors, ranging from the violet, in the shortest visible wavelengths, to the blues, greens, yellows, and reds. A body emitting radiation shows a characteristic distribution of energy emitted over the various wave-lengths under given temperature conditions of the body. With proper apparatus, this distribution can be analyzed in detail and the results can then be presented as plots of emissive power against wavelength for different temperatures. Such a plot is often called the emission spectrum of the body at the temperature in question. The spectrum of the sun shows a peak of emissive power in the visible wavelengths, but about half its total emission is outside the visible range in the infrared and ultraviolet wavelengths.

The spectrum sometimes is given in terms of frequency, in which we recognize that the product of wavelength and frequency is the speed of propagation—in this case the speed of light (300,000 km or 186,300 miles per sec). The wavelength or frequency is a characteristic property of

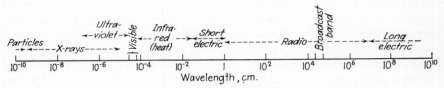

Fig. 2–1. The electromagnetic spectrum.

nearly all radiations found in nature or produced artificially, including long radio waves at one extreme and waves so short as to perhaps be better treated as particle emanations at the other extreme. All of these waves form a continuous arrangement which goes by the general name of *electromagnetic spectrum*. This continuous spectrum arrangement is illustrated diagrammatically in Fig. 2–1.

**Black-body Radiation.** The amount of energy radiated from a body depends largely upon the temperature of the body. It has been shown by experiment that, at a given temperature, there is an upper limit to the amount of radiant energy that can be emitted in a given time by a unit surface of a body. This maximum amount of radiation for a given temperature is called the *black-body radiation*. A body that radiates for every wavelength the maximum intensity of radiation possible at a given temperature is known as a *black body*. At a given temperature, this maximum is the same for every black body regardless of its structure or composition. A black body can also be described in terms of absorption by the fact that all the radiant energy reaching the surface of a black body is absorbed by the body.

The term "black body" is misleading in that it implies the concept of color. As a matter of fact, objects that do not under ordinary conditions appear black may radiate as black bodies. Physicists dealing with measurements of great accuracy are best able to produce black-body conditions in the form of radiation that passes out through a small cavity in a solid body at a uniform temperature. Surfaces especially prepared for producing black-body radiation usually consist of a screen or grid made up of a myriad of needle points, or some form of honeycomb structure that provides many cavities.

All black bodies emit a continuous spectrum. Gases, however, have a discontinuous spectrum, showing only emission and absorption in various parts of the spectrum, called *lines*. These lines are characteristic for each substance and serve as a means of identification.

**Definitions.** At this point it is appropriate to define some of the terms to be used in discussing the effects and modifications of radiant energy. The words that are used in the English language to describe the various processes have not been completely standardized, but the following terminology will be used here:

*Emissive Power.* The energy radiated from a surface per unit surface area per unit of time. It is expressed, in cgs units, in ergs per sec per square centimeter, but in meteorology the minute is often used as the unit of time and the gram-calorie per square centimeter, or langley, is used as the energy unit. One may speak of the total emissive power, referring to all wavelengths, or the monochromatic or characteristic emissive power, referring to a particular wavelength or spectral band.

*Absorption Rate.* For surfaces, the energy absorbed per unit of area per unit of time, expressed in the same units as emissive power. It depends on the incident radiation and the surface characteristics of the body. For partly transparent media, see *extinction coefficient*, defined below. Absorption rate may be considered for a band, a single wavelength, or the entire spectrum.

*Emissivity.* The ratio of the observed emissive power to that of a black body or surface under identical conditions. It varies with the wavelength and with the temperature. This quantity may be designated as a coefficient of emission, since it is a dimensionless number between 0 and 1.

*Absorptivity.* The fractional part of the incident radiation that is absorbed by the surface in question. It also varies with the wavelength of the incident radiation and with the temperature of the body. Like the emissivity, it is a dimensionless number between 0 and 1 and can be used as a coefficient of absorption. The term "absorptive power" is sometimes used to express this function, but it is illogical because power is the rate of doing work.

*Reflectivity.* The fractional part of the incident radiation that is reflected by a surface (total or monochromatic). It is sometimes called reflective power, but this is illogical. It also is a dimensionless number between 0 and 1.

*Transmissivity.* In a partly transparent medium such as the atmosphere or the oceans, the transmissivity is the fractional part of the radiation transmitted through the medium per unit of thickness along the path of the radiant beam. The thickness is often called the optical thickness and is usually expressed in units of mass of the absorbing and backscattering medium. The transmissivity is a dimensionless number between 0 and 1. It can be applied monochromatically or to the total spectrum. The fraction depleted per unit optical thickness defines the *extinction coefficient*, 1 minus the transmissivity.

Although absorptivity and reflectivity have been defined in terms of a surface, they are real effects, too, in the free atmosphere. If the molecules of a gas, because of their temperature, are in a state of oscillation compatible with the wavelength of the radiation, they will absorb energy through resonance. Thus the gases can absorb a portion of the wavelengths or lines in the spectrum. Reflectivity occurs in a gas through that component of the scattering which is directed against the oncoming radiation. Thus we can speak of absorptivity and reflectivity in the atmosphere. Since absorptivity, reflectivity, and transmissivity represent different fractions of the same incident radiation, their sum must be unity, or $A + R + T = 1$.

## RADIATION LAWS

In order to understand meteorological radiation processes, it is necessary to know some of the so-called "classic radiation laws," based on experimental and theoretical work of physicists of the late nineteenth and early twentieth centuries. Some of these radiation principles are easy to understand from common experience. For example, one can see that if two bodies of about the same emissivity but at different temperatures are suspended near each other, the warmer one will lose energy by radiation, part of which will be absorbed by the cooler one, so that the temperatures of the two bodies will approach the same value. If the surface of the cooler body is initially at the same temperature as other surfaces in its surroundings, it will not lose energy through its own radiation until it gets warmer than the surrounding surfaces.

A demonstration of the effects of different values of absorptivity and emissivity can be performed by taking a thin metal sheet or aluminum foil as the cool body and by trying two types of surface. The sheet can be coated with lampblack on one side to make the absorptivity and emissivity on that side close to that of a black body and the other side can be left in its more or less polished condition. If the blackened side is exposed to the radiation from the hot body, the temperature of the sheet will rise very fast because the absorptivity on the black side is high and the emissivity on the unblackened side is low. It should be noted that energy is also radiated from the blackened side but that this at most can be half of the black-body emission from the sheet since it represents only half of the surface area of the sheet. The surface area on the other side emits something less than half, so the total emission is considerably less than that of an equivalent black body while the absorption is at approximately the black-body rate. If the sheet is exposed with the unblackened side toward the hot body, its warming will be very slow because the sheet will emit its energy toward the surroundings on the blackened side approximately as a black body and absorb poorly on the other side. Actually, for the same temperature, the same amount of energy would be emitted as in the first case, but the absorption rate would be less. Intermediate rates of warming would be experienced if both sides were the same, with an all-black sheet warming up faster than an all-polished one.

**Kirchhoff's Law.** This law relates the emission of radiation of a given wavelength at a given temperature to the absorption of that radiation. Some consequences of the law have already been anticipated by the preceding discussions and definitions.

To visualize the fundamental form of the law, let us consider a closed cavity, the walls of which are kept at a constant high temperature and are radiating as a black body. If a non-black body is suspended by nonconducting threads in the cavity, a balance between it and the walls will be reached. This balance would involve the black-body energy emitted by the walls $E_B$, the radiant energy emitted by the non-black body $E_\lambda$, and the unabsorbed energy reflected from the non-black body. If the absorptivity of this body is $a_\lambda$, then the unabsorbed energy is $(1 - a_\lambda)E_B$. The balance is

$$E_B - E_\lambda - (1 - a_\lambda)E_B = 0 \qquad (2\text{--}1)$$

If we divide by $E_B$, we obtain

$$\frac{E_\lambda}{E_B} = a_\lambda \qquad (2\text{--}2)$$

By definition, the emissivity is

$$e_\lambda = \frac{E_\lambda}{E_B}$$

Therefore $\qquad\qquad\qquad a_\lambda = e_\lambda$

Kirchhoff's law requires that the absorptivity by a body of radiant energy of a given wavelength at a given temperature is equal to its emissivity in that wavelength at the same temperature. The subscript $\lambda$ which we have introduced is to indicate that $a_\lambda$, $E_\lambda$, and $e_\lambda$ have different values for the different wavelengths at a given temperature.

Put another way, Kirchhoff's law states that the emissivity at a given wavelength and temperature is equal to the absorptivity for radiation of the same wavelength from a black body at the same temperature. The law also stipulates that the ratio of the emissive power to the absorptivity is equal to the emissive power of a black body at the same wavelength and temperature. This is shown by taking the relationship given in Eq. (2–2),

$$\frac{E_\lambda}{a_\lambda} = E_B \tag{2-3}$$

For a given temperature, the rules hold for the total emission spectrum. They are also applicable to gases, with proper consideration given to the selective nature of absorption and emission in the characteristic *lines* of the spectrum. At the same temperature, the emission spectrum and absorption spectrum of a body match exactly. This is also true of a gas, even to the details of the spectral lines.

**Planck's Law.** This, one of the great fundamental laws of physics, relates the manner in which the emissive power of a black body in all of the different wavelengths depends on its temperature. For a temperature $T$ the emissive power is distributed over the spectrum of wavelengths according to the following relation:

$$E_\lambda = \frac{c_1 \lambda^{-5}}{e^{c_2/\lambda T} - 1} \tag{2-4}$$

where $c_1$ and $c_2$ are constants and $e$ is the base of the natural logarithms. It is beyond the scope of this book to go through the empirical and theoretical steps in the development of this equation. Its meaning is more easily understood by examining curves plotted for various temperatures in terms of a graph with wavelength and emissive power as coordinates. Samples of Planck curves are shown in Fig. 2–2. Figure 2–2a shows the curve for a black body at a temperature of 6000°K, the approximate temperature of the outer part of the sun. Figure 2–2b presents two curves, the upper one standing for a black body at 300°K and the lower one at 200°K, both within the range of temperatures in the atmosphere.

As may be determined from the equation and as may be seen from the curves, the higher the temperature, the greater the emissive power. This is true of all wavelengths. Note that Figs. 2–2a and b are not in the same scale or range. It is apparent that the total emissive power is that summed up (integrated) over all wavelengths and therefore is proportional to the area between the curve and the line $E_\lambda = 0$. It is also apparent from the curves that their maxima are found at shorter wavelengths at the higher temperatures.

Interest in the manner in which the curves are displaced with changing temperature led Wien, Rayleigh, and others to develop a *displacement*

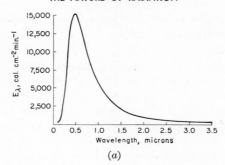

(a)

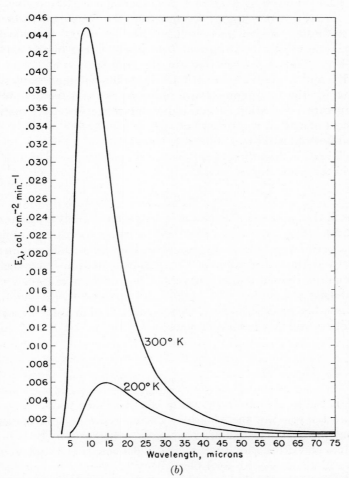

(b)

FIG. 2-2. Planck curves for black-body emission at a, 6000°K and b, 300°K (upper curve) and 200°K (lower curve).

*law.* As a result of their work it is possible to determine the wavelength of maximum emission from a black body at a given temperature by means of a very simple formula:

$$\lambda_m = \frac{2897}{T} \quad \text{microns}$$

This result can be obtained by taking the derivative of Planck's formula with respect to wavelength and solving for the maximum. Applying 6000°K to the formula, which is the effective radiating temperature of the sun, one finds the maximum to be in the visible part of the spectrum. (Our eyes are so constructed as to make maximum use of sunlight.) For the earth, with a temperature in the range from around 200 to 300°K, the maximum is well into the infrared. Specifically, the solar emission is at a maximum at 0.48 $\mu$ while that of the earth is at 10 to 14 $\mu$. Thus it is seen that we are dealing with emissions in two widely different parts of the spectrum. It should be noted, however, that the curve for the high-temperature radiation is at all points above the low-temperature radiation curves, indicating that a hot body emits more than a cool one at all wavelengths.

**Stefan-Boltzmann Law.** This law states that the total emissive power of a black body is directly proportional to the fourth power of its absolute or Kelvin temperature, or

$$E_B = \sigma T^4 \tag{2-5}$$

In terms of the total emissive power of a true black body, $\sigma$ has the value $5.673 \times 10^{-5}$ ergs cm$^{-2}$ deg$^{-4}$ sec$^{-1}$ and is called the Stefan-Boltzmann constant. The relationship expressed in the Stefan-Boltzmann law is derived from the integration of the Planck equation over the entire spectrum (area under Planck curve). The constant $\sigma$ applies only to the total spectrum.

For a non-black body the relationship can be used in a similar way if the true total emissivity $e$ is known, since

$$e = \frac{E}{E_B} \qquad E = eE_B$$
$$E = e\sigma T^4 \tag{2-6}$$

where $E$ is the total emissive power of the non-black body.

Because the gases of the atmosphere emit and absorb only in certain wavelengths, meteorologists are frequently concerned with the application of this and other radiation laws to a portion of the total spectrum. If a gas emits and absorbs as a black body between wavelengths $\lambda_1$ and $\lambda_2$, its total emission in that band is given by the portion between $\lambda_1$ and $\lambda_2$ of the total area under the Planck curve for a black body at the temperature of the gas. If this area is the fraction $\epsilon$ of the total area, then

$$E_{\lambda_1\lambda_2} = \epsilon\sigma T^4 \tag{2-7}$$

Thus the fourth-power law has general applicability.

**Transmissivity and Extinction.** These terms have been defined on page 16. Since the atmosphere is partly transparent to both the solar and terrestrial radiation, a great deal of attention must be given to the problem of atmospheric transmission and extinction of radiant energy in the various wavelengths.

If radiation of wavelength $\lambda$ reaches a point in a gas with intensity $I_{0\lambda}$ and has the intensity $I_\lambda$ after passing through a unit mass of the gas, the transmissivity $\tau$ of that gas for the wavelength in question will be expressed by the ratio

$$\tau = \frac{I_\lambda}{I_{0\lambda}} \tag{2-8}$$

The fractional change in intensity in passing through the small mass $\Delta m$, expressed in terms of unit mass, would be

$$\frac{I_0 - I}{I_0\,\Delta m} = 1 - \tau = k \tag{2-9}$$

where $k$ is an extinction coefficient. Expressed in terms of a differential equation, this becomes

$$\frac{dI_\lambda}{I_\lambda} = -k\,dm \tag{2-10}$$

the negative sign indicating decreasing intensity with accumulating mass. Integrating between the limits $I_{0\lambda}$ and $I_\lambda$, with $m = 0$ at $I_\lambda = I_{0\lambda}$, we find

$$k = \frac{1}{m}\ln\frac{I_{0\lambda}}{I_\lambda} \tag{2-11}$$

and
$$I_\lambda = I_{0\lambda}e^{-km} \tag{2-12}$$

When it is more convenient to use the common logarithms (base 10 instead of base $e$), a "decimal coefficient of extinction" $\alpha$ can be employed, such that

$$I_\lambda = I_{0\lambda} \times 10^{-\alpha m} \tag{2-13}$$

where $\alpha = 0.4343k$.

The above relationships apply only to parallel radiation. In the case of scattering of the magnitude observed in the atmosphere, this restriction can lead to appreciable error if not taken into account, especially in the case of solar radiation at low angles of the sun. Since the non-parallel effects are hard to correct for, situations in which these errors are large are usually avoided in making measurements and computations, so the above equations can be applied.

The intensities refer to 1 cm², so $m$ is the mass in a column 1 cm² in cross section, and $m = \rho L$, where $\rho$ is the density of the gas (grams per cubic centimeter) in the optical path length $L$ (centimeters). With $m$ as mass per unit area, $k$ is dimensionless. In considering the highly important extinction by water vapor in the atmosphere, it is customary to use "centimeters of precipitable water" for $m$. This refers to the depth the water would occupy if it were in a sheet of liquid. The density of the liquid water is assumed to be 1, so 1 g per cm² is 1 cm in depth.

It is important to recognize that the depletion or extinction in the atmosphere includes not only the energy absorbed by the gases and particles but also that reflected or scattered back by them. Further details of this problem will be discussed in later paragraphs.

**Greenhouse Effect.** Since the atmosphere absorbs selectively and in such a way as to transmit most of the solar radiation but to absorb a large part of the terrestrial radiation, it acts to conserve the heat energy of the earth. This is called the *greenhouse* effect. A greenhouse permits most of the short-wave solar radiation to pass through the glass roof and sides to be absorbed by the floor or ground and objects inside. These objects reradiate energy at their temperatures of about 300°K, and therefore, according to Wien's law, with principal intensity of around 10 $\mu$. The glass absorbs the energy at these wavelengths and sends part of it back into the greenhouse, causing the inside of the greenhouse to remain warmer than the outside. The atmosphere similarly acts as a greenhouse, the gases absorbing selectively in somewhat the same way as the glass.

**Reflection.** Everyone is familiar with the process of reflection of light. In general, our visual perceptions are approximately correct in indicating the wavelengths of greatest reflectivity, for they fall mostly within the visible spectrum. This means that only the solar radiation is reflected appreciably, while the reflection of the long-wave radiation from the earth and atmosphere may be neglected.

There is some variation in the reflectivity of various natural surfaces. The general reflectivity is called the *albedo*. Although this term is defined somewhat loosely, we shall think of it as the reflectivity covering all significant wavelengths for surfaces viewed from above. The albedo of the entire planet Earth is, on the average, considered to be about 0.36 (36 per cent reflected). By far the most important part of this reflectivity comes from the tops of clouds. The albedos of natural surfaces may be summarized as follows:

*Upper surfaces of clouds:* From 40 to 80 per cent, but with an average of about 55 per cent.

*Snow surfaces:* Over 80 per cent for cold, fresh snow; as low as 50 per cent for old, dirty snow.

*Land surfaces:* Most common surfaces, such as forests, grassy fields, plowed fields, and rocky deserts have an albedo averaging from about 10 to 20 per cent, but ranging from 5 per cent for dark forests to 30 per cent for dry sand.

*Water:* In general, the lowest albedos are found over water. It depends, however, on the zenith distance of the sun. According to List, who has tabulated the data in the Smithsonian Meteorological Tables (1951), the relation to the sun's zenith distance is as follows:

| Zenith distance, deg | 0 | 20 | 40 | 50 | 60 | 70 | 80 | 85 | 90 |
|---|---|---|---|---|---|---|---|---|---|
| Percentage reflected | 2.0 | 2.1 | 2.5 | 3.4 | 6.0 | 13.4 | 34.8 | 58.4 | 100.0 |

When the wind speed is sufficient to raise whitecaps, the albedo is greater than that of a nonfoaming condition.

The data indicate that, except for the effects of snow cover, there is no important geographical difference in the albedo of surfaces on the earth itself. If anything, water surfaces exhibit a slightly lower albedo than most land surfaces. Therefore, over the earth as a whole, one may conclude that *the albedo will be determined mainly by the presence or absence of clouds.* Extensive snow-covered areas will also be of importance. Under cloudless conditions, the greatest reflectivity would be found in high latitudes where snow and ice are present and over open water where the reflectivity would be appreciable owing to the low angle of the sun.

Obviously, the diminution of sunlight that we observe on an overcast day is due not so much to absorption within the cloud as to the large amount of light reflected from the top of the overcast layer. The strong reflectivity of a snow surface helps it to maintain its low temperature. Also, it emits long-wave radiation approximately as a black body. Thus a snow surface is a good refrigerant. Clouds exert a thermostatic control in reflecting the short-wave solar radiation and absorbing the long-wave terrestrial radiation.

**Scattering.** When light passes through a medium containing particles (including molecules) less in diameter than the wavelength of the light, a portion of the light is scattered in all directions. This is sometimes called *Rayleigh scattering* after Lord Rayleigh, who studied it in great detail. It is effective only for the short wavelengths, since it is proportional to $\lambda^{-4}$. Blue light is scattered more easily than red, and the blue color of the sky is ascribed to this effect. The sunlight, which starts out as white, comes to us with a reddish tinge. This is especially noticeable at sunset when the light passes through its longest path of atmosphere and is explained by the fact that the blue light has been scattered by the atmosphere and only the reddish portions reach us directly. The same effect is noticed when the sun shines through a smoke haze.

Particles larger in diameter than the wavelength of the light do not produce scattering. Thus cloud particles do not change the color of the light, because of their relatively large size. Fine dust particles often produce scattering. A yellowish cast is observed in the sun following dust storms or volcanic eruptions.

In conditions of clear skies, the amount of light sent back into space through scattering is slightly greater than that reflected from the surface of the earth. That transmitted outward is less than half of the scattered light, the remainder passing earthward as sky radiation.

Scattering is the process mainly responsible for reducing the visibility or distance from which standard objects can barely be seen. Under hazy or dusty conditions the light from a distant object may be completely attenuated by scattering before reaching the eye. Direct absorption by the haze particles is of some importance, but scattering is the principal effect. The visibility is also affected by the scattered light or "air light" coming from all directions with enough relative strength to weaken or overpower visual contrast between distant objects.

# CHAPTER 3

# THE HEAT BALANCE OF THE ATMOSPHERE

In the preceding chapter it was noted that the radiation intensity depends on the fourth power of the absolute temperature of the radiating body. This means that the more the sun heats up the earth the greater will be the amount of energy sent back into space again by terrestrial radiation. This rate of heat loss must exactly balance over a long period of time the amount of heat received from the sun, in order to prevent the earth from becoming continuously hotter or continuously colder, as the case may be.

In geological history, there have been periods when the earth was warmer or cooler than at the present time, and it seems at once evident that this must have been caused by changes in the incoming and outgoing radiation. However, at least one theory in explanation of the climates of the past is based on the assumption that the heat balance between the sun and the earth has always been the same. If the earth is now getting hotter or colder, it is doing so at such a slow rate that for our purposes we may consider that there is, over a long period of time, an absolute heat balance in the earth and its atmosphere in relation to solar radiation.

Meteorologists have found that the exact mechanism by means of which the heat balance is maintained in the earth and its atmosphere is extremely complicated. This is owing mainly to selective absorption of radiation by the various atmospheric constituents, such that it is necessary to consider the various wavelengths separately. In this chapter the mechanism of radiation balance in the atmosphere will be discussed, both to explain the observed conditions and to form a basis for the discussion of various radiation problems with which practical meteorologists must of necessity become acquainted.

In the cosmic sense, radiation is the only means of maintaining a complete heat balance, because it is only by radiation that heat energy can be transferred through space. If the outgoing terrestrial radiation were greater than the incoming solar radiation, the earth would become progressively colder. Not only must there be a balance between the earth's surface and the incoming radiation, but also a balance must exist that includes the atmosphere. The heat must escape outside of the atmospheric boundary.

If the atmosphere were totally transparent to the terrestrial radiation, the heat would go directly out into space, uninfluenced by the presence of the atmosphere. The atmosphere, however, strongly absorbs the radiation at some wavelengths, while at others it is perfectly transparent, so that only a portion of the radiation from the surface of the earth goes directly outward into space. The solar radiation is also influenced to a considerable extent by passage through the atmosphere; however, it is composed of wavelengths much shorter than those of the terrestrial radiation, and these shorter wavelengths are absorbed much less than the longer ones of the terrestrial radiation. In fact, the atmosphere, by comparison with its absorption of terrestrial radiation, can almost be regarded as transparent for the solar beam.

Although the absorption of solar radiation is slight, it is nevertheless important. Most important of all, however, are the effects of reflection, including both the direct reflection and the scattering. The amount that is lost by reflection back into space is, for average conditions of cloudiness, etc., and over the world as a whole, about 36 per cent of the total intercepted by the earth.

**The Depletion of Solar Radiation in the Atmosphere.** In order to know the manner and amount of depletion of solar radiation in the atmosphere it is necessary to consider the composition of the air. It consists of a mechanical mixture of several gases, sometimes called the *permanent* gases, that remain in fixed proportion to the total and other gases that vary markedly with time and location. A number of tabulations of the composition of the air have been made by various investigators, all in fairly close agreement. Table 3–1 is taken from recent sources compiled by Glueckauf.[1]

Through most of the atmosphere the permanent gases exist in nearly the same proportion at all heights, the remaining constituents showing generally a rapid decrease in percentage with height.

It is interesting to note that although water vapor usually comprises less than 3 per cent of the gases even with moist conditions at sea level, it absorbs nearly six times as much solar radiant energy as do all of the other gases combined. Furthermore it accounts for nearly all of the gaseous absorption of the terrestrial radiation.

Ozone is of special interest because of its photochemical reaction to certain wavelengths of the solar radiation, particularly in the ultraviolet. The height of maximum ozone density is between 20 and 30 km. Oxygen molecules are dissociated by the solar radiation into atomic oxygen which

[1] Glueckauf, E., The Composition of Atmospheric Air, *Compendium of Meteorol.*, 1951, pp. 1–10.

TABLE 3–1. COMPOSITION OF THE ATMOSPHERE

| Constituent | Per cent by volume | Parts per million |
|---|---|---|
| Nitrogen............... | 78.084 ± 0.004 | |
| Oxygen................ | 20.946 ± 0.002 | |
| Carbon dioxide.......... | 0.033 ± 0.001 | |
| Argon................. | 0.934 ± 0.001 | |
| Neon.................. | ............. | 18.18 ± 0.04 |
| Helium................ | ............. | 5.24 ± 0.004 |
| Krypton............... | ............. | 1.14 ± 0.01 |
| Xenon................. | ............. | 0.087 ± 0.001 |
| Hydrogen.............. | ............. | 0.5 |
| Methane ($CH_4$)......... | ............. | 2 |
| Nitrous oxide ($N_2O$)....... | ............. | 0.5 ± 0.1 |

| Important variable gases | |
|---|---|
| Water vapor......... | 0–3 per cent |
| Ozone.............. | 0–0.07 ppm (ground level) |
| | 0.1–0.2 ppm (20–30 km) |

combines with other oxygen molecules to form ozone $(O + O_2 \rightarrow O_3)$ which itself is dissociated to form $O_2$ and O. The three forms O, $O_2$, and $O_3$ react to achieve an equilibrium mixture which is different at various heights.

Suspended in the atmosphere are certain particles. By far the most important are the liquid water and ice particles of clouds. Not only in the radiation balance but also in the whole problem of heat transfer in the atmosphere they play a predominant part. Other particles are present which have less direct meteorological effects. They include dust, smoke, industrial effluents, various chemical particles that may be classified separately from dust and smoke, things of an organic nature such as pollens, spores, bacteria, fibers, etc., and particles recognizable only as ions or radiation particles.

Outside the atmosphere the solar radiation, at normal incidence, has a mean intensity of 1.94 g-cal $cm^{-2}$ $min^{-1}$, according to accepted standards. This value is called the *solar constant*. At the surface of the earth the solar radiation that can be absorbed is very much less because the rays are normal at only one point in the tropics at any given time and, more important for our purposes here, a considerable fraction of the radiation is depleted in the atmosphere. The depletion depends on the length of the optical path (determined by latitude, date, and time) and on the nature and quantity of absorbing, reflecting, and scattering matter in the atmosphere. The radiation reaching the earth or any point on a horizontal surface, including both direct and sky radiation, is called the *insolation* at that point. Figure 1–6 gives an example of the effects of the atmosphere on this quantity during the course of the year at Washington, D.C.

To get an idea of what happens to the solar radiation after it enters the atmosphere one can make up a table, such as Table 3–2, based on the

TABLE 3–2. FRACTION OF INCIDENT SOLAR RADIATION DEPLETED AND RECEIVED AT SURFACE UNDER AVERAGE CONDITIONS WITH CLEAR SKIES, OVERCAST SKIES, AND MEAN CLOUDINESS

1. Clear skies
   Reflection and back scattering:
   
   | | | |
   |---|---|---|
   | Atmospheric scattering | 0.09 | |
   | Surface reflection | 0.06 | |
   | Total | | 0.15 |
   
   Absorption:
   
   | | | |
   |---|---|---|
   | By water vapor | 0.13 | |
   | By other gases, dust, etc | 0.03 | |
   | Total | | 0.16 |
   | Total depletion | | 0.31 |
   | Absorbed at surface $(1 - 0.31)$ | 0.69 | |

2. Overcast skies

   | | | |
   |---|---|---|
   | Reflection and back scattering | 0.55 | |
   | Absorption | 0.10 | |
   | Total depletion | | 0.65 |
   | Absorbed at surface $(1 - 0.65)$ | 0.35 | |

3. Mean cloudiness of 0.52 over whole earth

   | | | |
   |---|---|---|
   | Absorbed at surface in clear spaces (0.48 of area), $0.48 \times 0.69$ | 0.33 | |
   | Absorbed at surface under cloud-covered spaces (0.52 of area), $0.52 \times 0.35$ | 0.18 | |
   | Total (mean fraction absorbed over the surface of the earth as a whole) | | 0.51 |

best estimates of reflection, scattering, and absorption with and without clouds and for the average cloud cover of the earth, which may be taken as 52 per cent. It can be seen that under average clear-sky conditions about 70 per cent of incident radiation outside the atmosphere is absorbed at the surface of the earth but under average overcast conditions only about 35 per cent gets through. Thus with slightly more than half the earth obscured by clouds on the daylight side, about 50 per cent of the solar energy intercepted by the planet is absorbed at its surface.

From the table it can be seen that the average albedo of the earth including its atmosphere should be 52 per cent of 0.55 plus 48 per cent of 0.15 or 0.36 (36 per cent).

**Terrestrial Radiation.** From the application of Planck's radiation formula, we find that energy emitted from a body having the temperature of the earth would be in the form of long waves, the maximum emissive power being in the neighborhood of 10 $\mu$. This is called *infrared*, or low-temperature, radiation. Of these wavelengths, a large proportion is absorbed by the gases of the atmosphere, with water vapor playing by far the predominant role. This will be true for perfectly clear skies as long as there is water present in the vapor form. Clouds will absorb the radiation from the earth even more effectively.

From Kirchhoff's law it is apparent that the radiant energy from the earth that is absorbed by the atmosphere would be reradiated. This energy would be radiated in all directions. However, since the horizontal temperature differences are negligible, horizontal radiations will cancel out, each particle losing in a horizontal direction the same amount of energy that it receives horizontally. Only the upward and downward flux of radiation need be considered. It follows from the Stefan-Boltzmann law that, if the earth is warmer than the overlying atmosphere, which is the normal state of affairs, the atmosphere will receive more terrestrial radiation than it emits. Under certain circumstances, a large portion of the atmosphere is found to be warmer than the ground, and the net radiation is downward. This, of course, is in addition to and at a different wavelength from that coming downward from the sun.

The atmospheric gases, including the all-important water vapor, are "selective" absorbers, i.e., they absorb some wavelengths but are transparent to others. For example, the water vapor in the atmosphere absorbs strongly at wavelengths greater than 27 $\mu$ and between 5.5 and 7 $\mu$. It has some narrow absorption bands below 4 $\mu$ and absorbs moderately from 4 to 5.5 $\mu$, 7 to 8 $\mu$, and 13 to 27 $\mu$. However, for wavelengths from 8 to 13 $\mu$ it is almost perfectly transparent. It is worthy of note that the wavelengths of transparency are in the portion of the spectrum in the vicinity of the peak of emissive power for a body having the temperature of the earth. Energy emitted by the earth at these wavelengths of transparency passes practically unimpeded through the atmosphere and directly into outer space.

The problem of the heat balance of the earth and its atmosphere may be divided into three parts, as follows:

1. The solar radiation, its reflection and absorption in the atmosphere and at the surface of the earth.

2. The reradiation of energy from the earth and its atmosphere to outer space.

3. The interplay of radiation between the surface of the earth and the atmosphere.

The first part of the problem has already been discussed. By comparison with the terrestrial-radiation part, it is extremely simple. Only by a series of approximations can the nature of the emission and absorption of the long-wave terrestrial radiation be determined.

**Water-vapor Absorption.** In order to study radiation processes in the atmosphere, the nature of the absorption by the most effective absorbing gas, viz., water vapor, must be known. Lack of sufficient information concerning the water-vapor absorption has been a serious deficiency in meteorological data. Recently, precise determinations of water-vapor absorption have been made in most regions of the spectrum associated with terrestrial radiation. They show the absorption spectrum to be made up of a myriad of absorption lines distributed through the various wavelengths. The computation of transmission functions in all of these spectral lines is a prodigious task even after the basic absorption measurements have been made in the laboratory and in the atmosphere. Until 1959 only incomplete empirical and analytical results were available.

The absorption rate of radiation of a given wavelength $\lambda$ passing through mass $m$ per square centimeter of a medium was expressed in Chap. 2 in terms of an extinction coefficient $k_\lambda$. In integrated form, the relation is

$$I_\lambda = I_{0\lambda}e^{-k_\lambda m} \tag{3-1}$$

where $I_{0\lambda}$ and $I_\lambda$ are, respectively, the incident and emergent radiation at wavelength $\lambda$. Since the equation and $k_\lambda$ hold for only a specified wavelength, this relationship cannot be applied conveniently to the whole spectrum or even a group of neighboring lines. The computation is complicated by the tendency of the radiation not to be parallel as required for the use of this equation, but to be partly diffuse. An even more troublesome complication arises from the fact that in each spectral line the absorption coefficient varies from a very high value in the center of the line to much smaller values on the sides. This variation may be of the order of 100 to 1. In addition, there is an effect on this last factor due to pressure and temperature, known as the "broadening" of the absorption lines such that the half-value width of each line increases with air pressure and temperature. In the atmosphere where the decrease in pressure with height is large (half an atmosphere in the first 6000 m), the pressure broadening is an important effect.

Reasonable success can be obtained by using simplifications of the absorption spectrum, based on average values, over every small range of the spectrum and by neglecting complicating factors. A widely used simplification developed by Elsasser[1] is shown in Fig. 3-1. The common logarithm of the extinction coefficients is plotted against the wavelength. Two coefficients are used: $k$, which is that derived from the conventional extinction equation (3-1) and $L$, which is that obtained

---

[1] Elsasser, W. M., Heat Transfer by Infrared Radiation in the Atmosphere, *Harvard Meteorol. Studies*, no. 6, 1942.

from a more complicated relationship. The coefficient $k$ applies to the part of the curve between the two short dashes, that is, from 8 to 27 $\mu$. The strong absorption band of carbon dioxide from 13 to 17.5 $\mu$ is indicated by a break in the water-vapor curve. This is done because, in practical computations, the carbon dioxide absorption overshadows that due to water vapor at these wavelengths. Infrared absorption by ozone, while perhaps not entirely negligible, is not considered. Thus the data may be applied to a cloudless atmosphere or to a part thereof containing water vapor.

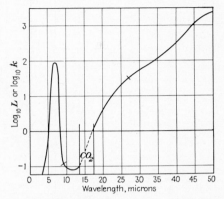

FIG. 3–1. Simplification of the water-vapor spectrum according to Elsasser.

The so-called "transparent band" or infrared "window" in which $k$ is approximately 0.1 (log $k$ near $-1$) should be noted. It lies between about 8 $\mu$ and the beginning of the $CO_2$ absorption at 13 $\mu$. It is through this band that terrestrial radiation can pass directly through the atmosphere into outer space with 80 per cent transmission or better, depending on $m$, the mass of water in the air column.

Plots of transmission as a function of $k$ (curve $I$) and $L$ (curve $II$), based on an atmospheric column containing 1 cm of precipitable water, a reasonable value, are shown in Fig. 3–2. When examined in conjunction with Fig. 3–1, it indicates that a small increase in the absorption coefficient at certain values corresponds to a very large increase in the amount of radiation absorbed. As $k$ increases from 1 to 4, the amount of energy transmitted decreases from a ratio $I/I_0$ of 0.37 to 0.02. For lesser amounts of water the transmissions would be greater, and vice versa. The precipitable water in an air column through the whole atmosphere varies from about 0.1 mm in extreme winter arctic conditions to perhaps 10 cm in the rainy season of the tropics. From Figs. 3–1 and 3–2 it is apparent that for appreciable water-vapor contents, the atmosphere may be considered practically opaque ($\tau < 20$ per cent) for wavelengths from 5.5 to 7 $\mu$ and greater than 27 $\mu$.

**Simpson's Analysis of Terrestrial Radiation.** A highly simplified yet useful treatment of the infrared radiation in the atmosphere by G. C. Simpson[1] was published in 1928. The method is illustrated graphically in Fig. 3–3, taken from Simpson's work. Two black-body Planck curves

[1] Simpson, G. C., Further Studies in Terrestrial Radiation, *Mem. Roy. Meteorol. Soc.*, vol. 3, no. 21, 1928.

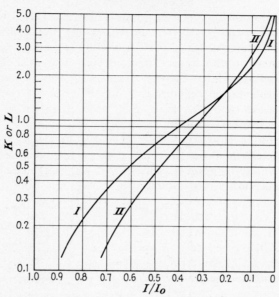

FIG. 3–2. Transmission as a function of absorption coefficients for 1 cm of precipitable water.

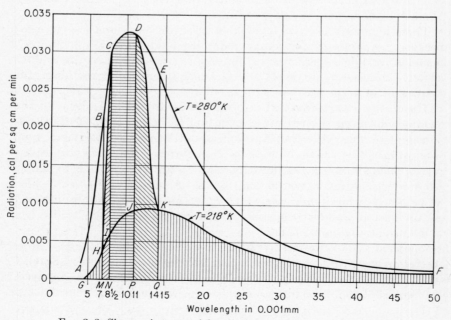

FIG. 3–3. Simpson's terrestrial-radiation curves for latitude 50°N.

are plotted representing the mean temperature of the earth and of the stratosphere, both for lat 50°N. The temperatures are 280°K for the surface (upper curve) and 218°K for the stratosphere (lower curve). Simpson assumed, with reasonable justification, that the portion of the outgoing energy that is completely absorbed in the atmosphere would be emitted to space from the top of the atmosphere as black-body radiation in the opaque bands at the temperature of the stratosphere. This assumes that the stratosphere temperature represents the effective radiating temperature of the outgoing radiation in the opaque bands as it might be measured outside the atmosphere; or, applying the Stefan-Boltzmann law only to those portions of the spectrum where the atmosphere is opaque, that

$$E_w = \sigma_w T^4 = \sigma_w 218^4$$
$$\sigma_w = \sigma\epsilon$$

where the $w$ subscripts refer only to the opaque radiation and $\epsilon$ has the meaning given in Eq. (2–7).

The absorption-emission spectrum is divided into the following three main regions:

1. Total absorption from 5.5 to 7 $\mu$ and upward from 14 $\mu$.
2. Complete transparency from 8.5 to 11 $\mu$.
3. Intermediate regions of partial absorption, "semitransparent bands," in the ranges from 7 to 8.5 $\mu$ and 11 to 14 $\mu$.

These limits are not the same as those stated on the preceding pages because Simpson had only early, more crude data to work with. The model is valid, however, in demonstrating the importance of the different effects. A mean value of 0.3 mm of precipitable water was taken, and clear skies were specified.

The energy represented by the areas $GHM$ and $QKF$, shown by vertical shading, is the energy that goes outward into space at the wavelengths of complete absorption. It is emitted at the 218° temperature of the stratosphere.

The radiation going out through the transparent band or "atmospheric window" is emitted at the temperature of the surface of the earth which, at 50°N, has a mean value of 280°K. The area $NCDP$, shaded by horizontal lines, represents this direct radiation to space.

Simpson found that any sort of line forming the upper limit of the semitransparent bands would divide the areas approximately into halves. Accordingly, he drew the lines $KD$ and $HC$ which suffice for this purpose. The areas $MHCIN$ and $PJDKQ$, shaded with diagonal lines, represent the radiation going out in these semitransparent bands.

The total energy emitted to space with clear skies and 0.3 mm precipitable water in vapor form under mean temperature conditions at

50°N is therefore represented by all of the shaded areas of Fig. 3–3. The unshaded areas under the upper curve represent the difference between the total energy emitted by the ground (at all infrared wavelengths) and that which gets out into space. This energy, absorbed by the atmosphere, is reradiated internally and contributes to the maintenance of the observed temperatures.

Similar curves were prepared by Simpson for other latitudes based on mean temperatures of the surface and the stratosphere at each latitude and based on reasonable values of the precipitable water. These were then modified by taking the mean cloud cover as 0.5, and the outgoing radiation was computed for the whole earth. Simpson found that this

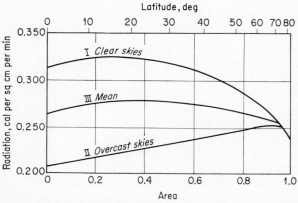

Fig. 3–4. Terrestrial radiation in terms of latitude under various sky conditions.

was in good agreement with the much more easily computed total incoming solar radiation. In effect, the heat balance of the atmosphere was accounted for.

Figure 3–4 shows the distribution according to latitudinal area of the terrestrial radiation going out into space under conditions of clear skies, overcast skies, and mean cloudiness. The data are averaged for all seasons of the year. For clear skies, the transmitted energy is greatest at about lat 15°. This is because the highest mean surface temperatures are observed in that latitude, giving large emission in the transparent region. Under overcast skies, the outgoing radiation is at a minimum at the equator because (1) the high amount of energy emitted by the surface at low latitudes in the transparent bands does not get through the clouds, and (2) the stratosphere is coldest at the equator, warmest at the poles. In the polar regions it is assumed that clouds make little or no difference since, on the average, they are at about the same temperature as the surface of the earth and are about equally effective as radiating surfaces.

A similar computation based on improved data and observations has been made by Houghton[1] for the Northern Hemisphere for all latitudes, longitudes, and seasons (Fig. 3–5). It is unlikely that the Southern Hemisphere conditions would produce a marked difference in the results, and so it seems permissible to take them as representing the balance for the entire earth. Curve II represents the same information conveyed by curve III of Fig. 3–4, since it also is based on mean cloudiness. The ordinate in Houghton's graph is in langleys per day, and since a langley

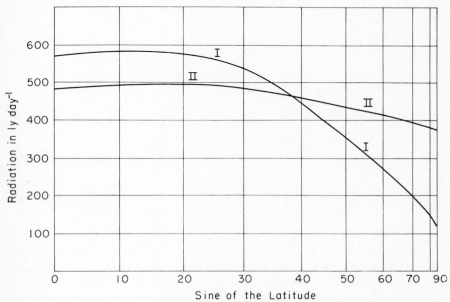

FIG. 3–5. Houghton's radiation curves; curve I, solar radiation absorbed by earth and atmosphere; curve II, long-wave radiation leaving the atmosphere.

is 1 cal per cm², Simpson's values in Fig. 3–4 when multiplied by the number of minutes in a day should give Houghton's values if they are in agreement. It is noted that the latter are considerably higher. Both investigators obtained an almost exact balance of mean outgoing long-wave radiation with absorbed solar radiation. The recent data from solar radiation measurements give higher values than Simpson used.

**Graphical Representation of the Heat Balance.** In Fig. 3–6 Houghton's graphical summary of the heat balance of the earth and atmosphere is presented with slight modifications. On the left side of the diagram

[1] Houghton, H. G., On the Annual Heat Balance of the Northern Hemisphere. *J. Meteorol.*, vol. 11, pp. 1–9, 1954.

the reflection, scattering, and absorption of the solar radiation are represented and on the right the terrestrial effects are shown. On the left side, 100 units of solar energy are shown entering the top of the atmosphere and 34 going out again from reflection and scattering (albedo of 0.34). On the right, the remaining 66 units go out through the transparent region of the water-vapor and carbon dioxide spectrum

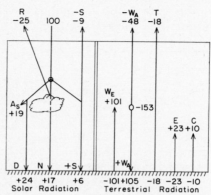

FIG. 3–6. The heat balance of the earth and its atmosphere as summarized by Houghton.

(18 units) and in the opaque region (48 units) to make up the external balance. The various symbols and quantities are as follows:

$A_s$ = solar radiation absorbed in the atmosphere, 19 units

$R$ = reflected solar radiation (depicted as coming from cloud, although some comes from the surface), 25 units

$-S$ = solar radiation scattered outward, 9 units

$+S$ = solar radiation scattered downward (sky radiation), 6 units

$D$ = direct solar radiation reaching the earth, 24 units

$N$ = diffuse solar radiation reaching the earth through clouds, 17 units

$W_E$ = emission from the earth in the absorbing portion of the water-vapor spectrum, 101 units

$+W_A$ = downward flux of infrared radiation from the atmosphere in the absorbing portion, 105 units reach the ground

$-W_A$ = upward flux of infrared radiation from the atmosphere in the absorbing portion, 48 units leave at top

$T$ = emission from the earth in the transparent region, 18 units

$E$ = latent heat carried to the atmosphere in the hydrologic cycle (evaporation, condensation, precipitation), 23 units

$C$ = heat transported upward by convection or turbulence, 10 units to the atmosphere

The balance is maintained as follows:

| Balance to space | | Surface balance | | | Atmospheric balance | | |
|---|---|---|---|---|---|---|---|
| In | Out | In | | Out | In | | Out |
| 100 | $-S$   9 | $D$   24 | $W_E$   101 | | $W_E$   101 | $-W_A$   48 |
| | $R$   25 | $N$   17 | $E$   23 | | $E$   23 | $+W_A$   105 |
| | $-W_A$   48 | $+S$   6 | $C$   10 | | $C$   10 | |
| | $T$   18 | $+W_A$   105 | $T$   18 | | $A_s$   19 | |
| 100 | 100 | 152 | 152 | | 153 | 153 |

Thus, averaged over the entire year for the earth as a whole, there is a balanced heat budget.

**Imbalance on the Earth.**    In thinking about the necessity of a radiation balance for the planet as a whole, including its surface and its atmosphere, one must not lose sight of the fact that there is a great imbalance between different parts of the earth and the atmosphere. This is demonstrated by the two curves of Fig. 3–5, which indicate a pronounced excess of incoming over outgoing radiation in low latitudes and a marked deficit in high latitudes. The total areas under the separate curves are approximately equal, indicating a total balance. This means that the whole earth is getting neither hotter nor colder. In view of the imbalance at high and low latitudes, one may ask why the high-latitude regions do not get colder and colder while the low-latitude areas keep heating up. The answer is to be found in the transport of heat by convection or, more specifically, advection from low to high latitudes. The air circulation of the atmosphere must equalize these differences.

After computing the data represented in Fig. 3–5, Houghton calculated the amount of heat that would have to be transported poleward across the various latitude circles in order to compensate for the radiation imbalance. The results for the Northern Hemisphere are given in Table 3–3. It should be noted that the flux would have to be greatest at lat 40° where the two curves of Fig. 3–5 cross. In the Northern

TABLE 3–3. REQUIRED POLEWARD FLUX OF HEAT ACROSS LATITUDE CIRCLES
IN UNITS OF $10^{19}$ CAL PER DAY
(From H. G. Houghton)

| Latitude, °N | Flux | Latitude, °N | Flux |
|---|---|---|---|
| 0 | 0 | 50 | 9.61 |
| 10 | 4.05 | 60 | 6.68 |
| 20 | 7.68 | 70 | 3.41 |
| 30 | 10.46 | 80 | 0.94 |
| 40 | 11.12 | 90 | 0 |

Hemisphere an appreciable amount of this heat (estimated roughly as 10 per cent) is transported by the ocean currents.

**Radiation in the Free Atmosphere.** Analyses such as Simpson's clearly indicate the importance of the vertical distribution of temperature and of water vapor in determining the heat exchange by radiation between the earth and its overlying atmosphere. Under normal conditions, with the temperature decreasing steadily with altitude, there will be a steady flow of heat upward by radiation, as long as an appreciable

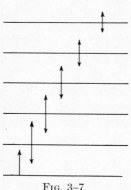

FIG. 3–7.

amount of water vapor is present. This can be seen in Fig. 3–7, where several successive layers of air are treated as to the amount of long-wave radiation received and emitted. The surface of the earth has the highest temperature and therefore radiates the greatest amount of energy. The first layer above the ground has a lower temperature, so that, although it absorbs a quantity equal to that emitted by the earth's surface, it reradiates a lesser amount of energy because it has a lower temperature, and this amount is divided into two parts, that going upward and that going downward. Thus the layer next above it receives only that portion of the energy which is radiated upward. This layer in turn radiates in all directions a lesser amount of energy than it receives, because it has a still lower temperature. Of course, the quantity that is radiated downward is absorbed again by the layers beneath, but this quantity of energy is less than that radiated upward by these lower layers, because the temperature is higher near the ground. In the figure, the length of the arrow pointing upward or downward gives in each case the relative amounts of radiation. It can be seen that the radiant energy that goes out into space at the top of the atmosphere must be emitted under black-body conditions characteristic of the temperature of the outer part of the atmosphere. In addition, as has been pointed out already, some radiation will find its way into space through the transparent bands in which a cloudless atmosphere plays no role.

The effects of a layer of temperature inversion, i.e., a layer where the temperature increases with height, are readily seen. If the overlying warm air contains an amount of water vapor comparable to that of the cooler air beneath, then the net transfer of heat by radiation will be downward. In many temperature inversions existing in the atmosphere, however, there is also a sharp decrease in the water-vapor content in passing upward into the warmer air. Considering the fact that absorption depends on the quantity of water vapor present as well as on the absorption coefficient, it is possible that in the case of very dry inversions there will be a net radiation loss upward, just as in the case of a normal temperature distribution. It is a difficult problem to determine the magnitudes and respective moisture distributions in temperature inversions required for a balance between upward and downward radiation. Recent studies of this problem in connection with the formation of fogs and low clouds along the California coast indicate that the strongest temperature inversions are often associated with the lowest quantities of water vapor in the upper air. In some cases, however, these inversions are so strong that even a relatively minute quantity of water vapor will radiate with sufficient intensity so as actually to cause an addition of heat to the layers beneath the inversion by radiation from those above. Weaker inversions, which nevertheless show a minute quantity of water vapor above them, represent the most favorable conditions for radiation heat loss at upper levels outward through the atmosphere. A study of these problems can be applied to many questions of meteorological research.

An interesting practical application of this knowledge is found in the explanation of the formation of cold air developing upward from the surface to great heights over high-latitude continental regions. Here the sudden cooling to which the air is subjected by passing from the warm oceans in winter to the snow-covered continents results in a temperature inversion immediately above the surface. There is then a net flow of heat downward from this inversion layer to the snow cover. This heat absorbed by the snow surface is radiated back again, but part of it goes out into space through the transparent bands. Thus the air just above the temperature inversion is continually losing heat to the snow surface, because it does not receive in return the same quantity that it radiates downward. Thus, by means of radiation processes, the air aloft over the cold continental regions gradually becomes chilled at great heights.

Several attempts to obtain an explanation of the observed distribution of temperature in the upper air over various parts of the world from an investigation of the energy transferred through radiation have been made. These attempts have in general failed, mainly because of incomplete data concerning the exact nature of the radiation phenomena. Simpson approached the subject from the opposite point of view, viz., by taking the observed temperature distribution, calculating the radiative transfer that would occur under these conditions, and determining whether or not this would produce a heat balance. It must be borne in mind that radiation is not the only process at work to distribute heat in the atmosphere. Convection currents, as has already been pointed out, are of extreme importance, and so far no very satisfactory way of taking them into consideration in the calculations has been found. In later chapters we shall learn that the whole subject of heat transferred throughout the atmosphere becomes very complicated when all the factors are taken into account.

**Absorption and Radiation by Clouds.** Several investigators, using films of water, have investigated the absorption spectrum of liquid water, and the data appear to be applicable to clouds. The measurements indicate that the liquid has approximately the same pattern of absorption bands as the vapor, but the values of the coefficients are nearly ten times as great. Even at about 10 $\mu$, which is in the middle of the transparent band for water vapor and in the portion of the spectrum where the absorption also is least for liquid water, a water film just 0.1 mm in thickness transmits only one hundredth of the incident unreflected radiation. According to accepted values of the water content of average clouds, the length of a path through a cloud that would contain 0.1 mm of liquid water per unit cross section would be 50 m. Thus a layer of cloud or fog a few meters thick can be treated as a black-body radiator.

Clouds therefore have a more pronounced effect than water vapor on the radiation balance of the atmosphere. We have already seen that they are powerful reflecting surfaces for the short-wave solar radiation, sending back into space by this process up to 80 per cent of the solar radiation incident upon them. Although their reflecting power is negligible for the longer wavelengths of terrestrial radiation, their importance as absorbing and radiating bodies for radiation of this type is great.

As black-body radiators, cloud layers at any level in the atmosphere strongly alter the interplay of radiant energy within the atmosphere. A cloud layer absorbs and emits radiation in all of the infrared wavelengths including the transparent bands of water vapor. In a normal atmosphere with the temperature decreasing with height, a cloud layer gains heat from below and loses heat by radiation at the top. As far as radiation to the upper atmosphere and to space is concerned, a cloud layer has the effect of creating a radiating surface that is approximately as effective as the ground but that is normally at a considerably lower temperature. The reduction of outgoing radiation, particularly in the transparent region, is marked.

The nighttime decrease of temperature at the ground is modified more by cloudiness than by any other factor. A cloud layer absorbs the radiation coming up from the earth and reradiates it down, so that the temperature falls but little. If the cloud base is warmer than the ground, as is sometimes the case in winter at high latitudes, it may emit more energy downward than comes up from the ground.

At the top of a thick cloud layer the emission of infrared radiation will operate to produce marked cooling, at least at night when there is no solar radiation to be absorbed. Owing to the strong absorption in the cloud of radiation coming up into it, the top layers receive little energy from below. From the top upward there is only a small amount of water vapor to absorb and radiate back down again the energy emitted by the top. In fact, a considerable fraction of this energy is in the transparent bands of water vapor which passes freely to outer space.

**Radiation Flux and Cooling in the Atmosphere.** The interplay of radiation in the atmosphere is somewhat like heat conduction. Radiant energy (heat) flows from warm to cold layers or, without temperature differences, from strong radiators to weaker ones. This is called the *flux* of radiation. In the simple case of Fig. 3–7 the net flux is uniformly upward because an atmosphere of steadily decreasing temperature and water-vapor content with height is assumed. Clouds, haze lines, and moisture and temperature irregularities change this picture.

It is common for layers in the atmosphere to have radiation cooling even without clouds or discontinuities in temperature and moisture. Consider the air in the space between any two horizontal lines in Fig. 3–7. The upward flux of radiation is given by the difference between the quantity of energy represented by the arrow pointing upward into this space from below and that pointing downward from above. If this difference increased with height, the upward flux would increase with height, and the layers would be transporting more heat upward than they were receiving. Thus they would cool. From a consideration of the temperature effect in the fourth-power law (Stefan-Boltzman law) one would say that this could not happen, as long as the temperature decreased with height. It does happen, and the reason is to be found in a rapid decrease with height of the water-vapor content. The decrease with height of the amount of energy absorbed and reradiated downward may then exceed the decrease in amount radiated upward. For a radiation flux to occur through layers of the atmosphere without changing the temperature of those layers, there must be for each vertical distribution of temperature a given vertical distribution of water vapor or other absorbing material. These may be called the "steady-state distributions." It is apparent that moisture and temperature distributions that would cause a layer to gain heat are also possible.

Details of the computation of the radiation flux in the actual atmosphere will not be discussed here, but some recent results on cooling rates from radiation flux will demonstrate the principal effects. Figure 3–8 contains results of several computations by Möller[1] of cooling by infrared radiation at various heights under various conditions in the atmosphere. The normal cloudless atmosphere in middle latitudes (curve *A*) shows

[1] Möller, F., Long-wave Radiation, *Compendium of Meteorol.*, 1951, pp. 34–49.

cooling at all heights up to 14 km.   This cooling results from an increase
in upward radiation flux with height despite a steady decrease of temperature through the first 10 km or more.   The cooling effect is ascribed to
the rapid decrease with height of the water-vapor content.   The cooling

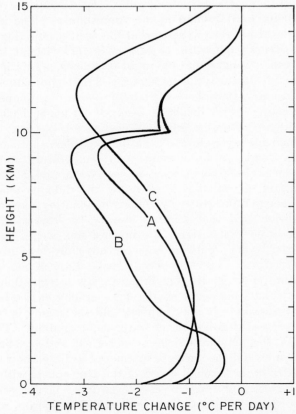

FIG. 3–8. Rates of cooling by infrared radiation at various heights in the atmosphere.
Curve A, middle latitudes, cloudless; curve B, average cloudiness; curve C, tropical
latitudes, cloudless.

reaches its maximum at about 9 km in layers of rapidly decreasing humidity.   The kink in the curve at about 10 km occurs at the base of the
stratosphere and is due to the sudden cessation of the temperature
decrease with height.   Above that height the temperature is approximately unchanging with height, although the water-vapor content continues to decrease.   Curve B for average distribution of clouds shows
some of the same characteristics as A, but the effect of the clouds is to

augment the cooling in their upper parts and to diminish it at their bases (1 to 2 km) as well as to cut down the net loss from the ground.

In curve C, the cloudless tropical atmosphere is seen to be not very different from that of middle latitudes except in the stratosphere. In the tropics the stratosphere is at a greater height than in middle latitudes, so the trend of increased cooling with height continues to about 12 km. The stratosphere is not entered until 16 or 17 km but the water-vapor content and the air density determine the distribution of cooling.

Figure 3–8 does not include the heating due to absorption of insolation by water vapor. Under favorable conditions in the tropics this may

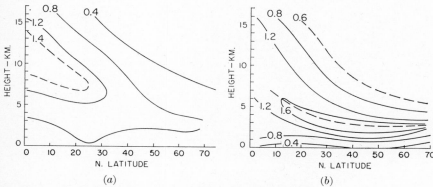

(a)                                    (b)

Fig. 3–9. Cooling rates in a north-south vertical cross section for clear skies (a) and for average cloudiness (b).

amount to 1°C or more per day. J. London[1] has carried out a computation including both the solar heating and the atmospheric radiation. In addition, he has calculated the net effects for various latitudes and heights. The result is shown in Fig. 3–9 where the lines of equal cooling rates are entered in north-south vertical cross sections. Figure 3–9a shows the distribution of net radiational cooling for clear skies and Fig. 3–9b shows the same for average cloudiness. The computations are for the month of March when the radiation budget of the atmosphere is somewhat similar to the average annual radiation budget.

It is noteworthy that the effect of clouds is to increase the cooling at most points in the atmosphere but to diminish it at or near the ground. In the polar regions the presence of clouds doubles the cooling rate at from 2 to 3 km. In the tropics the rate of cooling is not increased so

[1] London, J., The Distribution of Radiational Temperature Change in the Northern Hemisphere during March, *J. Meteorol.*, vol. 9, pp. 145–151, 1952.

much because of the presence of an average cloud distribution, but the level of maximum cooling is lowered.

What balances these cooling rates? The answer is to be found in the action of convection and advection. Through the general circulation of the atmosphere, which will be treated in detail in a subsequent chapter, the atmosphere mixes just enough to preserve, over a long period of time, a steady state. To put the argument the other way around, it may be said that the motions in the atmosphere come about as a result of the different rates of heating and cooling. Thus the atmosphere may be described as a huge thermodynamic engine.

# CHAPTER 4

# THE DISTRIBUTION OF TEMPERATURE

The temperature conditions of any place on the surface of the earth are determined by the following factors:

1. The intensity and daily duration of solar radiant energy received at the outside of the atmosphere over the place in question.

2. The depletion of this energy in the atmosphere by reflection, scattering, and absorption.

3. The albedo of the surface.

4. Important physical characteristics of the surface and its surrounding areas, e.g., whether land or water.

5. Heat budget of surface- and atmospheric-terrestrial radiation.

6. Heat exchanges involved in evaporation, condensation, freezing, and melting of water.

7. Importation of warm or cold conditions by horizontal air currents or ocean currents.

8. Transport of heat upward or downward by vertical currents, convection, and turbulence.

Numerous examples of pronounced temperature effects of these factors can be cited. Because of (1) we have the latitudinal differences in temperature. Differences in the effectiveness of (2) account for the deserts in middle latitudes being hotter than the tropics during their respective warmest seasons. The albedo (3) explains why temperatures of bright dry sand are lower than those of dark dry sand. Under (4) are found the great ocean versus land temperature contrasts. Differences in (5) account for the relatively warm nights in moist regions and relatively cool nights in dry climates. Evaporation, mentioned under (6), often accounts for the cooling during a rain shower, while the melting of ice delays the summer in high-latitude regions. Imported temperature climates (7) account for the pronounced differences in temperature, summer and winter, between west coast and east coast locations in our latitudes. Upward transport of heat by convection currents, mentioned under (8), prevents the temperature from reaching unbearably high values at the surface, while downward transport increases the winter temperatures of locations having mountains to windward.

The temperature changes with which everyone is most familiar are those depending on latitude and altitude. In general, temperatures decrease as one goes toward the poles and as one goes upward in the atmosphere. The change of temperature with altitude is by far the most important, amounting, on the average, to about 6°C per km or about 3.6°F per 1000 ft up to the stratosphere. This is approximately a thousand times greater than the average rate of change of temperature with latitude. The presence of continents and oceans with their greatly contrasting temperatures modifies the latitudinal effect in a very pronounced way in certain localities. For example, in Western Europe during most of the year the surface isotherms (lines of equal temperature) run mainly north and south instead of east and west as might be expected.

The vertical distribution of temperature is likewise affected by the type of underlying surface. The temperature decreases most rapidly with height over continental areas in summer and oceanic areas in winter. Owing to cooling by radiation losses at the surface or by contact of originally warm air with a cold surface, the vertical temperature lapse rate is often modified to the extent that the temperature actually increases somewhat with height through these lower layers. Layers through which the temperature increases with height are called *temperature inversions*. These inversions are most common over continents in winter and over oceans in summer; in other words, they are characteristic of regions that are cool for their latitude owing to the surface conditions.

**The Vertical Distribution of Temperature.** Attempts to arrive at the observed vertical distribution of temperature in the atmosphere by theoretical reasoning, based on radiation studies, have been mentioned. The necessity for taking into consideration processes other than radiation, such as convection, has been pointed out. It is appropriate at this point to make a general survey of the vertical distribution of temperature in the atmosphere to see what various conditions need explaining.

A conventional way of subdividing the atmosphere is to consider it as having three main parts—the troposphere, where the temperature normally decreases with elevation; the tropopause, the point where this decrease in temperature with elevation ceases; and above it the stratosphere, where temperatures change relatively little with elevation and which for the most part may be considered as having a nearly isothermal temperature structure. In meteorology the activities in the troposphere are our main concern, because storms and clouds are confined to it. However, studies of the tropopause and stratosphere have shown that these upper layers have a direct bearing on the conditions that occur in the troposphere and at the surface of the earth.

The troposphere averages from 8 to 18 km deep, depending on latitude and local weather conditions. It is deepest over the equator and shallow over the poles. The tropopause is simply a shallow layer that serves as a transition zone between the troposphere and the stratosphere which lies above. The atmosphere has no fixed outer boundary, but, instead, thins out gradually in the higher levels until the pressure, and therefore the quantity of gases present, eventually approaches zero. More than 90 per cent of the mass of the atmosphere lies below 20 km, yet there are traces of atmospheric matter at 1000 km.

Vertical cross sections of the temperature distribution between 5 and 75°N for summer and for winter are shown in Fig. 4–1. These cross sections were prepared by the U.S. Weather Bureau from balloon soundings throughout the Northern Hemisphere averaged for each latitude belt. They are meridional cross sections averaged for all the meridians, but extending only to 20 km, which is the highest altitude for which a representative geographical distribution of data is obtainable. Above that height only sporadic rocket soundings and indirect calculations are available. The lines in the figure are *isotherms* connecting points of equal temperature in centigrade degrees. The heavy line sloping upward toward the equator is the tropopause, and it is clear from the diagram that it forms a fairly well-marked discontinuity between the region of persistent temperature decrease with height in the troposphere and the region of slight temperature gradients in the stratosphere.

It is noted that the tropopause is lowest over the high-latitude stations and highest near the equator, with the maximum slope in middle latitudes. At all latitudes it is higher in summer than in winter and also has a more nearly constant and gradual slope in the warm season.

The troposphere exhibits stronger south-to-north temperature gradients in winter than in summer at all levels. Especially noteworthy on the winter cross section is the reversal of the isotherms north of lat 60° and below 3 km. This shows an increasing temperature with height, or temperature inversion, resulting from the strong winter cooling of the arctic and subarctic nights. Note also that the strongest horizontal temperature gradients are in middle latitudes, corresponding to the region of greatest slope of the tropopause. This is the region of greatest storm activity.

These charts show that the coldest portion of the atmosphere lies over the equatorial region in the vicinity of the tropopause. For example, in winter the temperatures in the tropics at 17 km are below $-75°C$, whereas near the pole at the same altitude they are higher than $-60°C$ with a maximum of $-55°C$ at the tropopause. In summer the polar

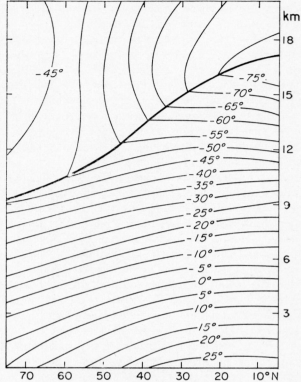

Fig. 4–1. Vertical cross sections of the meridional distribution of temperature in summer.

stratosphere has temperatures in excess of $-45°C$ and the equatorial temperatures are lower than $-75°C$ at 17 km, indicating a difference of about 35°.

When the stratosphere was discovered toward the end of the nineteenth century in Europe, it was identified as an isothermal region. While this is seen to be true, on the average, in the latitudes of Europe, soundings in lower latitudes and near the poles show that this is not the case. The tropical stratosphere is characterized by a temperature inversion, as is also the case in the polar regions in summer. In winter, the polar tropopause often is hard to find because the temperature continues to decrease upward. Until the 1920s meteorologists assumed that the isothermal stratosphere extended to the limits of the atmosphere, which, as we shall presently see, is far from the true state of affairs.

Another way to represent the temperature structure of the atmosphere is by means of soundings at individual stations plotted in a graph of temperature against height. Graphs of mean winter and summer

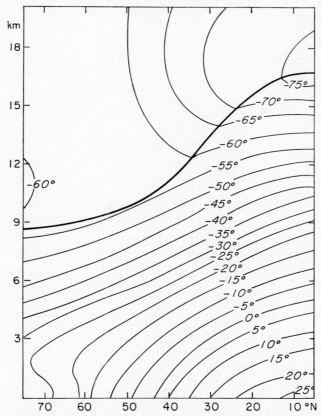

FIG. 4-1. (*Continued*) Vertical cross sections of the meridional distribution of temperatures in winter.

soundings in North America as represented by three stations are shown in Fig. 4–2. The stations are Swan Island, in the tropics; Point Barrow, Alaska, which is inside the Arctic Circle; and Omaha, Nebraska, a continental station of middle latitudes. Plotted with these curves is the so-called "standard atmosphere," adopted by the International Civil Aviation Organization, which approximates a year-round average of all latitudes. This standard, or minor variations of it, is used throughout the world for specifying altitudes and performance of aircraft. The stations on these graphs are a few of the hundreds used for the construction of the cross sections in Fig. 4–1, and they show the features representative of their latitude. As a continental station, Omaha shows the effects of continental cooling of the lower atmosphere in winter. The average sounding of winter shows approximately isothermal conditions through the first 2 km. This average is made up of day-to-day changes

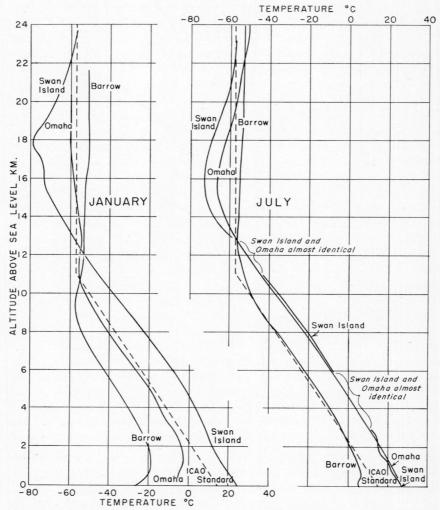

FIG. 4–2. Graphs of mean winter and summer soundings in the North American region.

from extreme inversions to conditions of appreciable lapse rates. In the summer mean soundings, Omaha has approximately the same troposphere temperatures as tropical Swan Island.

**Atmospheric Subdivisions.** A convenient subdivision of the atmosphere based on these soundings plus data from the higher atmosphere takes into consideration five zones or, with the high atmosphere further divided into six zones, a total of ten. They are as follows:

1. A lower region of frictional and diurnal influence about 0.5 to 2 km deep containing in many cases temperature inversions. The so-called "micro-layer" comprising the lowest two meters is included in this zone. It forms the center of interest of a special branch of meteorology known as micrometeorology or microclimatology.

2. The middle and upper troposphere, which has a "normal" rate of temperature decrease with height, viz., about 0.4 to 0.8°C per 100 m. This layer is practically uninfluenced by surface friction on the wind or by diurnal temperature changes.

3. The tropopause, or sometimes a zone of multiple tropopauses, where several small temperature inversions or isothermal layers occur beneath what can be generally classified as the stratosphere.

4. The stratosphere—the nearly isothermal region described above.

5. The high atmosphere—a region comprising several layers of different temperature characteristics which will be described presently.

**The Lower Region.** There is a wide variation in the structure of the lowest layers of the troposphere, depending upon the different relationships of heat transfer between the surface of the earth and these layers by radiation, convection, and conduction.

Variations with latitude are of considerable importance to practical meteorologists, because there is considerable exchange of air between the different latitudes, and because the structure of the lower layers of air from different regions of the earth as they invade other regions is important in determining the weather conditions to be observed. In high latitudes, where the outgoing terrestrial radiation is large, a cooling of the lower layers is pronounced. Therefore, we find that, in the polar regions, especially in winter when the incoming solar radiation is at a minimum, temperature inversions are of frequent occurrence. These are due to the cooling off of the air from below by contact with the radiation-cooled surface. Only the lower layers are at first affected, although eventually, if the air lies in a region of extremely low surface temperatures, this cooling effect may extend to upper layers.

Over tropical regions, where the incoming solar radiation exceeds the net loss due to terrestrial radiation by a considerable amount, one would expect that the heat added to the lower part of the atmosphere would prevent the development of any temperature distribution other than a steady decrease with height. This is true in some tropical locations, especially over land in daytime during the rainy season. However, one of the best-known inversions or near-inversions of temperature is the so-called "trade-wind inversion" characteristic of tropical ocean areas.

Geographical variations in the lower layer occur because of different types of surfaces, e.g., land as opposed to sea surfaces. As pointed out in Chap. 1, continental regions react more quickly to changes in the ratio between solar and terrestrial radiation, so that in summer, when the solar heating is intense, the continental regions achieve high temperature quickly, and in winter the low temperatures become quite pronounced. Over the oceans the summer surface temperatures are relatively lower and in winter considerably higher than over land. This results in a tendency for the creation of temperature inversions over the land in winter and over the oceans in summer. On some occasions the lower layer has the same characteristics as the middle troposphere with regard to temperature distribution and can not then be distinguished. Over relatively cold sea surfaces temperature inversions are due to the fact that the air moving into these regions comes from places where the surface temperatures are higher.

Over the continents, pronounced diurnal variations in the temperature structure of the lowest layers are noted. During the night there is a net loss of heat from the surface of the earth by terrestrial radiation, because there is no receipt of energy from the sun. One of the most common types of temperature inversion, the so-called "nocturnal inversion," is brought about in this way, so that on early-morning temperature soundings, even in summer, a marked inversion near the ground appears. This is usually broken down completely during the day, owing to the excessive heating of the earth's surface by the summer sun. For the same reason that diurnal changes occur, there are variations in the structure of the temperature with the seasons. In this respect, the winter may be compared with nighttime. Therefore, over the land, inversions are most common in winter. In fact, over continental areas they are the rule rather than the exception. In summer, inversions occur only over surfaces that are cold in relation to their surroundings, such as lakes and oceans, or over continental regions in the early morning.

To summarize the various effects of different kinds of surface on the temperature structure in the lower troposphere, it should be noted, then, that the greatest amount of heating and, therefore, the least opportunity for distinguishing between this layer and the middle and upper troposphere would occur over low-latitude continental regions during the daytime in summer. The lower layers best distinguish themselves from the upper and middle troposphere over continental regions at high latitudes during the winter night. Over the oceans, the greatest tendency for the formation of temperature inversions would be where cold water lies near a continental area. In summer the warm continental air is chilled as it passes over the ocean, producing inversions.

**The Middle and Upper Troposphere.** It appears obvious that the middle and upper troposphere could become heated in the same way as the lower region. However, in most places during the course of the day there is not enough solar radiation received at the surface of the earth to cause appreciable heating of the atmosphere above about 2 km. The absorption of direct solar radiation by these layers is negligible. The small amount of heating that does occur, mainly from terrestrial radiation and convection, is sufficient when considered in terms of several days of heating, so that there is an appreciable seasonal variation in the temperature of the middle and upper troposphere. This is shown in the curves of Fig. 4–2, which indicates that during summer the temperatures in the troposphere above 2 km are on the average, in our latitudes, about 20°C higher than in winter.

While it is obvious that the middle and upper troposphere is heated by convection, the process by means of which the troposphere is cooled at these heights is not so clear, mainly because cooling cannot proceed by convection when that cooling occurs mainly at the surface. The reason for this will be discussed in more detail in a later chapter, but it will suffice to say that temperature inversions that must result from surface cooling tend to prevent the free circulation of vertical convection currents. The cooling takes place mainly through radiation processes. These processes have been discussed in a paper by Wexler.[1] The cooling proceeds first in what we have called the lower region, and gradually, by a net loss of heat from the overlying warm air outward to space by way of the surface of the ground, it extends the lower region upward. In the extreme case over continental-polar regions in winter, the layer that we have characterized as the lower troposphere may extend from the ground to about 5 km. Since, under these conditions, the stratosphere or tropopause is at relatively low elevations, the region of normal lapse rate, which we have termed the middle and upper troposphere, may be only 2 or 3 km in thickness. In some extreme cases one finds the middle layer missing entirely.

**The Tropopause.** The tropopause is a transition layer between the troposphere and the stratosphere. Soundings made at single stations usually show a sharp delineation between the normal rate of temperature decrease occurring in the troposphere and the approximately isothermal distribution of the stratosphere. In some cases it is difficult to find such a well-marked discontinuity, especially when an attempt is made to locate a fixed tropopause over a large area from a network of sounding stations. A tropopause delineated at one station may have a pressure and temperature such that no atmospheric processes can be found that would associate this tropopause layer with that noted at some other station. Instead, the tropopause obtained at the first station may be recognizable in terms of temperature and pressure as a small discontinuity occurring at a level at the other station that would not be

[1] Wexler, H., Cooling in the Lower Atmosphere and the Structure of Polar Continental Air, *Monthly Weather Rev.*, vol. 64, pp. 122–136, 1936.

clearly defined as the tropopause. Consequently, meteorologists have come to recognize the principle of multiple tropopauses, in which it is realized that there is normally not one tropopause extending over a large area, but rather a series of overlapping steps in the tropopause, ranging from high elevations and low temperatures over equatorial regions to low elevations and high temperatures near the poles. These discontinuities may vary in location from day to day so that the mean data present only a smooth picture.

**The Stratosphere.** In a rough picturization of the stratosphere we usually think of a region in which the vertical distribution of temperature is isothermal. However, as more and more data are accumulated, it is brought out that it may in many cases consist of rather pronounced temperature irregularities. In many situations, for reasons that are not yet fully understood, the temperature may increase with elevation in the stratosphere to great heights. On other occasions, a number of small inversions and temperature lapses are indicated. Owing to the great difference in altitude of the stratosphere base over the earth, there is a wide variation in the temperatures observed in the lower part. The tropopause temperatures in the polar regions are very much higher than those over the tropics, but in the vicinity of the equator the temperature increases with elevation in the stratosphere, while in the polar stratosphere the temperature usually decreases with height. These two opposite temperature trends serve to diminish stratosphere latitudinal contrasts at levels near 20 km. In the polar stratosphere the decrease of temperature with height sometimes approaches that of the upper troposphere. Since the stratosphere is defined and distinguished only by having a temperature lapse rate markedly less than that of the underlying troposphere, one would be unable to locate a stratosphere in soundings made under these conditions. Such disappearance of the stratosphere over the antarctic region is a regular occurrence, according to Court.[1]

In going from high altitudes over the tropics to low altitudes over the polar regions the tropopause has its greatest slope in middle latitudes. It is here also that the greatest day-to-day and seasonal variations in tropopause heights are found. For example, in North America, more or less polar stratosphere conditions accompany cold winter weather while tropical heights and temperatures accompany warm weather of summer.

Theoretical meteorologists have devoted considerable attention to a quantitative explanation of the existence and temperature distribution of the stratosphere. None of these attempts has been entirely successful, and it is still difficult to present a concise explanation of why there must be a stratosphere or why the temperature is so distributed. We

[1] Court, A., Antarctic Atmospheric Circulation, *Compendium of Meteorol.*, 1951, p. 917.

may approach the problem by starting out with a cold isothermal atmosphere and allowing an accumulation of heat at the surface of the earth by absorption of the solar radiation. This would cause a rapid increase of temperature at the surface in such a way that the temperature would be highest there and would decrease with elevation up to a certain height. This height we might call the maximum altitude of effective heating of the atmosphere by the earth. (The atmosphere is not heated appreciably by the direct solar beam.) Vertical convection currents may arise that would carry heat upward or downward in the atmosphere, as the case might be, and, as will be pointed out in more detail later, these vertical convection currents would accomplish a rather complete stirring of the atmosphere and would produce within the stirred portion a uniform rate of temperature fall with height. There would be a certain maximum altitude of penetration of these convection currents. This height, which would also be the maximum altitude to which heating of the atmosphere would extend, would be the height of the tropopause. In the polar regions, where the amount of heating is small, this height would naturally be low, whereas in the tropics, where the heating is intense and convection can penetrate to high levels, the stratosphere would be found at much greater heights.

In addition to the convection effects, it is possible to obtain the approximately correct temperature distribution from theoretical radiation relationships. Such computations are beyond the scope of this book.

**The High Atmosphere.** Soundings by rockets and data deduced from physical and chemical effects show that layers having marked special properties exist above the heights normally reached by meteorological balloons. The temperature distribution shown in Fig. 4–3 is for the ICAO standard atmosphere, as in Fig. 4–2, extended provisionally to about 300 km. The standard is derived from rocket soundings. The "molecular-scale temperature" above 91 km is the ordinary kinetic temperature corrected for the lower molecular weight of the air at those heights, given by $T \times m_0/m$, where $m_0$ is the molecular weight of 28.966, considered constant up to 91 km, and $m$ is the molecular weight at the greater heights.

The increase of temperature with height above the isothermal stratosphere to 47 km is explained as being due to the intense absorption of ultraviolet radiation by the ozone which is concentrated there. The highest temperature is near the upper part of the ozone distribution where the radiation is first intercepted and absorbed.

From 80 to 130 km the atmosphere of nitrogen and oxygen ($O_2$) is gradually transformed into one of nitrogen and monatomic oxygen (O). The ultraviolet rays are responsible for dissociating the oxygen. It should be noted that this is the region in which the temperature increases

with height.   The reduction of the molecular weight of the air at these
levels is due to the dissociation of the oxygen.

Above 70 km are the layers of the *ionosphere*, well known to radio
amateurs and scientists as the important layers for long-distance radio
transmission.   Radiation from the sun in the extreme ultraviolet ionizes
the gases in these layers.   There are several ionized regions but the two

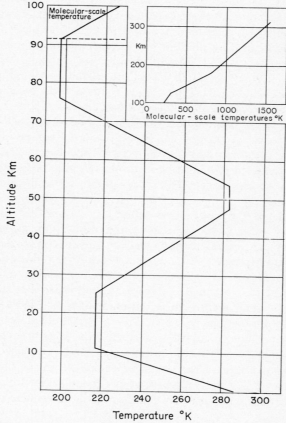

Fɪɢ. 4–3. ICAO standard atmosphere extended provisionally to about 300 km.

main zones of maximum ionization are the *E* layer and the *F* layer.
The ionosphere is considered as extending from 70 km to 500 km with
the *E* and *F* layers concentrated at 100 km and 250 km, respectively.
These heights are only approximate, and some authorities prefer to regard
the ionosphere as a single, deep, ionized section of the atmosphere.

That indefinable layer regarded as the outer limit of the atmosphere
can best be described as the region where molecules cannot be held in

the atmosphere, but escape into space. A height is reached where the collisions between molecules are extremely rare and a molecule from the denser atmosphere below has little likelihood of returning toward the earth by collision with molecules above. Matter exists in interplanetary space, some of it originating outside the solar system. Most of it appears to come from the sun, leading many scientists to regard the plasma beyond our atmosphere as representing the outer extension of the atmosphere of the sun. Magnetized clouds of particles from solar eruptions or flares reach the vicinity of the earth and cause disturbances in our magnetic field, known as magnetic storms.

**Horizontal Temperature Distribution.** Since ancient times people have been aware of differences in the average temperature conditions from place to place over the surface of the known earth. Likewise people have known that these temperatures were not wholly dependent on latitude. Furthermore the ancients knew that weather and temperature changes from day to day at a given locality are due to the transport by the winds of the temperature climates of warmer or colder regions—*advection*. Thus a connection between climatology—the average atmospheric conditions of the earth—and weather forecasting was established. Climatology is a special branch of meteorology and geography that treats of mean temperatures of regions of the earth along with a number of other atmospheric properties. In discussing mean temperatures in this chapter, only a broad view of world temperature distribution will be considered, a more detailed treatment being more in the province of a book on climatology.

Only the data for the horizontal distribution of temperature at the immediate surface of the earth are available in abundance. In the upper air, there are large gaps in the data, but available observations indicate that local differences are much less pronounced than at the surface.

In representing the temperature distribution at the surface, one encounters the difficulty that, because of mountains and plateaus, one is obtaining a combined horizontal and vertical view of temperature variations. It is desirable to have a means of comparing temperatures and representing them on the same horizontal surface. For this reason, climatologists favor having all temperatures reduced to sea level by adding an empirical factor. This eliminates a tangled maze of isotherms that would otherwise be found in mountainous regions where no two stations are likely to be at the same elevation, but it also produces some ridiculous results. For example, the reduction of temperatures to sea level makes the relatively cool plateaus of Mexico and Abyssinia appear as the hottest regions on earth in summer.

The two charts in Figs. 4–4 and 4–5 show the world distribution of mean surface temperature in January and July by means of isotherms. Several

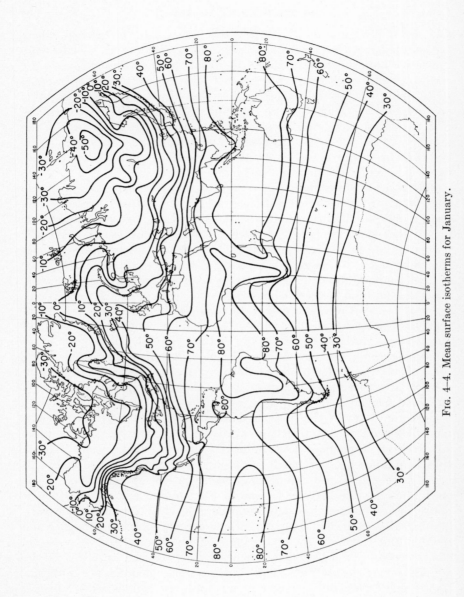

Fig. 4–4. Mean surface isotherms for January.

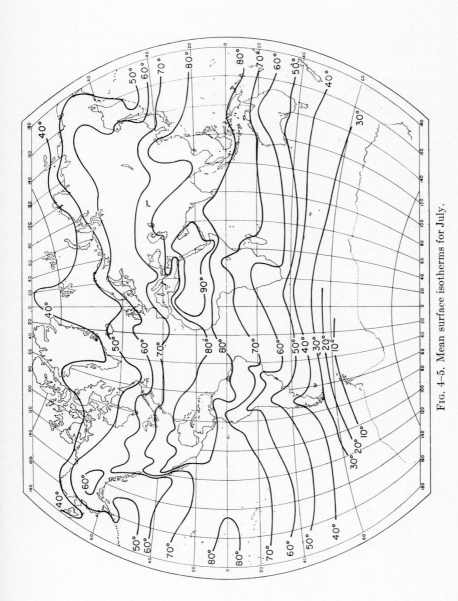

FIG. 4–5. Mean surface isotherms for July.

59

features of these charts should be noted.    In January the continents of the Northern Hemisphere show extreme winter conditions while the oceans exhibit mild conditions.    The trend of the isotherms in western Europe and along the Pacific Coast of North America indicates that the oceanic temperature climate is transported by westerly winds; the eastern coasts show relatively little marine influence.    The greatest south-to-north temperature gradient is over the continents, the least over the oceans.    The intense winter cold of northern Siberia is especially striking, and the effects of the warm Gulf Stream are noted in the Atlantic extending even to the north of Norway.    January is midsummer in the Southern Hemisphere.    The continents are relatively less conspicuous than in the Northern Hemisphere, but they nevertheless stand out as warm spots. The low temperatures along the coast of Peru and Chile and the western coast of South Africa are caused by cold ocean currents in those regions.

The July map shows the Northern Hemisphere continents as considerably warmer than the oceans.    The low temperatures along the Pacific Coast of the United States are due to the transported marine climate plus the effects of the cold California current, which is the counterpart of the cold current off the western coast of South America.    A similar cool belt is noted on the northwestern coast of Africa.    Eastern coastal locations of the Northern Hemisphere, particularly in the United States, show practically no marine influence, again suggesting the mechanism of a temperature climate transported from the continent.

# CHAPTER 5

# OBSERVATIONS AND STATION INSTRUMENTS

Meteorological observations may, for convenience, be considered as of two types—surface observations and upper-air observations. The latter have been made systematically only in recent years, but some form of weather observation by man from his position on the surface of the earth has been made since earliest times. As crude methods of measurement for various natural phenomena were developed, people became interested in knowing the depth of rain falling during a storm; the degree of heat or cold, i.e., the temperature; the strength of the wind, or wind velocity; the degree of dampness of the air, or humidity; and possibly the intensity of the sunshine. These are all quantities to which we are sensitive and which can be judged, or perhaps even measured in a rough way, by our own perceptions. With the development of barometry, a very important meteorological measurement, that of the pressure of the atmosphere, a quantity of which we were almost wholly unaware, could be made.

## MEASUREMENT OF TEMPERATURE

Modern thermometry has been developed to the point where temperatures can be measured to within a thousandth of a degree if desired. If an instrument measuring with such accuracy were exposed to the air under average conditions, it would show such rapid and large fluctuations in the temperature that it would be not only foolish but practically impossible to measure the temperature with this accuracy. The air, at least near the ground, does not ordinarily maintain a constant enough temperature to warrant reading to within less than 0.5°F. Under certain conditions, usually found when fresh cold-air outbreaks are occurring, temperature fluctuations of as much as 2 or 3°F in less than a minute have been observed. Ordinarily, however, no noticeable fluctuations occur in thermometers having a scale readable to a few tenths of a degree.

Of perhaps greater importance are the variations in the temperature read as the thermometer is moved about from place to place within a very short distance, especially over rough or rolling terrain, or as it is placed at different heights above the ground.   On clear calm nights, the net loss of heat by radiation from the surface of the earth is sufficient to make the temperature several degrees lower next to the ground than at a height, let us say, of 2 or 3 m.   On hot summer days, the temperature at the ground may be 2 or 3° higher than at a height of 1 m.   Obviously, under

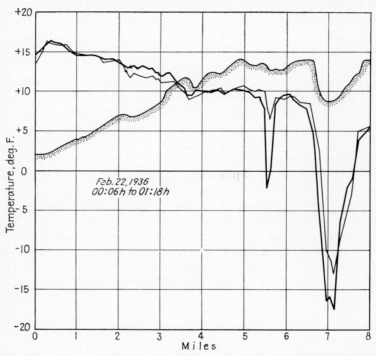

Fig. 5–1. Temperature variations recorded on a moving automobile in Toronto, Ontario, on a night of pronounced radiation cooling. The shaded line represents the profile of the terrain, greatly exaggerated, sloping from Lake Ontario on the left. The abscissa is the distance from the lake. The heavy line shows temperatures on the run toward the lake; the light line, away from the lake.

such conditions, very different temperature readings are going to be obtained depending upon the height at which the thermometer is placed. On cold nights, when there is not much wind to keep the air mixed, the coldest air, because of its greater density, settles into the hollows.   We have all experienced this perhaps in traveling through the country at night.

Figure 5–1 shows the results of temperatures recorded by a sensitive recording thermometer placed on an automobile driven through the streets of Toronto, Ontario, northward from the lake on a clear calm winter night. This record, obtained by Middleton and Millar,[1] is plotted in the figure as temperature against distance from the lake front, and superimposed on the record is a curve showing the profile of the terrain. The sharp drop in temperature as the thermometer is carried into low spots, particularly between 6 and 8 miles where a difference of about 26° in 1 mile is noted, represents admittedly extreme conditions but demonstrates the difficulty of obtaining truly representative temperatures of the air.

**Liquid-in-Glass Thermometers.** Thermometers based on the expansion of liquids with increasing temperature are the most convenient for temperature measurements of the accuracy required in meteorology. They are easy to manufacture, easy to read, and require no maintenance. The mercury thermometer is the most convenient and the most reliable, but in localities where the temperature is likely to reach the freezing point of mercury, $-38.9°C$, alcohol thermometers are used. The liquid expands into a glass tube out of a glass bulb at the bottom, and lengths in the tube are scaled off in terms of temperature to be read at the top point to which the liquid has expanded in the tube. For accuracy, the degree markings should be etched on the glass so that if the glass changes its position with respect to the frame or expands at a different rate, the readings are still reliable.

FIG. 5–2. Weather Bureau type of thermometer.

The thermometer used for official observations of the U.S. Weather Bureau is a glass tube about 10 in. long, mounted on a strip of metal for support and graduated in some 150 Fahrenheit degrees (Fig. 5–2). With a little practice, temperatures in tenths of a degree can be interpolated with good approximation. As stated above, there is no need for such close reading of the temperature, but it will be pointed out presently that in certain types of humidity determination involving wet- and dry-bulb thermometers, readings to this accuracy are important.

It is interesting to know the highest and lowest temperatures reached during any specified period. Weather Bureau records usually show the maximum and minimum temperature occurring each day. Except during rapid changes in the weather, the minimum temperature usually occurs in the early morning and the maximum in the middle or late afternoon. Self-registering thermometers that indicate the highest or

[1] *J. Roy. Astron. Soc. Can.* pp. 265–272, Sept., 1936.

lowest reading reached between times in which they are reset are used for this purpose. They look very much like ordinary thermometers. The maximum thermometer has a constriction in the glass tube which permits the mercury to pass when forced up the tube by temperature expansion, but gravity is insufficient to let the mercury down into the bulb as it cools; hence it stays at its highest reading until the thermometer is shaken or whirled. To ensure proper performance, the thermometer is mounted nearly horizontal but is read in the vertical position. The details of a maximum thermometer are shown in Fig. 5–3(b and c).

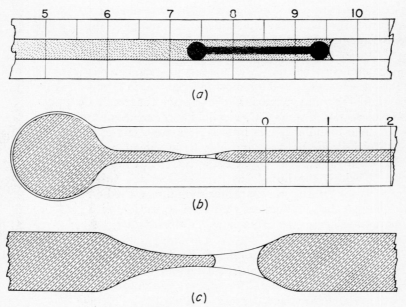

Fig. 5–3. (a) Details of minimum thermometer, (b and c) details of maximum thermometer. (U.S. Weather Bureau.)

The minimum thermometer is an alcohol thermometer with a small glass index having the appearance of a pin with a head at both ends. The index is in the bore inside the alcohol column, kept just below the meniscus by the surface tension there (Fig. 5–3a). The thermometer is mounted in a horizontal position, and as the meniscus retreats toward the bulb, it drags the index with it. As the temperature rises, the liquid leaves the index, so that it remains with its outer end still showing the lowest temperature reached. To reset the thermometer, the bulb end is tilted upward and this is sufficient to cause the index to float to the end of the alcohol column. There, again, the surface tension of the meniscus prevents the index from breaking out of the liquid column into the empty part of the bore.

**Deformation Thermometers.** When two strips of metal having different coefficients of thermal expansion are welded and rolled together, temperature changes will cause the bimetal strip made in this fashion to become distorted by the shearing stress between the two faces of the strip. With most metals at ordinary temperatures this bending can be reproduced time and again in exactly the same amount and thus can be calibrated in terms of temperature. Invar, a metal having an extremely

FIG. 5–4. Hygrothermograph, combining Bourdon-tube type thermograph and hair hygrograph (see next section). (*Friez Instrument Division, Bendix Aviation Corporation.*)

low coefficient of expansion, is commonly used for the inner portion of the arc-shaped strip, with brass or steel on the outer face.

The Bourdon thermometer consists of a curved tube, usually of elliptical cross section, made of metal and filled with some organic liquid. Expansion of the liquid with increasing temperatures forces the tube into a shape of less curvature.

Deformation thermometers are used not for direct measurements of the temperature, but rather for writing a record of it. An instrument designed to make a temperature record in this way is called a *thermograph*. In the usual arrangement, the bimetal or Bourdon thermometer moves a pen arm that writes with ink or scratches on a lampblacked surface on a drum rotated by clockwork (Fig. 5–4). These thermometers can also be made to operate a rheostat, make and break electrical circuits, control radio sets, etc., to make remote records of temperature. Their most common nonmeteorological use is in thermostatic controls, such as in house-heating installations, hot-water heaters, gas stoves, and innumerable manufacturing processes.

**Electric Thermometers.** For measuring and recording temperature accurately, with great sensitivity or in a very small space, electrical methods are best. Two general types of electrical thermometers are in use: (1) the thermocouple or thermopile and (2) the resistance thermometer. A discussion of these can be found in physics textbooks. The thermocouple is based on the fact that a current flows between two junctions of two metals if one junction is considerably hotter or colder than the other. The junctions, made of such pairs of metals as copper and constantan, can be made so small that they can be fitted or fused into a small space and, being almost massless, their sensitivity is high and time lag very small. In its use in meteorology the thermocouple is often arranged with the cold junction in a bath of dry ice and acetone or of liquid nitrogen and the other junction in the place where the measurement is wanted. The current may be amplified and recorded on any one of a number of suitable recorders either by direct wire or by a radio-transmitted signal.

Resistance thermometers are based on the principle that the electrical resistance of a conductor varies with its temperature. The platinum-wire thermometer is of this type. Recently it has been recognized that high sensitivity and highly satisfactory results can be obtained from ceramic resistors. These have negative resistance coefficients; that is, the resistance decreases with increasing temperature instead of increasing as it does in metals. One type of ceramic resistor in use, called the *thermistor*, has a very high negative coefficient, varying from approximately 20,000 to 2,000,000 ohms for the temperature range from +60°C to −90°C. This makes it very suitable for meteorological measurements. It is made 0.02 in. in diameter and 1 in. in length and is coated with a pigment which makes it more than 90 per cent reflective to the solar radiation. Its small mass assures good sensitivity. It is widely used for upper-air measurements, with the readings radiotelemetered to a ground recorder.

**Exposure of Thermometers.** One often hears people talking about the temperature "in the shade" as against that "in the sun." Actually, the temperature we measure is that of the air, and it is about the same whether it is over a shady spot or a sunny one. The air is perfectly free to move about to equalize itself by stirring any purely local horizontal heat differences that may develop. We feel cooler when we are in the shade, not because the air around us is cooler, but because our bodies are no longer receiving and absorbing the powerful rays of the sun.

A thermometer is also capable of absorbing heat if exposed to the sun or to radiation from any other surface. Since the air absorbs an almost negligible amount of the solar radiation, a thermometer in the sun will be warmer than the air, and the temperature it records will be not that of the air but that of its radiation-warmed bulb. The temperature thus recorded would be different for every design of thermometer, depending to a large extent on its mass and absorbing properties. By means of thermocouples or other suitable apparatus we can measure the temperature of such things as solid objects exposed to the sun and find that they are much warmer than those in the shade, but this will not be found to be true of the air.

In order for a thermometer to have the same temperature as the air, it must be protected from all kinds of radiation that it can absorb but which the air cannot. This can be accomplished by placing a lightweight highly polished tube around the thermometer, opened at both ends and with plenty of air space for ventilation. It is well to ensure ventilation in a stationary installation by drawing air through the shielding tube with a fan. As an extra precaution, the protection may consist of two concentric cylindrical tubes with air space between them. If properly shielded and ventilated in this way, the instrument should give the same readings whether mounted in the sun or in the shade.

For convenience when several instruments have to be used, a special shelter to house all the instruments, such as thermometers (wet and dry bulb, maximum and minimum) and humidity recorders, is installed. This instrument shelter, or thermometer screen, as it is sometimes called, is constructed as protection from the weather as well as from the sun or other radiating surfaces. It is usually made of wood and is shaped like a box with louvered sides and bottom and a double roof or top having a 2- or 3-in. air space. The shelter is painted white and mounted on an open framework, usually of such a height that the thermometers are about 5 ft above the ground. The shelter is set up with the door on the north side so that the sun cannot enter while the observer is reading the instruments. For winter observations or in northerly latitudes, the north side of the shelter may be left open, provided that there is no nearby building or other surface radiating from that direction. Two types of U.S. Weather Bureau shelters are shown in Fig. 5–5.

In spite of careful attention paid to details in the design of instrument shelters, on calm clear days of intense sunlight the air in the shelter may acquire a temperature as much as 4°F higher than that in the surroundings, owing to radiation absorbed by the shelter. On clear calm nights, the shelter may lose enough heat by net radiation to make its temperature

lower than that of the air. These radiation effects can be minimized by
proper ventilation. In any event, the shelter must be constructed so as
to permit free through passage of the air.

Older writings in meteorology were much concerned about the accuracy of thermometers. Now, however, meteorologists realize that a far
more significant problem is that of obtaining representative readings of

FIG. 5–5. Two types of U.S. Weather Bureau shelters.

the temperature. Even today we find some instrument shelters on the
tops of skyscrapers in cities while others are over cool lawns in the country;
some on the roofs of hangars or low buildings at dusty airports, others
hidden away in the forests. The city is a great mass of stone that heats
up intensely under the sun's rays, its cooling by radiation at night partly
intercepted by a blanket of smoke, its buildings in winter continuously
giving up part of the heat from their furnaces through the chimneys and
through the walls and windows. One doubts that the farmer cares much

about the temperature in the city or that the gas company is concerned about the temperature out in the country beyond its mains.

Under some circumstances, particularly when it is cloudy and the winds are strong, the differences due to radiation processes between different types of exposure are small. Sometimes great uniformity of temperature is reported over wide areas. However, in clear weather, without much wind, and particularly in winter, the exposure has much to do with the temperature. The curve for Toronto in Fig. 5–1 is an example.

## HUMIDITY MEASUREMENTS

By *humidity* we mean some measure of the quantity of water in *vapor* or gaseous form contained in a given portion of the atmosphere. This may be expressed directly as the number of grams of water vapor in a cubic meter, or in terms of the contribution of the water vapor to the total of the pressure of all the atmospheric gases. The latter is called the *vapor pressure*. It may be stated in terms of specific humidity, relative humidity, temperature of the dew point, or possibly some other quantities. All these water-vapor measures will be defined and discussed in detail in Chap. 8. We shall confine ourselves now to a discussion of instruments that will be sensitive to changes in the humidity or water-vapor content. Such instruments are called *hygrometers*.

**Absorption Hygrometers.** The most obvious way to measure the water-vapor content is to pass a sample of known volume or mass of the atmosphere through chemicals that absorb all the water vapor. By weighing the absorbing material before and after the measurement, the mass of water vapor in the sample can be determined. Sulfuric acid is one of the better known chemicals having this property, but it is difficult to use because of its corrosive nature. Certain salts, such as $CaCl_2$, $P_2O_5$, $NH_4Cl$, $Ca(NO_3)_2$, and $MgCl_2$ are well suited to this type of measurement.

The chemical-absorption method of measuring humidity, while supposedly quite accurate, is difficult to practice. It takes so much time to take a reading that it can be used accurately only to obtain a mean value over an hour or perhaps a whole day. In evaporation studies, in which an integrated value of the humidity over a considerable period of time is desired, chemical-absorption hygrometers are useful.

Another type of absorption hygrometer is based on electrical changes produced by the absorption of water on electrical-conducting materials. An instrument of this type developed by Dunmore has been used with considerable success in radio-balloon soundings (see page 100). This hygrometer measures the electrical resistance of a film containing lithium chloride, LiCl, which is hygroscopic. The resistance also depends on the temperature, so that a correction of the readings due to temperature is necessary.

**The Hair Hygrometer.** Anyone living in the variable climates of middle latitudes is familiar with the nuisance of doors and windows sticking in warm moist weather and being rather loose in dry conditions. This is caused chiefly by the swelling of the wood with increasing humidity. Other normally dry organic tissues, such as skin and hair, exhibit similar changes in dimensions with changing humidity. Animal hairs, partly because of their fine texture, are the most sensitive, and in this respect human head hairs are best.

The humidity reaction of hairs follows most closely that of the *relative humidity*. Relative humidity is defined as the ratio of the quantity of water vapor present to the quantity required for saturation at the given temperature and pressure. This means that at a given temperature and pressure there is a certain water-vapor *capacity*, so that further moisture that is added normally cannot remain in the vapor form but must start to condense as fog. When the capacity or equilibrium amount is reached, the water vapor is said to be at *saturation*, or the air space is said to be *saturated*. The relative humidity usually is expressed in percentage of saturation, so that at saturation it is 100 per cent, and when the water-vapor content is half the capacity or saturation value, the relative humidity is 50 per cent, etc.

The human head hair increases its length by about $2\frac{1}{2}$ per cent as it is brought from 0 to 100 per cent relative humidity. Different hair specimens have different ranges of total expansion, but there is fair uniformity in the relation between the relative humidity and the fraction of the total elongation. This relation is very closely logarithmic.

Like most materials, the hair also increases its length with increasing temperature. This requires a temperature correction that can be obtained only through calibration. The correction is not a constant one, being greater when the humidity is high. The temperature effect is quite small compared with the humidity effect on the hair, but it cannot be neglected.

The hair hygrometer is utilized where a written or transmitted record of humidity is required. Usually a single hair is not strong enough to support or drive a pen arm or switch. For this purpose a bundle of hairs is used. Much of the sensitivity of the hairs is lost in this way, and it has been argued that a single, coarser and stronger hair, such as a horsehair, might be better than a bundle of human hairs.

The hair hygrometer or hygrograph is far from being a satisfactory instrument. It is reliable only if calibrated frequently and carefully. Its chief disadvantage, especially for use in ascending airplanes or balloons, is that it has a very large time lag. Vertical gradients of humidity are often quite large in the atmosphere, and this instrumental lag is serious.    The electrical-absorption hygrometer has much less lag and is therefore preferred.    The greatest difficulty is encountered at low temperatures, since the hair lag increases as the temperature decreases, becoming approximately infinite at a temperature of $-40°$.   This means that at high levels or in polar regions the instrument is practically worthless.    A hair type of hygrograph is shown as part of Fig. 5–4.

**The Psychrometer.**    If an ordinary liquid-in-glass thermometer bulb is covered with a piece of tight-fitting muslin cloth, it becomes a wet-bulb thermometer; for, if the cloth-covered bulb is wetted with pure water and the thermometer is properly ventilated, the temperature reading will decrease to a certain point at which it will remain until all the water is evaporated.    This final temperature is called the *wet-bulb temperature*. The decrease in the temperature reading is caused by evaporation of the water from the bulb, resulting in a loss of heat from the wet surface in the form of the heat of vaporization.    This evaporation in a short time produces a steady-state temperature condition, which is the wet-bulb temperature.    The amount of evaporation that occurs, and therefore the amount of cooling, depends on the quantity of water vapor present in the surrounding air.    If the surroundings are already saturated, there will be no evaporation from the wet bulb, and it will read the same as a dry-bulb thermometer.

The humidity values obtained from the measurement depend on the difference between the dry- and wet-bulb readings, or what is called the *depression* of the wet bulb, and on the actual temperature.    The relationship is determined semi-empirically and is represented in various convenient tables, such as those of the Smithsonian Institution (Washington, D.C., 1952).

It is seen, then, that the determination depends on the reading of two temperatures, the wet and the dry.    A wet-bulb thermometer and an ordinary thermometer mounted side by side make up what, curiously, is regarded as a separate individual instrument called by the high-sounding name, *psychrometer*.

Most psychrometric tables are computed on the basis of a ventilation of from 4 to 10 m per sec.    Several methods of providing this ventilation are used.    In the United States the most common method is to whirl the two thermometers.    When the thermometers are mounted in an instrument shelter, they are whirled by turning a crank, geared for proper speed, or about 4 revolutions per sec.    For measurements in the open, a crank handle is attached to the upper end of the thermometer mountings.    This arrangement is known as a *sling psychrometer*.    Three types of psychrometer are shown in Fig. 5–6.

The Assmann psychrometer is considered standard for general use.

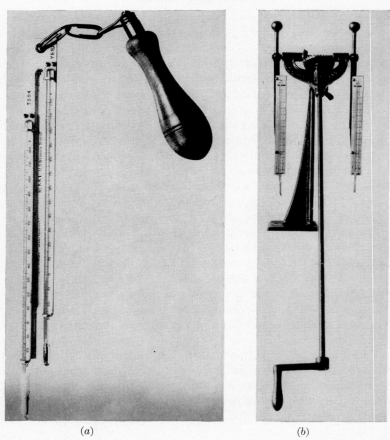

$(a)$                                      $(b)$

Fig. 5-6. Three types of psychrometer. (a) Sling psychrometer, (b) whirling psychrometer.

It ventilates the thermometers by drawing air past them by means of a fan through double-walled metal tubes in which the thermometers are mounted. The metal tubes also serve as radiation shields.

An important difficulty in using the psychrometer method is brought about by the fact that at low temperatures differences in wet-bulb depression of a few tenths of a degree may mean differences in relative humidity, for example, of perhaps 10 per cent. Therefore it becomes necessary to read the two temperatures to tenths of a degree. Even if the temperature is fluctuating widely, it should be possible, by reading the two thermometers practically simultaneously, to obtain proper values, *provided* that both thermometers have the same lag. Spilhaus[1] has noted that the lag

[1] *Trans. Roy. Soc. S. Africa*, vol. 24, pp. 184-202, 1936.

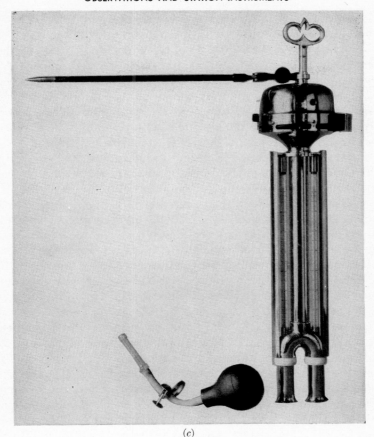

(c)

FIG. 5-6. (Continued) (c) Assmann psychrometer.

coefficient of the wet bulb is lower if the two thermometers are of the same size and are placed in the same air stream. This difficulty may be circumvented by increasing the ventilation of the dry bulb or by substituting a smaller thermometer.

**Dew-point Apparatus.** For every value of the water-vapor content, there is a temperature at which this quantity will produce saturation. Since supersaturation does not ordinarily occur, this temperature would be lower than the actual temperature or equal to it in the case of saturation in the beginning. This temperature is called the *temperature of the dew point*, and it may be achieved by cooling the air at constant pressure and without allowing the total water-vapor content to change. When a solid body is cooled to the dew point, dew begins to condense on it. If the temperature of the surface of such a body can be measured it would provide a means of obtaining the dew-point temperature. This quantity, once obtained, together with the temperature and pressure, can be converted into any other expression of the humidity that may be desired.

Some forms of the dew-point apparatus are crude and simple. A small reservoir of ether is placed behind a silvered disk or in a silvered tube. By bubbling air through the ether, it is made to evaporate and cool, and the silvered surface is supposed to cool at the same rate. The surface is so highly polished that one notices immediately the dulling of reflections caused by the condensation of dew. The temperature of the ether is read on a thermometer immersed in it, and if the instrument is properly constructed and the thermometer is read just at the right time, the reading will be the temperature of the dew point.

The principal difficulty with the instrument is in obtaining a clear-cut beginning of the dew formation so that the observer knows when to read the temperature. Furthermore, it is not possible for the observer to keep his eyes on the polished surface and the thermometer at the same time. This is sometimes serious, because the temperature is changing rapidly as the ether is cooled, and a slight delay in reading may introduce an appreciable error. Finally, the dew does not always disappear at the same temperature that it formed.

A modern recording dew-point hygrometer substitutes a photoelectric cell for the human eye and employs suitable electronic circuitry.[1] A tiny mirror is fused to the outside end of a copper rod, the main part of which is immersed in a refrigerant contained in a Dewar flask. The temperature of the mirror can be kept constant by induction heating to balance the conduction cooling. As dew forms on the mirror, the diminution of a light beam reflected from the mirror causes the photocell to actuate the heating circuit. The system can be made to supply just the right amount of heat to hold a steady condition in which the dew is neither thickening nor disappearing. The temperature is obtained through a thermocouple junction fastened to the back of the mirror, and recorded electronically.

## THE MEASUREMENT OF PRESSURE

The pressure is defined as the force per unit area exerted by the air,

$$p = \frac{F}{A}$$

It is not necessary to specify the direction of the force or the orientation of the unit area of surface, because the pressure is exerted equally in all

---

[1] See, for example, Barrett, E. W., and L. R. Herndon, Jr., An Improved Electronic Dew-point Hygrometer, *J. Meteorol.*, vol. 8, pp. 40–51, 1951.

directions. If the acceleration of gravity $g$ is the only acceleration present and if $M$ is the total mass of the overlying atmosphere, then

$$F = Mg$$

which is the weight of the atmosphere. Under these conditions, the atmosphere is said to be in static equilibrium, and the pressure is defined as the weight per unit area or the weight of a column of air of unit cross section to the top of the atmosphere, i.e.,

$$p = \frac{Mg}{A}$$

Under most circumstances this may be considered to be the case.

In the cgs system of units, the pressure is expressed in terms of dynes per square centimeter. For meteorological purposes, this unit is too small, so 1000 times this unit, the *millibar*, is used. A *bar* is one million dynes per cm² and a millibar is one thousandth of that, or 1000 dynes per cm². The average pressure at sea level, the "normal" pressure of physics and chemistry, is generally taken to be $1.0136 \times 10^6$ dynes per cm², or 1013.6 mb. In British units, the pressure would be in pounds per square inch, and the average at sea level is about 14.9 lb per sq in. The latter units are never used in meteorology for pressure values, the millibar being standard throughout the world.

Torricelli, in 1643, found that, when a tube 33 in. long, filled with mercury, was inverted and the open end immersed in a dish of mercury, a small quantity of mercury would run out of the tube until the mercury column stood at a height of about 30 in., thus leaving a vacuum above. This experiment amounted to measuring the pressure of the atmosphere by balancing it against the weight of a column of mercury, and it was found that the pressure of the atmosphere was equivalent to that exerted by approximately a 30-in. depth of mercury. This type of glass tube filled with mercury and having its lower end open and immersed in a dish or cistern of mercury is called a *Torricellian* tube and is essentially the standard form of modern mercury barometers.

The balancing of the atmosphere against a mercury column has become so common a procedure that in most practical work in the physical sciences the pressure is expressed in terms of the length of the supported mercury column, such as 760 mm, 29.92 in., etc., instead of the regular pressure units of dynes per square centimeter or pounds per square inch.

In a Torricellian tube, the cross-sectional area of the column does not affect the reading unless the tube is of such narrow bore that capillary forces between the glass and mercury occur. If the column is 3 cm² in cross section, the force, being pressure times area, is three times as great

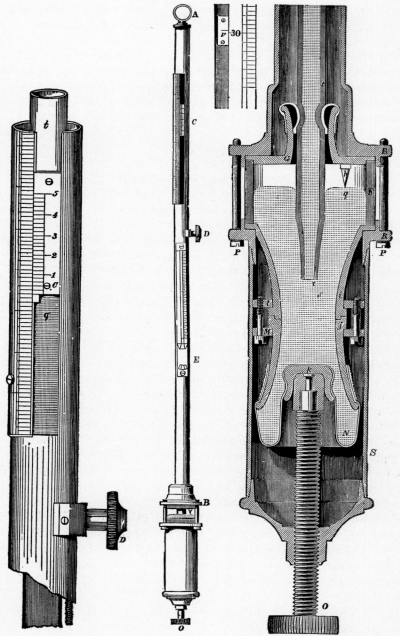

Fig. 5–7. Fortin-type mercurial barometer.   *Left*, details of vernier scale: the sliding
scale (*C*) is operated by a thumbscrew (*D*) on the housing over the tube (*t*).   The

as the force per unit area (the pressure); therefore the mercury will stand at the same height against a vacuum regardless of cross-sectional area as long as it is greater than capillary size.

The mercury in the glass also acts as a thermometer, expanding as the temperature rises, contracting as it decreases. In order to make comparable readings in terms of the length of the mercury column, the values are reduced to that which would be obtained if the mercury were at a temperature of 0°C. Therefore, when we state that the pressure is 760 mm Hg, we mean that the atmosphere has a pressure equal to that of mercury which at a temperature of 0°C would have a height of 760 mm.

To find out how much this pressure of 760 mm of mercury is, we need to know the weight of the mercury. From physical tables, the mass of a cubic centimeter of mercury at various temperatures can be obtained. This is known as the *density* or mass/volume. At a temperature of 0°C it is 13.6 g per cm³. Since pressure is expressed in terms of 1 cm² we need only consider a square centimeter portion of the mercury. Such a column 760 mm high would have a mass equal to the density times the height. The pressure exerted by the mercury column is

$$p = \frac{Mg}{A} = \rho g h$$

where $\rho$ is the density of the mercury and $h$ is the height of the column ($A = 1$). Taking $g = 980.6$ cm per sec², which is the value at sea level at lat 45°, the pressure is

$13.6 \times 980.6 \times 76 = 1.0136 \times 10^6$ dynes per cm², or 1013.6 mb

In the Torricellian tube, the length that is measured is that of the column extending above the level of the mercury in the dish, or *cistern*, as it is called. The measuring scale must therefore have its zero point at the level of the mercury in the cistern. In the barometers in general use, the designs are such as to eliminate the necessity of moving the scale as this level changes.

Two kinds of mercury barometer are in general use—the Fortin type and the fixed-cistern type. In the Fortin type, the level of the mercury in the cistern is raised to the zero point of the scale while the scale remains fixed. The bottom of the cistern is made of kidskin, which may be raised

---

slide rests at the apex of the meniscus of the mercury (*q*) for correct reading. *Center,* full view showing attached thermometer (*E*) for temperature correction, suspension ring (*A*), base (*B*), and screw (*O*) for adjusting zero of mercury column. *Right,* details of cistern: mercury (*q*) is adjusted to the level of the index pointer (*h*); the tube (*t*) enters the cistern through the collar (*G*). The portion (*N*) of the bottom of the cistern is kidskin, adjusted by the screw (*O*) through the head (*k*). (*U.S. Weather Bureau.*)

or lowered by a setscrew to the desired zero point before reading.   A
small ivory pointer indicates the zero point.   The reflection of this
pointer is seen in the mercury, and the screw is turned up until the ivory
tip just touches its image.   Air has access to the instrument through a
leather collar or porous gasket between the cover of the cistern and the
tube.   The Fortin-type barometer is shown in detail in Fig. 5–7.

In the fixed-cistern or Kew type, no attempt is made to have the zero
point always at the surface of the mercury in the cistern.   Instead, the fall
of the mercury in the cistern accompanying a rise in the tube is taken into
account by altering the graduations on the scale.   A change in pressure
of 1 cm will change the height of the mercury in the tube by an amount
less than 1 cm, depending on the relative areas in the tube and in the
cistern.   If the cistern is of large cross section compared with the tube,
this discrepancy will be small.   If $A$ is the area of the tube and $S$ that of
the cistern (minus intruding tube), then the rises or falls in the tube and
cistern will be in the following ratio:

$$\frac{\text{Rise in tube}}{\text{Fall in cistern}} = \frac{\text{area of cistern}}{\text{area of tube}}$$

$$\frac{x}{x'} = \frac{S}{A} \quad \text{and} \quad x' = \frac{xA}{S}$$

The pressure (or height of the mercury column above the mercury in the
cistern) changes by an amount equal to the rise in the tube plus the fall
in the cistern, or $x + x'$.   But

$$x + x' = x + \frac{xA}{S} = x\left(1 + \frac{A}{S}\right) = x\,\frac{(A + S)}{S}$$

The change in the tube $x$ as the pressure rises 1 cm ($x + x' = 1$) can be
determined by making the right-hand side of the above equation equal to
one, which is true when $x = S/(A + S)$ cm.

The barometer usually has $S$ about fifteen times as large as $A$ so that
the mercury in the tube rises nearly 0.95 cm or 0.95 in. for each whole
centimeter or inch of pressure rise.   The scale is graduated in units of
$S/(A + S)$ centimeters or inches, but labeled in the standard centimeters
or inches corresponding, therefore, to the true readings of the pressure.
The details of a fixed-cistern barometer are shown in Fig. 5–8.

All mercury barometers are constructed for accurate readings.   A
sliding vernier scale gives graduations to tenths of a millimeter or even
thousandths of an inch.   The scale is intended for a reading at the
highest point of the meniscus of the mercury.   A thermometer is attached
for the purpose of reducing the readings to correspond with a mercury
column at standard temperature, 0°C.   The temperature corrections are

to be found in the Smithsonian Meteorological Tables. The tables usually include also a correction for the temperature effect on the brass scale.

The fixed-cistern barometer has the advantage that it can be read quickly, easily, and accurately, but has the disadvantage that any loss of mercury during transportation affects the readings. The Fortin type is not affected by ordinary small losses of mercury, but the necessity for setting the cistern to zero before each reading presents a difficulty. Observers cannot be consistently sure of getting the exact zero in their settings. Considerable attention given to the lighting around the barometer, especially if the mercury has lost some of its luster, is necessary in order to ensure that the ivory pointer and its image can be matched exactly by semiskilled observers.

**Aneroid Barometers.** The aneroid barometer gets its name from the Greek word for *dry*, since no liquid is used. Just as in weighing machines there are those which balance the object to be weighed against known weights and those which use springs, so in barometry there are two types —those which balance against weights (mercury barometers) and those which operate with springs. The aneroid is of the latter type.

Fundamentally, the aneroid barometer consists of an evacuated chamber and a spring. The spring keeps the chamber from collapsing under the pressure of the atmosphere and restores the chamber to a larger shape when the pressure is reduced. The chamber is of thin metal that can expand or contract the chamber as the pressure changes. The best types are in

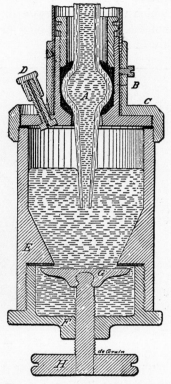

Fig. 5–8. Details of the cistern of a fixed-cistern barometer. The tube (*A*) rests in a collar (*B*). The thumbscrew and head (*H* and *G*) are used when carrying. (*U.S. Weather Bureau.*)

the form of metal bellows. The spring may be in the form of either a spring arm outside the chamber or a helical spring inside. Some newer forms have the bellows themselves built for resilience like a spring. A common type of aneroid is shown in Fig. 5–9.

The deflections of the spring and chamber are multiplied by levers so that they may operate a pointer on a dial marked with pressure readings.

The aneroid has a temperature correction due to temperature effects on the characteristics of the spring and on the small amount of gas contained in the chamber. Modern designs have been fairly successful in providing compensating mechanisms for these temperature effects.

A common use of the aneroid is for providing a written record of the pressure, i.e., *barographs*. Instead of a pointer, a pen arm is moved which writes on a drum rotated by clockwork. Barograph traces are of considerable importance in weather forecasting. A barograph is pictured in Fig. 5–10.

Fig. 5–9. Aneroid barometer. (*U.S. Weather Bureau.*)

The great advantage of the aneroid barometer is its portability. It is especially suitable for use on shipboard, because it is not affected appreciably by swaying, can be hung on any convenient wall, and is as easy to read as a compass. The disadvantage is that its pointer must be reset at fairly frequent intervals by comparison with the mercury barometer. Unfortunately there are many inferior aneroid barometers on the market and only a few excellent ones. No general statement about the performance or reliability of aneroids can be made because of the wide variation in design and workmanship. The U.S. Weather Bureau, however, uses aneroid barometers with great success at hundreds of secondary stations.

*Altimeters* are aneroid barometers made with a scale of altitude instead of pressure. This can be done because of the close relationship between height and pressure. Under average conditions, the pressure decreases with height in the lower part of the atmosphere at a rate of about 10 mb per 100 m or about 1 in. of mercury per 1000 ft.  The rate of decrease is not always the same, varying with temperature, pressure, temperature lapse rate, and humidity, stated in the order of their importance.   The altimeter, if it is accurate, measures the pressure correctly. By setting the zero of the scale to the pressure at sea level or at the ground, altitudes for a standard atmosphere can be read off directly. If the atmosphere is colder than standard, the altimeter will give too high an altitude and if it is warmer, the reading will be too low.   The readings probably never vary more than 5 per cent from true values.   The effects of other meteorological elements besides temperature can be neglected in

Fig. 5–10. Barograph, aneroid.   (*U.S. Weather Bureau.*)

practical air navigation.  Tables or slide rules can be made up for applying temperature corrections to altimeter readings.  It should be emphasized again, however, that these corrections have nothing to do with the instrument itself but apply to the pressure-height relationship that the graduations on the scale assume.  The correction should be applied in terms of the mean temperature of the atmosphere intervening between the altitude in question and the ground.

**"Exposure" of Barometers.**  Most meteorological instruments have peculiar problems of exposure to the air in order to obtain representative readings.  This is not true of barometers, because they measure not the properties of a "sample" of air, as do thermometers, hygrometers, etc., but simply the force exerted at the height of measurement by the overlying atmosphere. Barometers do not have to be exposed in the open; in fact, because of obvious convenience, they are always mounted indoors. The pressure inside a building is always the same as that at the same level outside, except for momentary differences in severe wind storms. In mounting a mercurial barometer, care must be taken not to place it where the temperature is likely to fluctuate appreciably, because the temperature correction is based on the assumption that the mercury in the barometer has the same temperature as that in the attached thermometer. The latter is more sensitive to temperature changes, and a wrong correction value may be obtained under fluctuating temperature conditions. For this reason it is best to keep the barometer on the inside wall of a room that is kept at a fairly uniform temperature. This is not much of a problem in most government or airport buildings in which meteorological offices are housed.

The problem of exposure of aneroids in airplanes is more difficult, since airplanes are especially built to create local pressure differences. The pressure in the vicinity of the instrument panel on most airplanes is far different from the static pressure of the free air. Therefore, airplane altimeters are connected to the outside air by means of a tube with its opening on some part of the airplane where no dynamic pressure effects are present. Such precautions are never necessary in the vicinity of ordinary structures, such as buildings. This emphasizes the very special nature of airplane design, for it is doubtful that any other structure could be found that would produce systematic dynamic pressure effects of this nature, even in the strongest winds. There is a nonsystematic dynamic pressure effect noticeable around many buildings in strong winds which causes the barometric pressure to oscillate very rapidly through a small range. This effect is called *pumping* and is especially marked when the winds are strong and gusty, particularly at observatories on mountain peaks. There is no satisfactory way to overcome or correct pumping.

**Sea-level and Gravity Reduction.** In charting atmospheric pressures over the earth, meteorologists are principally interested in pressure differences between one place and another, or the gradient of pressure. They are not interested in the small differences that may be due to differences in the acceleration of gravity at various locations. The acceleration of gravity varies with latitude and with elevation and is also affected by mountains. By international agreement, meteorologists reduce all their pressure observations to standard gravity, the value which prevails at sea level in lat 45° being specified. The value of 980.616 or 980.62 cm per sec$^2$ is used for this standard. If the local acceleration of gravity cannot be measured, it can be obtained by interpolation between measuring stations or by an empirical formula. Formulas and tables are given in the Smithsonian Meteorological Tables. At most stations the gravity correction may be considered a constant value to be added to all barometer readings.

In order to be able to compare readings at stations having different elevations, it is necessary to reduce all observations to a common level. Since most of the earth is at or near sea level, it is common practice to reduce all pressures to sea level for charting or other comparative purposes. In some sections, such as the western part of the United States, where much of the ground is on an elevated plateau, pressures reduced to some higher standard level, such as 5000 ft, are frequently used.

The problem of reduction of pressure to sea level is a very serious yet practical one and could well be made the subject of a complete book. For isolated mountain peaks the problem is not very difficult, being simply that of the airplane altimeter worked in reverse. Over great plateaus and elevated plains, such as in the Western United States, the problem defies exact solution, because there is no atmosphere intervening between the station and sea level about which temperature approximations can be made. In winter, small valleys in the elevated plateaus may be filled with cold air while surrounding stations may be in a place where cold air does not collect. Stations in the cold valley will use the low temperature as representative of the fictitious air column between them and sea level, while the other stations will use a much higher temperature. The colder stations will have a much larger reduction and will therefore have a pressure altogether too high at sea level. It is unfortunate that pressures, which can be measured with great accuracy, should become so inaccurate in certain regions for use on weather charts because of the necessity of reduction by crude methods through some thousands of feet of rock.

## THE MEASUREMENT OF WIND

There are many simple ways of determining the speed and direction of the wind. The ordinary farm windmill is a crude form of instrument that could be used for this purpose. The wind sock used at airports is an excellent wind-direction indicator as is also the wind vane found on many church steeples. The meteorological instrument used officially to measure the wind is a combination of the windmill principle and the old-fashioned wind vane.

A conventional design of wind vane is shown in Fig. 5–11. In order to function properly, the vane should be mounted on bearings that will reduce friction to a minimum, and the vane should be balanced at the point of rotation. The arrowhead, often made of lead, not only gives the vane a finished appearance but serves to balance the weight of the tail.

The cup anemometer, pictured in two forms in Fig. 5–12, has been used by meteorological services for many years. It has an advantage over the common windmill type in that the vertical axis of rotation obviates the necessity of keeping the instrument facing the wind. The instrument

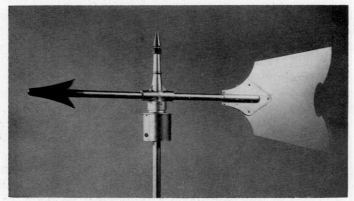

Fig. 5–11. Wind vane. (*U.S. Weather Bureau.*)

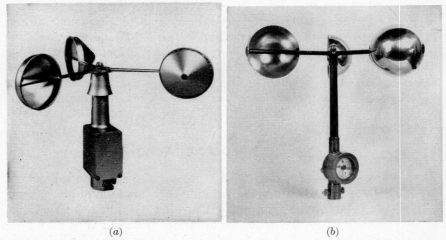

(a)  (b)

Fig. 5–12. Cup anemometers. (a) Airway type, (b) totalizing-dial type. (*U.S. Weather Bureau.*)

can be calibrated so that the number of revolutions in a given time may be translated into wind speed. Obviously the cup wheel must be carefully balanced and mounted in bearings that can be kept properly lubricated in any kind of weather.

A great deal of work has been done by instrument research workers toward perfecting the cup anemometer, but it still has disadvantages, and there is lack of agreement as to which design is best.   One of the chief difficulties is that in a gusty wind the anemometer, because of its inertia, indicates only the mean wind.   Furthermore, the cup accelerates more rapidly than it loses speed, so that the mean wind is registered slightly too high.   All winds are more or less gusty, and much valuable information concerning the turbulence of the lowest layers of the atmosphere is lost through use of this instrument.

The cup anemometer is usually arranged with a dial that counts the revolutions, translating them into miles of wind passage.   This information is not especially useful, since the instantaneous velocity, or at least that averaged over a minute or two, is desired.   Also, it is convenient for the record to be obtained at some distance from the cup wheel.   Some form of electrical contact is used to count the revolutions at a convenient place inside the office.   A common type works through reduction gears that finally make one complete rotation for each $\frac{1}{60}$ mile of air passage, making an electrical contact at each rotation.   By counting the number of contacts through a period of 1 min, the velocity in miles per hour is obtained.   The counting is often done by means of a light or a buzzer.

Fig. 5–13.   Wind-direction and wind-speed indicator.   The light in the center is used for counting contacts of the cup anemometer.   (*U.S. Weather Bureau.*)

A simple way to make the direction register remotely is to have electrical contacts for as many different directions as desired mounted on a small shaft that rotates with the wind vane.   These can be made to light small lamps mounted on a board in the same arrangement as on a compass.   For example, as long as the wind is from the north, the lamp at the upper part of the board will be lit, the lowest lamp for south, etc.   Such a recording board with lights is pictured in Fig. 5–13.

Written records of wind direction and speed can be obtained in several ways.   For recording speed, contacts of the anemometer may be made to pull a pen by closing a circuit into a magnetic coil.   A spring returns the pen to another position between contacts.   Thus, each mile of wind makes a nick in a straight line drawn by the pen across a sheet of paper moved by clockwork. By counting the number of nicks in an hour's displacement of the sheet, the average wind speed during that hour is obtained. The paper is usually mounted on a rotating drum.

For recording direction, perhaps the simplest way is to have four pens, for N, S, E, and W. Contacts on the wind vane can move the appropriate pen by means of an electromagnet once every minute. Combinations of NW, SE, etc., can be arranged by having two contacts made at once. By using a larger number of pens, directions to 16 compass points may be recorded.

FIG. 5–14. Sensing part of Aerovane. (*Bendix-Friez.*)

In recent years there has been an increasing need for detailed information concerning the wind structure near the ground, and anemometers capable of recording individual gusts as well as average speeds have been developed. A great variety of these has appeared in the literature and on the market, but only one which has been widely used in America will be described—the Friez aerovane.[1]

A general external view of the sensing part of the aerovane is shown in Fig. 5–14. The vertical tail fin serves to keep the head facing into the wind. The wind direction and rotation speed of the propellor are transmitted to recorders or indicators by self-synchronous motors or other suitable electronic devices. Wind-tunnel tests have shown the rotation

[1] Wood, L. E., Development of a New Wind-measuring System, *Bull. Am. Meteorol. Soc.*, vol. 26, pp. 361–370, 1945.

speed of the propellor to be essentially a linear function of actual wind speed.

**Exposure of Anemometers.** Unfortunately, many anemometers are exposed on the roofs of buildings in cities. Considering the extremely small portion of the earth occupied by urban settlements, it is obvious that we are not getting a representative record of the flow of the air over the earth. City structures produce friction against the wind flow which may reduce the speeds at some levels by as much as 50 per cent. This is overcome in part by the fact that many of the exposures are on the tallest buildings available—sometimes skyscrapers. In many cases, however, surrounding structures tower above the anemometer and interfere seriously with the wind flow from certain directions.

Airport exposures are usually better than city locations because the absence of tall buildings in the immediate vicinity is practically guaranteed. Here again, however, difficulties arise. The wind from a direction such that it has a sweep clear across the airport before reaching the anemometer will have very little frictional retardation, but the conditions will be very different when the wind is blowing along a line of hangars or through trees or buildings on the side away from the field.

In general, it is unfortunate that practically all installations are on the roofs of buildings. Other things being equal, such anemometers will always record too high a velocity because of the crowding of the streamlines as the air flows over the building. The building itself creates gusts and this effect may vary with wind direction, unless the installation is in the center of a circular building.

Because the wind increases rapidly with height near the ground, one of the first requirements of anemometer installations should be that they all be at the same height. Practical considerations of placing the instruments on city buildings or at airports are apparently so important that little attention is paid to standardizing the height. A height of 9 m has been suggested because it corresponds to the average height above the water at which winds are measured or estimated on shipboard. If such standardization were possible, and proper attention were paid to other details of exposure, winds over the entire earth would be directly comparable. To avoid building effects, the anemometer should be mounted on a tower or pole above a small hut containing the recording instruments or should be wired for remote recording. An ideal location would be in the center of a large field with no sizable trees or building nearby. In forested areas, if no large clearing is available, the anemometer should be above the treetops at the same height that it would be above bare ground.

**Beaufort Scale.** Most ships at sea are not equipped with any type of instrument for determining the wind. It then becomes necessary to estimate it. Admiral Beaufort of the British Navy devised in 1805 a scale for estimating the *wind force*, with definitions based on the effect of the wind on the sails carried. The scale is still used today, and since its first use, the wind speeds corresponding to the various forces, which are 12 in all, have been determined experimentally.

TABLE 5–1. BEAUFORT SCALE OF WIND FORCE

| Beaufort number | Deep-sea criterion (1874) | | Wind speed | | |
|---|---|---|---|---|---|
| | | | knots | mph | m per sec |
| 0 | Calm | | 1 | 1 | 0.4 |
| 1 | Just sufficient to give steerageway | | 1– 3 | 1– 3 | 0.4– 1.5 |
| 2 | That in which a well-conditioned man-of-war, with all sail set, and clean full, would go in smooth water from | 1–2 knots | 4– 6 | 4– 7 | 1.6– 3.3 |
| 3 | | 3–4 knots | 7–10 | 8–12 | 3.4– 5.4 |
| 4 | | 5–6 knots | 11–16 | 13–18 | 5.5– 7.9 |
| 5 | That to which she could just carry in chase, full and by | Royals, etc. | 17–21 | 19–24 | 8.0–10.7 |
| 6 | | Topgallant sails | 22–27 | 25–31 | 10.8–13.8 |
| 7 | | Topsails, jib, etc. | 28–33 | 32–38 | 13.9–17.1 |
| 8 | That to which she could just carry in chase, full and by | Reefed upper topsails and courses | 34–40 | 39–46 | 17.2–20.7 |
| 9 | | Lower topsails and courses | 41–47 | 47–54 | 20.8–24.4 |
| 10 | That with which she could scarcely bear lower main topsail and reefed foresail | | 48–55 | 55–63 | 24.5–28.4 |
| 11 | That which would reduce her to storm staysails | | 56–65 | 64–75 | 28.5–33.5 |
| 12 | That which no canvas could withstand | | Above 65 | Above 75 | Above 33.5 |

The Beaufort scale, with specifications for full-rigged sailing vessels of 1874 and corresponding speeds, is given in Table 5–1.

## MEASUREMENT OF PRECIPITATION

In the atmosphere there is a continuous process of evaporation, condensation, precipitation, and runoff that forms the so-called "water cycle." It makes no difference how we consider the cycle to be started, but in our thinking we may regard it initially in the form of the *evaporation* of water from the oceans. Some of the water vapor added to the atmosphere in this way is *condensed* in the form of clouds over the continents and out of these clouds water falls either in the liquid (rain) or ice (snow, hail, sleet) form to produce *precipitation*. Part of this water makes its way into the ground by *infiltration*, where it may be tapped by the digging of wells or may appear at the surface again in the form of springs. A larger part goes into *runoff*, by means of which the water flows through brooks, glaciers, lakes, and rivers back to the ocean again. The cycle is complicated by the fact that much of the evaporated water is returned *directly* to the ocean by rainstorms at sea and by the fact that a considerable amount of evaporation also occurs from land surfaces. The major currents of the atmosphere, however, are such that water evaporated in one locality is usually precipitated thousands of miles away, so that the cycle can almost never be completed locally.

Of the four processes of the cycle—precipitation, runoff, evaporation, and infiltration—the last two are the most difficult to measure. Only those parts of the cycle which involve the atmosphere come within the province of meteorology, viz., evaporation and precipitation. Runoff and infiltration are the concern of a borderline field between meteorology, engineering, and geology, known as *hydrology*. This will not be treated here.

Evaporation measurements are beset with numerous difficulties because of the complicated nature of the process. Progress in developing instrumental methods for measurement can be made only if the process of evaporation is thoroughly understood. Since the explanation of methods of measurement also requires a thorough understanding of evaporation, discussion of this topic will be reserved for a later chapter in which the whole problem will be treated in some detail.

Rainfall measurements are extremely easy to make at any given location. All that is needed is a bucket of uniform area and a measuring stick. The depth of the water in the bucket is measured after each rainstorm before the water begins evaporating, and the bucket is emptied to be ready for the next storm.

It is difficult to say to what extent a network of such observations represents the total precipitation falling over a large area. It is known that over level terrain in winter, precipitation amounts are fairly uniform, but summer showers may occur entirely in the space between rain gauges even though these may be less than 10 miles apart. In mountainous regions, great batteries of rain gauges on all watersheds would be required in order to estimate the total precipitation. A rain gauge catches an absurdly small sample of the depth of water over a large area. However, as the number of gauges increases from year to year, it is to be expected that we are getting more and more representative values.

Precipitation gauges may be classified into two types—recording and direct measuring. For nonrecording purposes, a cylindrical gauge 8 in. in diameter is standard in the United States (Fig. 5–15). In Canada a cylinder having an area of 10 sq in. (diameter 3.57 in.) is used, and the British standard is 5 in. in diameter. In these gauges, the precipitation that enters passes through a funnel into a measuring tube or bottle. In the U.S. Weather Bureau type, the measuring tube has one-tenth of

FIG. 5–15. United States standard 8-in. rain gauge with large overflow cylinder, funnel, inner measuring tube and stick. (*U.S. Weather Bureau.*)

the cross-sectional area of the exposed gauge, so that the depth of water in it is ten times that which has fallen. A depth of 10 in. therefore corresponds to 1 in. of rainfall. The water is measured by a measuring stick graduated in terms of a ten-times exaggerated scale so that the nearest hundredth of an inch is easily read. The funnel serves the dual purpose of running the water into the tube and preventing appreciable evaporation. The whole tube is enclosed in a large overflow cylinder so that the hole in the funnel is the only egress for evaporated water. The funnel and measuring tube are removed when snow is expected.

For recording purposes, the weighing-type gauge developed by Ferguson is now being used in the U.S. Weather Bureau (Fig. 5–16). In this instrument, precipitation is also caught in an 8-in. cylinder. It accumulates in a bucket resting on a spring-type weighing platform. The weight, transposed into inches of precipitation by means of proper link-ages, is written by a pen on a clock-driven drum. The capacity is 12 in. of precipitation, and the pen is of the dual traverse type, recording up to 6 in. on the upstroke and the remaining 6 on the downstroke. For detailed recording the mouth area is made larger in order to catch a greater amount of water. An increase in area of 2½ times results in a

Fig. 5–16. Weighing rain gauge, showing housing and 8-in. throat removed. (*U.S. Weather Bureau.*)

diameter approximately that of the outer shell of the gauge. This makes the full stroke of the pen correspond to 2.4 in. instead of 6 in. as in the case of the 8-in. mouth. The clock drum can be speeded up by using gears with a smaller reduction factor. When snow is not expected, a funnel is placed inside the gauge above the bucket to check evaporation of water after it is collected so it can be measured with a stick as a proof of the accuracy of the recording mechanism.

Since rain gauges affect the flow of the wind around them in producing upward currents on their windward sides and downward currents to leeward, it is advisable to provide windshields to smooth out the air flow. For the measurement of snow, this is positively necessary, since the feathery flakes are carried with the wind current in such a way that the gauge is an unlikely place for them to land. Several different designs of shield are in use. Two designs, one suggested by Brooks and the other

(a)           (b)

Fig. 5–17. Shielded snow gauges. (a) Alter design. (U.S. Weather Bureau.) (b) Mount Washington design. (C. F. Brooks.)

by Alter, are shown in Fig. 5–17. The problem of the proper construction of windshields is a difficult one in which only small progress has been made. The design has to be carefully checked so that it neither allows snow that would normally fall on a representative horizontal surface to escape the gauge nor acts as a snow "trap" to give too high readings.

Other types of recording gauges that are in use in various countries and in the United States will not be described here, since most of them are limited to the measurement of precipitation in the form of rain only.

Where a properly shielded and representative gauge is not available, it is possible to measure precipitation in the form of snow by carefully selecting a sample, cutting it out like a biscuit, then weighing it or measuring it in a graduate after melting. Care should be taken not to include old snow in the sample. If the snow has drifted badly, it is practically impossible to be assured of a representative sample and considerable guesswork is involved. For snow surveys in mountain regions, a sampling tube about 3 in. in diameter and having a sharp cutting edge is used, equipped with a spring balance for immediate weighing to determine the water equivalent. For general information, it may be stated that the water equivalent of snow is in the vicinity of one-tenth of its unmelted depth. In many cases this is quite far from correct.

Radar has been tried with considerable success as a means of getting the total rainfall over a specified drainage area, especially under showery conditions where rain-gauge networks are wholly inadequate.[1,2] The pulse transmitted by radars in the 3 to 10 cm wavelengths is scattered back by water and ice particles of raindrop size suspended or falling in the air. As a radar scans the horizon the rainy portions of all clouds that are producing rain are outlined on the radarscope. The ratio of the power returned to the power transmitted at a given wavelength and at a given distance of the scatterers from the radar is proportional to $na^6$, where $n$ is the number of spherical scatterers of radius $a$ per unit volume. The volume of water contained in such spherical drops is proportional to $na^3$. Thus the ratio of the echo intensity to the volume of water is proportional to $a^3$.

By comparing the volume and intensity of a radar echo with the rainfall rate at the same time and place over a dense network of recording rain gauges, the radar can be "calibrated" as a means of measuring rain. In practice, the area covered by the echo is used instead of the volume, since to get the volume requires vertical as well as horizontal scanning and ordinarily, therefore, two different types of radars. Instead of measuring the intensity, the shrinkage of the area as the receiver gain is reduced is noted. With these simplifications the method loses little in accuracy. Since only the more intense rainfall produces an echo at lower receiver gain, the various power settings produce areas on the scope that bear some correspondence to the areas enclosed by lines of equal rainfall (*isohyets*). Such a correspondence is shown in the map in

[1] Byers, H. R., and Collaborators, The Use of Radar in Determining the Amount of Rain Falling over a Small Area, *Trans. Am. Geophys. Union*, vol. 29, pp. 187–196, 1948.

[2] Stout, G. E., and J. C. Neill, Utility of Radar in Measuring Areal Rainfall, *Bull. Am. Meteorol. Soc.*, vol. 34, pp. 21–27, 1953.

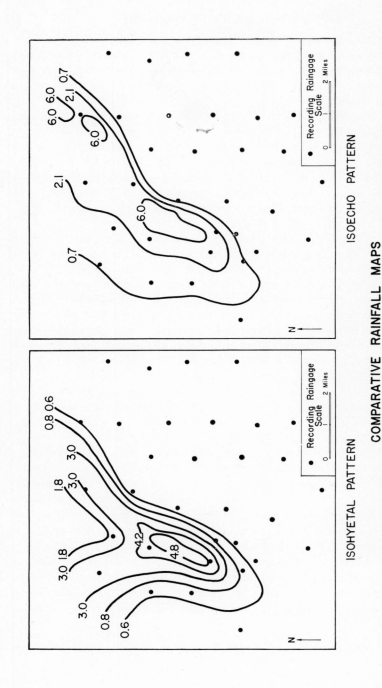

ISOHYETAL PATTERN                    ISOECHO PATTERN

**COMPARATIVE RAINFALL MAPS**

Rainfall in Inches per Hour at 2000 to 2001 C.S.T. On September 26, 1951

FIG. 5–18. *Left:* rainfall as recorded on the Illinois Water Survey rain-gauge micro-network. *Right:* rainfall as evaluated from radar return at same time. All figures are in inches. (*Illinois State Water Survey, Glenn E. Stout.*)

Fig. 5–18 from a thunderstorm studied by the Illinois State Water Survey, using radar and a rain gauge network of 33 gauges in a 50 sq-mile area.

Even with its greatest quantitative inaccuracies the radar will not miss a shower altogether, as the standard rain gauge networks sometimes do. The duration of rainfall over a given area is one of the most important factors in determining the total that falls. This time factor the radar obtains with complete accuracy.

# CHAPTER 6

# UPPER-AIR AND CLOUD OBSERVATIONS

Soundings of the troposphere and lower stratosphere with meteorological instruments were made on an exploratory basis in the latter part of the nineteenth century. Systematic daily measurements of this kind from a synoptic network of aerological stations available for forecasting purposes have been possible only since the 1930s.

In the early nineteenth century scientists were already learning from mountain observations that the pressure decreases rapidly with height, that the temperature does not always decrease upward through every layer of the atmosphere, and other details of the upper air. However, it was soon realized that mountain observations were not representative of the surrounding undisturbed atmosphere. It was not until near the close of the century that conditions in the *free* atmosphere were being reliably and systematically measured. Beginning in about 1885, serious attention was given to upper-air measurements. Ascensions in manned balloons were the sensation of the times, and scientists made use of them to obtain information about the vertical structure of the atmosphere. From 1888 to 1899, about 75 balloon ascensions were made near Berlin under the direction of R. Assmann, who developed a special type of psychrometer for this purpose (see Fig. 5–6c). At the same time, details of the air structure near the ground were obtained from captive balloons.

The foremost step in upper-air sounding came from a series of records of small free balloons (*ballonsondes*) carrying lightweight recording instruments. The record could be evaluated after the instrument, which had parachuted to earth when the balloon burst, was sent back to the research station by the finder. By means of a series of such soundings in France and Belgium, Teisserenc de Bort discovered the existence of the stratosphere. These recordings, while giving information from great heights in the atmosphere, could not be used for daily analysis and forecasting, because it took days, sometimes months or even years, to recover the record.

Following the meeting of the International Conference on Aerial Navigation at Chicago in 1893, renewed interest was taken in the use of kites for meteorological soundings, especially in the United States. Kites were constructed that, flown with heavy piano wire connected to a machine-driven winch, could carry recording instruments to a height of several kilometers. To obtain a sounding of this nature was laborious, required special ground stations, equipment, personnel, etc., and seldom furnished information from above 3 km. It was difficult to make the data available for forecasting.

In the United States the year 1934 marked the beginning of systematic daily soundings. In that year the Weather Bureau in cooperation with the Army and Navy organized a system of some 24 stations taking daily simultaneous soundings by airplane. The aerological network developed rapidly as a part of the regular Weather Bureau forecasting services. This integration of the third dimension of the upper air with the two-dimensional weather map in day-to-day forecasting marked an important turning point in meteorology.

In 1938, sounding balloons carrying instruments called *radiosondes* that *telemeter*, or send their records back to the ground by radio signals, replaced the airplanes in the network in the United States. During the Second World War, and subsequently, ground equipment was developed for radio direction finding from the radiosonde signal, thus making it possible to follow the drift of the balloon and compute the winds at the various levels through which the balloon rises in addition to recording the transmitted temperature, pressure, and humidity data. The name *rawinsonde* has been applied to this type of measurement in America.

## UPPER-AIR SOUNDING SYSTEMS

Before proceeding with a discussion of the radiosonde instrumental equipment, it is well to review briefly the more fundamental instruments used in kites, ballonsondes, and airplanes.

In order to determine the state of the atmosphere at rest at any given point, three quantities must be measured—pressure, temperature, and humidity. The relationship between pressure and height is such that, if the three quantities just named are measured, the altitude can be obtained. Therefore meteorological sounding instruments consist of apparatus for recording pressure, temperature, and humidity.

In previous sections, the standard methods of recording pressure, temperature, and relative humidity were described. The instruments for this purpose are, respectively, the barograph, the thermograph, and the hygrograph. It is possible to mount an aneroid, bimetal strip, and hair element to a single framework, each element connected to a separate pen writing on the same clock-driven drum. This is essentially the nature of the simplest type of kite, balloon, or airplane *meteorograph*. The

(a)

(b)

(c)

(d)

FIG. 6-1. Stages in the development of soundings of the upper air. (a) *Ballon-sondes*, 1890–1938; (b) kites, 1900–1934; (c) airplanes, 1921–1938; (d) ordinary radiosonde, 1937; (e) *rawinsonde*, 1943 to date—1956 model GMD-1, GMD-2, is shown. (a to d, *U.S. Weather Bureau; e, U.S. Army photograph, Signal Corps Engineering Laboratory*.)

(e)

modern airplane meteorograph or *aerograph* is much more complicated, since it has to be designed for airplanes of reasonably high speed. Details of the aerograph are beyond the scope of this book.

**The Radiosonde.** The radiosonde equipment involves special problems of engineering. In addition to the meteorological unit, the radiosonde must have a lightweight, cheap radio transmitter. The needs are best met by use of ultrahigh radio frequency, which requires a minimum of power. Extremely small dry-cell or storage batteries may be used for the energy supply.

The simplest meteorological unit is that based on the so-called "Olland cycle." The unit consists of a slowly rotating contact point, somewhat on the principle of an automobile distributor, driven by clockwork or some other constant-speed motor. Instead of making contact with fixed points, it operates with points that change their position in the cycle of rotation. The pressure, temperature, and humidity sensing elements cause these contact points to move as the measured values change. Two fixed points, easily identifiable because they are close together, are included for reference. As the measured quantities change, the time interval between the fixed reference and the variable sensing contacts changes. The signal transmitted at each contact is recorded on a chronograph at a receiving station where the spacing of the signals is calibrated in terms of meteorological quantities. This type of instrument is used in several countries.

The United States weather services and those of some other countries use an instrument in which the audio-output of a continuous signal of fixed radio frequency is modulated by the sensing elements. Distinguishing reference signals are also transmitted.

Two systems of modulation are in use, one in which the audiofrequency is modulated and the other with amplitude modulated. The latter is favored for direction finding, at least when used in a recent version of a 1680-mc transmitter. Both types are controlled by what is known as a blocking oscillator.

A special pressure-measuring and actuating system is used. An aneroid moves a contact arm over a series of strips. These strips are spaced in accordance with set intervals of pressure so that the pressure-change steps can be added together by counting the contacts. The temperature and humidity readings are transmitted with each set of contacts. The conducting strips are separated by insulating bands. When the switch arm is on an insulating portion, the signal modulated by the temperature is transmitted. When it is on a conducting strip, the humidity signal is actuated. Every few strips transmit reference signals (Fig. 6–2).

For sensing the temperature, a ceramic "thermistor" described on page 66 is used, while the humidity element is the lithium chloride-coated slide mentioned on page 69.

**Winds.** The most obvious way to measure the winds in the upper air is by measuring the drift of balloons or aircraft. In conditions of poor visibility, especially with clouds, this cannot be done visually. Readings

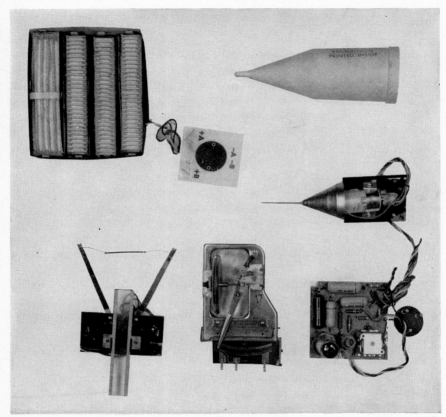

Fɪɢ. 6–2. Radiosonde, shown in parts. *Lower left:* thermistor (between arms of V), and humidity strip (extending vertically). *Lower center:* baroswitch. *Lower right:* radio transmitter and antenna. *Upper right:* antenna cover. *Upper left:* battery pack. (*U.S. Weather Bureau photograph.*)

by methods of radio direction finding are now made a part of regular radiosonde observations, thus making wind observations independent of visibility. Radar is also used on balloons carrying small targets.

Several types of rawinsonde systems, combining radiosondage with tracking of the radiosonde to get wind drift of the balloon, have been developed. A system devised by the United States Army Signal Corps Engineering Laboratories is used in the United States. The ordinary

United States radiosonde has its signal picked up on the ground by a receiver with a specially designed antenna and with a combined recording and tracking circuit. Automatic tracking is built into the equipment. Since the radiosonde transmits the meteorological elements in terms of audiofrequency, the receiver feeds the signal to what is essentially a frequency meter, but the electronic circuitry carries it through much more elaborate steps to provide automatic recording and computing.

The United States equipment, designated as the GMD-1 (see Fig. 6–1e), is so designed as to print the complete record of the flight in terms of numbers in tabular form on a roll of paper. This requires a built-in computer to calculate the winds. With the antenna pointed at all times at the balloon, the altitude and azimuth angles are obtained at stated intervals. At the same time the altitude above the point of launching can be obtained from the telemetered pressure. Thus three variables required to determine the position of the balloon in space are obtained.

Standard military radars can be used with balloons for obtaining winds without radiosonde data. A special reflector is employed, usually made of three squares of cardboard covered with metal foil and arranged to intersect in three mutually perpendicular planes. The squares are usually about 3 ft on a side. These so-called "corner reflectors" can be traced by the radar, which, in addition to giving azimuth and elevation angles, also gives slant range, thus providing three space variables for positioning the balloon.

Balloons used for obtaining visually the upper-air wind drift are called *pilot balloons*. They are much smaller than the radiosonde balloons, having a diameter of 24 to 36 in. when inflated. Pilot balloons carry no instruments of any kind.

The only direct measurements on pilot balloons are the azimuth and altitude angles, as sighted through a theodolite (similar to a surveyor's transit). If simultaneous sights are taken on the balloon from two points a known distance apart, the height can be computed from plane trigonometry. Ordinarily such double theodolite readings are not made. Instead, the balloon is assumed to have a constant rate of ascent so that by timing it from its starting point the height can be determined. This assumption of constant rate of ascent has been tested by a long series of double-theodolite observations and has been found to be valid within a reasonable limit of error.

Within a few seconds after it is released, the balloon reaches a so-called "terminal velocity," in which the air resistance exactly balances the buoyancy force. The air resistance decreases with the decreasing density of the air with height, but apparently this is almost exactly compensated for by increase in the size of the balloon owing to expansion against decreasing external pressure with height. At greater heights the diffusion of gas out of the balloon tends to correct for an increase in speed which might be expected.

Various formulas, all more or less the same, have been determined empirically for the vertical velocity of pilot balloons. The formula used in the United States and Canada is

$$v = \frac{72L^{0.63}}{(L + W)^{0.42}} \quad \text{m per min}$$

where $L$ is the so-called "free lift" in grams, or the mass in grams that the inflated balloon, carrying all its attachments (if any), is just able to support without rising or sinking, and $W$ is the weight of the balloon, with attachments, before inflation. In order to take into account effects near the ground that are ascribed to turbulence of the air, a certain decreasing percentage is added to $v$ in the first 5 min of the ascent.

**Constant-level Balloons.** During the Second World War, the Japanese demonstrated that nonextensible balloons could be made to float automatically at a level of constant air density across the Pacific Ocean in the upper westerly winds. The balloons were used as incendiary weapons, but later in the United States the idea was adapted for meteorological purposes.

The principle of a nonextensible balloon is that it can be filled to produce strong upward buoyancy at launching, but finally a level will be reached at which the buoyancy will be exactly balanced by the load. Another way of regarding this balance is on the basis that, since the volume is constant, a level is reached at which the weight of the balloon, gas, and load is the same as the weight of the same volume of air—the displaced air.

Balloon materials have been synthesized which allow very little diffusion of the gas through them and which can withstand a high internal pressure. Certain automatic controls are necessary to offset the small amount of leakage that occurs, to compensate for vertical currents in the atmosphere, to correct for the vertical motion of the balloon due to diurnal changes in the balloon's temperature, and to allow for the necessary valving of gas to prevent rupture of the balloon. A safety valve is easily installed. Liquid ballast can be released automatically if the atmospheric pressure rises above a desired value after the minimum has been reached. A balloon of this type is pictured in Fig. 6–3. After it has reached a fairly high altitude, the gas has forced the envelope into a more nearly spherical shape with a volume that remains constant.

Since the balloon travels great distances, it must be monitored by several stations and must have a more powerful and longer-lived radio transmitter than the conventional radiosonde. The instrument is heavier and more durable. Cloud photography can be included if the balloon can be prevented from crossing sensitive political boundaries. These balloons have been tracked through distances equal to half the circumference of the earth, obtaining valuable wind and temperature information.

FIG. 6–3. Constant-pressure balloon. (*U.S. Navy Photograph.*)

**Weather Reconnaisance and Dropsondes.** Over ocean and polar areas weather reconnaisance airplane flights supplement the radiosonde observations from stationary weather ships and ice islands. Temperature, pressure, humidity, and wind drift are the principal measurements obtained from the airplanes. They can fly at a constant pressure and measure their altitude with a radioaltimeter. Improved automatic systems are continually being devised. From flights at the higher altitudes, radio-telemetering instruments called *dropsondes* are launched, connected to parachutes which lower them slowly to the surface. The signal is received and evaluated automatically in the airplane. In this way a continuous recording of conditions at the level of the airplane and occasional soundings below it can be obtained. Airborne radars scan the horizon to show the detailed distributions of storm areas.

**Rockets and Satellites.** The outer regions of the atmosphere which are inaccessible to balloons are explored by rockets on a sporadic basis. Rocket technology is changing so rapidly that it is unwise to describe the measurement systems in anything as permanent as a book.

Satellites can provide information relating to the entire earth over long, more or less continuous periods of time. Among the useful meteorological measurements are those having to do with the radiation balance between the earth, sun, and space, the use of cloud-scanning devices similar to television, and the measurement of radiation particles entering the atmosphere.

## CLOUD OBSERVATIONS

The following information concerning clouds is of value to the meteorologist: (1) the amount of sky covered, (2) the direction from which the clouds are moving, (3) their speed, (4) the height of the cloud base—the ceiling, (5) the height of the cloud top, (6) the cloud form or type according to the international classification, and (7) the constitution of the clouds. These factors will be considered, in order, below.

**Amount of Clouds.** The amount of any kind of cloud is observed and written in the weather log in terms of the tenths of the visible sky covered by such clouds. Clouds may exist and be visible at more than one level and may be comprised of several different forms, so that an observer notes, for example, $\frac{2}{10}$ of one kind, $\frac{5}{10}$ of another, etc. At night, the cloud amount is more difficult to determine and depends on the observer's judgment derived from the obscuring of the stars by the clouds. In bright moonlight, the observation is not difficult. Formerly, data of this nature were available only for normal waking hours. In recent years, at least in the United States, weather offices and observatories have been active throughout the 24 hr of the day, and a complete unbroken chain of observations at intervals of 1 hr or less has been maintained.

**Cloud Direction.** If the clouds are made up of discrete elements that can be followed by the eye, it is possible to obtain roughly the direction from which they are moving by sighting along the anemometer tower or pole or some other tall structure. This method, of course, is not possible on a dark night or when the clouds are in a uniform sheet with no distinguishing surface features. Some clouds have strong vertical currents that should not be mistaken for horizontal components.

The most reliable method of obtaining the cloud direction is by noting the direction of a pilot balloon or other balloon as it enters the cloud. If the balloon is tracked it can also give the speed of the cloud. Clouds consisting of large-sized water drops or ice particles can be viewed by radar to obtain direction and speed of motion.

**Cloud Speed.** An instrument for measuring both cloud direction and speed that has long been in use but has not been favored in recent years is the *mirror nephoscope*. This consists of a disk of black reflecting glass mounted on a level stand, engraved with concentric circles a known distance apart. Around the disk are graduations in directional degrees. The observer chooses a distinguishable cloud feature to be observed and changes the position of his eye until that feature is in the center of the mirror disk. He then follows the reflection of this cloud element with a pointer until it moves off the edge of the disk or reaches, in convenient time, one of the concentric circles. Meanwhile, the movement has been timed. The direction of the pointer from the center gives the direction of motion, and the time required for the reflected element to move a known distance gives a rough measure of the speed. Actually, the speed at which the reflection of a cloud moves across the mirror depends on how near it is to the ground as well as on its speed. Tables for the speed measured to the concentric circles are made up in terms of a cloud height of 1000 m. One then has the *relative speed*, and if the height is known or can be estimated closely, the actual speed of the cloud at a height $H$ would be given by multiplying the relative speed by $H/1000$.

In the United States, where a network of about 150 upper-wind-finding stations is available making two to four runs a day, fairly complete information concerning the direction and speed of clouds is obtained from the indications of the balloons as they enter or float along in the clouds.

**Ceiling.** The most obvious way of determining the cloud base or ceiling is from an airplane flying at cloud levels. On a "let-down" through an overcast the pilot or copilot can note the altitude from which the ground can first be seen when looking straight down, the altitude at which a certain "slant visibility" to the runway becomes discernible, and the altitude at which the lowest cloud bases are in the horizontal line of sight. The philosophy behind methods of ceiling measurements is that of giving the pilot the latest conditions before he encounters them. Therefore the standard ceiling measurements are made from the ground.

At the more important airport stations of the U.S. Weather Bureau an automatic "ceilometer" system is used. This consists of a projector sending a beam of modulated light vertically from the ground. From 750 to 1500 ft away a detector is mounted which scans from the horizon to the vertical in the direction toward the beam. The detector consists of a photocell which is sensitive to the reflection of the light beam on the cloud base. As it scans it makes an impulse on the record when it is pointed toward the spot of light on the bottom of the cloud. This elevation angle is recorded electrically in the weather office and by solving the right triangle this can be translated into height. This method is made to work in daytime as well as at night by virtue of the fact that the light beam is modulated. A photocell is used which is sensitive only to such light and not at all to the steady daylight, even though the latter may be a million times brighter than the spot. A quartz water-cooled mercury arc lamp when illuminated by a 60-cycle current produces light modulated at 120 cycles. Other adaptations of this system, some without automatic recording, are in use in other countries.

Other methods of ceiling determination include obtaining the height of the disappearance of meteorological balloons into clouds, visual sighting on light spots of a known source with suitable angle-measuring sighting devices, and the somewhat crude method of noting at what contour the clouds lie on a mountain.

**Cloud Top.** Clouds in sheets or layers ordinarily have a more clearly defined top than base. The "top of the overcast" is easily determined by pilots flying through it. In most conditions over nonmountainous territory it is at the same height over thousands of square miles, except in storm areas.

An indirect method of determining the top of layer clouds is made possible because of the fact that they nearly always form under a *temperature inversion*, i.e., a region where the temperature increases with height for a short distance. These inversions are shown by radiosonde observations. The humidity indications of the soundings are also useful.

The base and top of a reasonably thick low-cloud layer can be determined by certain types of radar located on the ground. A radar wavelength of about 1.8 cm, the so-called "*k* band," detects cloud droplets of considerably less than raindrop size. The antenna points vertically and returns an echo only from that portion of the overlying atmosphere occupied by clouds. A picturization of a vertical slice through the cloud layer is obtained on the radarscope.

## CLOUD CLASSIFICATION

Meteorologists of the world have agreed on a uniform system of cloud classification. The World Meteorological Organization (WMO) fosters adherence to the system and is responsible for any changes or improvements that may be made from time to time. The present classification is an outgrowth of a system published in 1803 in England by Luke Howard, improved upon by the Frenchman Renou and the Swede Hildebrandsson. The WMO publishes the definitions and photographs of the different types in the form of an atlas. A two-volume atlas was published in 1957 in several languages.

The classification does not attempt to consider the processes forming the clouds but rather adheres to distinguishable shapes, shading, general appearances, and optical effects which a subprofessional meteorologist can be trained to recognize. The meteorologist at the analysis center can put together the cloud observations from a number of stations to obtain clues to the processes that are operating.

There are 10 *genera* of clouds, as listed in Table 6–1, which may be further subdivided into *species* and *varieties*.

TABLE 6–1. CLOUD GENERA

| | |
|---|---|
| Cirrus | Nimbostratus |
| Cirrocumulus | Stratocumulus |
| Cirrostratus | Stratus |
| Altocumulus | Cumulus |
| Altostratus | Cumulonimbus |

Surface and aircarft observations have shown that clouds are generally encountered over a range of altitudes varying from sea level to the height of the tropopause. That part of the atmosphere in which clouds are usually present in the troposphere has been divided into three "étages": high, middle, and low. Cirrus, cirrocumulus, and cirrostratus are in the

Fig. 6–4. Cirrus. (*U.S. Weather Bureau, J. W. Johnson.*)

high étage; altocumulus is in the middle étage; and stratus and stratocumulus are in the low étage. Altostratus is usually found in the middle étage, but it often extends higher; nimbostratus, cumulus, and cumulonimbus extend through several levels. The étages overlap and vary with latitude, but their approximate limits are given in Table 6–2.

TABLE 6–2. LIMITS OF ÉTAGES

| Étages | Polar regions | Temperate regions | Tropical regions |
|---|---|---|---|
| High............. | 3–8 km | 5–13 km | 6–18 km |
| Middle........... | 2–4 km | 2–7 km | 2–8 km |
| Low............. | Surface to 2 km | Surface to 2 km | Surface to 2 km |

In the following descriptions, the definitions of the 1957 World Meteorological Organization Cloud Atlas are given in italics, and additional information to help the student has been supplied by the author.

**Cirrus.** *Detached clouds in the form of white, delicate filaments or white or mostly white patches or narrow bands. These clouds have a fibrous (hair-like) appearance.*

The prefix *cirro-* is applied to forms at the same general level but having somewhat different appearance. Cirrus is the name for detached clouds as defined. A variety of forms is noted, such as tufts, delicate lines across a blue sky, branching plumes, curved lines ending in tufts, unshaded white smears against a blue sky, etc. Effects of perspective sometimes give the clouds the appearance of vertical extent or converging of bands to a point on the horizon, but this is a false impression.

Fig. 6–5. Cirrocumulus, *upper right,* with cirrus and cirrostratus. (*U.S. Army photograph.*)

All of the clouds of the cirrus or cirro- type are composed of ice crystals. The sun or moon shining through these ice-crystal clouds produces a halo. In the simple cirrus types, however, the irregular cloud distribution fails to produce this action on the light rays in a noticeable way.

Because of their great height and brightness, cirrus clouds are brilliantly colored well above the horizon at sunset and sunrise, often being of a bright yellow or red color upward from the horizon and almost directly overhead.

**Cirrocumulus.** *Thin, white patch, sheet or layer of cloud without shading, composed of very small elements in the form of grains, ripples, etc., merged or separate, and more or less regularly arranged; most of the elements have an apparent width of less than one degree.*

They often look like small flakes or very small globular masses. When well marked in a uniform arrangement they form what the sailors used to call a *mackerel sky*. Cirrocumulus is commonly connected with cirrus or cirrostratus. It occurs less frequently than the forms of cirrus and cirrostratus.

**Cirrostratus.** *Transparent, whitish cloud veil of fibrous (hair-like) or smooth appearance, totally or partly covering the sky, and generally producing halo phenomena.*

Sometimes the cirrostratus is so thin that it only slightly whitens the blue of the sky. At other times it has the appearance of a heavy white sheet. Occasionally it has irregular filaments. The border of the sheet of cirrostratus is usually indefinite, often ending in patches of cirrus or cirrocumulus. On rare occasions the edge of the sheet is straight and clear-cut. It never obscures the sun to the extent that shadows are not cast by objects on the ground, never at least when the sun is fairly high.

**Altocumulus.** *White or grey, or both white and grey, patch, sheet or layer of cloud, generally with shading, composed of laminae, rounded masses, rolls, etc., which are sometimes partly fibrous or diffuse and which may or may not be merged; most of the regularly arranged small elements usually have an apparent width of between one and five degrees.*

Altocumulus clouds have shapes somewhat similar to those of cirrocumulus; however, they are distinguishable from the latter in that they are larger and usually have definite dark shading underneath and in the middle of each cloud element. They do not produce halo phenomena. The edges of the elements are often thin and translucent and exhibit irisations (bright plays of colors) which are found only in this type of cloud.

Low-level altocumulus may be distinguished from stratocumulus by the size of the elements. Altocumulus may occur at more than one level at the same time. The fact that they do not produce halos should not be taken to mean that they do not occur at temperatures below freezing. As a matter of fact, altocumulus clouds, as well as altostratus, are often composed of liquid droplets undercooled to temperatures well below freezing.

**Altostratus.** *Greyish or bluish cloud sheet or layer of striated, fibrous or uniform appearance, totally or partly covering the sky, and having parts thin enough to reveal the sun at least vaguely, as through ground glass. Altostratus does not show halo phenomena.*

Altostratus is sometimes thin in light patches between very dark parts, but it never shows definite configurations. Under an altostratus sheet, shadows of objects on the ground are never visible.

Low altostratus may be distinguished from stratus or nimbostratus because of the darker, more uniform grey of the lower forms and the

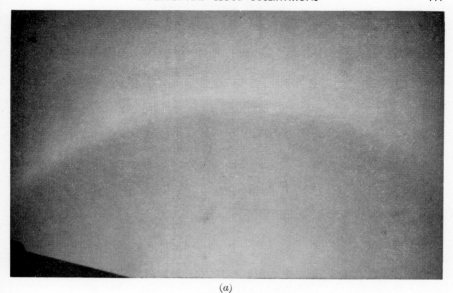

(a)

(b)

Fig. 6–6. Distinction between cirrostratus with halo (a) and altostratus (b) with sun appearing as through ground glass. (R. G. Beebe.)

fibrous structure and whitish gleam often visible in the altostratus. In a very smoky atmosphere it is almost impossible to make this distinction without some direct height measurement. If the sun or moon is completely hidden at all times, i.e., if not even a light spot shows in the vicinity of these luminaries, then one may conclude that the sheet is stratus or nimbostratus.

Fig. 6–7. Altocumulus, high, scaly.   (*U.S. Weather Bureau, J. W. Johnson.*)

Altostratus may result from a transformation of a sheet of altocumulus, and on the other hand altocumulus may represent a dissipating stage of altostratus.

**Nimbostratus.**   *Grey cloud layer, often dark, the appearance of which is rendered diffuse by more or less continuously falling rain or snow, which in most cases reaches the ground.   It is thick enough throughout to blot out the sun.*

*Low, ragged clouds frequently occur below the layer, with which they may or may not merge.*

The precipitation does not have to reach the ground.   The rain or snow may evaporate in the air, in which case the base of the cloud usually is ill-defined and has a "wet" look caused by trails of precipitation and low "scud" clouds (fractostratus).

Nimbostratus is most often a low cloud form.   It is distinguishable from stratocumulus in that it has no discrete or, at least, regular cloud

FIG. 6–8. Altocumulus, massive, closely packed.   (*U.S. Weather Bureau, J. W. Johnson.*)

elements and it is distinguishable from stratus in that it is darker, shows rain conditions, and has a highly variable lower surface.

In the usual storms of middle latitudes, nimbostratus often develops from a thickening and lowering altostratus.   Streaks of snow or rain not reaching the ground are called *virga*.   The fractostratus or scud clouds, sometimes also fractocumulus, form underneath the nimbostratus to give the sky a dark chaotic system of low clouds that are characteristic of bad weather.   Less frequently, nimbostratus may develop from stratocumulus.

**Stratocumulus.**   *Grey or whitish, or both grey and whitish, patch, sheet or layer of cloud which almost always has dark parts, composed of tassellations, rounded masses, rolls, etc., which are non-fibrous (except for virga)* *and which may or may not be merged; most of the regularly arranged small elements have an apparent width of more than five degrees.*

The arrangements of the cloud elements are in groups, lines, or waves, aligned in one or in two directions. Rolls often appear, sometimes so close that their edges join, but even when they cover the whole sky they have an undulated appearance on their lower surface.

Stratocumulus clouds often have an appreciable vertical development and are therefore likely to be confused with small cumulus. However, they have a softer, more irregular shape than cumulus and when viewed

Fig. 6–9. Stratocumulus. (*U.S. Weather Bureau, W. J. Humphreys.*)

from above are seen to have their tops at a uniform height and to exhibit a quilted pattern. Sometimes they are confused with large lumps of stratus that have broken off from a uniform stratus sheet or that result from the dissipation or precede the formation of a stratus sheet. Sometimes stratus changes into stratocumulus, but this does not happen simply by the breaking off of lumps of stratus. There must be some regular pattern and distinct masses.

A transition from stratocumulus to nimbostratus is sometimes seen. The elements of thick stratocumulus fuse together completely, and the cloud is called nimbostratus when, after the disappearance of the cloud elements, falling trails of precipitation destroy the clear-cut boundary of the lower surface.

Stratocumulus *vesperalis* are flat, elongated clouds that are often seen to form about sunset as the final product of the diurnal changes of cumulus. Another type is *cumulogenitus*, formed by the spreading out of the tops of cumulus clouds, which have disappeared.

**Stratus.** *Generally grey cloud layer with a fairly uniform base, which may give drizzle, ice prisms, or snow grains. When the sun is visible through the cloud, its outline is clearly discernible. Stratus does not produce halo phenomena except, possibly, at very low temperatures.*

*Sometimes stratus appears in the form of ragged patches.*

Fig. 6–10. Stratus in the Golden Gate, San Francisco, California. (*U.S. Weather Bureau.*)

When viewed from above, stratus always has a uniform top, usually marked by a temperature inversion or another thermally stable layer. It can have the same characteristics as a fog, except that it does not occur on the ground.

**Cumulus.** *Detached clouds, generally dense and with sharp outlines, developing vertically in the form of rising mounds, domes or towers, of which the bulging upper part often resembles a cauliflower. The sunlit parts of these clouds are mostly brilliant white; their base is relatively dark and nearly horizontal.*

*Sometimes cumulus is ragged.*

Over land areas, cumulus is most often found in the daytime, generally dissipating at night. Cumulus cannot produce more than light precipitation.   It often, however, makes the transition to cumulonimbus, which is the heavier shower cloud.

Cumulus clouds represent strong vertical convection currents; hence they occur in air that is heated from below or cooled from above, so that the warm air is displaced by surrounding colder air.   The "boiling" of the tops is often noticed, indicating the strong vertical currents.

Four species of cumulus are given in the International Cloud Atlas. They are cumulus *humilis*, cumulus *mediocris*, cumulus *congestus*, and

FIG. 6–11. Nimbostratus above low clouds of bad weather.   (*U.S. Weather Bureau, F. Ellerman, Mt. Wilson, California.*)

*fractocumulus.*  Cumulus humilis, often referred to as fair-weather cumulus, have little vertical development.   Nevertheless they have rounded tops and flat bases.   They are often more or less equally spaced but appear more crowded toward the horizon owing to perspective.   Also, in looking toward the horizon, one notes the flat bases in a series of steps or in *echelon.*  Cumulus congestus have marked vertical development, but not reaching the cumulonimbus stage.   The tops are seen to "boil" vigorously.   Cumulus mediocris and fractocumulus are obvious in their meaning.

**Cumulonimbus.**  *Heavy and dense cloud, with a considerable vertical extent, in the form of a mountain or huge towers.   At least part of its upper* *portion is usually smooth, or fibrous, or striated, and nearly always flattened; this part often spreads out in the shape of an anvil or vast plume.*

*Under the base of this cloud which is often very dark, there are frequently low ragged clouds either merged with it or not, and precipitation sometimes in the form of virga.*

At a distance, cumulonimbus is recognizable as the most massive and tallest of clouds. Its development from a collection of cumulus congestus indicates the strong vertical currents that are present. The cloud top often reaches to the cirrus level or bursts through the tropopause.

Fig. 6–12. Cumulus humilis growing to cumulus congestus. (*U.S. Navy photograph.*)

From underneath, the base of the cloud is like nimbostratus, having low scud clouds of fractocumulus character. In general, the turbulent motion of these ragged low clouds is much more noticeable than in nimbostratus. Cumulonimbus are outgrowths of cumulus, whereas nimbostratus occurs from clouds that have little vertical development.

Cumulonimbus is the great thundercloud so familiar in the summer weather of most of the United States, and at other seasons in the tropics. It always produces at least a pronounced shower. Its development is cellular, and there is always more or less clear space between two adjacent clouds of this type, except in certain general storm conditions. When the cloud is overhead and the features recognizable at a distance cannot be

(a)

(b)

(c)

Fig. 6–13.

seen, the fall of a real shower and sudden darkening of the sky is ample evidence of cumulonimbus.

Cumulonimbus gives rise to a great variety of associated clouds. The sky takes on a broken-up, menacing appearance in the low levels, and the spreading out or dissipation of the high parts forms layers of cirriform and alto-form clouds. In the forward portion of an intense cumulonimbus, a rolling scud cloud is seen just under the cloud base. Also in the forward portion, *mamma* forms, pendant from middle to low clouds like mammalian teats or udders, are sometimes observed.

## METEORS (NONASTRONOMICAL)

The general definition of meteors, given by nearly all dictionaries, is that they are any visible or optical phenomena in the atmosphere. Astronomical meteors entering the atmosphere from space are a special class, but since there is no other common word to describe them, they virtually monopolize the term in ordinary usage, at least in the English language.

The World Meteorological Organization has agreed on the definitions and descriptions of four classes of meteors: (1) *hydrometeors*, composed of water in various forms; (2) *lithometeors*, consisting of essentially dry particles and their visible manifestations; (3) *photometeors*, that is, optical phenomena; and (4) *electrometeors*, arising from atmospheric electrical phenomena. The definitions below are taken from Volume I of that organization's International Cloud Atlas, published in 1956 from the headquarters in Geneva.

**Hydrometeors.** *Rain.* Precipitation of liquid water particles, either in the form of drops of more than 0.5 mm diameter or in the form of smaller widely scattered drops. *Freezing rain* is recorded when the drops freeze on impact with the ground, with objects on the earth's surface, or with aircraft in flight.

*Drizzle.* Fairly uniform precipitation composed exclusively of fine drops of water (diameter less than 0.5 mm), very close to one another. *Freezing drizzle* is recorded when the drops freeze on impact with the ground, with objects on the earth's surface, or with aircraft in flight.

*Snow.* Precipitation of ice crystals, most of which are branched (sometimes star-shaped).

---

Fig. 6-13 (*facing page*). Stages in the development of a cumulus congestus. (*a*) Cumulus congestus with cumulus humilis around it. The greyness left of center may be the beginning of precipitation. (*b*) The same cloud 15 min later, spreading toward the left with precipitation. (*c*) The same cloud photographed 15 min after (*b*), showing definite cumulonimbus characteristics, and new cumulus congestus developing in the foreground. (*Institute of Atmospheric Physics, University of Arizona.*)

*Snow Pellets.* Precipitation of white and opaque grains of ice. These grains are spherical or sometimes conical; their diameter is from about 2 to 5 mm.

*Snow Grains.* Precipitation of very small white and opaque grains of ice. These grains are fairly flat or elongated; their diameter is generally less than 1 mm.

*Ice Pellets.* Precipitation of transparent or translucent pellets of ice, which are spherical or irregular, rarely conical, and which have a diameter of 5 mm or less.

Fig. 6–14. Cumulonimbus, spreading over the sky toward the photographer. (*U.S. Navy photograph.*)

*Hail.* Precipitation of small balls or pieces of ice (hailstones) with a diameter ranging from 5 to 50 mm or sometimes more, falling either separately or agglomerated into irregular lumps.

*Ice Prisms.* A fall of unbranched ice crystals, in the form of needles, columns, or plates, often so tiny that they seem to be suspended in the air. These crystals may fall from a cloud or from a cloudless sky.

*Fog.* A suspension of very small water droplets in the air, generally reducing the horizontal visibility at the earth's surface to less than 1 km.

*Ice Fog.* A suspension of numerous minute ice crystals in the air, reducing the visibility at the earth's surface.

*Mist.* A suspension in the air of microscopic water droplets or wet hygroscopic particles, reducing the visibility at the earth's surface. Note that in the International Codes for weather reports, the term "mist" is used when the hydrometeor mist or fog reduces the horizontal visibility at the earth's surface to *not less* than 1 km.

*Drifting Snow and Blowing Snow.* An ensemble of snow particles raised from the ground by a sufficiently strong and turbulent wind. *Drifting* means that the particles are raised to small heights and the visibility is not sensibly diminished at eye level. *Blowing* means that the particles are raised to moderate or great heights and the horizontal visibility at eye level is generally very poor.

Fig. 6–15.   Stratocumulus viewed from above.   (*U.S. Weather Bureau, Lois Bowen.*)

*Spray.* An ensemble of water droplets torn by the wind from the surface of an extensive body of water, generally from the crests of waves, and carried up a short distance into the air.

*Dew.* A deposit of water drops on objects at or near the ground, produced by the condensation of water vapor from the surrounding clear air.   *White dew* is a deposit of white frozen dew drops.

*Hoarfrost.* A deposit of ice having a crystalline appearance, generally assuming the form of scales, needles, feathers, or fans.

*Rime.* A deposit of ice, composed of grains more or less separated by trapped air, sometimes adorned with crystalline branches.

*Glaze (Clear Ice).* A generally homogeneous and transparent deposit of ice formed by the freezing of supercooled drizzle droplets or raindrops on objects the surface temperature of which is below or slightly above 0°C.

*Spout.* A phenomenon consisting of an often violent whirlwind, revealed by the presence of a cloud column or inverted cloud cone (funnel cloud), protuding from the base of a cumulonimbus, and of a "bush" composed of water droplets raised from the surface of the sea or of dust, sand, or litter, raised from the ground; *tornado,* or *waterspout.*

**Lithometeors.**    *Haze.*    A suspension in the air of extremely small dry particles invisible to the naked eye and sufficiently numerous to give the air an opalescent appearance.

Fig. 6–16. Nimbostratus tops breaking upward through stratocumulus or altocumulus. (*U.S. Weather Bureau.*)

*Dust Haze.*    A suspension in the air of dust or small sand particles, raised from the ground prior to the time of observation by a dust storm or sandstorm.

*Smoke.*    A suspension in the air of small particles produced by combustion.

*Drifting and Blowing Dust or Sand.*    An ensemble of particles of dust or sand raised, at or near the station, from the ground to small or moderate heights by a sufficiently strong and turbulent wind. *Drifting* means raised to small heights, and the visibility is not sensibly diminished at eye level. *Blowing* means raised to moderate heights, and the horizontal visibility at eye level is sensibly reduced.

*Dust Storm or Sandstorm.*    An ensemble of particles of dust or sand energetically lifted to great heights by a strong and turbulent wind.

*Dust Whirl or Sand Whirl (Dust Devil).*   An ensemble of particles of dust or sand, sometimes accompanied by small litter, raised from the ground in the form of a whirling column of varying height with a small diameter and an approximately vertical axis.

FIG. 6–17. Cumulus congestus penetrating upward through a haze layer.   (*U.S. Weather Bureau.*)

**Photometeors.**   *Halo Phenomena.*   A group of optical phenomena in the form of rings, arcs, pillars, or bright spots, produced by the refraction or reflection of light by ice crystals suspended in the atmosphere (cirriform clouds, ice fog, etc.).

*Corona.*   One or more sequences (seldom more than three) of colored rings of relatively small diameter, centered on the sun or moon.

*Irisation.*   Colors appearing on clouds, sometimes mingled, sometimes in the form of bands nearly parallel to the margin of the clouds.   Green and pink predominate, often with pastel shades.

*Glory.*   One or more sequences of colored rings, seen by an observer around his own shadow on a cloud consisting mainly of numerous small water droplets, on fog or, very rarely, on dew.

*Rainbow.*   A group of concentric arcs with colors ranging from violet to red, produced on a "screen" of water drops (raindrops, droplets of drizzle, or fog) in the atmosphere by light from the sun or moon.

*Bishop's Ring.* A whitish ring, centered on the sun or moon, with a slightly bluish tinge on the inside and reddish brown on the outside.

*Mirage.* An optical phenomenon consisting mainly of steady or wavering, single or multiple, upright or inverted, vertically enlarged or reduced images of distant objects.

*Shimmer.* The apparent fluttering of objects at the earth's surface, when viewed in the horizontal direction.

*Scintillation.* Rapid variations, often in the form of pulsations, of the light from stars or terrestrial light sources.

*Green Flash.* A predominantly green coloration of short duration, often in the form of a flash, seen at the extreme upper edge of a luminary (sun, moon, or sometimes even a planet) when disappearing below or appearing above the horizon.

*Twilight Colors.* Various colorations of the sky and of the peaks of mountains at sunset and sunrise. (A number of these color effects have been given special names which will not be recited here.)

**Electrometeors.** *Thunderstorm.* One or more sudden electrical discharges, manifested by a flash of light (lightning) and a sharp or rumbling sound (thunder).

*Saint Elmo's Fire.* A more or less continuous, luminous electrical discharge of weak or moderate intensity in the atmosphere, emanating from elevated objects at the earth's surface (lightning conductors, wind vanes, masts of ships) or from aircraft in flight (wingtips, propellers, etc.).

*Polar Aurora.* A luminous phenomenon which appears in the high atmosphere, in the form of arcs, bands, draperies, or curtains.

# CHAPTER 7

# THERMODYNAMICS AND STATICS

The atmosphere is a huge thermodynamic engine, driven by the energy received from the sun. The general circulation over the earth, all winds, storms, and clouds result from the differences in the amount and utilization of this energy. Since the radiant energy appears principally as heat, the student of meteorology must understand how the air reacts to heat changes; in other words, he must understand the *thermodynamics* of the atmosphere. Furthermore, since the thermal state of any portion of the atmosphere also determines its weight, a consideration of *statics* is required.

## THE GAS LAWS

The atmospheric circulations mentioned above come about through changes in pressure, temperature, and density relationships of the air. Considering first the density, we note that it is defined as the mass per unit volume $\rho = M/V$, and that in a rigid body of simple configuration the density can be obtained easily with a pair of calipers or measuring tape and a weighing balance or scale, making use of the defining relationship. In gases, the volume changes with changes in pressure or temperature, so that this simple measurement based on the relationship between density, mass, and volume cannot readily be made although the relationship still holds.

**The Laws of Boyle and Gay-Lussac.** The relationship between pressure, temperature, and volume (therefore, also density) in gases has been determined by early experiments of classical physics. One of the fundamental concepts derived from these early experiments is Boyle's law, which states that, in a gas that is kept at constant temperature,

$$pV = p'V' = \text{const}$$

where $p$ and $V$ are the pressure and volume at one stage and $p'$ and $V'$ at another stage of the constant-temperature, or isothermal, process.

This law is good for all common gases not too near their liquefaction temperature and is therefore applicable to the atmosphere.

We also make use of the law of Gay-Lussac, which shows how the volume of a gas changes when the temperature is changed but the pressure is kept constant. If $V_0$ represents the volume at a temperature of 0°C, then the volume $V$ at any other temperature $t$ is given by

$$V = V_0(1 + \alpha_p t)$$

at constant pressure, where $\alpha_p$ is the volume coefficient of expansion with constant pressure and has the numerical value of $\frac{1}{273}$. This means that, for any gas, a rise in temperature of 1°C increases the volume by $\frac{1}{273}$ if the pressure is held constant.

We can combine the laws of Boyle and Gay-Lussac by considering two constant-pressure processes, one at a pressure $p$, and the other at a standard pressure $p_s$, and both with the same temperature $t$. Then at the pressure $p$

$$V = V_0(1 + \alpha_p t) \tag{7-1}$$

and at the pressure $p_s$

$$V_s = V_{0s}(1 + \alpha_p t) \tag{7-2}$$

where the subscript $s$ refers to standard pressure conditions. From Boyle's law, since $p$, $V$, $p_s$, and $V_s$ all depend on the temperature $t$,

$$pV = p_s V_s = p_s V_{0s}(1 + \alpha_p t) = p_s V_{0s} \alpha_p \left( \frac{1}{\alpha_p} + t \right) \tag{7-3}$$

Let $p_s V_{0s} \alpha_p$ be called $C$ since they are all constant and

$$\frac{1}{\alpha_p} + t = 273 + t \tag{7-4}$$

be called $T$ (the absolute or Kelvin temperature that derives its definition in this way), then

$$pV = CT \tag{7-5}$$

**Avogadro's Law and the Meaning of $C$.** According to Avogadro's law, a gram molecule (the number of grams of the gas equal to its molecular weight) of any gas at the same temperature and pressure occupies the same volume; therefore, the volume of a gram molecule of any gas is a universal function of the temperature and pressure. At a temperature of 0°C and a pressure of 760 mm of mercury, the volume of a gram molecule of any gas is approximately 22,400 cm³. If $\mathbf{v}$ is the volume occupied by one gram-molecular weight (the gram-molecular volume) then $\mathbf{v} = V/n$ where $n$ is the number of gram molecules contained in $V$

(any volume). If we say that $C/n = R$, then

$$p\mathbf{v} = RT \qquad (7\text{--}6)$$

and, for one mole of gas, $R$ will then be a universal constant, applicable to any gas. Also, since $C = nR$, we can write the relationship

$$pV = nRT \qquad (7\text{--}7)$$

The last two equations are forms of the so-called "equation of state for an ideal gas," expressed in terms most often used in physics. In meteorology, where we are not dealing with controlled volumes, it is preferable to express the equation in slightly different form.

**Equation of State in Different Forms.** If $M$ is the mass of the volume $V$ and $m$ is the gram-molecular weight, then

$$n = \frac{M}{m} \qquad (7\text{--}8)$$

and therefore

$$pV = \frac{M}{m} RT \qquad (7\text{--}9)$$

but

$$\frac{V}{M} = \frac{1}{\rho} = \alpha \qquad (7\text{--}10)$$

where $\alpha$ is the specific volume or the number of cubic centimeters occupied by 1 g of the gas, and in these terms we can write the equation as

$$p\alpha = \frac{R}{m} T \qquad (7\text{--}11)$$

or

$$p = \rho \frac{R}{m} T \qquad (7\text{--}12)$$

These two forms are the ones in which the equation of state is expressed for meteorological purposes in terms of the universal gas constant. Sometimes the equation is written without the $m$, and it then becomes $p\alpha = R'T$ where $R'$ is the individual gas constant, different for every gas and equal to $R/m$.

Strictly speaking, air does not have a molecular weight since it is a mixture of gases and there is no such thing as an air molecule; however, it is possible to assign a so-called "molecular weight" to dry air, which will make the equation of state operative. It has the value 28.9. For water vapor it would have the value 18, which is the true molecular weight of water. The gas constant $R$ has the value of $8.314 \times 10^7$ ergs per degree K per mole. The pressure is expressed in dynes per square centimeter, $\alpha$ in cubic centimeters per gram, $T$ in degrees Kelvin, and $m$ in grams.[1]

Exact measurements indicate that the equation of state is only

[1] Mechanical units of energy are used for the most part throughout this and succeeding chapters. See standard physics texts for definitions.

approximately valid. The higher the pressure and the lower the temperature, i.e., the nearer the gas approaches liquefaction, the greater the departure from the conditions of the equation. An ideal substance that follows the equation exactly is called an *ideal gas*. Real gases conform to the equation of state approximately. In spite of this approximation, the gases as they exist in the atmosphere may be considered as ideal gases. This is permissible because the refinements of the equation are considerably greater than the limits of accuracy of the observations. There is hardly a relationship in meteorology that is more basic and important than the equation of state. The student and professional meteorologist must make regular and frequent use of it either as a descriptive concept or for computations. It will often be referred to in this book.

**Effects of Water Vapor—Virtual Temperature.** All the gases in the atmosphere, including the water vapor, exert their own partial pressures. Concerning this, we have Dalton's law, which states that the total pressure of a gas mixture is equal to the sum of the partial pressures. Also, we have the corollary that, in a mixture of gases, every gas occupies the whole volume of the mixture as if the other gases were not present. In meteorology we find it convenient to consider the mixture of "dry gases" forming one "gas" ("molecular weight" 28.9) and the water vapor (molecular weight 18) another.

The equation of state can be applied as in Eq. (7–12) to a mixture of gases provided that the relative quantities of the different gases in the mixture do not vary. Otherwise, the "molecular weight" $m$ would not be a constant. Water vapor is the only important gas in the atmosphere that varies in significant amounts, and it is found necessary to treat it separately or arrive at some means of taking into account the variable effects of its presence. Since water vapor has a lesser molecular weight than that ascribed to dry air, its presence at a given temperature and pressure would tend to lower the density of the mixture. We write the equation of state for water vapor in the form

$$e = \rho_w \frac{R}{m_w} T \tag{7–13}$$

or

$$\rho_w = \frac{e m_w}{RT} \tag{7–14}$$

where $e$ is the partial pressure of the water vapor and the subscript $w$ refers to water vapor.

We consider the other gases (dry air) separately and write

$$p_d = \rho_d \frac{R}{m_d} T \tag{7–15}$$

or

$$\rho_d = \frac{p_d m_d}{RT} \tag{7–16}$$

The two equations of state can be combined in such a way as to take into account the effects of water vapor. To do this, meteorologists find it is not convenient to vary the "molecular weight" but instead to ascribe a fictitious temperature to the mixture, which would depend partly on the amount of water vapor present. This can be interpreted from a recognition of the fact that an increase in water vapor decreases the air density, and an increase in temperature also decreases it. We assign a fictitious increase to the temperature in just the right amount to correspond to the lowered density caused by the water vapor. The new temperature is called the *virtual temperature*. It may be defined as the temperature of dry air having the same total pressure and density as the moist air.

The combination of the equations of state for dry air and water vapor in terms of the virtual temperature and the total density $\rho$ is accomplished as follows:

$$\rho = \rho_w + \rho_d = \frac{em_w + p_d m_d}{RT}$$

$$= \frac{em_w + (P - e)m_d}{RT} \tag{7-17}$$

where $P$ is the total pressure $(p_d + e)$. If we multiply and divide the numerator by $Pm_d$, we obtain

$$\rho = Pm_d \frac{\dfrac{e}{P}\dfrac{m_w}{m_d} + \left(1 - \dfrac{e}{P}\right)}{RT}$$

$$= \frac{Pm_d}{RT}\left(1 - \frac{3}{8}\frac{e}{P}\right) \tag{7-18}$$

since $\dfrac{m_w}{m_d} = \dfrac{18}{28.9} = \dfrac{5}{8}$ (approximately). If we call $T^* = \dfrac{T}{1 - \frac{3}{8}e/P}$, then

$$\rho = \frac{Pm_d}{RT^*} \tag{7-19}$$

where $T^*$ is the virtual temperature. It will be pointed out later that $e/P$ is a function of the *specific humidity q*, which is the number of grams of water vapor in a gram of air, so that we also have

$$T^* = \frac{T}{1 - \frac{3}{5}q} \tag{7-20}$$

By means of the virtual temperature, it is possible to use the equation of state in terms of the total pressure and the "molecular weight" of dry air. Since $q$ or $e/P$ seldom exceed 0.02, $T^*$ seldom exceeds $T$ by more than 2 or 3°.

The correct equation of state for air is, then,

$$P\alpha = \frac{R}{m_d} T^*$$  (7–21)

or

$$P = \rho \frac{R}{m_d} T^*$$  (7–22)

## THE FIRST LAW OF THERMODYNAMICS

**The Concept of Internal Energy.** The kinetic theory of gases states that the temperature observed in a gas depends on the rate at which the molecules are moving about and is, in fact, proportional to the mean kinetic energy of the moving molecules. The heating of the gas will be accompanied by an increased speed of motion of the molecules, and therefore by an increased kinetic energy. On the other hand, if no heat is added but the gas is compressed, the kinetic energy will also be increased by the compression, and the temperature of the gas will rise. The kinetic theory reveals that this increase in temperature is brought about by the greater speed with which the molecules rebound from the contracting walls that confine them. This kinetic energy of the molecules goes to make up what is known as the *internal energy* of the gas, and from the foregoing reasoning it is apparent that an increase in internal energy must be accompanied by an increase in temperature and vice versa.[1]

**Statement of the First Law.** The first law of thermodynamics states that an increase in the internal energy can be brought about by the addition of heat or by performing work on the gas, or by a combination of both. If we represent the change in internal energy by $dE$, positive for an increase and negative for a decrease, and the heat added as $+dQ$, and $dW$ represents the work done *on* the gas, negative for work done *by* the gas, then we have the following relationship:

$$dE = dQ + dW$$  (7–23)

Thus, in the case mentioned above, where the gas is compressed without adding heat, we would have

$$dE = dW$$  (7–24)

In other words, the increase in internal energy would be caused by work (compression) performed on the gas. In the case of direct heating where no work is done

$$dE = dQ$$  (7–25)

---

[1] In some gases whose molecules contain two or more atoms, a part of the internal energy is stored as energy not only of translatory motion but also of rotation and vibration of individual molecules.

and it is not difficult to conceive of a process in which both heating and mechanical work would be involved.

**Work Done by External Forces.** In considering the work done on a gas, we are mainly concerned with pressure. Pressure is defined as force per unit area.

$$p = \frac{F}{A}$$

or
$$F = pA \qquad\qquad (7\text{--}26)$$

Consider Fig. 7–1, which represents a parcel of air in the atmosphere. Any pressure $p$ which may be applied in the atmosphere would act equally in all directions. Therefore this pressure would be exerted on the parcel from all sides, causing it to be compressed to a smaller volume by an amount

$$-dV = A\, dn \qquad (7\text{--}27)$$

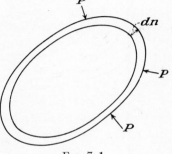

Here $dn$ is the distance between the outer surface of the parcel in the two positions and $A$ is the area of this surface, assumed to be the same in both cases because $dn$ is taken as infinitesimal. The work done on the parcel in this compression is given, as

Fig. 7–1.

always, by the product of the force acting on the parcel times the distance through which the force acts, measured in the direction of the force.

$$dW = F\, dn \qquad\qquad (7\text{--}28)$$

and by substituting for $F$ from Eq. (7–26), we obtain the work done on the parcel in terms of pressure and volume, viz.,

$$dW = pA\, dn = -p\, dV \qquad\qquad (7\text{--}29)$$

**The Internal Energy.** It can be shown by experiment that the internal energy of an ideal gas varies only with its absolute temperature. Since the state of a gas is determined by pressure and volume, in addition to temperature, one may consider a temperature change as made up of changes in the two components $p$ and $V$. The temperature may be changed by holding the volume constant and varying the pressure, or by keeping the pressure constant and varying the volume. This may be seen in Fig. 7–2, where the equation of state is represented in a $pV$ diagram, with temperatures shown in the curved lines (rectangular hyperbolas). It is apparent that the temperature may be changed by following along a horizontal line $p = $ const, or along a vertical line $V = $ const.

We shall arrive at the change in internal energy by considering these two processes.

Having obtained the expression for the work done $dW$, we may now write the equation for the first law as

$$dE = dQ - p\,dV \qquad (7\text{--}30)$$

If we consider a constant-volume process, $p\,dV = 0$. The heat added $dQ$, corresponding to a change in temperature $dT$, will be given by the mass times the heat required to raise unit mass 1°C at constant volume, i.e., the specific heat, multiplied by $dT$, or

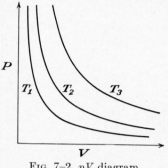

$$dE = MC_v\,dT \qquad (7\text{--}31)$$

FIG. 7–2. $pV$ diagram.

where $C_v$ is the specific heat at constant volume.

It has been shown experimentally that for a "perfect" gas the internal energy depends only on the temperature and that this may also be considered to hold for the gases comprising the air in their observed states in the atmosphere. $C_v$ is determined by experiment and is found to be constant. The expression (7–31) is taken as the definition of the change in internal energy and can be substituted for $dE$ whether one is dealing with a constant-volume process or not.

Equation (7–31) is a statement of Eq. (7–30) for the case of heat added at constant volume so that $dV = 0$ and no external work is involved. The heat added all goes toward changing the internal energy. If heat is added at constant pressure, $dV \neq 0$ and the gas performs work against the environment through expansion as it is heated. We get two different results depending upon which of these two conditions is imposed during the heating. The amount of heat required to raise the temperature of a given mass of the substance by one degree will be different in the two cases. That is another way of saying that there are two specific heats of a gas, the specific heat at constant volume $C_v$ and the specific heat at constant pressure $C_p$, both constant.

To see how the two specific heats differ, we may consider a constant-pressure process involving the same change in internal energy $dE$ as in the constant-volume process of Eq. (7–31). We substitute for this $dE$ in the fundamental Eq. (7–30) and apply the heat $dQ$ at constant pressure:

$$MC_v\,dT = dQ - p\,dV \qquad (7\text{--}32)$$

At constant pressure, the heat added would be $MC_p\,dT$, where $C_p$ is the specific heat at constant pressure. The change in internal energy in the constant-pressure process would be

$$dE = MC_v \, dT = MC_p \, dT - p \, dV \qquad (7\text{--}33)$$

This may be written in the form

$$M(C_p - C_v) \, dT = p \, dV \qquad (7\text{--}34)$$

The equation of state (7–7) in differential form is

$$p \, dV + V \, dp = nR \, dT \qquad (7\text{--}35)$$

In this constant-pressure process $dp = 0$ and, by algebra, we may solve for $(dT/dV)_p$, the change in temperature with volume change at constant pressure, in both (7–34) and (7–35), obtaining

$$\left(\frac{dT}{dV}\right)_p = \frac{p}{M(C_p - C_v)} = \frac{p}{nR} \qquad (7\text{--}36)$$

and

$$C_p - C_v = \frac{nR}{M} = \frac{R}{m} \qquad (7\text{--}37)$$

since, from Eq. (7–8), $n/M = 1/m$. The difference $C_p - C_v = R/m$ is sometimes called the *molecular heat difference*, since it is inversely proportional to the molecular weight $m$. The ratio of the specific heats, which can be obtained from Eq. (7–37) by dividing by $C_v$, is

$$\frac{C_p}{C_v} = 1 + \frac{R}{mC_v} \qquad (7\text{--}38)$$

It is nearly the same in all gases in the same class, as defined by the number of atoms contained in their molecules. For example, in monatomic gases like helium it has the value 1.67; in diatomic gases ($N_2$, $O_2$, etc.), about 1.40; in gases with from 3 to 5 atoms per molecule, ($H_2O$, $CO_2$, $NH_3$, etc.), about 1.30.

**Application to the Atmosphere.** Substituting the values obtained for $dE$ and $dW$ into the complete equation of the first law, we have

$$MC_v \, dT = dQ - p \, dV \qquad (7\text{--}39)$$

or

$$dQ = MC_v \, dT + p \, dV \qquad (7\text{--}40)$$

This represents the equation in terms of temperature, pressure, and volume; but in the atmosphere, volume measurements are difficult, and it is preferable to use the equation in terms of pressures and temperatures only. It will also be more convenient, since in the atmosphere we are not dealing with fixed masses of air, to consider unit mass (1 g). For unit mass we shall write the equation, after dividing by $M$, as

$$dq = C_v \, dT + p \, d\alpha \qquad (7\text{--}41)$$

where $dq$ is the heat added to unit mass and $d\alpha$ is the change in specific volume. This equation can be reduced to terms of pressure and temperature by writing the equation of state in differential form

$$p\alpha = \frac{R}{m} T$$

$$p\,d\alpha + \alpha\,dp = \frac{R}{m} dT$$

$$p\,d\alpha = \frac{R}{m} dT - \alpha\,dp \qquad (7\text{-}42)$$

and substituting for $p\,d\alpha$ with the result

$$dq = C_v\,dT + \frac{R}{m} dT - \alpha\,dp \qquad (7\text{-}43)$$

But since
$$C_p - C_v = \frac{R}{m}$$

and therefore
$$C_v + \frac{R}{m} = C_p$$

we note that
$$dq = \left(C_v + \frac{R}{m}\right) dT - \alpha\,dp$$

and therefore
$$dq = C_p\,dT - \frac{R}{m} T \frac{dp}{p} \qquad (7\text{-}44)$$

the last term on the right being obtained by solving the equation of state for $\alpha$, i.e., by making use of the relationship

$$\alpha = \frac{RT}{mp}$$

Equation (7-44) is another of the half dozen or so highly important basic equations used to describe the properties, motions, and transformations of the atmospheric medium. It is a statement of the first law of thermodynamics in terms of the easily measured atmospheric variables, temperature and pressure, and requires no consideration of measured or controlled volumes or masses. It sometimes is described as the expression of the first law of thermodynamics for open systems, as contrasted with the closed systems usually dealt with in the laboratory and in engineering. The latter are represented by Eq. (7-40). It will now be shown how in the atmosphere we often find Eq. (7-44) simplified by the prevalence of processes in which $dq = 0$.

**Adiabatic Process.** The adiabatic process is defined as one in which there is no heat added or taken away, i.e., one in which $dq = 0$. In an adiabatic process the change in internal energy of the gas would, therefore, be due entirely to the work performed on it, particularly by forces compressing the gas, or by the work done by the gas in the form of an expansion. In the atmosphere both adiabatic and nonadiabatic processes are occurring. The addition of heat to the atmosphere near the ground when the surface is warmer than the overlying air and the removal of heat in the same manner when the surface is colder are continuous non-adiabatic processes. In the free atmosphere where there is no solid or liquid surface to give off or remove heat and where the amount of energy absorbed from the sun's rays or lost by direct radiation is insignificant by comparison, we are justified in assuming that all short-period processes are essentially adiabatic. Since in the atmosphere the pressure decreases rapidly with elevation, adiabatic temperature changes, which as is seen above, are determined solely by pressure changes, occur most readily when portions of the air undergo motions having a vertical component. Thus, a parcel of air carried upward cools adiabatically with the decreasing pressure that it experiences, and conversely, a descent with increasing pressure causes an increase in the temperature.

From the first law of thermodynamics it is possible to obtain an equation by means of which, if given the temperature and pressure of a parcel or sample of air at the beginning of an adiabatic process, its temperature at any known pressure in which it is found later on during that process can be calculated. The derivation of such an equation affords the best opportunity to introduce the concept of *entropy*. The complete explanation of entropy is derived from the second law of thermodynamics. However, since the second law involves mainly concepts that are not generally applied in meteorology at the present time, no effort will be made to enter into a general discussion of it here. For our purposes we shall have to be satisfied with a mere definition of entropy. We shall make use of the specific entropy, which is the entropy applicable to unit mass of the substance. Expressing it in differential form $d\varphi$, meaning the change in entropy, we have the relationship applicable to any reversible process

$$d\varphi = \frac{dq}{T} \qquad (7\text{--}45)$$

In other words, the increase in entropy is given by the ratio of the heat added to the temperature at which it is added. We see from this relationship that a reversible adiabatic process is one in which the entropy does not change; therefore, it is what we call an *isentropic* process.

By making use of the entropy differential, we have for an adiabatic process

$$d\varphi = \frac{dq}{T} = C_p \frac{dT}{T} - \frac{R}{m}\frac{dp}{p} = 0 \qquad (7\text{--}46)$$

and

$$C_p \frac{dT}{T} = \frac{R}{m}\frac{dp}{p} \qquad (7\text{--}47)$$

We start out in an adiabatic process with the temperature $T_0$ and the pressure $p_0$ and wish to find the temperature $T$ at some other pressure $p$. To do this, we integrate the last equation from $T_0$ to $T$ and from $p_0$ to $p$ as follows:

$$\int_{T_0}^{T} C_p \frac{dT}{T} = \int_{p_0}^{p} \frac{R}{m} \frac{dp}{p} \tag{7-48}$$

which becomes $C_p \ln T - C_p \ln T_0 = \dfrac{R}{m} \ln p - \dfrac{R}{m} \ln p_0$

or

$$C_p \ln \frac{T}{T_0} = \frac{R}{m} \ln \frac{p}{p_0} \tag{7-49}$$

which is the same as

$$\left(\frac{T}{T_0}\right)^{C_p} = \left(\frac{p}{p_0}\right)^{R/m} \tag{7-50}$$

$$\frac{T}{T_0} = \left(\frac{p}{p_0}\right)^{R/mC_p} \tag{7-51}$$

This is known as Poisson's equation. The exponent $R/mC_p$ is usually given the value $2/7$, or 0.286.

In physics and engineering, the thermodynamic processes of gases, such as isothermal processes, adiabatic processes, etc., are represented on the so-called "$pV$ diagram," having pressure and volume as coordinates. This diagram has the property that the work involved in any closed cycle, made up of any series or combination of processes bringing the gas back to its starting pressure and volume, is directly proportional to the area enclosed by the plot of the cycle on the diagram. From Eq. (7–29), it is seen that the work done on the gas in compression to change its volume by an amount $-dV$ would be $dW = -p \, dV$. The total work done in a cyclic process would then be

$$W = -\int_c p \, dV \tag{7-52}$$

where the integral sign with the subscript $c$ indicates integration around a closed path (line integral). This is then the area enclosed by the closed path on the $pV$ diagram. The negative sign means work done *on* the gas and the positive sign would denote work done *by* the gas, according to the convention adopted in Eq. (7–23).

In the atmosphere, where we are not dealing with controlled volumes, it is more convenient to represent the processes in terms of pressure and temperature. It is desirable to retain, however, the work-measuring property of the $pV$ integral. This can be done in terms of $p$ and $T$ with a suitable transformation. Since in the atmosphere it is more convenient to deal with unit mass and specific volume, we measure the work on a unit mass,

$$dw = -p \, d\alpha \tag{7-53}$$

Again substituting from the equation of state in differential form as in the development of Eq. (7–42), we note that

$$dw = \alpha \, dp - \frac{R}{m} \, dT \qquad (7-54)$$

and the integral becomes

$$w = \int_c \alpha \, dp - \int_c \frac{R}{m} \, dT \qquad (7-55)$$

But the second integral on the right is equal to zero. This can be shown mathematically by proving that $dT$ is an exact differential and by using a theorem from the calculus which shows that the integral of an exact differential around a closed path is zero.

The $\alpha$ in the first term on the right can be changed to an expression of $p$ and $T$ by means of the equation of state, so we have

$$w = \frac{R}{m} \int_c T \frac{dp}{p} = \frac{R}{m} \int_c T \, d(\ln p) \qquad (7-56)$$

Thus a diagram with $T$ and $\ln p$ as coordinates will have the desired property of representing work by an area.

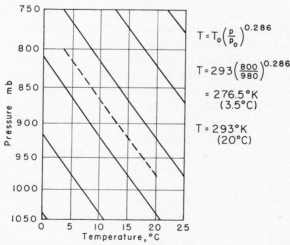

$$T = T_0 \left( \frac{p}{p_0} \right)^{0.286}$$

$$T = 293 \left( \frac{800}{980} \right)^{0.286}$$
$$= 276.5°K$$
$$(3.5°C)$$

$$T = 293°K$$
$$(20°C)$$

Fig. 7–3. Adiabatic chart illustrating the graphical solution of Poisson's equation.

This is particularly fortunate for atmospheric studies since height is very nearly a function of the logarithm of pressure, and a diagram with temperature as abscissa and logarithm of pressure, decreasing upward, as ordinate has the appearance of a temperature-height graph. These points will be demonstrated in the next section of this chapter. Another fortunate circumstance is that the exponent in Eq. (7–51) has such a value ($k = 0.286$) that $dp^k$ is proportional to $d \ln p$ at atmospheric values so the ordinate in the diagram can be $p^k$ with close approximation. This has the advantage of making the adiabats, or lines representing the adiabatic process, straight lines. A portion of an adiabatic chart of this nature is shown in Fig. 7–3. The sloping lines are the adiabats.

Poisson's equation (7–51) can be solved graphically by means of this diagram. Suppose we have a sample of air at a temperature of 20°C ($T_0 = 293$) and a pressure ($p_0$) of 980 mb, as in the figure. If we want to find the temperature after the sample has been carried through an adiabatic process in which it has been brought to a pressure $p$, let us say of 800 mb, the required temperature $T$ can be read off the scale below, which in this example turns out to be 3.5°C.

Poisson's equation also can be expressed in terms of the derivative $dT/dp$, to give the rate at which the temperature would change with pressure during an adiabatic process (therefore, with the slopes of the adiabatic lines). From Eq. (7–47), rearrangement of terms gives the result

$$\frac{dT}{dp} = \frac{R}{m}\frac{T}{C_p p} \tag{7–57}$$

**Hydrostatic Equation.** Ordinarily the only force operating vertically on the whole atmosphere is that force produced by the acceleration of gravity. Transient upward or downward accelerations of the air are noted in certain situations which may on occasion have noticeable effects on readings of sensitive barographs, but except under special conditions in mountainous areas, the effects are trivial. The force produced by the acceleration of gravity $g$ on a mass $M$ is $F = Mg$. This, of course, is the definition of weight and for the atmosphere it would be the weight of the total overlying air. By definition, the pressure is the force per unit area, and in the cgs units the unit of area is 1 cm². The pressure at any point in the atmosphere would be equivalent to the weight of an air column of a 1 cm² cross section extending to the top of the atmosphere. If the atmosphere were of constant density with height we would have $M = \rho V$ and $p = \rho g H$, where $H$ is the height of the air column extending to the outside of the atmosphere.

Actually, since $\rho$ varies with height, we must express the equation as a differential in which each layer of infinitesimal thickness $dz$ and density $\rho$ contributes a pressure increase $dp$. In differential form the equation is

$$dp = -\rho g \, dz \tag{7–58}$$

the minus sign indicating that $z$ is measured upward in the direction of decreasing pressure.

It should be emphasized again, as on page 74, that the pressure is exerted equally in all directions. It is apparent from the hydrostatic relationships that the pressure depends only on the density and thickness of the overlying atmosphere. Thus, if there are two small volumes or parcels of air next to each other but each has a different density, the pressure in each will nevertheless be the same. It will be shown in this chapter that two such parcels will not remain together at the same level.

Equation (7–58) is called the hydrostatic equation and is applicable to bodies of fluid and gaseous atmospheres. It is the third equation of great basic importance which we have derived in this chapter. We now are in a position to extend the three basic relationships (equation of state, first law of thermodynamics, and hydrostatic equation) to a variety of problems of thermodynamics and statics in the atmosphere.

**Adiabatic Temperature Changes in Terms of Height.** To obtain the adiabatic rate of temperature change with height, we substitute $dp$ from the hydrostatic equation (7–58) into the differential form of the adiabatic equation (7–47) with the result

$$C_p \frac{dT}{T} + \frac{R\rho g\, dz}{mp} = 0 \qquad (7\text{–}59)$$

and since, from the equation of state $\rho = pm/RT$,

$$C_p \frac{dT}{T} = -\frac{mp}{RT} \frac{Rg\, dz}{mp} \qquad (7\text{–}60)$$

$$C_p\, dT = -g\, dz \qquad (7\text{–}61)$$

and

$$\frac{dT}{dz} = -\frac{g}{C_p} \qquad (7\text{–}62)$$

This gives us an expression for the rate of change of temperature with height in an adiabatic process, the negative sign indicating that the temperature would decrease with altitude. The term $g/C_p$ has the value of approximately $10^{-4}°C$ per cm, or $1°C$ per 100 m.

This is the rate at which a sample or portion of dry air[1] would change its temperature if caused to ascend or descend. The negative sign indicates that the temperature would decrease with increasing height and increase with decreasing height—in each case at a rate of $1°C$ per 100 m.

It is often useful in meteorology to consider adiabatic ascent or descent of small parcels of air through the surrounding atmosphere, the latter not taking part in the vertical motion and therefore not changing its temperature. Unless the surrounding atmosphere has a rate of temperature fall with height that is exactly the same as the adiabatic rate of cooling

---

[1] The relevance of the term "dry" will be discussed on p. 145.

for ascending air, a parcel displaced from its original position would have a temperature different from that of its surroundings. Therefore, its density would be different. The pressure-height relationship of Eq. (7–59) should then be determined in terms of the density of the surrounding air. At any given level the pressure in the parcel and in the environment would be the same, because the parcel is equally as compressible as the surrounding air. For the parcel method, the two temperatures in Eq. (7–60) would be different, and $dT'/dz$ where $T'$ is the temperature of the rising parcel ($T$ that of the surroundings) would be given by

$$\frac{dT'}{dz} = -\frac{T'}{T}\frac{g}{C_p} \tag{7–63}$$

For temperature differences of the order likely to occur in the atmosphere, the factor $T'/T$ is so close to 1 that it has a negligible effect on the numerical value of the expression. Therefore Eq. (7–62) is used in most cases. It might be added that Eq. (7–62) is also useful because we are not always thinking in terms of displaced parcels in the atmosphere.

**Determination of Altitude.** On the adiabatic chart, altitudes can be represented conveniently because all three factors, pressure, temperature, and humidity, determine the altitude. The relationship between pressure and height at a given temperature may be determined from the hydrostatic equation

$$dp = -\rho g\,dz$$

or, by substituting from the equation of state,

$$dp = -\frac{pmg}{RT^*}\,dz$$

where $T^*$ is the virtual temperature. This equation is then integrated from sea level, where the pressure is $p_0$, to the height $z$, having the pressure $p$, as follows:

$$\int_{p_0}^{p}\frac{dp}{p} = -\frac{mg}{R}\int_0^z\frac{1}{T^*}\,dz = \ln\frac{p}{p_0} \tag{7–64}$$

$$p = p_0 e^{-\frac{mg}{R}\int_0^z\frac{1}{T^*}dz} \tag{7–65}$$

It is convenient and feasible to divide the atmosphere into layers of about 100 mb in thickness, using the mean virtual temperature of each layer to determine its depth. The various depths are then added together to obtain the total height. Hence we have for a layer between $z_1$ and $z_2$, having the mean virtual temperature $\bar{T}^*$,

$$\int_{p_1}^{p_2} \frac{dp}{p} = - \frac{mg}{\bar{T}^*R} (z_2 - z_1) \tag{7-66}$$

$$\ln p_2 - \ln p_1 = - \frac{mg}{R\bar{T}^*} (z_2 - z_1)$$

$$z_2 - z_1 = \frac{R\bar{T}^*}{mg} (\ln p_1 - \ln p_2) \tag{7-67}$$

This is known as the *hypsometric formula,* and the total height is the sum of the thicknesses of the layers.

These relationships show that, if temperature in a sounding is plotted against pressures on a *logarithmic* scale, we have, at least for a certain mean virtual temperature $\bar{T}^*$, an exact plot of temperature against height

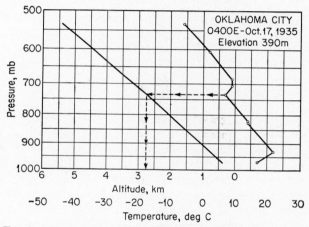

FIG. 7-4. Determination of altitudes on the adiabatic chart.

on a linear scale. Some adiabatic charts are constructed with the pressure ordinate on a logarithmic scale, and the pressure-height relation indicated exactly for a mean virtual temperature of 0°C. It turns out, however, that a scale of $p^{0.286}$ is very close to that of $\ln p$ and has the advantage of straight lines for the dry adiabats. In casual inspection, a plot of a sounding on a chart having $p^{0.286}$ as ordinate looks like a plot against altitude, or $\ln p$. In either type of diagram a supplementary curve must be plotted showing the exact pressure-height relationship. It is most convenient to construct the pressure-height curve in the manner illustrated in Fig. 7-4. The linear temperature scale of the abscissa is also used as an altitude scale, with altitude increasing toward the left by 100 m for each degree centigrade in the temperature scale. To obtain the altitude of any point of inflection of the temperature, follow a line horizontally from the point on the temperature curve to the pressure-height curve. Then follow down vertically to read the height on the altitude scale of the abscissa. The process is indicated by the dashed arrows in Fig. 7–4, which shows that the altitude of the base of the temperature inversion in the Oklahoma City sounding is 2760 m.

**Geodynamic Altitude.** A horizontal surface on the earth or in the atmosphere is one that everywhere parallels the surface of the sea, or in other words, a surface that is everywhere at the same distance above (or below) mean sea level. One learns in elementary physics that a particle in straight steady frictionless horizontal motion neither performs nor requires work in its motion. In the gravitational field of the earth, the work performed in lifting a mass $M$ from a height $z_1$ to a greater height $z_2$ is said to be $Mg(z_2 - z_1)$. To be more exact, we should say that the work involved in a displacement of a mass $M$ from any point 1 to any other point 2 is given by

$$W = \int_{z_1}^{z_2} Mg \, dz \qquad (7\text{–}68)$$

or, for unit mass,

$$= \int_{z_1}^{z_2} g \, dz \qquad (7\text{–}69)$$

If the acceleration of gravity were constant in a horizontal plane all over the earth, then a surface of $z = $ const, in other words, a horizontal surface, would be one along which air particles could move in straight frictionless flow without work. Such a surface would then be one of constant potential energy in the earth's gravitational field ($Mgz = $ const). We should call such surfaces *equipotential surfaces* or *geopotential surfaces* or *level surfaces*. However, we know that $g$ is not constant at any given height over the earth, that it varies especially with latitude, being at a maximum near the pole and at a minimum near the equator. Therefore, *horizontal surfaces are not level surfaces.* In order for an air particle to move in a horizontal surface over the earth, work must be performed, for, although in so doing it goes from point 1 to point 2 with $z_1 = z_2$, there is a difference in $g_1$ and $g_2$.

If we start with zero at sea level, we may define a geopotential given by

$$\Phi = \int_0^z g \, dz \qquad (7\text{–}70)$$
$$d\Phi = g \, dz \qquad (7\text{–}71)$$

In meteorology and oceanography, heights or depths are given in terms of this geopotential under the name *geodynamic height* or *depth*, sometimes simply *dynamic height* or *depth*. In order to make this appear in units similar to meters, the value is divided by $10^5$, and the geodynamic height is given in *geodynamic* (or *dynamic*) *meters*. For example, a height of 4000 metric meters where $g = 980$, would be 3920 geodynamic meters. We have

$$\Phi' = \frac{1}{10^5} \int_0^z g \, dz \qquad \text{geodynamic meters}$$

Since there are fewer dynamic than metric meters in a given height, the dynamic meter is, obviously, a larger unit. One dynamic meter would be $(10^5/g)$ cm.

The geodynamic height is conveniently substituted in the hydrostatic equation, for

$$dp = -\rho g \, dz = -\rho \, d\Phi = -\frac{pm}{RT^*} \, d\Phi \qquad (7\text{--}72)$$

and

$$\int_{p_1}^{p_2} \frac{dp}{p} = -\frac{m}{R} \int_{z_1}^{z_2} \frac{1}{T^*} g \, dz = -\frac{m}{R} \int_{\Phi_1}^{\Phi_2} \frac{1}{T^*} \, d\Phi \qquad (7\text{--}73)$$

and

$$\ln p_2 - \ln p_1 = -\frac{m}{\bar{T}^* R} (\Phi_2 - \Phi_1)$$

$$\Phi_2 - \Phi_1 = \frac{R\bar{T}^*}{m} (\ln p_1 - \ln p_2) \qquad (7\text{--}74)$$

Tables or graphs for obtaining the geodynamic thickness of 100-mb layers in the atmosphere under various conditions of mean virtual temperature are available. Although the geodynamic meter has been adopted by international agreement, the U.S. Weather Bureau finds it convenient to use 0.98 geodynamic meter, which is approximately the same as the metric meter formerly used. This makes the older and present-day records comparable.

It is also possible to determine altitudes by a direct graphical method. This is done by making use of the simple relationship of 1°C per 100 m for the dry adiabats. By following the dry adiabat nearest the temperature curve in the layer in question, every degree of temperature decrease along this adiabat corresponds to 100 m altitude. These adiabatic slopes may be transferred to form a single altitude curve for all the layers by means of parallel rulers or sliding triangles, the segments of altitude curves for each layer being added as a continuation of the one below.

**Altimeters.** The hypsometric formula shows that, in order to determine the height, the pressure at a known height (the ground or sea level) and at the level in question and also the mean virtual temperature of the intervening air column must be known. The quantities are $p_0$, $p$, and $\bar{T}^*$. The airplane altimeter is an aneroid barometer which measures $p$ only. By setting the zero of the altitude scale at $p_0$ as given by that or a similar instrument on the ground, the altitude at $p$ will be obtained, provided that the scale can be adjusted for $\bar{T}^*$.

Altimeters have no provision for adjusting the altitude scale for variations in the mean virtual temperature of the air column underneath. The conditions of the so-called "standard atmosphere" are always assumed.[1] This standardized temperature distribution, which is internationally accepted, is based on what are thought to be the average conditions over the earth as a whole. A temperature of 15°C is assumed at sea level with a lapse rate of 0.65°C per 100 m. As a result of this simplified assumption, altimeters indicate altitudes that are too high in cold weather and too low in warm weather. The error is negligible when flying near the ground, provided that a correct setting for the ground elevation is obtained. Manufacturers sometimes supply with their altimeters corrections based on the temperature at the flying level. This is not a complete correction, since it must assume a certain lapse rate. It should be kept in mind that the mean virtual temperature of the air column between the airplane and the ground determines the temperature factor. If there is a reasonably uniform lapse rate, this mean can be determined accurately enough if the temperatures at the ground and at the flying level are known. If one or more important temperature inversions exist, the mean temperature cannot thus be obtained from the two end points of the curve.

## POTENTIAL TEMPERATURE AND STABILITY OF DRY AIR

**Potential Temperature Defined.** *The potential temperature of any sample of air is the temperature it would have if brought dry-adiabatically to a pressure of* 1000 *mb* ($10^6$ *dyne per cm*$^2$). The expression for it is therefore to be derived from Poisson's equation, taking $p_0$ as 1000 mb and $T_0$ as the potential temperature, which we will designate as $\theta$. We have, then

$$\frac{T}{T_0} = \left(\frac{p}{p_0}\right)^{R/mc_p} \tag{7-75}$$

$$\frac{T}{\theta} = \left(\frac{p}{1000}\right)^{R/mc_p} \tag{7-76}$$

$$\theta = T \left(\frac{1000}{p}\right)^{R/mc_p} \tag{7-77}$$

where $p$ is expressed in millibars.

**Constant θ, Adiabatic and Isentropic.** Since on the $T \ln p$ or similar diagram a dry-adiabatic line can intersect the 1000-mb line at only one

---

[1] The complete specifications of the standard atmosphere call for a sea-level pressure of 1013.25 mb, a surface temperature of 59°F (15°C), and a lapse rate of 3.566°F per 1000 ft or 0.65°C per 100 m until a temperature of −67°F (−55°C) is reached, thence isothermal. The altimeter is based on the observed ground pressure, but the other factors are the same.

point, every point on an adiabatic line must be characterized by one and the same potential temperature. Therefore, dry-adiabatic lines are constant potential-temperature lines, and each can be designated according to its potential temperature. In Fig. 7–3 we may label the sloping lines, starting from the left, as 280, 290, 300, etc., in terms of potential temperature. A dry-adiabatic process in the atmosphere is a constant potential-temperature process. Furthermore, since under atmospheric conditions a dry-adiabatic process does not involve a change in the specific entropy, the terms *constant potential temperature, dry-adiabatic,* and *isentropic* are used to describe one and the same process.

At this point it might be explained that the word "dry" applied to an adiabatic process does not require that the air should contain no water vapor. The process operates up to the saturation point of the water vapor or, in other words, at all relative humidities below 100 per cent. The effect of water vapor on the air density is essentially negligible in the atmosphere, but it can be considered by using the virtual temperature and the virtual potential temperature derived from it.

This also is a good place to introduce the term *lapse rate*, which is the rate of temperature decrease with height in the atmosphere overlying a point on the surface of the earth at any particular time. It is the type of distribution discussed, for mean conditions, in Chap. 4. This quantity $-dT/dz$ should not be confused with the $dT/dz$ of Eq. (7–62) which, as in Eq. (7–63), should more properly be labeled $dT'/dz$, where $T'$ is the temperature of a vertically moving parcel. $T$ would then be the temperature of the environment through which the parcel is moving. We return to this point later in this chapter.

A *dry-adiabatic lapse rate* is defined as a lapse rate equal to the dry-adiabatic rate of temperature decrease with height in ascending air. In this case $-dT/dz = -dT'/dz = g/C_p = \gamma_0$, where $\gamma_0$ is a constant of approximately $10^{-4}°C$ per cm or $1°C$ per 100 m.

**Distribution of Potential Temperature.** In an atmosphere with a dry-adiabatic lapse rate, the potential temperature would not change with altitude. Except under certain circumstances near the ground, lapse rates are nearly always less than this value, which means that the potential temperature must normally increase with altitude. If the potential-temperature values are entered on the dry-adiabatic lines of Fig. 7–3 this point can be demonstrated; for any normal lapse rate must produce a line with a smaller decrease of temperature with decreasing pressure than the adiabats and thus show increasing potential temperature with decreasing pressure (upward in the atmosphere).

In considering the three-dimensional distribution of potential temperature, it is to be noted that, since the potential temperature depends on pressure and temperature, it would, at any given pressure (and therefore, roughly, at any given level), be greater the higher the temperature. Thus, we find that the potential temperature increases toward the equator. These normal latitudinal and vertical distributions require, then, that, in a north-to-south vertical cross section through the atmosphere, the potential-temperature lines or isentropic lines should slope upward toward the north, as shown in Fig. 7–5.

The potential-temperature or isentropic lines such as in the illustration become potential-temperature or isentropic surfaces when extended east and west to complete the three-dimensional picture. Since all processes in the free atmosphere tend to be largely adiabatic as long as no condensation occurs, air particles should remain on the same isentropic surface until saturation is reached. The true paths of air particles can best be traced on the surfaces along which they move—the isentropic surfaces. This tracing of paths or "flow patterns" is accomplished by mapping an

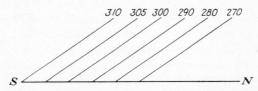

Fig. 7–5. Slope of potential-temperature surfaces from south to north in the Northern Hemisphere.

isentropic surface to produce from the upper-air data a so-called "isentropic chart." Contour lines of the surface in terms of either altitudes or pressures are drawn, and the flow patterns are traced by means of identification of air particles through some quantity that measures the absolute water-vapor content. Isentropic charts will be discussed in detail in a later chapter.

**The Importance of Vertical Motions.** The modern application of the principles of physical hydrodynamics to the weather has given conclusive evidence that the vertical components of air motions are the principal factors in producing the more important meteorological phenomena. Their chief significance comes from the rapid changes in temperature and moisture of the air caused by these upward and downward movements. For, when compared with the rate of increase or decrease of temperature and moisture in horizontally moving air, the rapidity of change of these properties in vertical currents is tremendous.

The weather phenomena of perhaps greatest practical interest are those having to do with *condensation*—clouds, fog, rain, snow, ice, hail, and sleet. Condensation occurs when the amount of water vapor contained in a given volume in the atmosphere reaches the capacity of that volume. Since the vapor capacity of the volume depends only on the temperature, it is possible to produce condensation by lowering the capacity (i.e., lowering the temperature) or by adding more and more water vapor. Observations show that condensation can be produced more easily and quickly in the atmosphere by the first method (cooling) than by the addition of moisture, especially at altitudes above the surface where no moisture supply is readily available.

The principal processes that bring about this cooling of an element of air are *radiation, contact with cold bodies, mixing with colder air masses,* and *adiabatic cooling with expansion* of the air.[1] It is not difficult to show that the last (adiabatic expansional cooling) is the most effective process, a fact that will become more apparent in the following discussions. Adiabatic cooling of a volume of air results from an expansion under decreasing pressure, i.e., from movement from high to lower pressure, unaccompanied by any exchange of heat with the environment. Here again, comparing the pressure decrease in horizontally moving air, which is seldom more than 5 mb in 100 miles, with the pressure decrease with height, which is normally about 500 mb in the first 3 or 4 miles above the surface, it is easily seen that *the principal cause of adiabatic cooling is upward motion.* Precipitation seldom, if ever, occurs without upward-moving air as its direct cause. For clouds that do not produce precipitation, and especially for fogs, the other cooling processes are of importance, but these phenomena will be discussed in a later chapter. In view of the fact that condensation, as well as many other important atmospheric processes, depends on rapid changes in temperature of a mass of air and that adiabatic temperature changes are of the greatest consequence, a thorough familiarity with adiabatic processes in the atmosphere is necessary for the student of meteorology.

In the atmosphere, we can regard vertical motions and the accompanying expansion or compression as occurring so rapidly that the absorption or loss of heat by radiation, conduction, or convection is negligible; thus the process is adiabatic in accordance with the definition. It is apparent, then, that as long as air is unsaturated it will always cool at the rate of 1°C for every 100 m that it is lifted; and on the other hand, if it is carried downward in the atmosphere, the moving air will be heated 1°C for every 100 m of its descent.

**The Adiabatic Rate of Cooling and the Prevailing Lapse Rate.** The student is likely to confuse the adiabatic rate of cooling for upward-moving air with the rate of temperature decrease with altitude ordinarily observed in the atmosphere. Temperature lapse rates are observed from data recorded on balloons or airplanes passing through a great many different parcels or samples of air. If it were possible to select a condi-

---

[1] For an early discussion, see Bjerkens, J., and H. Solberg, Meteorological Conditions for the Formation of Rain, *Geofys. Publikasjoner,* vol. 2, no. 3, 1921.

tion when upward motion is prevalent, and if we could take an individual element of air and follow it along as it went upward, recording the temperature of this and no other air element, we would find that it would cool approximately 1°C for every 100 m of its ascent. During this time, the surrounding air through which it was rising might have had quite a different temperature distribution.

A simple case to illustrate the distinction between lapse rate in the atmosphere and cooling rate of vertically moving air will be helpful. Consider a small island on a windy day. Suppose that the air is moving perfectly horizontally over the water, and that within this air the temperature decrease with height is 0.5°C per 100 m. The surface air has a temperature of 10°C. Some of the air will strike the island and in doing so will be forced upward over it, to produce lines of flow as shown in Fig. 7–6. Elsewhere, the air will pass undisturbed. The air forced up over

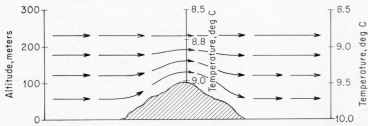

Fig. 7–6. Adiabatic cooling by forced ascent compared with observed lapse rate in surrounding air.

the island will cool at the rate of 1°C per 100 m so that the air just above the crest of the island, having been lifted exactly 100 m, will have a temperature 1° lower than it had over the surface of the water. It has been cooled from 10 to 9°. The air surrounding the island, however, will still have a temperature of 9.5°C at this height, because it has been moving horizontally.

Thus, in meteorology, it is the practice to speak of small, isolated elements of air lifted or lowered through the atmosphere. These elements during this motion are heated or cooled adiabatically, depending on whether they are displaced downward or upward, while the temperature decrease with altitude in the surrounding air through which they are moving remains unchanged.

The data on the temperature distribution in the atmosphere presented in Chap. 4 show that normally the temperature decrease with height is less than the rate at which air would be heated or cooled in passing downward or upward through the same height. The example of Fig. 7–6 represents the normal state of the atmosphere. This means that an upward motion would usually make the air in the rising current colder than the air at the same height in the surrounding, horizontally moving air. If the temperature lapse rate is the same as the rate for adiabatic changes in dry air, we say that the air has a *dry-adiabatic* lapse rate. If it is greater, the lapse rate is called *superadiabatic*.

**Temperature Lapse Rate and Stability.** Stability is sometimes defined as that condition in the atmosphere in which vertical motions are absent or definitely restricted; and, conversely, instability is defined as the state wherein vertical movement is prevalent. The more fundamental definition comes from a consideration of the temperature distribution. By noting at any given level the difference in temperature between an upward-moving element and the surrounding atmosphere, definite conclusions can be drawn as to the stability or instability. The surrounding atmosphere is described as stable or unstable depending on whether its temperature lapse rate brings about a decrease or an increase of the

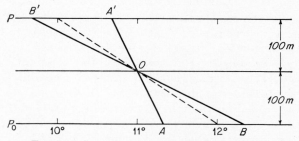

Fig. 7–7. Graphical determination of stability.

buoyancy forces on an upward-moving element. In the normal case, such as in Fig. 7–6, the rising air has at a corresponding level a lower temperature than the surroundings. That this represents stability will be seen in the following generalization of the principles of vertical motions through the atmosphere.

Suppose that an unsaturated layer in the atmosphere is 200 m thick and has the prevailing lapse rate represented by the curve $AA'$ of Fig. 7–7, which, it is seen, is less than the dry-adiabatic lapse rate. Suppose that an element of air at $O$, midway between the top and bottom of the layer, is displaced upward, encountering steadily lowering pressures and therefore cooling at the adiabatic rate of 1°C for every 100 m of ascent. Its course through the layer in terms of temperature and pressure is shown by the upper half of the *broken line* passing through $O$. It will be noted that along its path, as soon as it leaves the original level, its temperature is less than that of its surroundings (represented by $AA'$) and that this temperature difference between moving element and surrounding atmosphere becomes larger the greater the displacement. Knowing from the equation of state that at the same pressure and, therefore, at the same height in the atmosphere the density of the air depends inversely on the temperature, it is evident that the moving element becomes heavier than its surroundings; and as the temperature is lowered more and more by expansion, this difference in density will become greater. Therefore, unless a strong mechanical force pushes it strongly upward, it will sink back to the original level. Similarly, if the element moves downward from $O$, represented by the lower part of the broken line, it will become increasingly warmer than its surroundings and therefore lighter, so that the buoyancy forces will tend to return it to the original position. Thus we say that the curve $AA'$ represents a stable lapse rate or that the atmosphere in this case is stable, meaning that its density distribution suppresses any vertical motions that may be started.

The lapse rate $BB'$ is characteristic of an unstable atmosphere. This is seen by again moving an element from $O$ through this unstable air, for now it is continually becoming lighter than its surroundings as it moves upward, and heavier (colder) as it sinks. Given an impetus upward from $O$, this air will continue to rise of its own accord; and if pressed downward, it will continue to sink at an accelerated rate.

We have yet to consider the case where the lapse rate of the surrounding atmosphere is dry adiabatic. In such a condition, the rising or descending element would always have the temperature of its surroundings; and while the atmosphere would offer no resistance to vertical motions, neither would it favor them.

The necessary condition, then, for the support of vertical motions, up or down, in dry air is a superadiabatic temperature lapse rate.

If we represent the actual lapse rate $-dT/dz$ by $\gamma$ and the adiabatic rate by $\gamma_0$, then we may write the following conditions:

$$\gamma < \gamma_0 \quad \text{stable}$$
$$\gamma = \gamma_0 \quad \text{neutral}$$
$$\gamma > \gamma_0 \quad \text{unstable}$$

Also, since a dry-adiabatic line is a line of constant potential temperature $\theta$, we may refer to Fig. 7–3 and note the following conditions:

$$\frac{d\theta}{dz} > 0 \quad \text{stable}$$

$$\frac{d\theta}{dz} = 0 \quad \text{neutral}$$

$$\frac{d\theta}{dz} < 0 \quad \text{unstable}$$

The requirements for stability and instability[1] under conditions of water-vapor saturation, that is with 100 per cent relative humidity, are quite

[1] Note that in English the adjective is unstable and the noun is instability.

different from these.   We then speak of *saturation-adiabatic equilibrium*, a condition which will be studied in a later section after we have become familiar with the properties and thermodynamics of water vapor.

**Nature of Vertical Accelerations.**   The force causing warm parcels to rise in the air and cold ones to sink is the *buoyancy force.*  This is sometimes called the *Archimedean force.*  According to the principle of Archimedes, a body floating or immersed in a fluid is subjected to an upward-directed buoyancy force equal to the weight of the amount of fluid that the body displaces.   The body will rise, sink, or remain at the same level depending on whether this force is greater than, less than, or equal to, respectively, the downward force on the body due to the acceleration of gravity (the weight of the body).

Instead of a fixed body, we are here dealing with a parcel of air, which would have the weight $\rho'Vg$, where $\rho'$ is its density, $V$ its volume, and $g$ the acceleration of gravity.   The weight of the displaced fluid (air) is $\rho Vg$, where $\rho$ is the density of the surrounding, displaced air.   The volumes are the same.   The resultant force $F$, positive upward, would be

$$F = M'a = \rho Vg - \rho'Vg = (\rho - \rho')Vg \qquad (7\text{--}78)$$

where $a$ is the acceleration upward and $M'$ is the mass of the accelerated parcel.   However, $M' = \rho'V$, so that the upward acceleration is

$$a = g\,\frac{\rho - \rho'}{\rho'} \qquad (7\text{--}79)$$

It is more convenient to express this acceleration in terms of the temperature of the parcel and of its surroundings.   This may be done by substitution from the equation of state, viz.,

$$\rho = \frac{pm}{RT}$$

and
$$\rho' = \frac{p'm}{RT'}$$

Realizing that the parcel is under the same pressure as its immediate surroundings $p = p'$, we may write

$$a = g\,\frac{T' - T}{T} \qquad (7\text{--}80)$$

This shows that, as long as the temperature of the displaced element is higher than that of the air it is displacing, the element will be accelerated upward.   When the surroundings are warmer, the element is accelerated downward.   It should be noted that the acceleration, not the speed, is proportional to this temperature difference.   The speed will increase until temperature equilibrium is again reached.

**Auto-convective Lapse Rate: Homogeneous Atmosphere.**   Under ordinary conditions the density decreases rapidly with height, even when the prevailing lapse rate is considerably greater than the dry-adiabatic rate.   When the density is the same throughout, we have what is called a *homogeneous atmosphere*, which is of only theoretical interest, for such a condition never exists.   However, there are evidences of its occurrence in a restricted layer next to the ground on days of intense solar heating, and it is believed that conditions of this kind sometimes exist in tornadoes.

The lapse rate of a homogeneous atmosphere may be calculated from the hydrostatic equation and the equation of state in differential form. The hydrostatic equation is

$$dp = -\rho g \, dz$$

or
$$\frac{dp}{dz} = -\rho g$$

The equation of state in differential form is

$$p \, d\alpha + \alpha \, dp = \frac{R}{m} dT$$

or
$$dp = \rho \frac{R}{m} dT - \rho p \, d\alpha$$

In the homogeneous atmosphere $d\alpha/dz = 0$, and so

$$\frac{dp}{dz} = \rho \frac{R}{m} \frac{dT}{dz} \tag{7-81}$$

or, going back to the hydrostatic equation,

$$\frac{dp}{dz} = -\rho g = \rho \frac{R}{m} \frac{dT}{dz}$$

and
$$\frac{dT}{dz} = -\frac{mg}{R} \tag{7-82}$$

With numerical values in the equation, we have, assuming $g$ to be 980,

$$\frac{dT}{dz} = \frac{-28.9 \times 980}{8.314 \times 10^7} = -3.41 \times 10^{-4} \text{ °C per cm}$$

or $-3.41°C$ per 100 m.

This is called the *critical auto-convective lapse rate* or often simply the *auto-convective lapse rate* because if it is exceeded no displacement of a parcel from its initial level is necessary for upward acceleration to occur. The parcel would already be less dense than the air immediately above it, so vertical overturning must take place spontaneously. Over desert regions, large dust whirls or "dust devils" almost the size of small tornadoes are apparently caused by auto-convective lapse rates near the ground. Smaller dust whirls seen in almost any locality may arise from similar conditions on a very local scale.

A homogeneous atmosphere, having no decrease in density with height, would have a fixed upper surface. While this is not a reasonable assumption, the concept of a homogeneous atmosphere finds usefulness in many theoretical problems. The height of the homogeneous atmosphere can be calculated by using the hydrostatic equation and substituting for the density from the equation of state, giving

$$dz = - \frac{RT}{mg} \frac{dp}{p}$$

But the density at all heights is the same, so that

$$\rho = \frac{pm}{RT} = \frac{p_0 m}{RT_0} = \rho_0$$

and

$$p = p_0 \frac{T}{T_0}$$

where the subscript 0 refers to the bottom of the atmosphere. We therefore have

$$dz = - \frac{RT_0}{mgp_0} dp$$

which we may integrate through the depth of the atmosphere to the top $H$, where the pressure would be zero.

$$\int_0^H dz = - \frac{RT_0}{mgp_0} \int_{p_0}^0 dp = H = \frac{RT_0}{mg} \qquad (7\text{-}83)$$

For a surface temperature of $T_0 = 273°$, we would have

$$H = \frac{8.315 \times 10^7 \times 273}{28.9 \times 980} = 8 \times 10^5 \text{ cm (approx)}$$
$$= 8000 \text{ m (approx)}$$

It is evident that the temperature at the top of this atmosphere would be absolute zero. We could have obtained, therefore, the top of the atmosphere by dividing the surface temperature by the lapse rate.

**Layer Stability.** In addition to the ascent or descent of isolated parcels of air through their atmospheric environment, there are numerous occasions when whole layers of air many hundreds of meters thick undergo lifting or sinking (subsidence). The lifting may occur through the upslope motion of a large-scale current in a mountainous region or when a warm current ascends over a colder one. Subsidence may occur to compensate for the lateral spreading out of the air of the lower part of an area of high pressure. These processes will be described in detail in later chapters, but at present we shall examine only the thermodynamic effects of lifting and subsidence.

The weight or mass of a layer per vertical column of unit area is given by the pressure difference between the top and bottom of that layer. The weight is then given by the hydrostatic formula, which may be expressed in the following manner:

$$W = Mg = p_1 - p_2 = \bar{\rho}g(z_2 - z_1)$$

where the subscript 1 refers to the bottom, 2 to the top of the layer, and $\bar{\rho}$ is the mean density of the layer. If the changes in $g$ with height are neglected, this pressure difference will also be a measure of the mass. The mass of air contained, let us say, between two isentropic surfaces as boundaries can change only by the lateral addition or removal of mass. The addition of mass in this way is called *lateral convergence*, and the removal is called *lateral divergence*. If no convergence or divergence occurs, the pressure difference between top and bottom will remain the same during lifting or subsidence. If there is convergence, the pressure difference will become greater, and if there is divergence it will become less.

The changes in lapse rate involved in lifting and subsidence are best illustrated on the adiabatic chart. Suppose that a layer of very dry air lying between the 1000- and 900-mb surfaces (Fig. 7–8) is lifted in such a way that there is no lateral convergence or divergence. The pressure difference between the top and the bottom would remain the same, but the altitude difference corresponding to a given pressure difference is greater at high altitudes, so the condition as shown in Fig. 7–8 results. During the lifting, which is an adiabatic process, the lower part of the layer at $A$ will cool to $A'$ and the upper part with the temperature at $B$ will cool to $B'$. From the diagram, it is obvious that the stability is decreasing with the lifting.

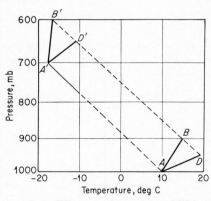

FIG. 7–8. Effects on lapse rate of lifting, sinking, divergence, and convergence.

By taking the layer under the condition $A'B'$ and noting the effects of subsidence, the reverse process is followed, and it is apparent that the lapse rate becomes more stable.

If the layer were superadiabatic in the beginning, the lifting would make the lapse rate less superadiabatic, and the subsidence would make it more superadiabatic. If the lapse rate were in adiabatic equilibrium in the beginning, no change in lapse rate could occur.

We have the rule: *Lifting causes the lapse rate to approach the dry-adiabatic and subsidence causes it to depart more and more from the adiabatic.*

In lateral divergence, the horizontal dimension of the volume occupied by the air is enlarged at the expense of the vertical thickness. The result of the divergence is seen in Fig. 7–8 by the line $AD$ corresponding to the lapse rate of $AB$ or $A'B'$ under the combined effects of subsidence and divergence. $A'D'$ shows the type of temperature distribution resulting from lifting of $AB$, accompanied by divergence.

In lateral convergence, the effect would be the reverse, i.e., convergence would tend to make the lapse rate $AB$ become less stable. For superadiabatic lapse rates convergence would tend to make the lapse rate less superadiabatic and divergence would decrease the instability.

We have the rule: *Lateral convergence causes the lapse rate to approach the adiabatic, and lateral divergence causes it to depart more and more from the adiabatic.*

Thus it is seen that convergence and lifting work in the same direction in affecting the lapse rate, and divergence and subsidence work together. It is possible in the atmosphere to have these processes working in opposition, as for example, lifting and divergence or subsidence and convergence. It is possible to compute the relative magnitudes of these opposing effects that would make them just cancel each other.[1]

[1] Byers, H. R., Combined Effects of Ascent and Divergence on the Lapse Rate, *Bull. Am. Meteorol. Soc.*, vol. 23, pp. 319–320, 1942.

# CHAPTER 8

## WATER VAPOR AND ITS
## THERMODYNAMIC EFFECTS

The presence of water either in the invisible vapor form or as visible cloud has been shown in previous chapters to have a pronounced effect on the transmission of radiation. Equally important are the thermodynamic effects. Water is present on our planet at a temperature far below its boiling point, but it is sufficiently volatile to change from the liquid or ice state to the gaseous state by the process of evaporation (liquid to gas) or sublimation (ice to gas) at atmospheric temperatures and pressures. Conversely, it changes from gas to liquid by condensation and from gas to solid by crystallization (sometimes also called sublimation) in the free air to form clouds and on surfaces to form dew or frost. Melting and freezing also occur at temperatures commonly found in the atmosphere. The precipitation of water from the clouds in the form of rain, snow, hail, etc., affects the heat distribution in the atmosphere. Electrical as well as thermal energy is transformed by these phenomena, as shown by the occurrence of precipitation static or of lightning.

Water is supplied to the atmosphere by evaporation from the surface of the earth, from the land as well as from the oceans. Precipitation returns water to the surface. Some of the water precipitated over the land flows to the oceans in rivers to complete the so-called "hydrologic cycle." For balance, this means that precipitation must exceed evaporation when averaged over an entire continent, while over the oceans as a whole evaporation must be greater than precipitation. The continental excess and the oceanic deficit are equalized by the discharge of rivers and glaciers into the oceans.

Although the percentage of water vapor in the atmosphere is quite small compared with the other gases, about six times more water is transported in the atmosphere over North America, for example, than is transported by all the rivers combined.[1] This water in its various actions of

---

[1] Benton, G. S., and M. A. Estoque, Water-vapor Transfer over the North American Continent, *J. Meteorol.*, vol. 11, pp. 462–477, 1954.

cloud, fog, and precipitation formation is responsible for what we usually call *weather*.   For these reasons we are much concerned with measuring the water-vapor content of the atmosphere and understanding its thermo-dynamic effects.

**Vapor Pressure and Saturation.**   Fundamentally, all measures of water vapor or atmospheric humidity are based upon quantities related to evaporation and condensation over a flat surface of pure water.   From a water surface that is evaporating, the excess of molecules of water leav-ing the surface over those coming back in is expressed and measured as a pressure.   This pressure, called the *vapor tension*, depends only on the temperature of the water surface.   This concept is based on measure-ments made in a closed space.   Let us consider a closed container about half-filled with water.   We shall assume that the water and the air space above it are kept at the same temperature.   If the air is relatively dry to begin with, the water will start to evaporate and introduce additional water vapor into the space above.   If the pressure in this space is meas-ured during the process, it will be noted that the pressure is increasing slightly as the new vapor is added.   This increasing pressure is due to an increase in the partial pressure of the water vapor, known as the *vapor pressure*.   The vapor pressure in the space will increase until it is exactly equal to the vapor tension of the water surface.   When this balance of pressure is reached, no further evaporation will occur, and if the overlying gases and the water are at the same temperature, the closed space above is then *saturated* with water vapor.   If the water had been exposed to the open air, equilibrium would not have been reached and all the water would eventually evaporate.   If the temperature of the overlying gases is different from that of the water, quite another equilibrium will be required.

The *saturation vapor pressure* of pure water vapor is defined as the pres-sure of the vapor when in a state of neutral equilibrium with a plane sur-face of pure water at the same temperature.   It is then equal to the vapor tension of the water surface at this temperature.   It varies with the tem-perature exactly as does the vapor tension of the water, so that the higher the temperature, the greater the vapor pressure required for saturation.   We can look at this from another point of view and say that any volume has a certain water-vapor capacity depending upon the temperature of the water vapor and other gases in that volume.   When this capacity is reached, we have saturation.

The dependence of the saturation vapor pressure on temperature is a specific characteristic; it is independent of the pressure of the other gases at all atmospheric pressures.   It has been determined empirically for both the liquid and the solid phases of water over a wide range of temperature.   The values in Table 8–1 include the pressures over both ice and liquid water at temperatures below freezing.  This is important in meteorology since there is a marked tendency for water in the atmosphere, especially in clouds, to remain in liquid form at temperatures many degrees below the established freezing point of pure bulk water.  Water in the liquid form at these temperatures is said to be *supercooled* or *undercooled*. Psychrometric tables for use with dry- and wet-bulb thermometer readings embody the vapor pressure with respect to ice at subfreezing temperatures because the wet-bulb thermometer gives a more constant reading if the water on it is allowed to freeze.

TABLE 8–1. SATURATION VAPOR PRESSURE OVER WATER AND OVER ICE,
IN MILLIBARS
(Values over water at subfreezing temperatures in italics)

| Tens | Temperature, °C | | | | | | | | | |
| | Units | | | | | | | | | |
| | 0 | 1 | 2 | 3 | 4 | 5 | 6 | 7 | 8 | 9 |
|---|---|---|---|---|---|---|---|---|---|---|
| 40 | 73.777 | 77.802 | 82.015 | 86.423 | 91.034 | 95.855 | 100.89 | 106.16 | 111.66 | 117.40 |
| 30 | 42.430 | 44.927 | 47.551 | 50.307 | 53.200 | 56.236 | 59.422 | 62.762 | 66.264 | 69.934 |
| 20 | 23.373 | 24.861 | 26.430 | 28.086 | 29.831 | 31.671 | 33.608 | 35.649 | 37.796 | 40.055 |
| 10 | 12.272 | 13.119 | 14.017 | 14.969 | 15.977 | 17.044 | 18.173 | 19.367 | 20.630 | 21.964 |
| +0 | 6.1078 | 6.5662 | 7.0547 | 7.5753 | 8.1294 | 8.7192 | 9.3465 | 10.013 | 10.722 | 11.474 |
| −0 | 6.1078 | 5.623 | 5.173 | 4.757 | 4.372 | 4.015 | 3.685 | 3.379 | 3.097 | 2.837 |
| | *6.1078* | *5.6780* | *5.2753* | *4.8981* | *4.5451* | *4.2148* | *3.9061* | *3.6177* | *3.3484* | *3.0971* |
| −10 | 2.597 | 2.376 | 2.172 | 1.984 | 1.811 | 1.652 | 1.506 | 1.371 | 1.248 | 1.135 |
| | *2.8627* | *2.6443* | *2.4409* | *2.2515* | *2.0755* | *1.9118* | *1.7597* | *1.6186* | *1.4877* | *1.3664* |
| −20 | 1.032 | 0.9370 | 0.8502 | 0.7709 | 0.6985 | 0.6323 | 0.5720 | 0.5170 | 0.4669 | 0.4213 |
| | *1.2540* | *1.1500* | *1.0538* | *0.9649* | *0.8827* | *0.8070* | *0.7371* | *0.6727* | *0.6134* | *0.5589* |
| −30 | 0.3798 | 0.3421 | 0.3079 | 0.2769 | 0.2488 | 0.2233 | 0.2002 | 0.1794 | 0.1606 | 0.1436 |
| | *0.5088* | *0.4628* | *0.4205* | *0.3818* | *0.3463* | *0.3139* | *0.2842* | *0.2571* | *0.2323* | *0.2097* |
| −40 | 0.1283 | 0.1145 | 0.1021 | 0.09098 | 0.08097 | 0.07198 | 0.06393 | 0.05671 | 0.05026 | 0.04449 |
| | *0.1891* | *0.1704* | *0.1534* | *0.1379* | *0.1239* | *0.1111* | *0.09961* | *0.08918* | *0.07975* | *0.07124* |
| −50 | 0.03935 | 0.03476 | 0.03067 | 0.02703 | 0.02380 | 0.02092 | 0.01838 | 0.01612 | 0.01413 | 0.01236 |

**Absolute Humidity.**  The equation of state for water vapor is written

$$e = \rho_w \frac{R}{m_w} T \qquad (8\text{–}1)$$

The $\rho_w$ is the vapor density or *absolute humidity*.  It is usually expressed in grams per cubic meter.  At saturation, $\rho_{ws}$ is given by

$$\rho_{ws} = \frac{e_s m_w}{R T_s} \qquad (8\text{–}2)$$

where the subscript $s$ refers to saturation conditions.

Values of the saturation absolute humidity are given in Table 8–2. These values, which represent the water-vapor capacity of a cubic-meter volume, are dependent only on the temperature. This is because $e_s$ is also a function of the temperature only.

TABLE 8–2. WATER-VAPOR CAPACITY OF A CUBIC-METER VOLUME ($\rho_{ws} \times 10^6$) AT VARIOUS TEMPERATURES

| Temp, °C | Grams | Temp, °C | Grams |
|----------|-------|----------|-------|
| −40 | 0.120 | 0 | 4.847 |
| −35 | 0.205 | 5 | 6.797 |
| −30 | 0.342 | 10 | 9.401 |
| −25 | 0.559 | 15 | 12.832 |
| −20 | 0.894 | 20 | 17.300 |
| −15 | 1.403 | 25 | 23.049 |
| −10 | 2.158 | 30 | 30.371 |
| − 5 | 3.261 | 35 | 39.599 |
|     |       | 40 | 51.117 |

**Specific Humidity.** The specific humidity is defined as the weight of water vapor contained in a unit weight of air (dry air plus water vapor), expressed in grams per gram or grams per kilogram. Designating it as $q$, we have

$$q = \frac{M_w}{M_a}$$

where $M_w$ is the mass or weight of the water vapor and $M_a$ that of the air in which it is contained. Since all the gases occupy the same volume $V$, and since $M_w = \rho_w V$ and $M_a = (\rho_d + \rho_w)V$, the $V$'s cancel and

$$q = \frac{\rho_w}{\rho_w + \rho_d} \tag{8-3}$$

the denominator being the total density of the dry gases $\rho_d$ plus the water vapor $\rho_w$. To express this in terms of easily measurable quantities, we substitute from the equations of state for dry air and for water vapor

$$\rho_d = \frac{p_d m_d}{RT}$$

$$\rho_w = \frac{e m_w}{RT}$$

to form the equation

$$q = \frac{m_w e}{m_d p_d + m_w e} \tag{8-4}$$

the $RT$ canceling out. We then divide both the numerator and the denominator by $m_d$ to obtain

$$q = \frac{m_w}{m_d} \frac{e}{p_d + (m_w/m_d)e} \tag{8-5}$$

The total pressure is $P = p_d + e$; therefore $p_d = P - e$, which we may substitute in the equation thus:

$$q = \frac{m_w}{m_d} \frac{e}{P - [1 - (m_w/m_d)]e} \qquad \text{g per g} \qquad (8\text{--}6)$$

which gives us the specific humidity in terms of the easily obtainable quantities $e$ and $P$.

Using numerical values, we have 18 as the molecular weight of water $(m_w)$ and 28.9 for $m_d$, so that $\dfrac{m_w}{m_d} = \dfrac{18}{28.9} = 0.622$. Then

$$q = 0.622 \frac{e}{P - 0.378e} \qquad \text{g per g} \qquad (8\text{--}7)$$

For ordinary values of the vapor pressure, we can safely say, without appreciable error, that

$$q = 0.622 \frac{e}{P} \qquad \text{g per g (approx)} \qquad (8\text{--}8)$$

The specific humidity at saturation may be written as

$$q_s = 0.622 \frac{e_s}{P - 0.378e_s} \qquad (8\text{--}9)$$

A table of saturation specific humidities, similar to Table 8–2, can be written to illustrate the saturation phenomena. These data are given in Table 8–3. In the previous table, no mention was made of pressure because the *saturation absolute humidity* does not change with pressure. Considering a constant mass (1 kg) of air, a change in its volume takes place with changing pressure, thus requiring a different quantity of water vapor to produce saturation. Values for every even hundred millibars pressure are given in Table 8–3. Using a graph of pressure on a logarithmic scale and temperature on a linear scale as rectangular coordinates, one finds that the saturation specific humidities become very nearly straight lines.

**The Mixing Ratio.** The mixing ratio is defined as the weight of water vapor contained in mixture with a unit weight of dry air, expressed in grams per gram or grams per kilogram. It differs from specific humidity only in that it is related to dry air instead of to the total of dry air plus vapor. Designating it as $w$, we have

$$w = \frac{\rho_w}{\rho_d} \qquad (8\text{--}10)$$

TABLE 8–3. QUANTITY OF WATER VAPOR REQUIRED FOR SATURATION AT
VARIOUS TEMPERATURES AND PRESSURES
(In grams per kilogram of moist air, saturation specific humidity)

| Temp, °C | Pressure, mb | | | | | | |
|---|---|---|---|---|---|---|---|
|  | 1000 | 900 | 800 | 700 | 600 | 500 | 400 |
| −40 | 0.118 | 0.131 | 0.147 | 0.168 | 0.196 | 0.235 | 0.294 |
| −35 | 0.195 | 0.217 | 0.244 | 0.279 | 0.326 | 0.391 | 0.488 |
| −30 | 0.317 | 0.353 | 0.397 | 0.453 | 0.529 | 0.635 | 0.793 |
| −25 | 0.503 | 0.559 | 0.629 | 0.719 | 0.839 | 1.007 | 1.259 |
| −20 | 0.784 | 0.871 | 0.980 | 1.120 | 1.307 | 1.569 | 1.962 |
| −15 | 1.20 | 1.33 | 1.49 | 1.71 | 1.99 | 2.39 | 2.99 |
| −10 | 1.79 | 1.99 | 2.23 | 2.55 | 2.98 | 3.58 | 4.48 |
| − 5 | 2.63 | 2.92 | 3.29 | 3.76 | 4.39 | 5.27 | 6.59 |
| 0 | 3.80 | 4.23 | 4.76 | 5.44 | 6.35 | 7.62 | 9.54 |
| 5 | 5.44 | 6.05 | 6.81 | 7.79 | 9.09 | 10.92 | 13.67 |
| 10 | 7.67 | 8.53 | 9.60 | 11.0 | 12.8 | 15.4 |  |
| 15 | 10.7 | 11.9 | 13.4 | 15.3 | 17.9 |  |  |
| 20 | 14.7 | 16.3 | 18.4 | 21.1 |  |  |  |
| 25 | 20.0 | 22.2 | 25.0 |  |  |  |  |
| 30 | 26.9 | 29.9 | 33.7 |  |  |  |  |
| 35 | 35.8 | 39.8 |  |  |  |  |  |
| 40 | 47.3 |  |  |  |  |  |  |

and from the equations of state, we get

$$w = \frac{m_w e}{m_d p_d}$$

or
$$w = 0.622 \frac{e}{P - e} \tag{8–11}$$

The relationship between $q$ and $w$ can be seen by taking the expression for $q$, viz.,

$$q = \frac{\rho_w}{\rho_d + \rho_w}$$

and dividing both the numerator and the denominator by $\rho_d$, obtaining

$$q = \frac{\rho_w/\rho_d}{1 + (\rho_w/\rho_d)}$$

However, $\rho_w/\rho_d$ is the mixing ratio $w$, so

$$q = \frac{w}{1 + w} \tag{8–12}$$

Since $w$ seldom exceeds 0.02 g per g, it can be seen that, in an extreme case,

$$q = \frac{0.02}{1 + 0.02} = \frac{w}{1 + w}$$

or approximately, $q = w$, and no appreciable error results if $q$ and $w$ are used interchangeably.

**Relative Humidity.**  By international agreement, the relative humidity is defined as the ratio of the observed mixing ratio to that which would prevail at saturation at the same temperature.  Expressed as a percentage, it is given as

$$f = \frac{w}{w_s} \times 100 \tag{8-13}$$

The relative humidity is also given by

$$f = \frac{e}{e_s} \times 100 \tag{8-14}$$

$$= \frac{\rho_w}{\rho_{ws}} \times 100 \tag{8-15}$$

and, with more than ample accuracy,

$$f = \frac{q}{q_s} \times 100 \tag{8-16}$$

**Temperature of the Dew Point.**  The dew-point temperature is defined as the temperature at which saturation barely would be reached if the air were cooled *at constant pressure* without the removal or addition of moisture.  In other words, it is the temperature at which the quantity of water vapor actually present in the atmosphere would be the capacity amount.

It should be pointed out that there are two ways to produce saturation: (1) by decreasing the temperature and thereby reducing the capacity for water vapor and (2) by increasing the amount of water vapor.  The dew-point temperature is defined in terms of the first process.

**Isentropic-condensation Temperature.**  The isentropic-condensation temperature is the temperature at which saturation barely would be reached if the air were cooled *adiabatically* without the removal or addition of moisture.  It differs from the dew-point temperature in that it is defined in terms of an adiabatic instead of a constant-pressure process.  It is always less than the dew-point temperature, because in an adiabatic process, due to expansion, the water vapor has an increasingly large volume to saturate.

In the adiabatic or isentropic process, condensation will occur at a level or pressure specified by the potential temperature and the specific humidity of mixing ratio.    Thus we speak of the *isentropic-condensation pressure* of an air sample, which for a given isentropic surface, will depend only on the specific humidity or mixing ratio.

In determining the base of clouds formed by an isentropic process up to the condensation level (i.e., cumulus and other convective cloud types), the dew-point temperature should never be used directly; instead, the computation should be based on the isentropic-condensation pressure or temperature.    A practical formula has been devised for obtaining the isentropic-condensation level from a given dew point and pressure.

**Variability of Humidity Quantities.**    *Vapor Pressure.*    If the quantity of water vapor present does not vary, i.e., if there is no addition by evaporation or removal by condensation, the vapor pressure will remain constant *provided* that the total pressure of all the gases does not change. In an adiabatic expansion, for example, the partial pressures of all the gases, including water vapor, decrease.    Thus the vapor pressure is an absolute measure of the quantity of water vapor present so long as we do not have to consider vertical displacements.

*Relative Humidity.*    The relative humidity is a highly variable quantity.    It involves the ratio of two vapor pressures, the actual and the saturation.    The actual vapor pressure changes with the pressure, as noted above, and the saturation vapor pressure varies with temperature. Therefore, relative humidity changes markedly in an adiabatic process and in all other processes involving a change in temperature or pressure. At most stations, relative humidity has a wide diurnal variation, changing inversely with the temperature.

*Absolute Humidity.*    The absolute humidity varies with all volume changes, since it is expressed in terms of the amount of moisture contained in a unit volume.    It is used mainly in physics and engineering where fixed volumes are dealt with.

*Specific Humidity and Mixing Ratio.*    Since these quantities are based on measurements of the weights of water vapor and air, the law of conservation of matter requires that they cannot be changed unless water vapor is actually added or removed.    They are the only measures of the moisture content that cannot be changed by any process except by actual removal or addition of water vapor from or to the portion of the air in question.    During an adiabatic process the specific humidity and mixing ratio are unchanged except after saturation is reached.    In an adiabatic cooling at saturation these quantities show a decrease because water vapor is then being changed into liquid that cannot be included in the measurement.

*Dew-point Temperature.*    The temperature of the dew point changes in the same way as does the vapor pressure.    It is conservative for non-adiabatic processes involving no pressure change provided that there is no evaporation or condensation. It is useful for comparing the absolute quantities of moisture present at stations having roughly the same elevation.

*Isentropic-condensation Pressure (or Temperature).* Remains unchanged in the same sense as specific humidity or mixing ratio as long as the potential temperature does not change.

**Water-vapor Content of an Air Column.** It is frequently useful to know the total water-vapor content of the atmosphere over a given place. Such a determination gives an idea of the possible amount of rain that may be expected from the overlying air if conditions become favorable for precipitation of the moisture. Also, in radiation studies it is necessary to know this quantity, called *the precipitable water,* expressed in centimeters.

Consider an air column having a cross-sectional area of 1 cm$^2$. The total mass of water vapor contained between the height 0 and the height $z$ would be

$$W = \int_0^z \rho_w \, dz \qquad (8\text{-}17)$$

where $\rho_w$ is the vapor density or absolute humidity. Substituting from the hydrostatic equation $dp = -\rho g \, dz$, where $\rho$ is the total air density, we have

$$W = \int_p^{p_0} \frac{\rho_w}{\rho} \frac{1}{g} \, dp$$
$$= \frac{1}{g} \int_p^{p_0} q \, dp \qquad (8\text{-}18)$$

where $q$ is the specific humidity, defined as $\rho_w/\rho$. This can be integrated in steps or by making a plot of the specific humidity against pressure and finding the area between the plotted curve and $q = 0$ and the lines $p$ and $p_0$. Actually, it is simpler to express the quantity in terms of vapor pressure and pressure. Since, approximately, $q = 0.622e/p$, we can write

$$W = \frac{0.622}{g} \int_p^{p_0} e \frac{dp}{p} \qquad (8\text{-}19)$$

$$W = \frac{0.622}{g} \int_p^{p_0} e \, d(\ln p) \qquad (8\text{-}20)$$

$W$ is in grams per square centimeter of area. Taking the density of the precipitable water as one, we see that, since $\rho$ and $A$ are both one, $W = \rho V = AD = D$ where $D$ is the depth of precipitable water. The last integral can be obtained graphically, for if a vapor-pressure curve is plotted from the sounding on the adiabatic chart with $p$ on a logarithmic scale, the water vapor contained in a vertical column can be determined by measuring the area under this curve.

Figure 8-1 shows maps of the distribution of the mean precipitable water, in inches, for the months of January and July over the United States, taken from a publication by Shands.[1] The values are given only for that part of the atmosphere lying below 8 km; it is found that in the mean the contribution above that height is of the order of hundredths of an inch in summer and thousandths of an inch in winter. At locations near sea level the principal concentration of water vapor is in the lowest 2 km.

For comparison purposes, it might be pointed out that for a *saturated* atmosphere with a sea-level temperature of 28°C (82.4°F) and in saturation-adiabatic equilibrium, the precipitable water would be 4.15 in.; under the same conditions for a sea-level temperature of 20°C (68°F) it would be 2.08 in., while at 0°C (32°F) it would be 0.33 in.

**Change of Phase.** Water is the one substance in the atmosphere that occurs commonly in all three of its phases—vapor, liquid, and solid. This has many consequences of great importance, not the least of which is the condensation and precipitation in the form of rain or snow. At this point, however, we are concerned with the thermodynamic effects.

It can be shown experimentally that heat energy is added or removed in these changes of phase. In the case of change from liquid to vapor (evaporation), the energy involved is called the *heat of vaporization*, and in the change from liquid to solid (freezing) it is called the *heat of fusion*. It is also possible to have a change from solid to vapor directly, as we often see in the case of the disappearance of snow without melting on a clear dry day. This process, called *sublimation*, involves energy in the form of the *heat of sublimation*, which is the sum of the heat of vaporization and the heat of fusion.

In the case of evaporation, there is a considerable increase in the volume occupied by the water. Since this occurs against a definite vapor pressure in the air, external work must be done by the vapor as it leaves the liquid surface. Also, the molecules and atoms themselves have their potential energy increased. Both these processes involve a removal of energy from the evaporating surface, and the remaining liquid must be cooled unless heat is added from the outside.[2] In nature, evaporation has many noticeable cooling effects, such as the cooling caused by the evaporation of the rain that falls in a summer shower, or the cooling a person notices when he steps dripping out of a warm bath. Certain other liquids, which are more volatile than water, such as ether, alcohol, carbon tetrachloride, etc., exhibit a much more pronounced cooling effect.

[1] Shands, A. L., Mean Precipitable Water in the United States, *U.S. Weather Bur. Tech. Papers*, no. 10, 1949.

[2] In the case of water being boiled, heat is added from the stove or flame as rapidly as it is removed by evaporation. The more rapidly the heat is supplied, the greater the rate of evaporation.

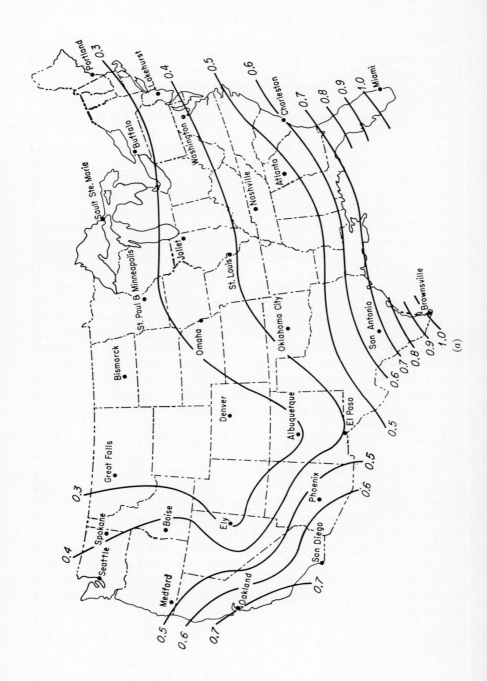

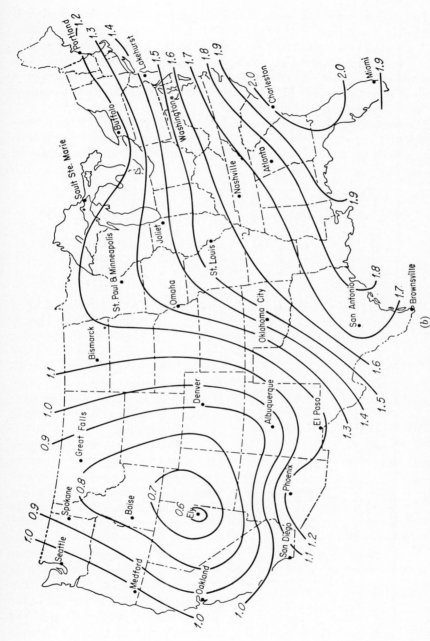

FIG. 8-1. Precipitable water, in inches, for the months of (a) January and (b) July.

(b)

167

The energy removed from the liquid surface in the evaporation is carried latent in the water vapor. When the vapor condenses again, each gram of vapor gives off the energy that it acquired from the evaporating surface. Thus we have the reverse of the heat of vaporization in the *heat of condensation*. We may say, therefore, that evaporation on a surface or in a sample of air has a cooling effect, while condensation gives off heat to the surface or air sample.

The heat of vaporization is defined as the heat removed by the evaporation of 1 g of the substance. For water at normal atmospheric temperatures, it has a value close to 600 cal per g but decreases with increasing temperature as shown in Table 8–4.

TABLE 8–4. LATENT HEAT OF VAPORIZATION OF WATER
(From Smithsonian Meteorological Tables, 6th ed.)

| Temp, °C | Latent heat, cal/g | Temp, °C | Latent heat, cal/g |
|---|---|---|---|
| −40 | 621.7 | 0 | 597.3 |
| −30 | 615.0 | 10 | 591.7 |
| −20 | 608.9 | 20 | 586.0 |
| −10 | 603.0 | 30 | 580.4 |
|  |  | 40 | 574.7 |

The heat of fusion is defined as the heat removed in the freezing of 1 g of the substance. For water, it has the value of approximately 80 cal per g. Within the limited ranges of pressure in the atmosphere, the freezing point of water may be considered to be always at 0°C and the removal of heat energy to cause freezing or its addition to produce melting must occur isothermally at this temperature.

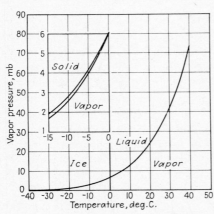

FIG. 8–2. Saturation vapor pressure. *Inset:* saturation vapor pressure over ice (lower curve) and over liquid (upper curve) at subfreezing temperatures.

In Fig. 8–2 is a $pT$ diagram of the saturation vapor-pressure curve for water at temperatures above and below freezing. It is seen that below the curved line the conditions support the vapor only, whereas above the line one finds conditions for liquid at temperatures above freezing and solid at temperatures below freezing. For saturation at the freezing point, the three phases, vapor, liquid, and solid, may theoretically occur in equilibrium together. This point is called the *triple point*. It occurs in water at a temperature of 0°C and with a vapor pressure of 6.11 mb.

In the inset, two curves of the saturation vapor pressure are shown for subfreezing temperatures. The lower one is for saturation with respect to a plane surface of ice, and the upper one is for saturation with respect to a plane liquid surface supercooled to these temperatures. All these values are the same as those given in Table 8–1. Without the presence of supercooled water, there would be direct sublimation at temperatures below freezing.

At all points below the line in Fig. 8–2, i.e., in the vapor phase, the relative humidity is less than 100 per cent. At all points above the line (or lines, in the case of subfreezing temperatures) there is greater than 100 per cent relative humidity, or *supersaturation*. On the line, the water is exactly at saturation. In the atmosphere, the natural processes of condensation and evaporation occur in such a way that appreciable supersaturation does not exist. In the atmosphere, then, one probably never finds conditions represented by points appreciably above the line or lines, and for all practical purposes one may consider that saturation is not exceeded and that the conditions along the lines exactly represent those in water or ice clouds.

As pointed out previously, meteorologists have discovered that supercooled water is prevalent in clouds at subfreezing temperatures down to about $-15°C$. Therefore the upper of the two curves in the inset diagram of Fig. 8–2 would represent the conditions in clouds at those temperatures.

**The Adiabatic Process at Saturation.** After air has been cooled sufficiently, either by adiabatic expansion or otherwise, a temperature is reached where there is no longer room for all the water contained in it to remain in vapor form, and so some of it starts to condense into fog or cloud. This temperature is called the *saturation* or *dew point* for cooling at constant pressure, and the *temperature of the condensation level* when we speak of adiabatic cooling. The distinction between the two is necessary, for in the case of adiabatic cooling, the saturation is delayed owing to the increasing volume to be saturated, a fact apparent in Table 8–3. As the air is further cooled, more and more of the vapor turns to liquid droplets or solid particles, until finally, at some low temperature that is probably never reached, all the vapor has changed to solid or liquid.

The humidity relationships derived thus far say nothing about the liquid water in the clouds. In a parcel of cloud air in which there is no exchange with the surroundings, all of the water vapor which condenses would go to increasing the liquid-water content, such that $-dw = dx$ where $w$ and $x$ represent vapor and liquid-water content, respectively, per gram of air. The water-vapor mixing ratio or specific humidity is constant during an adiabatic process before condensation, but after saturation is reached it decreases steadily. This is because it measures only the vapor and not the liquid water, and as more and more vapor changes to liquid, the specific humidity goes down, even though the relative humidity is still 100 per cent.

Adiabatic cooling will be counteracted to a certain extent after saturation in the cooling air is reached, for then every small amount of expansion cooling will cause the condensation of a little more of the water vapor and thereby the liberation of the latent heat of condensation. The net effect is that, after saturation, the rate of cooling with expansion is much less than that for dry air.

The mathematical expression for the adiabatic rate at saturation cannot be derived as simply as can that for the unsaturated case. An approximate expression may be obtained by simply adding the heat released by the condensation of the water vapor to the equation for the first law of thermodynamics. We recall Eq. (7-44) which is, for the dry-adiabatic case,

$$dq = C_p \, dT - \frac{R}{m} \, T \, \frac{dp}{p} = 0$$

We know that the heat added to an air parcel of unit mass by the condensation of the amount $dw$ of its water vapor would be $L \, dw$, where $L$ is the latent heat of condensation in ergs per gram and $w$ is the mixing ratio, decreasing in condensation. If this were simply additive, we would have

$$dq = -L \, dw = C_p \, dT - \frac{R}{m} \, T \, \frac{dp}{p} \tag{8-21}$$

$$C_p \, dT - \frac{R}{m} \, T \, \frac{dp}{p} + L \, dw = 0 \tag{8-22}$$

This is not the correct expression, however, because the amount of heat given off in this way depends on the process by means of which it is realized. The amount of water falling out of the cloud as rain should enter into the equation as well as the terms involving the specific heats of the liquid water and the vapor. Actually, the above equation serves quite well in representing almost any kind of saturation-adiabatic process in the atmosphere because greater accuracy is not needed. This is only a coincidence, however, as a consequence of the small numerical value of the other terms under atmospheric conditions, and the student should not retain the impression that the thermodynamic equations can be treated with such disrespect. The correct derivation may be found in more advanced textbooks.[1] The assumptions upon which one may base the thermodynamic interpretations are discussed on succeeding pages. The saturation-adiabatic rate varies inversely with the temperature and is also

[1] For example, Haurwitz, B., "Dynamic Meteorology," pp. 46-48, McGraw-Hill Book Company, Inc., New York, 1941.

affected by the pressure.    At a temperature of 20°C at sea level, the rate
of cooling of a rising element of air at saturation is less than half the rate
for dry air; at low temperatures, the two are nearly the same.    The name
saturation- or moist-adiabatic rate is given to the temperature decrease
rate for this process.    It is obvious that a lapse rate that would be quite
stable for dry air is sufficient for autoconvection to develop in moist air.
Thus, in warm and very moist air masses, it is possible to start strong
vertical motions in lapse rates only slightly steeper than the normally
observed values.

**Conditional Instability.**    In tracing the altitude-temperature curve
of a moving element that contains moisture but is not at saturation, the
lapse rate followed is practically the dry-adiabatic until the condensation
level is reached, after which the air will cool at the slower saturation rate.
If the prevailing lapse rate in the surrounding atmosphere is between the
dry- and saturation-adiabatic rates,
an element lifted upward would first
encounter resistance to its vertical
motion because it would cool with
altitude at the faster dry-adiabatic
rate.    After condensation, it would
follow the saturation-adiabatic rate,
which is slower than that of the surrounding atmosphere, so that the
line traced on the altitude-temperature graph by the moving element
would finally intersect the curve for

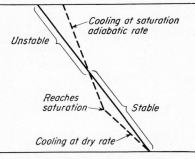

FIG. 8–3. Conditional instability.

the surrounding atmosphere and pass from stable to unstable, i.e., from
heavier to lighter than its surroundings.    The process is illustrated in
Fig. 8–3, where the solid line represents the prevailing lapse rate, and the
other parts of the figure are as indicated.

This type of temperature distribution (lapse rate between dry- and
saturation-adiabatic rates) is called *conditional instability*.    The conditions that must be fulfilled before the element may become unstable with
respect to its surroundings are

1. A sufficient amount of moisture in the air so that the moving element
becomes saturated soon enough to follow a saturation-adiabatic line
which intersects the prevailing lapse-rate curve.

2. A mechanically produced lifting of sufficient strength to overcome
the stabilizing forces at the lower levels and to carry the element to the
equilibrium point.

**The Condensation Adiabatic Processes and Precipitation.**    The
combined effect of adiabatic temperature changes and changes caused by
the latent heat of the moisture content has been investigated in its theo-

retical aspects with results that are of use to the practical meteorologist. The theory considers the condensation processes in an upward-moving element of air.    In the development of the theory, it is necessary to make certain simplifying assumptions relative to the manner in which the condensation and precipitation take place.    One assumption is that none of the condensed water falls out in the form of rain, hail, or snow but is carried along in the upward-moving current.    Under this simplification, it is known as the reversible-condensation adiabatic process.    The irreversible or pseudoadiabatic process comes from another assumption, viz., that the condensed water falls as precipitation as rapidly as it is formed. These two assumptions are at wide variance, and it seems apparent that somewhere between these two extreme processes lies the real condition of clouds and precipitation.    However, except when the formation of hail is considered, the use of one or the other of the hypotheses produces closely similar results.

The reversible case will be considered first.    A classical concept of this process has been developed which divides it into four successive stages— the dry stage, rain stage, hail stage, and snow stage.

*Dry Stage.*    As the element is lifted, it first cools at the dry-adiabatic rate of 1°C per 100 m until saturation is reached.    This stage, with the condensation level as its upper limit, is called the *dry stage*, shown by the lowest branch of the curve in Fig. 8–4.    The height of the condensation level depends on the initial temperature of the element and the amount of moisture that it contains.

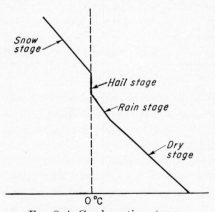

FIG. 8–4. Condensation stages.

*Rain Stage.*    After saturation, the air cools at the saturation-adiabatic rate described in the preceding paragraphs.    Under the reversible assumption, the cloud droplets are carried along with the upward-moving air so that, as condensation continues, more and more liquid water has formed until a maximum is reached at the top of this so-called "rain stage."    The top of the stage is encountered as soon as the element is cooled to the freezing point.

*Hail Stage.*    When a temperature of 0°C is reached, the water that has been carried along begins to freeze.    A large amount of heat, called the *heat of fusion* (80 cal per g), must be given up by the water to the surrounding air in order for it to freeze.    Since all the water must change to ice at this temperature, there will be no further cooling of the air until the freezing is complete. If the freezing were instantaneous, the hail stage would reduce to a point on the diagram, but it takes some time for the freezing to be accomplished. Meanwhile, the element of the air continues to rise. The heat of fusion has a complete nullifying effect on the expansional cooling, as contrasted with the heat of condensation liberated in the rain stage, which merely slows down the rate of adiabatic change. This is because the water freezes all at one given temperature, viz., 0°, while the water vapor condenses to liquid a little at a time during the rain stage. The hail stage is an isothermal process; i.e., the temperature remains constant (0°) in the rising air until all the liquid water is frozen.

*Snow Stage.* After all the liquid water has turned to ice, there is still some water vapor left which passes through the rain and hail stages without condensing. After the hail stage, the temperatures are all below freezing, and the remaining water vapor no longer condenses into a liquid form but goes directly into ice crystals. This part of the process is known as the snow stage and continues as the element is lifted upward in the atmosphere until all the water vapor is condensed, after which, necessarily, the process is again dry-adiabatic. Condensation directly into ice is called *crystallization*, or sublimation, and it gives off heat just as does the passage from vapor to liquid, but the amount per unit mass of water is greater because it combines both the heat of condensation and the heat of fusion. However, the temperature and amounts of moisture in the snow stage are so much lower that the rate of cooling is faster than in the rain stage. The ice formed in the hail stage is still carried along through the snow stage, but its effect is only slight, amounting to a very small amount of heat being given off.

Throughout the various stages of the process outlined above, whatever moisture forms develop, whether vapor, liquid water, hailstones, or snow crystals, are carried along through the successive stages, and none falls out as precipitation. Under this assumption, the process is a reversible one; i.e., if at any time the rising element is stopped and moved back downward through the atmosphere, it will follow through the same process, only in the reverse direction. The snow would evaporate, the hail would melt, and the liquid water would evaporate, each of these processes absorbing from the element of air the same amount of heat given to it during condensation, fusion, and crystallization; thus the element would arrive at its original position with the same temperature and moisture that it had before it was lifted.

**Pseudoadiabatic Process.** In the case of the immediate precipitation of the condensed water, which is called the *pseudoadiabatic* or irreversible process, the dry stage is the same. The rain stage differs only in the loss of a very small amount of heat which would have been given off by the liquid droplets had they not fallen out. The hail stage is nonexistent because no liquid remains to be frozen. The snow stage differs from that of the reversible-condensation process in the same way that the rain stage does, except that the heat lost is from ice crystals instead of from water droplets. The important point to note about the pseudo-adiabatic process is that, unlike the reversible-condensation process, it is irreversible. If then the ascent and expansion stop and the parcel starts downward with accompanying compression, the heat gained by the air through condensation and crystallization is retained, since there is no water in any form to melt or evaporate. The parcel follows a dry-adiabatic course downward and arrives at any given level with a temperature higher than it had at that level during the ascent. Theoretically, if the process were carried out with an extreme expansion, a point would be reached at which all of the water vapor would have been removed. A parcel carried completely through such a process and brought back to its original pressure would be completely dry and would have a temperature derived from the release of all the heat contained in the water vapor present at the start. This new temperature is called the *equivalent temperature* and is often used as a convenient expression of the temperature and moisture content in one thermodynamic term.

Researches into the nature of condensation in the atmosphere show not only that the two assumptions we have just considered are unrepresentative of the facts but also that the general classical theory of condensation is only partly tenable for the atmosphere. It is especially notable that the rain stage may extend to temperatures far below freezing. In fact, liquid water in clouds supercooled below the ordinary freezing point of water is the rule rather than the exception in the growing collection of observational material. This phenomenon is of the greatest importance in considering ice formation on aircraft. The prevalence of supercooled water in the atmosphere indicates that in most cases only the dry stage and rain stage need be considered as far as condensation is concerned. It is also quite likely that the hail stage can be neglected in most cases. It seems to be a generally accepted principle among meteorologists that large snowflakes are first formed in the presence of a certain amount of liquid water, although this idea has never been satisfactorily verified. In practically all thermodynamic diagrams representing the condensation processes, the rain and snow stages are represented by a continuous saturation-adiabatic line. With this simplification, the reversible and pseudo-adiabatic processes are almost identical for rising air.

**Entrainment.** The most serious departure from reality in the processes just described comes from the basic assumption of an isolated parcel of air. In the type of convection which gives rise to cumulus and cumulonimbus clouds, a certain amount of mixing between the cloud air and the environment air occurs. It has been shown that in order not to be decelerated in its upward growth the ascending parcel must be warmer than its environment. The mixing of colder environment air into the cloud has the effect of reducing the temperature of the rising air and thus of reducing or destroying its buoyancy. By bringing in dry air the cloud is unable to maintain itself unless some of the liquid water already present can be evaporated to make up the water-vapor deficit, thus preserving saturation. The resultant cooling by evaporation of cloud droplets further reduces the temperature in the cloud. The greater the proportion of outside air in the mixture and the lower its initial water-vapor content, the greater must be the evaporation of cloud water. The limiting case would be that in which the liquid content in the mixture is equal to or less than the saturation deficit in the mixture; in this case the cloud would dissipate in that portion.

Without introducing appreciable errors, we may describe the ascent and mixing as taking place in the following three steps:

1. Take 1 kg of air at saturation and lift it through a pseudoadiabatic expansion some chosen small distance to a new $T'$, $p$.

2. Mix this with $M$ kg of environment air having the temperature $T$ and the specific humidity $q$ to make a mixture of $1 + M$ kg. In this step the *thermodynamic* effects of changing the specific humidity will not be considered. The temperature of the mixture would then be the weighted mean

$$T_m = \frac{T' + MT}{1 + M} \tag{8-23}$$

and the specific humidity of the mixture would be the weighted mean

$$q_m = \frac{q' + Mq}{1 + M} \tag{8-24}$$

Here $q'$ is the saturation specific humidity which the isolated parcel would have at $T'$, $p$. Since $q$, the environment specific humidity, is less than the saturation value, $q_m$ is not sufficient to saturate the mixture. We must evaporate some of the cloud water to provide the necessary amount of water vapor for saturation. This we do in the next step.

3. Evaporate enough of the cloud water to keep the mixture at saturation. This involves the exchange of a certain amount of latent heat of vaporization. This heat can be calculated by using Eq. (8–22) for constant pressure ($dp = 0$), since no pressure change is involved in this step. The change in temperature is then

$$dT = \frac{-L}{C_p} dw \tag{8-25}$$

Here we recognize that by evaporating an amount of liquid water $-dx$ we produce an amount of vapor $+dw$. Also, since we are dealing with a mixture, it is more convenient to use the specific humidity change $dq$ in place of the change in mixing ratio $dw$, as justified on page 161. The new temperature, then, is

$$T'' = T_m + dT = T_m - \frac{L}{C_p} dq = T_m - \frac{L}{C_p} (q'' - q_m) \qquad (8\text{--}26)$$

where $T''$ and $q''$ are the actual temperature and specific humidity, respectively, resulting in the cloud.

Always in making these computations it is necessary to determine whether or not there is enough liquid water in the cloud at the end of step 1 to accomplish the saturation in step 3. The amount of water in liquid form $x_2$ contained in an isolated parcel going from point 1 to point 2 is given by

$$x_2 = x_1 + (q_{s1} - q_{s2})$$

where the quantitites in the parentheses are the saturation specific humidities at points 1 and 2, respectively. As shown on page 161 they can be determined directly from the temperatures and pressures of the two points.

The name *entrainment* has been given to this process of incorporation and mixing of environment air into the ascending cloud mass. Its precise thermodynamic significance was first pointed out by Stommel.[1] He used the term because he recognized that the ascending current in the cumulus cloud was essentially like a jet of air whose physical analysis always requires a consideration of entrainment of some of the still air into which it is injected.

In considering the ascent of air in convection currents in the atmosphere, it is customary to refer to the entrainment in terms of the percentage increase of mass by mixing in a given pressure interval. In cumulus clouds of restricted development Stommel found entrainment rates of 100 per cent in 100 mb while Byers and Braham[2] obtained a rate of 100 per cent in 500 mb for bulging cumulus growing into thunderstorms.

After a further discussion of thermodynamic diagrams and thermodynamic properties of the atmosphere in the next few pages, a simple graphical method of following the ascent of air with and without entrainment will be shown.

**The Adiabatic Chart and Thermodynamic Diagram.** Data from soundings of pressure, temperature, and humidity are always entered and computed on some form of adiabatic chart. In its simplest form this is a diagram with temperature in degrees centigrade as abscissa and

---

[1] Stommel, H., Entrainment of Air into a Cumulus Cloud, *J. Meteorol.*, vol. 4, pp. 91–94, 1947.

[2] Byers, H. R., and R. R. Braham, Jr., "The Thunderstorm," U.S. Government Printing Office, Washington, 1949.

pressure in millibars as ordinate.   The temperature is on a linear scale but the pressure is usually on a logarithmic scale, decreasing upward. There is some advantage in having the ordinate in terms of $p^{.286}$, making the dry-adiabatic or potential-temperature lines straight.   The potential temperature is given by

$$\theta = T \left(\frac{1000}{p}\right)^{.286}$$

as shown in Eq. (7-77).

A true thermodynamic diagram is one which is a transformation of the $pV$ diagram, which permits the computation of energy exchanged in a closed cycle.   As shown on page 137, this transforms into $T \ln p$ where, as in the atmosphere, we desire to use pressure and temperature in place of pressure and volume.   Coordinates of $T$ and $p^{.286}$ are a close approximation to $T$ and $\ln p$.   A useful diagram based on the latter approximation is the *Stüve diagram,* named after the German meteorologist who had much to do with its development.

A Stüve diagram is shown in Fig. 8–5, with various lines for atmospheric computations.   The potential-temperature or dry-adiabatic lines are the straight lines sloping upward from right to left and labeled 273, 283, 293, etc.   The lines of saturation mixing ratios are the dashed lines labeled 8, 10, 12, 14, . . . , 28 g per kg.   They are based on data similar to that given in Table 8–3 and connect points in terms of temperature and pressure where the amount of water vapor represented by each line will just produce saturation.   From these, the isentropic-condensation temperature or pressure may be obtained.   For example, if an air sample starting from $A$ and having a mixing ratio of 10 g per kg ascends, it will reach condensation at the point where its dry-adiabatic or potential-temperature line intersects the line for saturation for 10 g per kg.   This point is represented by $S$—an isentropic-condensation pressure of 900 mb and condensation temperature of 12°C.   If the air sample starting out at $A$ were cooled at constant pressure, it would reach saturation where a horizontal line from $A$ intersects the 10-g line.   This would be the temperature of the dew point, or about 14°C.

The pseudoadiabatic lines are the curved set of light, solid lines that are not labeled.   The variation in slope of these lines with variation in temperature should be noted.   At high temperatures, a given decrease in temperature of a saturated parcel results in a greater reduction in saturation mixing ratio than in the case of low temperatures.   In other words, condensation proceeds more rapidly in warm air than in cool air for a given decrease of temperature.   This means that there will be more heat released by condensation at the higher temperatures, which, in turn, will decrease the rate of adiabatic temperature drop.   At very low temperatures the pseudoadiabats approach the dry adiabats.

Conditional instability is also illustrated in Fig. 8–5. After the rising air parcel goes from $A$ to the condensation level at $S$, it follows along a pseudoadiabat $SB$. If $AC$ is the prevailing lapse-rate curve, we have conditional instability indicated as in Fig. 8–3. The point where the two curves cross, which in Fig. 8–5 is at 770 mb, is sometimes called the *level of free convection*, because above that level the rising parcel is unstable

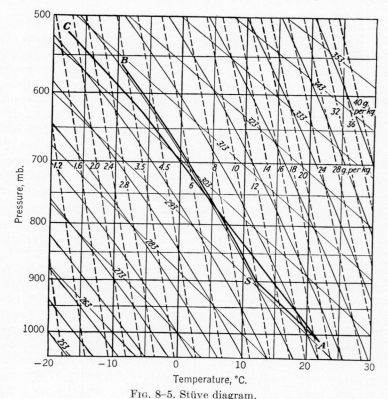

Fig. 8–5. Stüve diagram.

with respect to its surroundings and convection will proceed without added impulse.

A number of equal-area transformations of the $T \ln p$ diagram have been made and are used regularly by meteorological services. They are aimed at easier plotting, reading, and computation of the various quantities. Since adiabatic equilibrium or departures from it are important features to be looked for, some of the diagrams feature the dry adiabats as horizontal lines or vertical lines, so that departures from adiabatic equilibrium stand out more clearly. It is argued that neither isothermal nor constant-pressure conditions are of special interest in the atmosphere and that the vertical lines and horizontal lines on the conventional diagram are of no great help in recognizing critical situations. In one transformation the important pseudoadiabats for summer convection stand approximately vertical. In addition to the $T \ln p$ diagram, two true energy diagrams, the *tephigram* and the *skewed diagram*, have gained wide acceptance.

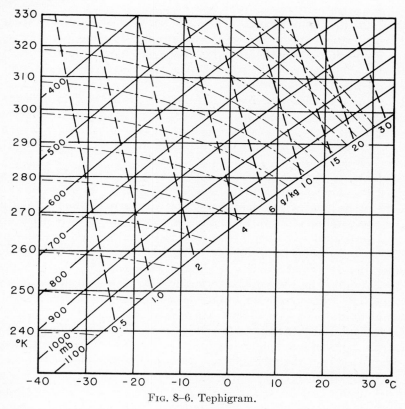

Fig. 8–6. Tephigram.

*Tephigram.* This derives its name from its coordinates of temperature and entropy $(T, \varphi)$. It was introduced by Sir Napier Shaw.[1] A line of constant entropy is a line of constant potential temperature, so the ordinate in Fig. 8–6 is labeled in terms of potential temperature. The pressure lines are diagonals with the lowest values in the upper left. Again, the moisture lines are the straight, dashed lines and the pseudo-adiabats are curved. This chart has been favored by British, Canadian, and some American meteorologists.

[1] Shaw, N., "Manual of Meteorology," vol. 2, p. 36; vol. 3, pp. 223–224, Cambridge University Press, London, 1926, 1930.

*Skewed Diagram.* Certain desired characteristics are obtained by making the coordinates nonrectangular while preserving the $T \ln p$ areal representation. A diagram of this type, used in the United States Air Force in 1952 and subsequently, has the conventional $\ln p$ scale as the ordinate, but the temperature lines are rotated somewhat less than 45° clockwise. This produces the maximum angle of intersection (90° in the standard atmosphere at 500 mb) between the lines of temperature and of potential temperature. The angle between dry-adiabatic (potential temperature) and pseudoadiabatic lines is also large. At temperatures in the low atmosphere characteristic of summer convection, the pseudoadiabats are nearly vertical. The Air Force skewed diagram is not reproduced here.

In addition to these equal-area transformations of the $T \ln p$ diagram, there is the closely approximate $Tp^k$ or Stüve-type diagram described on preceding pages. A diagram similar to the one shown in Fig. 8–5 has been used extensively by the U.S. Weather Bureau and the commercial airlines.

Students, teachers, and professional meteorologists should be warned against developing strong prejudices for or against a specific diagram. On the other hand, the promulgation of a new arrangement should not be on the basis of whim or even a desire to emphasize certain features. In meteorological work one becomes accustomed to certain visual patterns whose meanings are quickly recognized and understood. One is temporarily slowed down in one's work when confronted with a new picturization. The best advice to follow is to be willing to adapt to a new pattern where required but to expect a cool reception from any attempt to impose a new diagram on the profession.

**Graphical Computations on the Diagrams.** In practical meteorological work the thermodynamic diagrams are used for computing a variety of quantities from the given data. Radiosondes provide measurements of pressure, temperature, and relative humidity. The soundings are plotted on the diagram and from the plot other variables can be read off or plotted on related curves. Some of the data obtainable in this manner are as follows:

*Potential temperature* is obtained by following the dry adiabat to 1000 mb and reading the temperature there, or, more easily, by noting the values of potential temperature printed on the dry-adiabatic lines.

*Saturation mixing ratio* is read immediately at any point on the temperature-pressure plot by interpolation from the mixing-ratio lines.

*Mixing ratio* is obtained by multiplying the saturation mixing ratio by the measured relative humidity.

*Dew-point temperature* is obtained as the temperature at the point where the actual mixing-ratio line or interpolated line intersects the observed pressure line.  It is useful to plot this for every significant level of the sounding to produce a curve that is a plot of both the mixing ratio and the dew-point temperature.  From such a curve, working in a reverse sense, one can get the relative humidity from the ratio of the mixing ratio to the saturation mixing ratio.

*Condensation pressure, temperature (isentropic)* is found at the intersection of the potential-temperature line and the mixing-ratio line which corresponds to the value at the starting point.  For certain purposes it is convenient to plot this quantity for the various significant levels.

*Wet-bulb temperature,* for reasons that will be explained in the next section, can also be computed from a thermodynamic diagram.  This is done by following a pseudoadiabatic line from the condensation point back to the original pressure and reading the temperature there.

*Wet-bulb-potential temperature,* to be discussed in the next section, is obtained in the same way as the wet-bulb temperature except that the pseudoadiabat is followed to 1000 mb where the temperature is read.  A plot of the condensation points is also a plot of wet-bulb-potential temperature as read from the pseudoadiabats.  The latter often are labeled according to their corresponding wet-bulb-potential temperatures.

**Wet-bulb Temperature.**  At constant pressure, there are two separate ways of producing saturation: (1) by lowering the temperature to the dew point by means of cooling without any change in the water-vapor content, (2) by evaporating water into the air without adding or removing sensible heat.[1]  The process of evaporation in a closed container described on page 157 involves a combination of both of these methods, since in order to preserve a constant temperature in the enclosure, heat must be added.  The first of the two processes is easy to understand, but in the second it is necessary to determine the cooling effect involving the heat of vaporization.  In particular, it is necessary to know how much water has to be evaporated to produce saturation and what the temperature at saturation will be.  It is not a simple matter of raising the moisture content to that required for saturation at the beginning temperature of the air, because the temperature will decrease owing to the evaporative cooling.  In other words, we can't raise the dew point to the initial dry-bulb temperature because the latter will be falling and they will meet somewhere at an intermediate temperature point.  We must now find out at what temperature this saturation will occur.

At constant pressure $dp = 0$, the equation for the condensation process, Eq. (8–22) becomes

$$C_p \, dT = -L \, dw$$

---

[1] Sensible heat is heat that can be sensed or felt as contrasted with latent heat which cannot be sensed directly.

Let us start with temperature $T$ and mixing ratio $w$ and find the temperature $T_w$ and mixing ratio $w'$ at which the added water vapor will produce saturation.   The equation becomes

$$C_p(T - T_w) = -L(w - w') = L(w' - w) \qquad (8\text{--}27)$$

Solving for the new temperature $T_w$ we have

$$T_w = T - \frac{L}{C_p} (w' - w) \qquad (8\text{--}28)$$

Note that since water vapor has been added $w' > w$, so $T_w < T$.

At the beginning of this process we know only $T$ and $w$.   It is apparent that at the end $T_w$ is the actual temperature and $w'$ is the actual mixing ratio which at this point is at saturation.   Since $w'$ is a function of $T_w$ (saturation mixing ratio at a given pressure depends on temperature only), we can solve for $T_w$ or can use tables to find a $w'$ that fits the relation or, better still, can solve graphically.

Actually, $T_w$ is the wet-bulb temperature.[1]   The cooling of the wet bulb to its equilibrium temperature involves the same relationship between changes of latent and sensible heats as expressed in Eq. (8–22). At equilibrium, the transfer of sensible heat from the air to the cooler bulb is exactly equal to the heat transferred from the bulb by evaporation.   At a given air temperature, a low mixing ratio means a high rate of evaporational cooling of the bulb and a large temperature difference requires a correspondingly large transfer of sensible heat from the air to the bulb.   In a somewhat analogous sense we can say that for the cooling of air by evaporation, equilibrium is reached when the temperature has been reduced by an amount corresponding to the heat removed from the air by the evaporation.   The drier the air initially, the greater must be the amount of water evaporated to produce saturation equilibrium and the greater must be the temperature reduction.

The wet-bulb temperature of a mass of air may be defined as the temperature at which the air reaches saturation when water is evaporated into it without any other heat exchange.   It is the lowest temperature to which the air can be cooled by evaporating water into it.   These statements apply to a constant-pressure process.

It can be shown also that a wet-bulb temperature can be achieved through a saturation-adiabatic process.   This temperature differs so little from that obtained from a constant-pressure process that for practical purposes it may be considered the same.   On page 181 it was stated that the wet-bulb temperature lies on the intersection of the isobar in question and the saturation-adiabatic line which passes through the

---

[1] It is also the temperature $T'''$ of Eq. (8–26).

condensation point.  It was pointed out on page 172 that, in terms of the values obtained, it makes no difference whether the saturation adiabat is reversible or irreversible (pseudoadiabatic).  To obtain the wet-bulb temperature adiabatically we can go through the following theoretical process:

Lift a sample parcel of the air to its condensation point.  Then add enough liquid water in the form of cloud drops to keep the air parcel saturated by evaporation of these drops during descent to the original level.  If there is more than the required amount of water the result will not be affected.  With the water continually evaporating, the parcel will descend along a reversible saturation-adiabatic line, which is numerically essentially the same as a pseudoadiabatic line.  Where this line intersects the original pressure the wet-bulb temperature is achieved.

In this process, instead of adding water vapor by evaporation at constant pressure as described in the previous section, we have added the same amount of water during descent from the condensation level.  By definition, the mixing ratio $w$ at the condensation point is the same as the initial mixing ratio of the parcel.  In obtaining the wet-bulb temperature adiabatically, one must use Eq. (8–22) which differs from the equation (8–25) used in the isobaric case in that the term $(RT/m)(dp/p)$ must be taken into account.  When we say, as above, that the results of the two processes are the same, we are saying that this term integrated up to the condensation point and back to the original pressure is zero.  Actually it is not zero because a small amount of work has to be expended in the process, but this amount is too small to bother about in practice.

The wet-bulb-potential temperature is defined by this process carried to the 1000-mb pressure.  It is seen that each saturation-adiabatic or pseudoadiabatic line corresponds to one and only one wet-bulb-potential temperature as indicated at its intersection with the 1000-mb line.  Since there can be only one pseudoadiabat going through a given condensation point and since the condensation point is uniquely determined by the pressure, temperature, and mixing ratio or, more specifically, by the potential temperature and mixing ratio of the parcel, it follows that the wet-bulb-potential temperature is a function of $p$, $T$, and $w$ or of $\theta$ and $w$ or $\theta$, $p_c$ (the condensation point).  The student can satisfy himself about the truth of these statements by going through the processes graphically on the diagram.

**Equivalent Temperature and Equivalent-potential Temperature.** The *equivalent temperature* is a measure of the degree of heat obtainable after increasing the sensible temperature by realizing all of the latent heat of the water vapor.  The resulting temperature depends to some extent on the manner in which this heat is released.  It is specified that this shall be accomplished by an irreversible condensation process carried to the theoretical extreme where all of the water has been removed, $w = 0$, $x = 0$, then returned to the original pressure. The return is along a dry-adiabatic line, so the resulting temperature is higher than the original. The *equivalent-potential temperature* is obtained if the dry-adiabatic line is followed to 1000 mb.

As in the case of the wet-bulb relationships, the equivalent temperature and equivalent-potential temperature are uniquely determined by the condensation point. On examining a thermodynamic diagram extending to fairly low pressure, one will note that each pseudoadiabat approaches and apparently eventually joins a dry-adiabatic line. Thus the pseudo-adiabatic lines, in addition to being labeled in terms of wet-bulb-potential temperature, can be labeled by the potential temperature of the dry adiabat which they approach in the upper atmosphere. These would be the values of equivalent-potential temperature. It is apparent that the isentropic-condensation point or, simply stated, the condensation point, is unique for determining thermodynamic properties of a moist atmosphere.

**Properties Used in Tracing Air Parcels.** Some of the thermodynamic properties are useful in tracing, both horizontally and vertically, the paths of air parcels through the atmosphere. Those properties which under ordinary circumstances do not vary appreciably, called "conservative" properties, can be used for this purpose. In Table 8–5 the relative variability of thermodynamic properties which can be measured or derived easily from the observations of the conventional radiosondes is given. Those properties which are constant, at least before saturation,

TABLE 8–5. VARIABILITY OF AIR-MASS PROPERTIES IN ASCENT

| Property | Before condensation (dry-adiabatic) | After condensation (saturation-adiabatic) |
|---|---|---|
| Temperature | Decreases | Decreases |
| Virtual temperature | Decreases | Decreases |
| Vapor pressure | Decreases | Decreases |
| Relative humidity | Increases | Constant, 100% |
| Dew-point temperature | Decreases | Decreases |
| Absolute humidity | Decreases | Decreases |
| Specific humidity or mixing ratio | Constant | Decreases |
| Potential temperature | Constant | Increases |
| Isentropic-condensation pressure or temperature | Constant | Not defined |
| Equivalent temperature | Decreases | Decreases |
| Wet-bulb temperature | Decreases | Decreases |
| Equivalent-potential temperature | Constant | Constant |
| Wet-bulb-potential temperature | Constant | Constant |

are classified as conservative.  It will be noted that wet-bulb-potential temperature and equivalent-potential temperature are the only two properties that are constant before and after saturation.  As tracers, however, they are not as useful as specific humidity or mixing ratio, because over large sections of the atmosphere, and even over large horizontal distances, the values are observed to be unchanging with altitude. This means that a parcel displaced from its original location will not carry a distinctive value to differentiate it from its surroundings.  The water-vapor mixing ratio has normally a highly nonuniform distribution and any parcel carried away from its initial position is more easily recognized.  Over the large regions studied daily on synoptic charts, the areas of saturation are relatively small and their effects on the mixing ratio as a tracer are not usually serious.

A method of tracing the air flow in terms of moisture has been introduced on isentropic charts, mentioned briefly on page 146.  On a map of an isentropic or potential-temperature surface, which is a sloping surface whose contours are determined from the radiosonde network, the mixing ratios or the corresponding condensation pressures are plotted and charted.  Isentropic charts will be discussed in more detail in a later chapter.

The great bodies of air called *air masses*, coming from different "source" regions of the earth, can be traced and identified by plots of the distribution in the vertical of the conservative properties.  A diagram for this purpose was introduced by Rossby,[1] using the three properties equivalent-potential temperature, mixing ratio, and dry-air-potential temperature. The latter is the potential temperature obtained by starting with the same temperature but with the partial pressure of the dry air, $p_d = p - e$. In Fig. 8-7 this diagram is shown with plots of mean winter distributions of three principal American air masses—continental arctic $cA$, maritime polar $mP$, and maritime tropical $mT$.

It will be noted that the $cA$ air, which comes from northern Canada, not only has lower values of all three properties but also shows a marked increase of potential temperature and equivalent-potential temperature with height.  The $mP$ air shows an almost constant equivalent-potential temperature.  This is a characteristic of moist air masses in which a great deal of convective overturning and mixing has occurred.  Somewhat the same condition exists at San Antonio in the $mT$ except that all the values are higher.  The decrease of equivalent-potential temperature with height in this air mass indicates that convection has not been very active up to this point.  The dryness above 2 or 3 km is brought about

[1] Rossby, C. G., Thermodynamics Applied to Air Mass Analysis, *Mass. Inst. Technol., Meteorol. Papers*, vol. 1, no. 3, 1932.

by the prevalent sinking in the upper parts of the subtropical high-pressure area from which this air mass is drawn.

The use of either equivalent-potential temperature or wet-bulb-potential temperature in diagrams of this kind can be a matter of personal preference. The diagonal lines of Fig. 8–7 could be labeled in terms of wet-bulb-potential temperature.

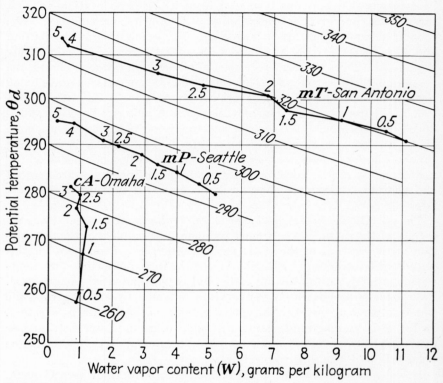

Fig. 8–7. Rossby diagram showing curves for the three principal air masses of the United States in winter. The numbers along the plots indicate heights in kilometers.

Certain other elements which could serve as tracers have been suggested from time to time. Among them are ozone, radioactive isotopes such as oxygen 18, trittium or radioactive krypton, not to mention radioactive substances introduced artificially by atomic or thermonuclear explosions. The expense and difficulty of making synoptic measurements of these quantities would require, before adoption, that they prove to be many times superior to water vapor, which apparently they are not. Measurements of the concentrations of radioactive materials in the free atmosphere after explosions have been used to obtain air trajectories. Without the benefit of these measurements meteorologists have demonstrated that they can obtain the trajectories from regular meteorological data about as well as they can with the measurements.

**Energy Diagrams.** The determination of conditional instability and the calculation of the energy available therefrom may be made graphically from the thermodynamic diagram. This is a step toward predicting the occurrence of strong vertical currents, especially thunderstorms, from

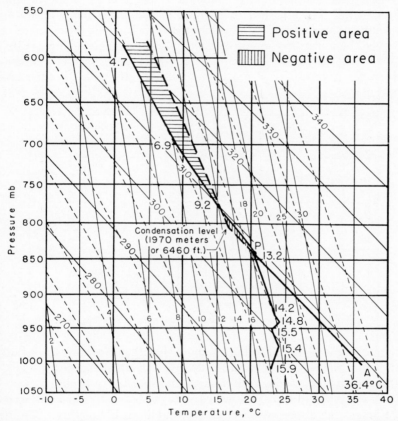

Fig. 8–8. Energy diagram prepared from an early morning sounding at Washington, D.C.

upper-air soundings. On the $T \ln p$ diagram or equal-area transformations of it the buoyant energy that can be realized in cumulus-cloud convection may be determined by measuring the areas between the prevailing lapse-rate curve and the adiabats followed by an ascending parcel. Areas on the diagram where the rising air is warmer than its surroundings are *positive areas* and the parts where the moving parcel is colder are *negative areas*. Figure 8–8 shows an energy diagram in terms of $T \ln p$

for a selected sounding and Fig. 8–9 shows the same sounding on a tephigram.

As a forecasting aid, the energy diagram is usually constructed from an early morning or late evening sounding and the conditions for the time of maximum temperature the ensuing day are analyzed. In Figs. 8–8 and 8–9 the calculations are based on expected afternoon conditions, reasoning that at the time of maximum temperature a dry-adiabatic lapse rate will prevail below the point $P$, so that the temperature at $A$ will result at the ground. The adiabatic mixing in this layer is expected to reduce the moisture content of the air at the ground to 15 g per kg, or to about the average of the values (entered to the right of the curve) between the ground and $P$. A sample of this ground air is then lifted.

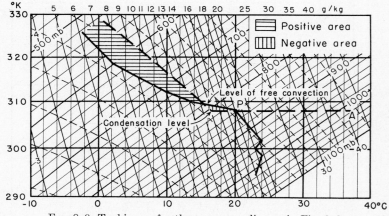

FIG. 8–9. Tephigram for the same sounding as in Fig. 8–8.

In this example, it is noted that a small negative area needs to be overcome before the ascending sample of air in the cloud reaches the *level of free convection* whence the positive area and instability begin.

The energy diagram just described is based on the full parcel method. Entrainment, as discussed on page 174, modifies this picture. To illustrate this, let us take a magnified portion of the plot in Fig. 8–9 between 950 and 600 mb and perform an entrainment computation, as shown in Fig. 8–10. For simplicity, the computation is made in 100-mb steps assuming an entrainment rate of 50 per cent per 100 mb of ascent.

The 1-kg parcel at $Q$ (pressure 810 mb) in Fig. 8–10 is carried along the pseudoadiabat to 710 mb, point $R$, where its temperature $T'$ becomes 11.8°; the environment temperature $T$ is 9.9° while the corresponding specific humidities $q'$ and $q$ are 12.6 and 7.2 g per kg, respectively. The environment $q$ is interpolated between the two points having 9.2 and 6.9

g per kg. Adding 50 per cent or 0.5 kg of environment air gives for the mixture, from Eqs. (8–23) and (8–24),

$$T_m = \frac{T' + 0.5T}{1.5} = \frac{11.8 + 5.0}{1.5} = 11.2°C$$

$$q_m = \frac{q' + 0.5q}{1.5} = \frac{12.6 + 3.6}{1.5} = 10.8 \text{ g kg}^{-1}$$

We obtain the point $S$ for this mixing by finding $T_m \equiv 11.2$ at 710 mb. It is noted that $q_m$ is less than the saturation value at this point. Some of the liquid water must evaporate to produce a new temperature and specific humidity. Actually, this new temperature is the wet-bulb

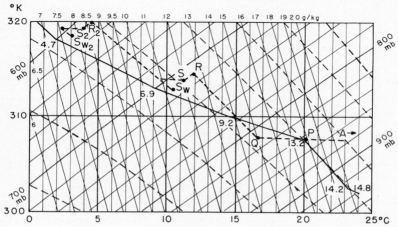

FIG. 8–10. Graphical computation of entrainment in 100-mb steps, magnified from Fig. 8–9.

temperature of the air at $S$, as is apparent from the thermodynamic definition of that quantity. It can be obtained by the usual graphical method of following a dry adiabat to the condensation point and tracing a pseudoadiabat back to the initial pressure. This procedure produces the point $S_w$, with temperature 10.3°C and specific humidity of 11.3 g per kg (read from the diagram).

The necessary bookkeeping, tabulated in Table 8–6, shows that from $Q$ to $R$, 2.4 g of water vapor, representing the difference between the saturation specific humidities (mixing ratios) at the two points, passed into liquid form in the 1-kg parcel of air. Putting this amount into 1.5 kg of air by the mixing reduces its concentration to 2.4/1.5 or 1.6 g per kg as the liquid-water content. After evaporating the 0.5 g (11.3 − 10.8) necessary to bring the mixture to saturation at the wet-bulb temperature, there is still 1.1 g per kg of liquid water left. This is added to the liquid-water load of the parcel through the next step of the ascent.

TABLE 8–6. VALUES OBTAINED IN COMPUTATION OF ENTRAINMENT
IN FIG. 8–10

a. Temperature and water vapor, assuming adequate supply of liquid water

| Point | $T'$ | $q_m$ | $q_{sat}$ | Environment $T$ | Environment $q$ |
|-------|------|-------|-----------|-----------------|-----------------|
| $Q$    | 16.6 | .... | 15.0 | 17.4 | 11.2 |
| $R$    | 11.8 | .... | 12.6 | 9.9  | 7.2  |
| $S$    | 11.2 | 10.8 | 12.0 | 9.9  | 7.2  |
| $S_w$  | 10.3 | .... | 11.3 | 9.9  | 7.2  |
| $R_2$  | 4.5  | .... | 8.7  | 2.6  | 4.9  |
| $S_2$  | 3.9  | 7.5  | 8.3  | 2.6  | 4.9  |
| $S_{w2}$ | 3.1 | .... | 7.8  | 2.6  | 4.9  |

b. Check as to adequacy of liquid-water contents, grams per kilogram

| From points | Added by condensation | Result of dilution by mixing | Removed by evaporation | Net carried forward |
|-------------|----------------------|------------------------------|------------------------|---------------------|
| $Q$ to $R$      | $15.0 - 12.6 = 2.4$ | ......... | .................. | 2.4 |
| $R$ to $S$      | ................. | $\dfrac{2.4}{1.5} = 1.6$ | .................. | 1.6 |
| $S$ to $S_w$    | ................. | ......... | $10.8 - 11.3 = -0.5$ | 1.1 |
| $S_w$ to $R_2$  | $11.3 - 8.7 = 2.6$ | ......... | .................. | 3.7 |
| $R_2$ to $S_2$  | ................. | $\dfrac{3.7}{1.5} = 2.5$ | .................. | 2.5 |
| $S_2$ to $S_{w2}$ | ............... | ......... | $7.5 - 7.8 = -0.3$ | 2.2 |

All net values positive, therefore liquid-water contents adequate for all required processes.

Taking $S_w$ as the new starting point, we go up another 100 mb, repeating the procedure to obtain $R_2$, $S_2$, and $S_{w2}$ as shown in the figure and recorded in the table. The entrainment moist-adiabatic ascent curve would be obtained by constructing straight line segments between $Q$ and $S_w$ and between $S_w$ and $S_{w2}$. For a clearer explanation of the process, this was not done in Fig. 8–10.

The results indicate that the buoyancy in the cloud is greatly reduced by the entrainment. In the actual atmosphere this reduced buoyancy represents the true state of affairs in cumulus clouds, except in the cores of giant ones where little environment air is able to penetrate.

**Layer Stability, Convective Instability.**   In Chap. 7 the consequences of lifting, sinking, stretching, and shrinking of layers in dry-adiabatic processes were described.

The results may apply to saturation as well as to dry conditions if the saturation- or pseudoadiabatic is used in place of the dry-adiabatic.

In nature, the saturation conditions would not appear to be applicable for descent. Superadiabatic lapse rates with respect to saturation are common in the atmosphere, and it is under these conditions that the effects on a superadiabatic lapse rate are important. For example, divergence in an ascending layer at saturation but superadiabatic with respect to saturation would preserve steep lapse rates during ascent.

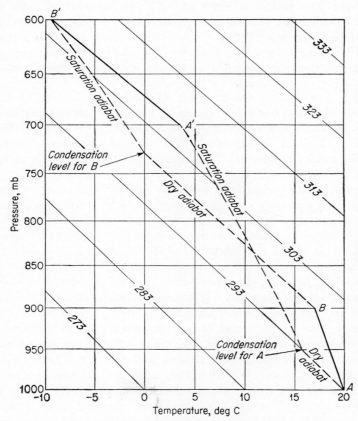

FIG. 8–11. Graphical representation of convective instability.

Frequently the vertical distribution of moisture within the lower layers of the atmosphere is such that, when they are lifted, the bottom part reaches its condensation level before the upper. This condition arises most often when the relative humidity decreases with height within the layer in question. The result of lifting in such cases is a very rapid steepening of the lapse rate, for now, in addition to the gradual change brought about in any lifting process as previously described, the top is cooling more rapidly than the bottom of the layer. If the air is very moist in the low levels, the difference between the saturation, and dry-adiabatic rates is large so that steep temperature drops with height within the air layers can develop with great rapidity. The process is shown in Fig. 8–11, where $AB$ is the original lapse rate in the layer. $A$ reaches saturation much earlier than $B$, and the results of the different rates of cooling at the two points are shown by $A'B'$.

Air layers that exhibit this property of sharp lapse-rate changes due to different condensation levels are designated as convectively unstable or as possessing the property of convective instability. Layers that are originally quite stable or that may even consist of temperature inversions are often convectively unstable because of the pronounced stratification of moisture.

Rossby[1] has studied the problem of convective instability in considerable detail and has shown that a layer will be convectively unstable if the equivalent-potential temperature decreases with height through the layer. This is the accepted definition of convective instability, although wet-bulb-potential temperature may be substituted in the definition.

With the introduction of convective instability, confusing terminology appears. We generally test convection by the parcel method, considering the conditional instability, whereas convective instability refers to layer conditions and has little reference to convection as we generally know it. It is a form of *potential* instability in which a layer that may at the present time be stable can become unstable with the appropriate amount of lifting. On the other hand, conditional instability refers to the character of the layer *now*. It is possible for a layer to be convectively unstable and not conditionally unstable.

An interesting case arises when a fairly deep layer that is convectively unstable becomes saturated not by lifting but by the evaporation of water into it from rain falling from a higher cloud layer. Once this layer becomes saturated, it is absolutely unstable. It has been noted on some occasions that thunderstorms develop from rain falling out of an altostratus layer. The saturation of the convectively unstable layer by evaporation of the falling rain is thought to be the cause. The student can verify the instability of this situation by plotting decreasing wet-bulb-potential temperatures with height and recognizing that this will be the actual lapse rate if saturation is reached.

[1] *Ibid.* p. 185.

# CHAPTER 9

# HORIZONTAL MOTION IN THE ATMOSPHERE— THE WINDS

The wind is simply air in motion, usually measured only in its horizontal component. It is an essential part of the thermodynamic mechanism of the atmosphere, serving as a means of transporting heat, moisture, and other properties from one region of the earth to another. While vertical motions, when they occur, are extremely important for the production of clouds, precipitation, thunderstorms, etc., their total sustained magnitude is quite small in comparison with the total horizontal flows of the atmosphere.

The physical-mathematical treatment of the flow of air particles over the surface of the earth is complicated by the fact that both the earth and the atmosphere are rotating. Before discussing the action of forces in the wind motions, it is necessary to outline some of the principles of rotational motion derived from elementary physics. For a more complete statement of these fundamentals, the reader is referred to physics textbooks.

**Angular Velocity.** The rate of rotation of a body is called its *angular velocity*. It is expressed as the angle through which a body turns in unit time; for a particle moving in the arc of a circle, it is the angular displacement in a unit time. It is customary to state the angular velocity in units of *radians per second*. (A complete circle of 360° is $2\pi$ rad, 180° is $\pi$ rad, 90° is $\pi/2$ rad, etc.)

Rotational motion may be expressed in terms of either the linear velocity or the angular velocity, and it is convenient at times to use them interchangeably according to a known relationship. Consider a particle moving in an arc the distance $s$ from $A$ to $B$ in Fig. 9–1 with a linear speed $v$ in the time $t$. Designating the radius of the circle by $r$, the angle $AOB$ by $\varphi$, and the angular velocity by $\omega$, we have

$$s = vt \qquad \text{and} \qquad \varphi = \omega t$$

The total circumference of the circle is $2\pi r$, and the arc is the fraction $\varphi/2\pi$ of the total circumference. Therefore $s = \varphi r$. By substitution of

$\varphi$ in the above, the following relationship between linear and angular velocity is obtained:

$$\omega = \frac{v}{r} \qquad v = \omega r \qquad (9\text{--}1)$$

In terms of the calculus, a small arc $\Delta s$ subtended by the angle $\Delta\varphi$ is determined by the relationship $\Delta s = r\,\Delta\varphi$, if $r$ is constant. We have, then

$$\left[\frac{\Delta s}{\Delta t}\right]_{\Delta t \to 0} = \frac{ds}{dt} = r\,\frac{d\varphi}{dt} \qquad (9\text{--}2)$$

where $ds/dt$ is the linear velocity and $d\varphi/dt$ is the angular velocity.

**Angular-velocity Vector.** The rotation of a surface, a volume, a system of points, or a frame of reference can be represented by a vector. The vector is in the axis of rotation, perpendicular to the plane of rotation.

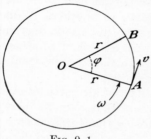

FIG. 9–1.

The convention has been adopted that the vector should point in the direction of advance of a screw being turned in the same direction of rotation. Thus a vector representing the rotation of the hands of a clock would point into the clock from the face because a screw turned with the hands would advance toward the back of the clock. The length of the vector is proportional to the angular velocity. The minute hand of the clock has an angular velocity of $2\pi$ rad per hr or $\pi/1800 = 1.745 \times 10^{-3}$ rad per sec. Taking a centimeter of length as representing $10^{-3}$ rad per sec, one would draw a vector 1.745 cm long pointing inward from the front of the clock to represent this angular velocity.

**Components at a Point on the Earth.** The earth rotates, when viewed from above the Northern Hemisphere, in a counterclockwise manner. At the North Pole the angular-velocity vector would point outward along the axis of rotation and at the South Pole it would point inward. Note that when viewed from over the Southern Hemisphere the earth rotates in the same direction as the hands of a clock. The two identical vectors are indicated at the North and South Poles in Fig. 9–2. Their magnitude is $2\pi$ rad per sidereal day or $7.292 \times 10^{-5}$ rad per sec.

At any point on the earth, other than at the pole and on the equator, the rotation can be resolved into two components—a radial component and a tangential component. At the pole it is all radial and at the equator it is only tangential. For a spherical earth the radial direction is vertically upward from the surface and the tangential direction is northward. The local vertical component represents a local turning of the surface of the earth in the tangential plane or, locally speaking, in the plane of the earth's surface.   The tangential component represents a turning in the radial or vertical plane. This latter component can affect the atmosphere, which is free to move in the vertical when not in static balance with the acceleration of gravity acting in this plane.

The components at latitude $\varphi$ of the earth's rotational vector $\Omega$ are illustrated in Fig. 9–3.   The vector $\Omega$ forms the angle $\alpha$ with the radial line which forms the vertical line at latitude $\varphi$.   But $\alpha = 90 - \varphi$, as shown by the construction.   The vertical component at latitude $\varphi$ is therefore $\Omega \sin \varphi$, in accordance with the rules of elementary trigonometry.   The northward component is $\Omega \cos \varphi$ as shown in the figure.

Fig. 9–2. Vector representation of the rotation of the earth.

The vertical component of the rotation, that is, the turning of the surface at all latitudes except the equator (where $\sin \varphi = 0$), has a profound influence on atmospheric motions and has to be referred to in all computations concerning the air in motion.   It should not be confused

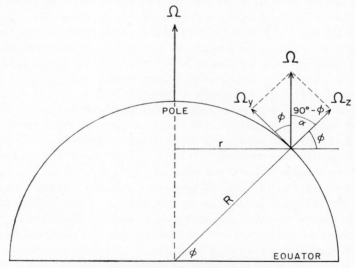

Fig. 9–3. Components of rotation at latitude $\varphi$.

with the movement of a point on the earth about the axis of rotation. All points on the earth move around the axis with the same angular velocity.   As already shown by Eq. (9–1), the linear velocity would be given by $v = \Omega r$ where $r$ is the distance from the axis of rotation.   Since $r$ decreases with increasing latitude, $v$ would be a maximum at the equator and go to zero at the poles where $r$ is zero.   If, as in Fig. 9–3, the radius of the earth is $R$ and the distance of the surface from the axis at latitude $\varphi$ is $r$, then $r = R \cos \varphi$. At any latitude, $\varphi$, the linear velocity of a point fixed on the surface of the earth, is

$$U = \Omega R \cos \varphi \qquad (9\text{-}3)$$

**Foucault's Pendulum Experiment.** In 1851 the French physicist Foucault, inventor of the gyroscope, demonstrated experimentally the presence and the magnitude of the local vertical component of the earth's rotation. He placed a freely suspended long, heavy pendulum attached inside the high dome of the Pantheon in Paris. The point of suspension was 200 ft above the floor. On the floor he heaped a ring of sand in such a way that near the end of each swing the pointed tip placed on the weighted ball of the pendulum would make a mark in the sand. The pendulum was started in free oscillation in a chosen plane. It was not long before it was noted that either the pendulum was gradually changing its plane of oscillation or the floor was rotating under it. Foucault explained to the spectators that it had to be the latter effect and, after 24 hr, demonstrated that the turning had amounted to that fraction of a complete circle equal to the sine of the latitude of Paris, or $2\pi \sin \varphi$ rad.

Foucault pendulums have been set up in many places throughout the world and today the student may see them in operation at the Museum of Science and Industry in Chicago, the Franklin Institute in Philadelphia, in the United Nations building in New York, and at exhibits in London, Paris, and a number of other cities, college campuses, etc.

**Centripetal Force.** According to Newton's first law of motion, a body in motion will continue in the same direction in a straight line and with the same speed unless acted upon by some external force. This means that, in order for a body to move in a curved path, some force must be continually applied. The force restraining bodies to move in a curved path is called the *centripetal force*, and it is always directed toward the center of rotation. When a rock is whirled around on a string, the centripetal force is afforded by the tension of the string. In the game of "crack-the-whip," the end man goes off on a straight line when the centripetal force required to keep him moving in a circle can no longer be maintained.

The centripetal force sometimes is regarded in the reverse sense as a *centrifugal force*. This is not exact, however, since the force applied in curved motion is inward. When one is standing fixed on a rotating platform one has the definite impression of an outward-acting centrifugal force. Actually, this feeling comes from the action of the body in its tendency toward motion in a straight path. On the rotating surface of the earth, where it is convenient to refer motions and forces to the rotating system rather than fixed stars, the apparent centrifugal force becomes quite real.    Meteorologists and others in the geophysical sciences often forego formalities and refer to it directly as a centrifugal force.

It is easiest to derive the expression for centripetal force by graphical means.    Consider a particle moving at constant speed through the arc $PQ$ about a center $O$ in Fig. 9–4.    At $P$ it has the velocity $v$ and at $Q$ the velocity $v'$.    The distance from $P$ to $Q$ is $\Delta s = \bar{v}\,\Delta t$, where $\bar{v}$ is the average velocity between $P$ and $Q$.    In the diagram to the right, the difference of the two velocity vectors $v$ and $v'$ shows a component of velocity inward which has been added due to the average acceleration $\bar{a}$ during the time $\Delta t$ required for the motion from $P$ to $Q$.    Since $v$ and $v'$ are tangential they are therefore perpendicular to $OP$ and $OQ$, respectively.    Consequently, the small vector triangle is similar to the triangle $OPQ$, consisting of the chord $PQ$ and the two radii.

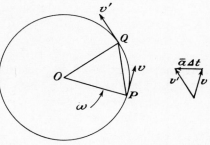

Fig. 9–4.

Now, as $\Delta t$ approaches zero, the chord approaches the arc and we may consider $\bar{v}\,\Delta t$ as the length of the chord and $\bar{v} = v$, $\bar{a} = a$.    Then, forming the ratios of the similar triangles, we have

$$\frac{a\,\Delta t}{v\,\Delta t} = \frac{v}{r}$$

$$a = \frac{v^2}{r} \qquad (9\text{–}4)$$

The vector $\bar{a}\,\Delta t$ shows the direction of the acceleration, and although it is perpendicular to the chord $PQ$, its direction approaches that of $OP$ as a limit as $\Delta t$ approaches zero.    Therefore, the instantaneous acceleration $a$ is directed toward the center.

According to Newton's second law of motion, the acceleration is related to the force that is acting by the equation

$$F = ma$$

where $m$ is the mass of the body accelerated.    The centripetal force is therefore given by

$$F = \frac{mv^2}{r} \qquad (9\text{–}5)$$

Ordinarily in meteorology the forces on a unit mass (equal to the acceleration) are considered.

**Conservation of Angular Momentum.**   Consider a particle rotating around an axis at radius $r$ with velocity $v$.   In order to decrease the radius of rotation, it is necessary to perform work against the centrifugal action and increase the centripetal force.   The work done on the particle would be $-F\ dr$, the negative sign indicating that $r$ is decreasing and $F$ denoting the centripetal force.[1]   We know from elementary physics that the work done on a body is equal to the gain of kinetic energy of the body and that the kinetic energy is $E = \frac{1}{2}mv^2$.   We have, then, the relationship

$$dE = -F\ dr$$

$$d\left(\frac{mv^2}{2}\right) = -mv^2\frac{dr}{r}$$

But the derivative of $E$ (inside the parenthesis) is $mv$, and dividing through by $m$, we have

$$v\ dv = -v^2\frac{dr}{r}$$

which becomes, upon multiplying both sides by $r/v$ and equating to zero,

$$r\ dv + v\ dr = 0 \qquad\qquad (9\text{–}6)$$

Upon integrating, we obtain

$$vr = \text{const} = \omega r^2 \qquad\qquad (9\text{–}7)$$

or

$$mvr = k = m\omega r^2$$

$mvr$ is by definition the *angular momentum* of the body.

The equation above expresses the principle of conservation of angular momentum.[2]   It means that, as the distance from the center of rotation to the particle becomes smaller, the particle must increase its linear and angular velocity.   This applies provided that there are no external torques on the particle, such as friction forces, etc.   The principle can be illustrated by spinning a weight on the end of a string around your finger, then allowing the string to wrap around the finger so as to decrease the radius of rotation.   A pronounced increase in the speed of rotation will be noted.

This principle has an important application in the atmosphere, which, when at rest with respect to the earth, is rotating with the earth.   A dis-

---

[1] The student should recall the fundamental principle of physics which defines work as the product of the force times the distance the body moves in the direction of the force.

[2] Another derivation of the equation, based on the moment of inertia of the particle $I = mr^2$, might be suggested.   $I$ has properties for rotational motion similar to those of mass in linear motion.   By analogy, since the conservation of linear momentum is stated by $mv = \text{const}$, the conservation of angular momentum would be expressed by $I\omega = \text{const}$, or $m\omega r^2 = \text{const}$.

placement of air particles poleward brings them nearer the axis of rotation and results in an increase of their angular velocity. This produces an apparent acceleration toward the east.

It will be noted from the derivation of the equation for the conservation of the angular momentum that to decrease the radius of curvature requires work. Over the earth, work must be performed on the air particles to move them poleward, and the particles must perform work against the centripetal force in going equatorward. This characteristic of the conservation of angular momentum does not exist in the conservation of linear momentum ($mv =$ const), since the latter involves no change in kinetic energy.

**Apparent and True Gravity.** We wish to investigate the motion of a particle on a rotating earth where we shall assume that the only real force acting is the attraction of gravity. On the rotating earth, however, the gravitational acceleration that we usually measure and use for our calculations includes also the centrifugal effects of the rotation, and as such, is known as the "apparent" gravity. The centrifugal effects are of great importance, e.g., the flattening of the earth at the poles results from them.

The inverse-square law of attraction between two bodies should be well known to students of elementary physics. Between two bodies there is a force of attraction proportional to the product of the masses and inversely proportional to the squares of their distances apart, and independent of the nature of the bodies. This law of attraction or gravitation may be stated in the formula

$$F = G \frac{mm'}{r^2}$$

where $G$ is called the *constant of gravitation*. Newton demonstrated that a sphere that is either homogeneous or may be regarded as made up of concentric shells, each of which is homogeneous, will attract as if the mass of the sphere were concentrated at its center. A particle of mass 1 g on the surface of the earth would be attracted toward the center of the earth by the force, which we know is about 980 dynes. Since this is the force acting on a unit mass, it is termed the *acceleration due to true gravity*. The earth being an imperfect sphere does not attract exactly toward its center but very nearly so.

The effects of rotation modify this true gravity considerably. Let us consider the earth as represented in Fig. 9–5. A particle at the point $P$ on the surface is subjected to a centrifugal action indicated by the vector $C$, acting outward from the axis of rotation. The true force of gravity is represented by the vector $T$. The resultant force is the vector $A$, which is the *apparent gravitational attraction*. Note that in the figure the earth is not represented as a perfect sphere and that the vector $A$ is perpendicular to the surface at $P$. The earth has adjusted its shape in such a way that there is no net force along the surface; the southward component of the centrifugal vector $C$ is exactly balanced by the northward component of the true gravity $T$. In the figure, the magnitude of the vector $C$ is exaggerated in comparison with $T$, thus making the earth appear less spherical than is actually the case. The exaggeration is for purposes of clarity in the diagrammatic representation.

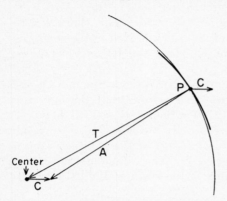

FIG. 9–5. Vectorial representation of the true force of gravity $T$ directed toward the center of the earth; the apparent gravitational attraction $A$, which is perpendicular to the surface of the earth; and the centrifugal component $C$.

A plumb line at $P$ would point in the direction of the vector $A$. The apparent gravity is the actually measured value of the acceleration of gravity at any point on the earth. The vertical component of the centrifugal action $C$ varies with latitude, being zero at the poles and a maximum at the equator. The true attraction, however, increases toward the poles because of the decreasing distance from the center of the flattened earth. The resulting apparent attraction is greatest at the poles because of both the nearness to the center and the absence of a vertical centrifugal action. At sea level at lat 45° the acceleration of gravity is taken as 980.616. From this value it varies with latitude $\varphi$ according to the formula

$$g_\varphi = 980.616(1 - 0.0026373 \cos 2\varphi + 0.0000059 \cos^2 2\varphi)$$

Note that for $\varphi = 45°$, $\cos 2\varphi = 0$. The decrease with height is small through the altitude intervals within the atmosphere. A formula for this variation, given in the Smithsonian Meteorological Tables, Sixth Edition (1951), is as follows:

$$g = g_\varphi - (3.085462 \times 10^{-4} + 2.27 \times 10^{-7} \cos 2\varphi)Z$$
$$+ (7.254 \times 10^{-11} + 1.0 \times 10^{-13} \cos 2\varphi)Z^2$$
$$- (1.517 \times 10^{-17} + 6 \times 10^{-20} \cos 2\varphi)Z^3$$

where $Z$ is the height in meters. At 10 km ($Z = 10^4$ m), the correction for altitude to be applied to $g_\varphi$ would be about 3 cm sec$^{-2}$.

**Motions in Accelerating Coordinate Systems.** In considering motions in the atmosphere, it is desirable to use a system of coordinates that is fixed on the surface of the earth, such as the coordinates of latitude and longitude or, more simply, north-south and east-west coordinates measured from any convenient point of origin on the earth. Since the earth is rotating, such a system of coordinates is also rotating. In applying Newton's laws of motion to rotation as in Eq. (9–4), we note that at any point not at the center of rotation there must be a centripetal acceleration acting. So also, in terms of Newtonian mechanics, any system of coordinates that is fixed on a rotating surface is an *accelerating* system of coordinates.

Before examining the rotating case, it may be helpful for an understanding of the problem to consider the simplest case of an accelerating system of coordinates—cartesian axes which are accelerating in a straight line at a uniform rate without rotation. If you were an observer moving with this system, an object moving through the area would appear to you with respect to your moving system as having an acceleration equal and opposite to your own acceleration. Perhaps you have had the experience of looking out the window of a train standing in a railroad station and seeing another train alongside appear to accelerate toward your rear, only to discover that your own train is accelerating forward instead.

Another example arises when, while moving along with your accelerating coordinate system, you see an object in that system that is to all appearances stationary. Actually it must be subjected to the same acceleration that you have, but you would not be able to discern this or state it quantitatively unless you were completely aware of your own acceleration.

With this point of view in mind, let us suppose you have established a coordinate system on a turntable. When the turntable is rotating, all objects fixed upon it would be subjected to a centripetal acceleration. Yet in your system no acceleration would be discernible. If you should place a ball free to roll on the turntable without friction, it would have an apparent acceleration outward and backward. If the platform is rotating in a counterclockwise direction, as seen from above, the ball would inscribe a path with respect to the turntable in which it would be continuously accelerated in an outward spiral to the right. Yet, in terms of a fixed coordinate system, the ball would move in a straight line; it has moved according to Newton's first law.

The motion in fixed coordinates is illustrated in Fig. 9–6a. The straight dashed line represents the path of the ball in fixed coordinates starting from 0. Each heavy dot represents the position at each 1-sec interval. Meanwhile the rotating coordinate system (the turntable) makes one complete revolution in 6 sec, as represented on the circle in the diagram. To simplify the picture, the $x$ axis is tangential and the $y$ axis is radial. In Fig. 9–6b the coordinates of the ball with respect to the

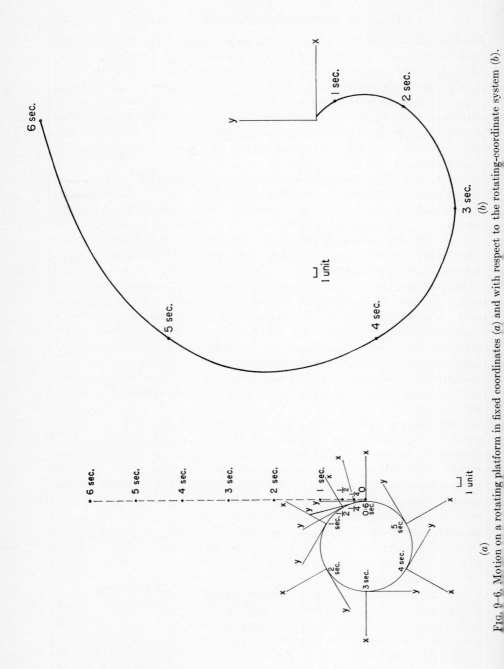

Fig. 9–6. Motion on a rotating platform in fixed coordinates (a) and with respect to the rotating-coordinate system (b).

rotating $x$ and $y$ axes are plotted, showing the apparent accelerating outward spiral to the right. The $x$ and $y$ coordinates measured from the moving origin are here plotted for the ball under the assumption that the axes are fixed. This is how it would appear on the turntable to an observer unaware of any fixed reference system and this is the actual path the ball would inscribe on the turntable, although in fixed space it would be traveling in a straight line at constant speed. The acceleration noticeable from the plot by virtue of the increasing separation of the points taken at one-second intervals is an *apparent* acceleration which appears because the coordinate system is accelerating, and it is known that the centripetal acceleration is acting. Figure 9–6 can, in fact, be used as a form of graphical demonstration that rotational motion is accelerated motion.

A quick demonstration of the relative path can be obtained by placing a cardboard disk on a phonograph turntable and, while it is turning, rapidly drawing a pencil line on the cardboard from near the center straight toward some fixed object, such as a corner of the machine. It would be most like the ball case just described if the pencil were started from a place where it would be going initially in a tangential rather than a radial direction.

The term *apparent* in dealing with an acceleration or force of this kind should not be taken lightly because in terms of the rotating surface it can be very real. For example, one might mount a toy railroad with the track running straight along a radial line upon the turntable. If the train is sent along the track while the platform is rotating counterclockwise, an added force would be exerted by the train on the right-hand rail. If the rotation were in a clockwise sense the force would be exerted on the left-hand rail. This is theoretically true for trains traveling over the surface of the earth.

**Inertial, Noninertial Forces.** A better way to denote the apparent forces described above is to call them noninertial forces. We start by defining an inertial force as one which, in accordance with Newton's second law, is equal to the rate of change with time of the momentum, or

$$F = \frac{d}{dt}(mv) = ma$$

the last equality being obtained by considering $m$ as constant and letting $dv/dt = a$, the acceleration. In the case of the ball on the rotating platform there was no change in momentum and therefore no inertial force. In terms of the rotating system, an acceleration and therefore a force appeared which was noninertial. In the case of the train, there was an inertial force driving the train along the track and a noninertial sidewise force.

Noninertial forces or accelerations in terms of rotating coordinate systems of the kind described above are called *coriolis forces* or *accelerations* after G. G. Coriolis, the French mathematical physicist who in 1844 first demonstrated quantitatively these effects. Many physicists go through their careers with only a very slight acquaintance with them, but to the meteorologist and the oceanographer the coriolis force or acceleration acting on the winds and ocean currents is just as important as the inertial forces. It is important to note that this type of acceleration occurs on a particle or mass only when it is in motion relative to the rotating axes.

**Quantitative Determination in a Rotating Plane.** We now wish to obtain an expression for the coriolis acceleration of the ball on the rotating turntable. In order to conform with a later application to the spherical earth, a coordinate system different from that of Fig. 9–6 will be used. As illustrated in Fig. 9–7, the $y$ axis points radially inward and the $x$ axis is tangential, positive in the direction of the counterclockwise rotation. Initially, the radial component $r$, positive outward from the center in a sense opposite to that of $y$, will be used. The velocity in the $x$ direction will be designated as $u$ and in the $y$ direction as $v_p$, where the subscript refers to a plane as contrasted with a sphere, to be treated later. To simplify the derivation, the relative motion will be considered separately in its two components. We will treat first the acceleration acting on $v_p$.

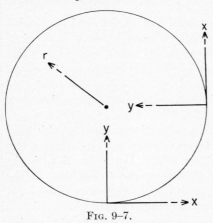

Fig. 9–7.

Since there is no inertial force acting, the absolute momentum will remain constant and this applies also to the absolute angular momentum. As the ball starts out from its initial position at a distance $r_0$ from the center, it has the angular momentum of a fixed point at $r_0$ which is $\Omega r_0{}^2$. After it has moved radially to a point at the greater distance $r$ from the center, it has developed an angular velocity $\omega$ relative to the turntable, involving at $r$ a linear velocity $u$, so its total angular velocity is $\Omega + \omega$. With the conservation of the absolute angular momentum, as expressed in Eq. (9–7), we have

$$\Omega r_0{}^2 = (\Omega + \omega)r^2 = \left(\Omega + \frac{u}{r}\right)r^2 = \Omega r^2 + ur \qquad (9\text{--}8)$$

$$u = \frac{\Omega r_0{}^2}{r} - \Omega r \qquad (9\text{--}9)$$

We wish to obtain the acceleration to the right or left of the radial direction, therefore in the tangential or $x$ direction. This acceleration is

$$\frac{du}{dt} = -\frac{\Omega r_0{}^2}{r^2}\frac{dr}{dt} - \Omega\frac{dr}{dt} \tag{9-10}$$

$$= -\left(\Omega + \frac{u}{r}\right)\frac{dr}{dt} - \Omega\frac{dr}{dt} \tag{9-11}$$

the part in the parentheses being substituted from Eq. (9–8). Combining terms and substituting $\omega$ for $u/r$, we obtain

$$\frac{du}{dt} = -2\Omega\frac{dr}{dt} - \omega\frac{dr}{dt} \tag{9-12}$$

Here $dr/dt$ is the radial component of velocity, positive outward from the center. In terms of the opposite $v_p$ the acceleration becomes

$$\frac{du}{dt} = 2\Omega v_p + \omega v_p \tag{9-13}$$

The first term on the right is defined as the coriolis acceleration. The second term involves $\omega$, which is the *relative* angular velocity with respect to the platform and which at any given instant would be in the $x$ component. The term can be considered as acting totally on the $x$ component of the relative motion.

Equation (9–13) shows that if $v_p$ is positive, that is, if the ball is moving inward, the acceleration is in the positive $x$ direction, or toward the right. If the ball is moving outward, $v_p$ is negative and the coriolis acceleration is in the negative $x$ direction, also accelerating the ball toward the right. If the rotation were clockwise, $x$ could be made positive in the opposite tangential direction and the acceleration would be toward the left.

The nature of the coriolis acceleration, at least in the $y$ component of relative motion, is to accelerate the object toward the right over a counterclockwise rotating surface and toward the left if the rotation is clockwise, and in both cases, for a given rotation speed, with a magnitude proportional to the relative speed of the object. We will next show that this is also true of the $x$ component of the relative motion.

In arriving at the acceleration acting on the radial component of velocity we utilized the effect of the conservation of absolute angular momentum to obtain an expression for a tangential-velocity component which would develop therefrom. We then took the derivative of this generated tangential velocity to obtain the acceleration. A somewhat different approach will be taken in considering the acceleration acting on the tangential or $x$ component of the velocity. The tangential motion may be considered as taking place instantaneously or over a very short period of time in the arc of a circle about the center of rotation. To an observer on the platform the ball will have an acceleration equal and opposite to his own centripetal acceleration plus an acceleration due to the angular velocity of the ball itself around the center of rotation measured with respect to the turntable. The ball has the velocity $U$ of the turntable plus its velocity $u$ with respect to the rotating system. An apparent *centrifugal* acceleration outward in the direction of increasing $r$ is given by

$$a_r = \frac{(U + u)^2}{r} \tag{9-14}$$

which, expanded, becomes

$$a_r = \frac{U^2}{r} + \frac{2Uu}{r} + \frac{u^2}{r} \tag{9-15}$$

But $U/r$ is $\Omega$ and $u/r$ is $\omega$ which may be substituted to give

$$a_r = \Omega^2 r + 2\Omega u + \omega^2 r \tag{9-16}$$

The second term on the right is the coriolis acceleration. The first term is the apparent opposing force of the centripetal acceleration of a mass point fixed on the turntable at distance $r$ from the center. It is balanced by the centripetal acceleration which holds it there. Therefore it has no effect in accelerating or deviating an object moving relative to the turntable, and it does not enter into our consideration of the non-inertial accelerations. The third term represents the apparent outward acceleration equivalent to the centripetal acceleration of the body due to its relative rotation around the turntable at distance $r$ from the center. It is equivalent to the centripetal acceleration that would be required if the platform were stationary and the ball were constrained to move around the center with angular velocity $\omega$ at distance $r$.

Considering our $y$ axis pointing inward and the velocity component $v_p = -dr/dt$, and discarding the first term in Eq. (9–16), we have for the relative acceleration

$$\frac{dv_p}{dt} = -2\Omega u - \frac{u^2}{r} \tag{9-17}$$

In the example in Fig. 9–6*b* the tangential component of the relative velocity is always clockwise, hence negative. Correspondingly, in our present notation $u$ would be negative, so $dv_p/dt$ is positive, indicating an inward acceleration which is to the right of the path of motion. If $u$ were in the positive direction, the acceleration would be negative (outward) and also to the right. By suitable conventions for signs in clockwise rotation, the acceleration will be found to be toward the left in that case.

The general conclusion we can draw from this analysis is that on a plane surface rotating counterclockwise a moving object will be accelerated toward the right.   If the rotation is clockwise, the acceleration is toward the left.   The magnitude of the acceleration is determined by the relative speed of the object at any given rotation speed (angular velocity).

**Coriolis Acceleration on the Spherical Earth.**   The derivation of the coriolis acceleration in cartesian coordinates on a rotating sphere can be accomplished by the same methods used for the rotating plane.   On the earth the $x$ and $y$ axes will be taken in a plane tangential to the spherical surface.   We can take into account the curvature of the earth by taking a new tangential plane for every point in question so that we may have as many as we like.   The $y$ axis is chosen so as to point toward the North Pole and the $x$ axis is taken as positive toward the east, in the sense of the earth's rotation.   A third or $z$ axis, positive upward, will be considered.

The $y$ component is not the same as that in the platform, not being radial now except at the pole itself.   The radial distance $r$ is not measured from the North Pole but from the axis of rotation and, as shown on page 196, is given as $r = R \cos \varphi$, where $R$ is the radius of the earth and $\varphi$ is the latitude.   We take the derivative of this $r$ to substitute for $dr/dt$ in the platform equation (9–12), which then gives the equation for the eastward acceleration on a rotating spherical earth as follows:

$$\frac{du}{dt} = (2\Omega + \omega) R \sin \varphi \frac{d\varphi}{dt} \qquad (9\text{–}18)$$

But by Eq. (9–2) we note that $R \, d\varphi/dt$ would be the linear velocity on a meridian circle, or $dy/dt = v$.   The acceleration then may be written:

$$\frac{du}{dt} = 2\Omega v \sin \varphi + \omega v \sin \varphi \qquad (9\text{–}19)$$

It is interesting to note that, as shown in Fig. 9–3, $\Omega \sin \varphi$ is the local vertical component of the earth's rotation at latitude $\varphi$.   The first term on the right therefore is the velocity multiplied by twice the local vertical component of the rotation.   It is defined as the coriolis acceleration. More will be said about the last term in a subsequent paragraph.   At the pole, where $\sin \varphi = 1$, Eq. (9–19) reduces to Eq. (9–13).

In considering the effects on motions in the $x$ direction, we recognize that the apparent radial acceleration of Eq. (9–17) has a component toward the equator, that is, in the negative $y$ direction.   It also has a vertical or $z$ component, to be treated in a subsequent paragraph.   Figure 9–8 illustrates these components.   It is seen from the construction of the small right triangle that $-a_y = a_r \sin \varphi$.

Applying this to Eq. (9–17), we obtain

$$-a_y = -\frac{dv}{dt} = a_r \sin \varphi = -\frac{dv_p}{dt} \sin \varphi = 2\Omega u \sin \varphi + \frac{u^2}{r} \sin \varphi$$

$$a_y = \frac{dv}{dt} = -2\Omega u \sin \varphi - \frac{u^2}{r} \sin \varphi \qquad (9\text{–}20)$$

Here again the first term on the right, defined as the coriolis acceleration, consists of the velocity multiplied by twice the local vertical component of rotation.

For the vertical acceleration we have, as seen in Fig. 9–8,

$$a_z = \frac{dw}{dt} = a_r \cos \varphi = 2\Omega u \cos \varphi + \frac{u^2}{r} \cos \varphi \qquad (9\text{–}21)$$

This is an acceleration in the $x$, $z$ plane and is due to the northward component of the earth's rotation as described on page 196. The coriolis acceleration here is given by the $u$ component of the velocity multiplied by twice the local northward component of the rotation. Note that it can operate only on the $u$ component of velocity.

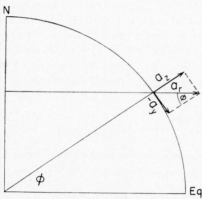

FIG. 9–8. Accelerations at latitude $\varphi$.

It is evident that the spherical case is the same as that of the plane except that the local rather than the total rotation is used. The acceleration on a particle is that which it would have if it were moving on a plane rotating at the speed $\Omega \sin \varphi$ at a given latitude $\varphi$. For example at lat 30° the acceleration would be that corresponding to a plane rotating at half the speed of the earth.

When we compare, in each of the Eqs. (9–13), (9–17), (9–19), and (9–20), the last term with the coriolis term, we find that in most cases it can be neglected. In Eq. (9–19) the relation of the first term to the second is

$$\frac{2\Omega v \sin \varphi}{v\omega \sin \varphi} = \frac{2\Omega}{\omega} = \frac{2U}{u}$$

the last ratio being obtained by substituting $U/r$ for $\Omega$ and $u/r$ for $\omega$. In Eq. (9–20) the ratio is

$$\frac{2\Omega u \sin \varphi}{\omega^2 r \sin \varphi} = \frac{2\Omega \omega r}{\omega^2 r} = \frac{2\Omega}{\omega} = \frac{2U}{u}$$

In Eq. (9–3) the linear velocity of a fixed point on the earth was found to be $U = \Omega R \cos \varphi$ where $R$ is the radius of the earth, approximately 4000 miles. If we take an extreme case of relative wind $u$ of 100 mph, we find that the ratio of $2U/u$ is 21 at the equator, 18 at 30°, 10 at 60°, and 4.6 at 80°. Therefore, except very near the poles, we are justified in neglecting the second term in meteorological applications. In the polar regions one would not use this type of cartesian-coordinate system anyway. With more nearly normal winds in middle latitudes, such as 10 mph at 45°, the ratio is about 150 to 1. Thus we can conclude that only the first term in Eqs. (9–19) and (9–20) is needed to represent the noninertial acceleration.

Considering force per unit mass, which is the same as the acceleration, we have the noninertial force expressed as the coriolis force in the components:

$$F'_x = 2\Omega v \sin \varphi \qquad (9\text{–}22a)$$
$$F'_y = -2\Omega u \sin \varphi \qquad (9\text{–}22b)$$
$$F'_z = 2\Omega u \cos \varphi \qquad (9\text{–}22c)$$

The student who has obtained a thorough grasp of the significance of the coriolis force or acceleration has overcome one of the worst hurdles in the study of meteorology. As soon as the air is put into motion this force plays its part in governing the path the air follows and in balancing the other forces. From the relationships that have been derived, it is clear that in the Northern Hemisphere a moving particle is accelerated to the right and in the Southern Hemisphere to the left. In the case of the Southern Hemisphere one can either take $\Omega$ as negative or reverse the coordinates.

**Pressure Gradient.** As soon as systematic weather charting was practiced, an expected relationship between the winds and the horizontal distribution of pressure was noted. The flow of the air was found to be associated with a horizontal pressure difference somewhat as the flow of fluid through a pipe is governed by a pressure difference between the ends of the pipe. It was at once evident, however, that in the atmosphere some extremely important modifications or complications are involved which ordinarily do not enter into laboratory or engineering flow problems.

The pressure effect in wind flow, if comparable to ordinary fluid flow in the laboratory, would be such that the air would move from high to low pressure by the most direct route. This direct path from high to low pressure is the one along which the pressure is changing most rapidly and is called the *pressure gradient*. It is customarily measured in the direction of *decreasing* pressure.

Thus it is seen that the gradient has a direction as well as a magnitude; in other words, it is a vector. This can be illustrated in terms of pressure

lines on a map, as in Fig. 9–9. The lines connect points having the
same pressure at a given level (sea level in this case) and are con-

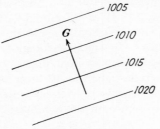

FIG. 9–9. Pressure gradient.

structed for intervals of 5 mb. Such lines
are called *isobars*. It is obvious that the
pressure is decreasing with distance most
rapidly along the arrow marked $G$, and it is
to be noted that the gradient $\vec{G}$ will always
be in a direction normal to (at right angles
to) the isobars.

If the horizontal pressure gradient provided the only horizontal force acting on
the air, the wind would blow directly across
the isobars in the direction of $\vec{G}$ and, for a given mass, with an acceleration proportional to the magnitude of the gradient $\vec{G}$.

In the form of a derivative, $\vec{G} = -\partial p/\partial n$, or the decrease in pressure
with unit distance measured along a line $n$, normal to the isobars. We
may express $\vec{G}$ in terms of its components along two perpendicular axes,
$x$ and $y$, to obtain $\vec{G} = \vec{G}_x + \vec{G}_y$, the sum of two vectors. The magni-
tude of $\vec{G} = -\partial p/\partial n$ is $\sqrt{(\partial p/\partial x)^2 + (\partial p/\partial y)^2}$ as indicated in Fig. 9–10.

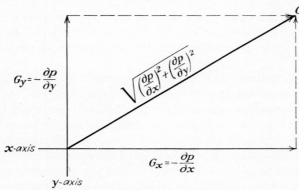

FIG. 9–10. Components of the gradient.

To indicate how the pressure gradient exerts a force, we may consider
a small rectangular block of the atmosphere having the dimensions $\delta x$,
$\delta y$, and $\delta z$ as in Fig. 9–11. The pressure acting over the area of the left
end may be considered as producing a force $F_1$ and over the right end $F_2$.
If $F_1 > F_2$, there will be a net force toward the right along the $x$ axis equal
to the difference between the forces at the two ends, or $F_1 - F_2$. But

since pressure is force per unit area, $F_1 = p_1 \, \delta y \, \delta z$, $F_2 = p_2 \, \delta y \, \delta z$, and $F_1 - F_2 = (p_1 - p_2) \, \delta y \, \delta z$.  In terms of a gradient,

$$p_1 - p_2 = -\frac{\partial p}{\partial x} \cdot \delta x$$

The net force in the $x$ direction, therefore, is given by

$$F_1 - F_2 = -\frac{\partial p}{\partial x} \, \delta x \, \delta y \, \delta z = -\frac{\partial p}{\partial x} \, V$$

where $V$ is the volume of the block.

Again, we wish to deal with the force acting on a unit mass.  In that case the volume would be that occupied by a unit mass, the specific volume $\alpha$.  Per unit mass, the force is

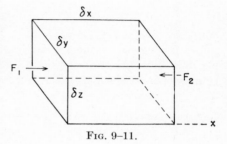

$$F_x = -\alpha \frac{\partial p}{\partial x} \qquad (9\text{–}23a)$$

Fig. 9–11.

and, similarly in the other components

$$F_y = -\alpha \frac{\partial p}{\partial y} \qquad\qquad (9\text{–}23b)$$

$$F_z = -\alpha \frac{\partial p}{\partial z} \qquad\qquad (9\text{–}23c)$$

These are the components of the pressure-gradient force which acts in the direction of decreasing pressure.  Its actual direction would be down the gradient, normal to the isobars, so that the total force per unit mass would be

$$F_n = -\alpha \frac{\partial p}{\partial n} \qquad\qquad (9\text{–}24)$$

In the cartesian coordinates which we have applied to the earth, the relations show that if the pressure increases toward the east, $F_x$ will be toward the west, etc.  In the $z$ component, $\partial p/\partial z$ is always negative, so $F_z$ is always positive, that is, upward.  As will be seen presently, this component is balanced by the acceleration of gravity in hydrostatic equilibrium.

**Balance of Forces.**   We have outlined two forces acting on a unit mass in the atmosphere—the coriolis force $F_x'$, $F_y'$, $F_z'$ and the pressure-gradient force $F_x$, $F_y$, $F_z$.   If we designate all other forces in the $x$ direction by $X$, in the $y$ direction by $Y$, and in the $z$ direction by $Z$, then all forces will be in balance when

$$F_x + F'_x + X = 0$$

or

$$\alpha \frac{\partial p}{\partial x} = 2\Omega v \sin \varphi + X \qquad (9\text{--}25a)$$

and

$$F_y + F'_y + Y = 0$$

or

$$\alpha \frac{\partial p}{\partial y} = -2\Omega u \sin \varphi + Y \qquad (9\text{--}25b)$$

and

$$F_z + F'_z + Z = 0$$

or

$$\alpha \frac{\partial p}{\partial z} = 2\Omega u \cos \varphi + Z \qquad (9\text{--}25c)$$

Let us dispose of the vertical component first.   A very strong force per unit mass, the acceleration of gravity $g$, acts downward in the vertical component.   We substitute it for $Z$ to obtain

$$\alpha \frac{\partial p}{\partial z} = 2\Omega u \cos \varphi - g \qquad (9\text{--}26)$$

Without the first term on the right, this is merely the hydrostatic equation (7–58).   If we substitute approximate values occurring in the atmosphere, we have $10^3$ cm$^3$ g$^{-1}$ for $\alpha$ and 1 dyne cm$^{-2}$ cm$^{-1}$ for $\partial p/\partial z$, giving $10^3$ dynes g$^{-1}$ for the term on the left.   The value of $g$ is approximately 980 dynes.   For $2\Omega$ we have $1.4 \times 10^{-4}$ sec$^{-1}$ and, taking $u$ to be $10^3$ cm sec$^{-1}$ and cos $\varphi$ as 1 ($\varphi = 0$), we get 0.14 cm sec$^{-2}$ for the first term on the right.   Each of the other terms is seen to outweigh it by almost 10,000 to 1.   Thus we neglect the northward component of the coriolis force and write the vertical balance in the form of the hydrostatic equation

$$dp = -\rho g \, dz$$

In the horizontal plane, two forces in addition to the coriolis and pressure-gradient forces are important, namely (1) the frictional force, including frictional stresses at the surface of the earth and internal stresses within the atmosphere, and (2) a centripetal force which arises when the air is moving in a curved path relative to the earth.   We will defer discussion of these two forces until after we have dwelt upon the situation that exists when these two forces are absent or negligible.   In this situation the air is said to have *geostrophic motion*.

**Geostrophic Balance.**   For frictionless flow in a straight path on a horizontal plane, the coriolis force and the pressure-gradient force are in balance.   This is known as the *geostrophic balance*.   It is represented by the equations

$$\alpha \frac{\partial p}{\partial x} = 2\Omega v \sin \varphi \qquad (9\text{-}27a)$$

and

$$\alpha \frac{\partial p}{\partial y} = -2\Omega u \sin \varphi \qquad (9\text{-}27b)$$

The velocities $u$ and $v$ are the components of the *geostrophic wind*. If the gradient is measured directly to determine $-\partial p/\partial n$, where $n$ is the distance measured in a direction normal to the isobars, then we may write

$$-\alpha \frac{\partial p}{\partial n} = 2\Omega c \sin \varphi \qquad (9\text{-}28)$$

where $c$ is the total geostrophic-wind velocity, having the magnitude $\sqrt{u^2 + v^2}$ and a direction always specified as 90° toward the right of the pressure gradient in the Northern Hemisphere and toward the left in the Southern Hemisphere. Solving for $c$ and designating $2\Omega \sin \varphi$ by $f$, we obtain the simple practical equation

$$c = \frac{\alpha G}{f} \qquad (9\text{-}29)$$

where $G = -\partial p/\partial n$.

Since $\Omega$ is $2\pi$ rad per sidereal day or $2\pi/86{,}164 = 7.29 \times 10^{-5}$ rad per sec, $f = 1.458 \times 10^{-4} \sin \varphi$ and has the following values at the various latitudes:

| $\varphi°$ | 0 | 10 | 20 | 30 | 40 | 50 | 60 | 70 | 80 | 90 |
|---|---|---|---|---|---|---|---|---|---|---|
| $f \times 10^4$ sec$^{-1}$ | 0 | 0.253 | 0.499 | 0.729 | 0.938 | 1.117 | 1.263 | 1.370 | 1.436 | 1.458 |

It has the value of exactly $10^{-4}$ at lat 43°18′30″.

From Eq. (9-29), it is apparent that, in magnitude, the geostrophic wind is greater the steeper the pressure gradient, the lower the latitude, and the higher the specific volume (the lower the density). The relationship is such that a given pressure gradient at a given density or specific volume of the air would be associated with a stronger wind in low latitudes than near the poles. Also, the wind would be stronger for a given gradient at high altitudes (lower density).

The direction of the steady geostrophic wind in relation to the pressure gradient and coriolis forces is shown for the two hemispheres in Fig. 9–12. One may visualize a particle in the Northern Hemisphere starting out down the pressure gradient but deflected toward the right more and more until it reaches a point where further deflection would give it a component against the gradient. This would be at the time it is moving at right angles to the gradient, i.e., parallel to the isobars, with high pressure to the right and low pressure to the left.   During the turning, the coriolis force is always acting to the right; therefore its direction is finally adjusted 90° to the right of the actual wind, or 180° from the direction of the pressure-gradient force.   In geostrophic balance, the coriolis force is an apparent force directed toward high pressure, and the pressure-gradient force is directed toward low pressure.

These considerations bear testimony to the old rule of meteorology, *Buys Ballot's law,* which states: *If, in the Northern Hemisphere, you stand with your back to the wind, the high pressure is on your right and the low pressure on your left; in the Southern Hemisphere, the high pressure is on your left and the low pressure on your right.*

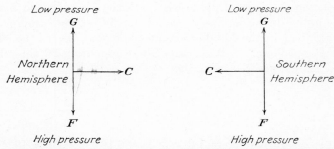

Fig. 9–12.  Geostrophic balance in the Northern and Southern Hemispheres.   *G* is pressure-gradient force, *F* is coriolis force, and *C* is geostrophic wind.

**Cyclones and Anticyclones.**   Centers or areas of low pressure are called *cyclones* and centers or areas of high pressure are called *anticyclones.*[1]   Cyclones are usually a few hundred miles in diameter and anticyclones are generally somewhat larger and often more eccentric, having in some cases elongated axes of 2000 miles or more.

The frictionless wind, in the case of geostrophic motion, flows along the isobars.   In cyclones and anticyclones the isobars are curved but the wind follows them.   Therefore the circulation around cyclones is counterclockwise in the Northern Hemisphere and clockwise in the Southern Hemisphere.   Around anticyclones, the air circulates clockwise in the Northern Hemisphere and counterclockwise in the Southern Hemisphere.

In Fig. 9–13 the appearance of cyclones and anticyclones on a surface weather map is shown.   Certain details (fronts) of the cyclones are left out.   It will be noted that the dimensions of the anticyclones are greater and the curvatures less sharp than in the cyclones.

---

[1] In newspapers and popular conversation in the United States the name *cyclone* is often applied to very intense, twisting storms of diameter less than a mile, more properly called *tornadoes.*

**Effects of Friction.**  At a given speed of motion and roughness of the surface boundary, the frictional effect on a homogeneous fluid or gas depends on its viscosity, or tendency for the molecules to retard each other by rubbing together.  Compared with molasses, air has an extremely low viscosity.  A much greater effect than the molecular viscosity in the atmosphere is produced by the *eddy viscosity*.  The air flows turbulently in eddies of various sizes and shapes which interfere with the direct progress of the motion.  Since eddies often carry air parcels vertically from their original positions, the thermal stability of the layer in question

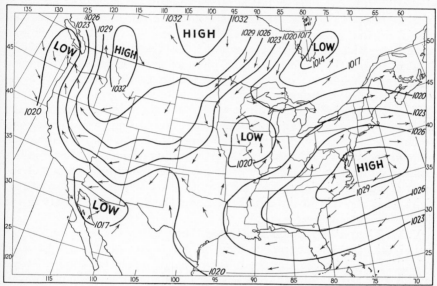

Fɪɢ. 9–13. Surface weather map (sea-level isobars) made from simultaneous observations over the United States, showing high-pressure centers (anticyclones), low-pressure centers (cyclones), and approximate wind-flow arrows.

affects the growth and dissipation of the eddies, so we find the eddy viscosity varying through a wide range of values from hour to hour, from day to day, and from place to place.  The roughness of the underlying surface, the mean wind speed, and the wind gradient or shear all affect it.

The eddy viscosity cannot be specified under any conditions except indirectly through special measurements and information not readily available.  An entire branch of meteorology is devoted to studies of it and of turbulent flow in general, including the transfer by eddies of energy and properties of the air.  At this point in our study of forces in atmospheric motion we are compelled by these circumstances to forego an attempt at an entirely logical and detailed examination of all the forces; we set aside one of them—the frictional force—for later examination.

Qualitatively, it can be seen that friction reduces the wind speed near the surface of the earth and thus reduces the magnitude of the coriolis force. The wind at the surface is not strong enough for the coriolis force to balance the pressure-gradient force, so the latter dominates and the air moves with a component across the isobars toward lower pressure. In the free atmosphere, above the first 500 to 1000 m, the friction is so slight in relation to the other forces that the flow is essentially parallel to the isobars.

The frictionally retarded surface air exerts a frictional drag on the air above it. Thus the air at 100 m above the surface shows the effects of friction, although it is not in contact with a rough surface. The *gradient-wind level*, that is, the height at which the wind is in equilibrium flow in accordance with the surface pressure gradient, is usually found at 500 to 1000 m above the surface. If the pressure gradient itself is changing rapidly with height through the first few hundred meters, there may be no level at which the surface-gradient wind is noted.

Since friction influences both the speed and direction of the wind, the wind vectors, starting out with low speeds and strong cross-isobar components in the bottom layer, increase in magnitude and take on a direction more in keeping with the isobars as the retarding effect of the lower layers gradually diminishes upward. Thus a balloon rising upward out of the layer of surface friction would curve, in the first 500 m or so, toward the right as it ascends in the Northern Hemisphere, toward the left in the Southern Hemisphere.

V. W. Ekman[1] in 1905 demonstrated theoretically the form the vectors would take in a homogeneous fluid on a rotating earth. If the wind velocities for, let us say, every 100 m of height up to the gradient-wind level are represented by vectors having a common origin, the curve connecting the end points of these vectors, called a *hodograph*, should be in the form of a logarithmic spiral, the *Ekman spiral*. The model is shown in Fig. 9–14. The end points of the vectors are projected down to the base rectangle and lines representing the vectors are drawn on the base area. The hodograph is seen to have a spiral form, resulting in the three vectors just below the top one having greater than geostrophic speeds, for the top vector represents geostrophic balance.

The idealized form of the Ekman spiral is not usually found even from very exacting pilot-balloon observations. The spiraling character of the hodograph is either nonexistent or very difficult to find as the spiral tightens near the top of the frictional layer. A serious difficulty in matching observed hodographs to Ekman's theoretical one comes from the fact that the atmosphere is seldom homogeneous, even in the hori-

---

[1] Ekman, V. W., On the Influence of the Earth's Rotation on Ocean Currents, *Arkiv. Mat. Astron. Fysik, Stockholm*, vol. 2, nos. 1–2, 1905.

zontal sense, as Ekman's theory assumes.   Density gradients require a change of the geostrophic wind with height, as an application of the hydrostatic equation for various densities will show.   These changes with height of the geostrophic wind will be examined in detail at the end of this chapter.

At anemometer levels over the oceans and flat grasslands the angle between the wind and the isobars is on the order of 20°.   Over rooftops in cities the angle is from 30 to 45°, depending on details of the exposure, and in mountainous areas, especially in the valleys, the flow only approximates the large-scale isobaric pattern.   Of course one could never apply Buys Ballot's rule in the bottom of the Grand Canyon or on a street corner in downtown New York.

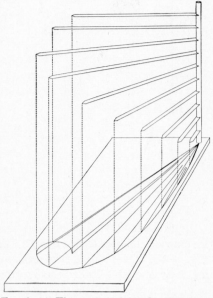

**Motion in a Curved Path.**   In terms of our earth-bound frame of reference, mass points moving in a

Fig. 9–14. Ekman spiral for the Northern Hemisphere.

curved path with respect to the earth are subjected to a local centripetal force.   For a unit mass, this force is given, as usual, as

$$F_c = \frac{c^2}{r}$$

where $c$ is the velocity, having the components $u$ and $v$ (horizontal motion only being considered) and $r$ is the radius of curvature.

In frictionless flow in a curved path the balance of forces is

$$F_n + F' \pm F_c = 0$$

or
$$-\alpha \frac{\partial p}{\partial n} + 2\Omega c \sin \varphi \pm \frac{c^2}{r} = 0 \tag{9–30}$$

The two alternative signs in the last term indicate that, with respect to the direction $n$, $F_c$ will be positive or negative depending on whether the rotation is counterclockwise or clockwise.   Since $F_c$ acts inward, it will be positive in the direction of increasing pressure in an anticyclone of the Northern Hemisphere and positive in the direction of decreasing pressure in a cyclone.   Thus in the Northern Hemisphere it will have the same sign as $\partial p/\partial n$ in an anticyclone and the opposite sign from $\partial p/\partial n$ in a cyclone.   For an anticyclone the balance is

$$-\alpha\frac{\partial p}{\partial n} + 2\Omega c \sin\varphi - \frac{c^2}{r} = 0 \tag{9-31}$$

$$\alpha\frac{\partial p}{\partial n} + \frac{c^2}{r} = (2\Omega \sin\varphi)c \tag{9-32}$$

$$c^2 - (2r\Omega \sin\varphi)c + \alpha r\frac{\partial p}{\partial n} = 0 \tag{9-33}$$

and for a cyclone

$$-\alpha\frac{\partial p}{\partial n} + 2\Omega c \sin\varphi + \frac{c^2}{r} = 0 \tag{9-34}$$

$$\alpha\frac{\partial p}{\partial n} - \frac{c^2}{r} = (2\Omega \sin\varphi)c \tag{9-35}$$

$$c^2 + (2r\Omega \sin\varphi)c - r\alpha\frac{\partial p}{\partial n} = 0 \tag{9-36}$$

Equations (9–33) and (9–36) permit balanced flow to be along the isobars in curved, frictionless motion.   The balance of the forces is shown in Fig. 9–15.   The Southern Hemisphere case is obtained either by regarding $\Omega$ as negative or by considering the south latitudes as negative.   In

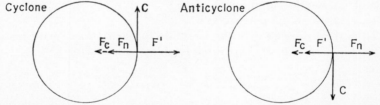

FIG. 9–15. Balance of forces in a cyclone and anticyclone of the Northern Hemisphere. $F_c$ is centripetal force, $F'$ is coriolis force, and $F_n$ is pressure-gradient force.

the Northern Hemisphere anticyclone the centripetal and coriolis forces both act inward, whereas in the cyclone they act in opposite directions. The reverse is true in the Southern Hemisphere.

For a given pressure gradient and radius of curvature in a given latitude, the expressions (9–33) and (9–36) have the form of a simple quadratic $ax^2 + bx + c = 0$, with $a = 1$, $b = 2r\Omega \sin\varphi$, and $c = r\alpha\,\partial p/\partial n$. The student may recall from high school or college algebra that the solutions of this take the form

$$x = \frac{-b \pm \sqrt{b^2 - 4ac}}{2a}$$

Solving for $c$ of our expressions, we have

$$c = r\Omega \sin \varphi \pm \sqrt{(r\Omega \sin \varphi)^2 - r\alpha \frac{\partial p}{\partial n}} \qquad (9\text{--}37)$$

for an anticyclone, and

$$c = -r\Omega \sin \varphi \pm \sqrt{(r\Omega \sin \varphi)^2 + r\alpha \frac{\partial p}{\partial n}} \qquad (9\text{--}38)$$

for a cyclone.

To determine whether the positive or the negative root is valid in each case, we introduce the requirement that when $\partial p/\partial n = 0$, $c = 0$; in other words, that there can be no motion without a pressure-gradient force. In Eq. (9–37) only the negative root and in Eq. (9–38) only the positive root will satisfy this requirement. Without this requirement, the positive root in Eq. (9–37) with $\partial p/\partial n = 0$ describes what is called *inertial motion* in which

$$c = 2r\Omega \sin \varphi \qquad (9\text{--}39)$$

This type of anticyclonic motion without a pressure gradient can be produced in laboratory models, and is of theoretical interest in the atmosphere. A mass point following this motion would inscribe a path on the surface of the earth which, if latitude changes along the path were neglected, would form a circle, called the *inertia circle*, having the radius $r$ of Eq. (9–39) or

$$r = \frac{c}{2\Omega \sin \varphi} \qquad (9\text{--}40)$$

With latitude changes during the motion, the inertial path forms an elongated loop.

In the cyclonic case, the alternative root (negative) has no physical meaning, since it would produce negative values of $c$. In deriving these equations we specified that $c$ would always have the proper direction, 90° to the right of the pressure gradient in the Northern Hemisphere, therefore always positive. In the anticyclonic case the quantity under the radical sign could become negative when $r\alpha \, \partial p/\partial n > (r\Omega \sin \varphi)^2$. When these two are equal, the radical is zero and $c$ has its maximum real value. If the radical is not to become negative, then $\partial p/\partial n$ must decrease rapidly as $r$ decreases. An anticyclone ought to obey the condition that

$$\frac{\partial p}{\partial n} \gtrless \rho r(\Omega \sin \varphi)^2 \gtrless kr \qquad (9\text{--}41)$$

the constant $k$ being appropriate when considering one latitude and one density. We find, in fact, that in anticyclones $\partial p/\partial n$ is very small near the center where $r$ is small and that high-pressure areas are characterized by a large central region with no appreciable pressure gradients and with calm winds.

Under certain conditions the wind appears to curve anticyclonically and with a fairly steep gradient so that $\partial p/\partial n > kr$. This seems to occur over small areas for short periods of time and is regarded as a dynamically unstable type of flow. Consider an example at 43° lat with air density of $10^{-3}$ g per cubic centimeter and a radius of curvature of 400 km. We have $\Omega \sin \varphi$ with a value of $0.5 \times 10^{-4}$, so

$$\rho r(\Omega \sin \varphi)^2 = 10^{-3} \times 4 \times 10^7 (0.5 \times 10^{-4})^2 = 10^{-4}$$

If $\partial p/\partial n$ is to be less than this, it must be less than $10^3/10^7$ dynes per cubic centimeter or 1 mb per 100 km. These are rare but wholly reasonable values, and it is seen that this type of dynamic instability with $\partial p/\partial n > kr$ is entirely possible in the atmosphere.

**Summary of Motions.** The principal types of balanced motion in the atmosphere for frictionless flow may now be listed.

*Geostrophic Wind.* The pressure gradient and coriolis forces are in balance and

$$c = -\frac{\alpha\, \partial p/\partial n}{2\Omega \sin \varphi} = \frac{\alpha G}{f} \tag{9-42}$$

*Gradient Wind.* The pressure gradient, coriolis forces, and centripetal forces are in balance and

$$c = r\Omega \sin \varphi - \sqrt{(r\Omega \sin \varphi)^2 - r\alpha \frac{\partial p}{\partial n}} \tag{9-43}$$

for anticyclones,

$$c = -r\Omega \sin \varphi + \sqrt{(r\Omega \sin \varphi)^2 + r\alpha \frac{\partial p}{\partial n}} \tag{9-44}$$

for cyclones.

*Inertia Motion.* The pressure-gradient force is zero and the coriolis force balances the centripetal force in the anticyclonic sense, so that

$$c = 2r\Omega \sin \varphi = rf \tag{9-45}$$

*Cyclostrophic Wind.* The pressure-gradient force balances the centripetal force and

$$c = \sqrt{r\alpha \frac{\partial p}{\partial n}} = \sqrt{r\alpha G} \tag{9-46}$$

All of the possible combinations of the three forces in frictionless flow have been defined, but only the first two—the geostrophic wind and the gradient wind—are of importance. The cyclostrophic balance has not been mentioned before. It is important near the centers of tropical cyclones (hurricanes or typhoons) in low latitudes where the centripetal force may outweigh the coriolis force by as much as 25 to 1.

The geostrophic wind is the basic wind relationship used as a starting point in a great variety of meteorological applications. The curvature effect can be added as a correction term to the geostrophic wind to obtain the gradient wind. Writing the gradient wind equation (9–30) in the form

$$\alpha G = fc \pm \frac{c^2}{r} \tag{9–47}$$

we divide through by $f$ to obtain

$$\frac{\alpha G}{f} = c \pm \frac{c^2}{fr}$$

where $c$ is the gradient wind. Then

$$c = \frac{\alpha G}{f} \pm \frac{c^2}{fr} \tag{9–48}$$

the plus sign in this last equation being for an anticyclone and the minus sign for a cyclone [note that the opposite is true in Eq. (9–43)]. The first term on the right is the geostrophic "component" of the wind. From a geostrophic-wind scale or tables, one can obtain $c = \alpha G/f$. Ordinarily the geostrophic instead of the gradient wind is substituted in the second term to arrive at the true value of the gradient wind by steps of approximation from the geostrophic wind.

Equation (9–48) shows that with the positive correction we have the anticyclonic case. This means that *for a given pressure gradient*, winds in an anticyclone are stronger than in a cyclone, and also stronger than geostrophic. In spite of this, winds are nearly always stronger in cyclones than in anticyclones because the pressure gradients are very much stronger.

**Representation on Constant-pressure Surfaces.** In meteorological practice it has been found that the more important types of computation are simplified if the motion is considered on a constant-pressure surface instead of on a horizontal or level surface. The equivalence of height contours on a constant-pressure surface to isobars on a level surface is seen qualitatively in Figs. 9–13 and 9–16. Figure 9–16 is a contour map of the 1000-mb surface for the same situation as that represented in terms of sea-level isobars in Fig. 9–13. The contours are labeled according to height in feet above sea level. Figure 9–17 shows schematically a vertical cross section through the lower atmosphere along the 40th parallel. The western edge of the map is on the left. The vertical scale is exaggerated to 10,000 times the horizontal scale in order to make

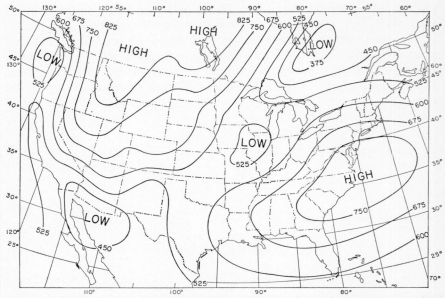

FIG. 9–16. Same map as in Fig. 9–13, represented as contours of the 1000-mb surface.

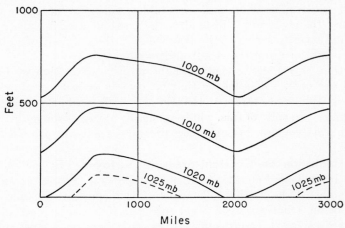

FIG. 9–17. Vertical cross section along the 40th parallel of latitude showing the slopes of the isobaric surfaces for the situation represented in Figs. 9–13 and 9–16.

the isobaric slopes noticeable.    It is evident from a comparison of the three figures that where the pressure on a level surface is low, the pressure surfaces have dipped downward, and where high pressure exists, the pressure surfaces have bulged upward.    Just as one represents relief features by contours on a map of a section of the earth's surface, so on a pressure surface, one uses contours to reveal such features as troughs, ridges, domes, and depressions (low centers). From these representations it should be clear that isobars on a level surface delineate the intersections of the corresponding pressure surfaces with that surface. Also, it can be shown that for a given rate of pressure decrease with height (therefore a given vertical spacing of the pressure surfaces) the horizontal pressure gradient will be given by the slope of the isobaric surfaces. Finally, as evidenced by the extreme vertical exaggeration necessary to reveal the slopes as in Fig. 9–17, motion on pressure surfaces differs immaterially from that on a level surface at the same height.

The transformation from horizontal pressure gradient to slope of a pressure surface and the use of the latter in the equations of motion can

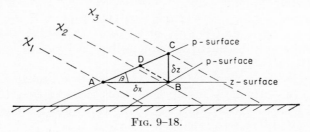

Fig. 9–18.

be considered with reference to Fig. 9–18. The pressure surfaces represented in vertical cross section slope upward in the direction of $x$. Let $\delta x$ and $\delta z$ represent, respectively, the horizontal and vertical separations of two parallel isobars with one unit of pressure difference between them, and let $\beta$ be the angle of intersection with a horizontal surface. The slope of the upper pressure surface is defined as

$$\tan \beta = \frac{\delta z}{\delta x}$$

But $\delta z$ is the change in $z$ per unit decrease in pressure and therefore is equal to $-\partial z/\partial p$ while $\delta x$, being the increment of distance per unit increase in pressure, is equal to $\partial x/\partial p$. The slope of the pressure surface then may be written

$$\left(\frac{\partial z}{\partial x}\right)_p = -\frac{\partial z/\partial p}{\partial x/\partial p} = -\frac{\partial p/\partial x}{\partial p/\partial z} \tag{9-49}$$

The differential quotients may be treated algebraically because $p$ is a continuous function of the space coordinates $x$, $y$, and $z$ (also $n$).

Under hydrostatic equilibrium,

$$-\alpha \frac{\partial p}{\partial z} = g$$

which may be substituted into Eq. (9–49) to give

$$\left(\frac{\partial z}{\partial x}\right)_p = \frac{\alpha}{g}\frac{\partial p}{\partial x} \tag{9–50}$$

We do not need to carry along the $g$ if, remembering the geodynamic height relationship of Eq. (7–71) $d\Phi = g\,dz$, we make the substitution

$$\left(\frac{\partial \Phi}{\partial x}\right)_p = \alpha\frac{\partial p}{\partial x} \tag{9–51}$$

This is especially convenient if upper-air observations are given in geodynamic heights.

Wherever the term $\alpha\,\partial p/\partial n$ or $\alpha\,\partial p/\partial x$, etc., appears in the equations of motion, $g(\partial z/\partial n)_p$ or $(\partial \Phi/\partial n)_p$ or $(\partial/\partial x)_p$, $(\partial/\partial y)_p$ of these height quantities may be substituted to express the equations of motion on a constant-pressure surface.

One simplification resulting from using constant-pressure surfaces instead of level surfaces is already apparent: the specific volume or its reciprocal, the density, has dropped out. Since $\alpha$ varies with temperature and pressure and increases rapidly with height, it is helpful to be rid of it. Now the same geostrophic-wind scale can be used for all heights or pressures at the same latitude. Getting rid of the acceleration of gravity $g$ is not so important since its variation with altitude and from place to place is relatively slight. The equations are written either in terms of $z$ or in terms of $\Phi$. One has to remember that the $g$ goes along with $z$ and not with $\Phi$.

**Other Properties on Constant-pressure Surfaces.** The transformation to a constant-pressure surface of any property of the atmosphere which is a continuous function of the space coordinates can be obtained from well-known theorems of the calculus. It can be demonstrated in simple terms by reference to Fig. 9–18. The dashed lines are isolines of any property $\chi$ which is distributed in the atmosphere. Since the pressure surface slopes, the distribution along it is made up of a horizontal component and a vertical component.

Consider the small triangle $ABC$ of Fig. 9–18. The change or gradient of $\chi$ from $A$ to $C$ on the pressure surface is to be determined. The change in the horizontal is that occurring from $A$ to $B$ in the distance $\delta x$. In the same horizontal distance $\delta x$ projected on $AC$ there is an additional change represented by the difference in value of $\chi$ between $D$ and $C$ which is the same as the difference between $B$ and $C$. So the change from $A$ to $C$ is the change from $A$ to $B$ plus the change from $B$ to $C$. In other words:

Change on $p$ surface = change on $z$ surface + change through $\delta z$

or
$$\left(\frac{\partial \chi}{\partial x}\right)_p \delta x = \left(\frac{\partial \chi}{\partial x}\right)_z \delta x + \frac{\partial \chi}{\partial z} \delta z \qquad (9\text{–}52)$$

but
$$\delta z = \delta x \tan \beta = \delta x \left(\frac{\partial z}{\partial x}\right)_p$$

which, when substituted in (9–52), results in a common factor $\delta x$ throughout, leaving

$$\left(\frac{\partial \chi}{\partial x}\right)_p = \left(\frac{\partial \chi}{\partial x}\right)_z + \frac{\partial \chi}{\partial z} \left(\frac{\partial z}{\partial x}\right)_p \qquad (9\text{–}53)$$

Stated in words, this demonstrates that the increase in value of any property $\chi$ in a given direction on a constant-pressure surface is given by the increase in that direction on a horizontal surface plus the change in the quantity with height multiplied by the slope of the pressure surface in the direction in question.  Since the slopes of pressure surfaces are slight, the last term will be small in most cases and the gradients of properties on the pressure surface will be essentially the same as on level surfaces.

It is also of interest at this point to introduce a vertical velocity in terms of pressure instead of in terms of $z$.  Vertical velocity has been expressed as $w = dz/dt$, but now we want to define a velocity of air particles downward through the pressure surfaces as $w_p = Dp/Dt$.  The capitalized $D$ is used here, in accordance with a common practice in fluid mechanics, to indicate the change that would be measured while moving along with the particle.  This distinction is necessary because pressure may also change at a fixed point, causing the height of the pressure surfaces to change.

If the pressure surfaces remain fixed, the capitalized $Dp/Dt$ is the only pressure change with time, and we may transform the differentials in our space-determined field as follows:

$$w_p = \frac{Dp}{Dt} = \frac{dz}{Dt} \frac{dp}{dz} = -\frac{g}{\alpha} w \qquad (9\text{–}54)$$

An advantage in using $w_p = Dp/Dt$ is seen when the change in thermodynamic properties of ascending air is examined.  Consider, for example, Eq. (8–22)

$$C_p \, dT - \frac{R}{m} T \frac{dp}{p} + L \, dq = 0$$

which represents the temperature change during a saturation-adiabatic expansion.  (Specific humidity $q$ is used here in place of mixing ratio $w$ in order to avoid the confusion created by also using $w$ for vertical velocity). Since this is a temperature change that would occur in ascent following along with the parcel, the derivatives should be written with a capital $D$. The time derivative is

$$\frac{DT}{Dt} = \frac{RT}{pmC_p}\frac{Dp}{Dt} - \frac{L}{C_p}\frac{Dq}{Dt}$$

but

$$\frac{Dq}{Dt} = \frac{Dq}{Dp}\frac{Dp}{Dt} \quad \text{and} \quad \frac{RT}{mp} = \alpha$$

so

$$\frac{DT}{Dt} = \frac{\alpha}{C_p}\frac{Dp}{Dt} - \frac{L}{C_p}\frac{Dq}{Dp}\frac{Dp}{Dt} = \frac{w_p}{C_p}\left(\alpha - L\frac{Dq}{Dp}\right) \tag{9-55}$$

The first term on the right is the temperature change for the dry-adiabatic process and the second term is the temperature change in the parcel due to evaporation or condensation. All of the variables are in terms of pressure, and it should be pointed out that $Dq/Dp$ can be measured directly on a thermodynamic diagram by counting the intersections of saturation mixing-ratio lines as one traces along a pseudoadiabatic line, in the case of pure parcel ascent or along the computed entrainment adiabat when mixing occurs. It can also be argued that vertical velocities obtained from aircraft flights must always be based on pressure changes. This point is trivial, however, since through a small temperature range, height changes are a direct function of the change in the logarithm of the pressure which the altimeter or rate-of-climb indicator measures.

A special feature of representation on a pressure surface is that, with allowance for inherent differences in dimensions, the isolines (isopleths) of the various properties of state of the air, such as temperature, potential temperature, specific volume, and density, will coincide. From the equation of state, it is seen that for constant $p$,

$$\frac{T}{\alpha} = \rho T = \text{const}$$

and, from Poisson's equation (7-51),

$$\frac{\theta}{T} = \text{const}$$

Thus all of these properties have a given numerical ratio to each other on a given pressure surface; their values and their gradients will vary together. A set of lines showing the distribution of one of these properties will give the distribution of the others.

**Change of the Geostrophic Wind with Height.** Hydrostatic equilibrium requires that the concentration in the vertical of a given set of isobars shall be inversely proportional to the mean temperature through the vertical height in question, in accordance with the relationship of the hydrostatic equation

$$\frac{\Delta p}{\Delta z} = -\rho_m g = -\frac{pmg}{RT_m}$$

If the atmosphere is warm, the pressure changes slowly with height; if it is cold, the pressure changes rapidly with height.

Let us consider the system of isobaric surfaces represented in vertical cross section in Fig. 9–19.    In this case it is assumed that there is either no pressure gradient at the ground or that the cross section is taken along a surface isobar or pressure contour.    The air to the right is warm, and hence the pressure decreases slowly with height.    The air on the left is cold; hence the pressure there decreases rapidly with height.    The result is that aloft there is an increasingly steep slope of the isobaric

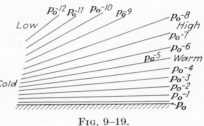

FIG. 9–19.

surfaces and increasingly strong pressure gradient from high pressure in the warm region to low pressure in the cold region.    This would result in a geostrophic-wind component directed into the page, with the high pressure and warm air on the right.    If this is considered to be a north-south cross section with north to the left, then the given temperature distribution would give an increasingly strong westerly-wind component with height.    At the surface, since the cross section is taken along an

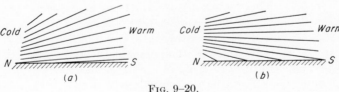

FIG. 9–20.

isobar running in a north-south direction, the geostrophic wind would be either from the north or the south.    For Southern Hemisphere conditions, all upper winds would be in the reverse sense.

The case of a west wind at the ground with cold air to the north and warm air to the south, as in the Northern Hemisphere, is illustrated in Fig. 9–20a.    In this case, the south-to-north pressure gradient, and hence the west wind, increases with height.    Figure 9–20b shows the same temperature distribution but with an east wind at the surface.    The north-to-south pressure gradient decreases with height, disappears, and finally reverses to a south-to-north gradient and a westerly wind at upper levels. With the normal temperature gradient of the Northern Hemisphere having cold air to the north and the Southern Hemisphere having cold air to the south, the great persistence of westerly components in the upper air in both hemispheres is verified. It should be noted that in the stratosphere and substratosphere levels the temperature gradients are reversed, as shown in Fig. 4–1; hence the westerlies increase to a maximum in the upper troposphere and decrease upward through the stratosphere.

One way of studying the details of the change of the wind with height is by means of the hodograph, already introduced on page 216. A hodo-

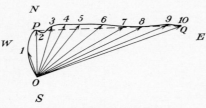

FIG. 9–21. Hodograph.

graph that might be considered as corresponding to the conditions in Fig. 9–19 is shown in Fig. 9–21. Here the wind vectors are drawn from the common origin $O$ for each 1000 ft, starting with a south-southeast wind at the surface. In this case the isobars run from south to north at the surface with the pressure decreasing toward the west. The geostrophic wind is therefore from the south and occurs at the top of the Ekman spiral, which is at about 2000 ft. At 10,000 ft the wind has turned to west-southwest and is quite strong.

The vector difference between the velocity at one level and some other level below is a vector in the general direction of the hodograph curve as shown in the dashed line from $P$ to $Q$ in Fig. 9–21 and as shown in detail in Fig. 9–22 for the 4000- and 5000-ft levels. In vector notation, $\overline{OB} - \overline{OA} = \overline{AB}$. The vector $\overline{AB}$ is called the *shear vector* because it measures the shear of the wind with height. It has a direction that is parallel to the isotherms of mean temperature of the layer, with high temperatures on the right and low temperatures on the left. Furthermore, it has a magnitude proportional to the gradient of this mean temperature. Because of this relationship to the temperature field, it is also called the *thermal-wind vector*. A vector from $O$ normal to $\overline{AB}$ and extending to $\overline{AB}$, designated in Fig. 9–22 by the vector $\overline{OC}$, represents the cross-isotherm component of the wind in the layer from 4000 to 5000 ft. This component of the wind can bring in warm air by advection if no heat

FIG. 9–22. Details of hodograph.

is added or removed from air parcels during the process. Warm-air advection is indicated in this case because it is coming from the right of the vector $\overline{AB}$. If the situation were reversed, so that $\overline{OB}$ were the 4000-ft wind and $\overline{OA}$ the 5000 ft, the shear or thermal-wind vector would be

$\overline{OA} - \overline{OB} = \overline{BA}$ which would point in the opposite direction from vector $\overline{AB}$ of the figure, so the vector $\overline{OC}$ would be coming in from the left of $\overline{AB}$ and would therefore represent cold-air advection.

A wind which changes in a clockwise direction is said to *veer* while a wind changing in a counterclockwise direction is said to *back*. These names came from old nautical terminology. In Figs. 9–21 and 9–22 the winds are veering with height. We have the rule: *Winds veering with height indicate warm-air advection; winds backing with height indicate cold air advection.* The rule is reversed in the Southern Hemisphere.

The physical-mathematical expression for the change of the geostrophic wind with height is obtained from a combined application of the geostrophic-wind equations and the hydrostatic equation. We shall begin with the geostrophic-wind equations in terms of isobaric surfaces. The geostrophic-wind equations are

$$\frac{g}{f}\left(\frac{\partial z}{\partial x}\right)_p = v \qquad (9\text{–}56a)$$

$$\frac{g}{f}\left(\frac{\partial z}{\partial y}\right)_p = -u \qquad (9\text{–}56b)$$

and the hydrostatic equation

$$\frac{\partial z}{\partial p} = -\frac{\alpha}{g}$$

We want to obtain the change of $u$ and $v$ with pressure. We have

$$\frac{\partial v}{\partial p} = \frac{g}{f}\frac{\partial}{\partial p}\left(\frac{\partial z}{\partial x}\right)_p = \frac{g}{f}\frac{\partial}{\partial x}\left(\frac{\partial z}{\partial p}\right) = \frac{g}{f}\frac{\partial}{\partial x}\left(-\frac{\alpha}{g}\right) = -\frac{1}{f}\left(\frac{\partial \alpha}{\partial x}\right)_p \quad (9\text{–}57)$$

From the equation of state, noting that $\partial\alpha/\partial x$ is on a surface of constant pressure, we have

$$\frac{\partial v}{\partial p} = -\frac{R}{fmp}\left(\frac{\partial T}{\partial x}\right)_p \qquad (9\text{–}58a)$$

Similarly for the variation of $u$ we have

$$\frac{\partial u}{\partial p} = -\frac{g}{f}\frac{\partial}{\partial y}\left(\frac{\partial z}{\partial p}\right) = \frac{1}{f}\left(\frac{\partial \alpha}{\partial y}\right)_p = \frac{R}{fmp}\left(\frac{\partial T}{\partial y}\right)_p \qquad (9\text{–}58b)$$

The reader may wonder about the interchange of derivatives represented by the second equality in Eq. (9–57), so at least a graphical demonstration is in order.

Consider two isobaric surfaces in Fig. 9–23 having one unit of pressure difference between them. The two vertical segments are taken unit distance apart in the $x$ direction. The slope of the lower isobar is $\delta z_0$ divided by the distance between the two verticals. But since this distance is 1, the slope is $\delta z_0$. Similarly the slope of the upper isobar is $\delta z$. The vertical separation of the two isobars on the right is $\Delta z_1$ and on the left the separation is $\Delta z_0$. Since there is one unit of pressure between the two isobars, $\Delta z_1/\Delta p$ is the same as $\Delta z_1$ and $\Delta z_0/\Delta p$ is equivalent to $\Delta z_0$. From the figure it is seen that

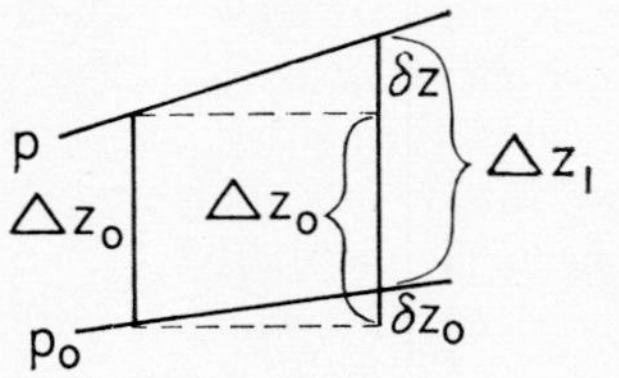

$$\Delta z_1 = \Delta z_0 + \delta z - \delta z_0$$

$$\Delta z_1 - \Delta z_0 = \delta z - \delta z_0$$

Expressed as derivatives, these equalities are

FIG. 9–23.

$$\left(\frac{\partial z}{\partial p}\right)_1 - \left(\frac{\partial z}{\partial p}\right)_0 = \left(\frac{\partial z}{\partial x}\right)_p - \left(\frac{\partial z}{\partial x}\right)_{p_0}$$

On the left is the gradient of thickness of the isobaric layer along $x$ and on the right is the change of the isobaric slope as we go from one isobar to another. The equation is equivalent to

$$\frac{\partial}{\partial x}\left(\frac{\partial z}{\partial p}\right) = \frac{\partial}{\partial p}\left(\frac{\partial z}{\partial x}\right)_p$$

Returning to Eqs. (9–57) and (9–58$b$) we note that the change in the geostrophic wind as we go upward through the isobaric surfaces is determined by the horizontal gradient of the thickness between the isobaric surfaces or, to repeat,

$$\frac{\partial v}{\partial p} = \frac{g}{f}\frac{\partial}{\partial x}\left(\frac{\partial z}{\partial p}\right) \qquad \frac{\partial u}{\partial p} = -\frac{g}{f}\frac{\partial}{\partial y}\left(\frac{\partial z}{\partial p}\right) \qquad (9\text{–}59)$$

If these two components are integrated between two pressure surfaces $p_1$ and $p_2$, the result is the thermal wind for the layer, or

$$v_T = v_2 - v_1 = \frac{g}{f}\frac{\partial}{\partial x}\int_{p_1}^{p_2}\frac{\partial z}{\partial p}\,dp = \frac{g}{f}\frac{\partial}{\partial x}\int_{z_1}^{z_2}dz = \frac{g}{f}\frac{\partial Z}{\partial x} \qquad (9\text{–}60)$$

and similarly

$$u_T = u_2 - u_1 = -\frac{g}{f}\frac{\partial Z}{\partial y} \qquad (9\text{–}61)$$

where $Z$ is the thickness between the two pressure surfaces. The vector difference of the total wind gives the true or total thermal wind

$$\vec{c_T} = \vec{c_2} - \vec{c_1} = -\frac{g}{f}\frac{\partial Z}{\partial n} \qquad (9\text{–}62)$$

where the arrows indicate that these are vector quantities and the difference is a vector difference. The direction of the thermal wind is along the thickness lines with high values to the right and $n$ is normal to these lines pointing toward lower values of $Z$, down the gradient and to the left of the thermal wind.

It is a frequent practice for meteorologists to plot isolines of thickness on upper-air charts, such as those for the thickness between the 700- and 500-mb surfaces. The magnitude of the gradient of this quantity at any point on the map is easily seen.

The change $\partial c/\partial p$ is also seen from Eq. (9–57) to depend on the gradient of specific volume along the pressure surface in question. Since, from the equation of state, $\alpha$ is proportional to $T/p$, it can be represented on a constant-pressure surface simply by $T$. From isotherms plotted on maps of isobaric surfaces, the temperature gradient is apparent.

A study of the relationships reveals that the contours and isotherms must coincide in equilibrium geostrophic flow in the upper atmosphere. A common situation seen on synoptic charts constructed for the surface and various levels is one in which the low-level winds, and therefore the contours, cross the isotherms at a considerable angle, but from the middle troposphere upward to the tropopause the contours and isotherms coincide. In storm conditions, nonequilibrium distributions can exist through a considerable portion of the atmosphere, but the tendency toward in-phase isotherm and contour patterns is always present.

# CHAPTER 10

## CHARACTERISTICS OF FLUID FLOW
## APPLIED TO THE ATMOSPHERE

In the preceding chapter the air flow which would result from a balance of forces was discussed. The tendency for a mutual adjustment of these forces is so marked in the atmosphere that it is difficult to observe or measure any broad-scale imbalance. Yet it is recognized that nothing but constant and steady motion would ever occur in a completely balanced atmosphere; disturbed weather would be unheard of, no new flows would be initiated, and what is more serious, no mechanism would develop for accomplishing the general circulation of the atmosphere which is necessary to prevent the latitudinal and geographic heat differences from getting out of hand. An imbalance, however small and difficult it may be to detect, must exist either continuously or sporadically. Predicting whether nonequilibrium conditions will or will not develop is one of the chief problems of weather forecasting.

Characteristics of fluid flow which are well known from classical hydrodynamics can be applied to the atmosphere to help in solving these problems. It is found that in the accelerating coordinates of the earth the development of some important systems of relative motion (wind systems) can be accounted for in this way; this would never result from a consideration of balanced flow.

**Vorticity.** When the equation representing the relation between linear velocity and angular velocity $c = \omega r$ is differentiated with respect to $r$, the result is

$$\frac{\partial c}{\partial r} = \omega$$

For solid rotation, $\omega$ at any given instant is constant throughout and the linear speed must increase at a fixed rate $\omega$ with radial distance. Fluids, since they are not constrained to rotate as solids, may turn at varying speeds both in time and in space, and not all of the particles of the fluid may have the same center of rotation or the same radius of curvature.

To obtain a quantitative understanding of these fluid motions, we first consider fluid elements which are small enough so that the change of $\omega$ in the infinitesimal distances used is zero. It is convenient to express the motion in the cartesian coordinates $x$ and $y$. The rotation is considered for two infinitesimal lines of fluid particles represented initially in $dx$ and $dy$ on the $x$ and $y$ axes as in Fig. 10–1. The $v$ component represents the linear velocity of the rotation at the $x$ axis and the $u$ component at the $y$ axis. The angular velocity does not vary in the distance $dx$ or $dy$ but it may be different on the two axes. If rotation is considered positive in a counterclockwise sense,

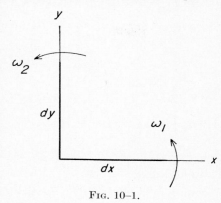

FIG. 10–1.

$$v = \omega_1 x \qquad -u = \omega_2 y$$
$$\frac{\partial v}{\partial x} = \omega_1 \qquad -\frac{\partial u}{\partial y} = \omega_2$$

The average of the two angular velocities is

$$\frac{1}{2}(\omega_1 + \omega_2) = \frac{1}{2}\left(\frac{\partial v}{\partial x} - \frac{\partial u}{\partial y}\right) \qquad (10\text{–}1)$$

The quantity enclosed in the parentheses is called the *vorticity*, or

$$\zeta = \frac{\partial v}{\partial x} - \frac{\partial u}{\partial y} \qquad (10\text{–}2)$$

which is $2\omega$ (twice the local average angular velocity). Since only the $x,y$ plane has been considered, this is only one component of the vorticity, but in the atmosphere the other two components are seldom taken into account because of the overwhelming tendency for the air to flow in laminar fashion. Just as in the case of earth rotation, this is called the vertical component of the vorticity and is represented vectorially by a vertically pointing vector.[1]

In practical computations of the vorticity, finite distances are used over which $\omega$ may vary considerably. It is then simpler in many cases to consider the motion on curved streamlines or lines of flow. Radial lines from the center of curvature are normal to these lines. If $R$ is the

---

[1] In the notation of vector algebra $\zeta = k \cdot \nabla \times C$, where $k$ is a unit vertical vector. $\nabla \times C$ is called the *curl* of $C$.

radius of curvature at any point on a streamline, the velocity is

$$c = \omega R$$

Since $R$ is everywhere normal to the direction of $c$, the vorticity reduces to

$$\zeta = \frac{\partial c}{\partial R} = R\frac{\partial \omega}{\partial R} + \omega \tag{10-3}$$

but

$$R\frac{\partial \omega}{\partial R} = \frac{\partial c}{\partial n}$$

where $n$ is the normal to $c$, so

$$\zeta = \frac{\partial c}{\partial n} + \omega = \frac{\partial c}{\partial n} + \frac{c}{R} \tag{10-4}$$

It is thus evident that the vorticity can be expressed as the sum of a shear term $\partial c/\partial n$ plus a curvature term $c/R$. In the equation, $n$ should be considered positive toward the right of $c$ because that is the direction in which the velocity increases in counterclockwise rotation, which has been taken as positive rotation and positive vorticity.

For geostrophic flow there is no curvature term and we have the *geotrophic vorticity*

$$\zeta_g = \frac{\partial c}{\partial n} \tag{10-5}$$

Note that in fluid mechanics, rotational motion exists whenever there is a velocity shear whether the path is curved or not. This is not true of a rigid body. Pure solid rotation is possible only if $\partial v/\partial x = -\partial u/\partial y$, for then $\omega_1 = \omega_2$. For a fluid, rotation as a solid is only one of an infinite variety of forms of rotation. In the atmosphere in the Northern Hemisphere, positive or counterclockwise vorticity is cyclonic vorticity. Regardless of wind direction, the relative vorticity is cyclonic in the Northern Hemisphere if the linear speeds of the winds increase toward the right. Anticyclonic vorticity is indicated by linear speeds increasing toward the left.

One is reminded that the earth has its own counterclockwise vertical component of vorticity, given by $f = 2\Omega \sin \varphi$, also twice the local angular velocity. We then define the *absolute vorticity* as the sum of the two vorticities $f + \zeta$. $\zeta$ is measured relative to the surface of the earth and is referred to as the relative vorticity.

It should also be noted that the vorticity expressions are valid on constant-pressure surfaces if the winds in these surfaces are used. The normal to a pressure surface is so nearly vertical that the vorticity component is still called vertical.

The principal use of the vorticity in studying air flow comes from the property that it is advected with the air; in other words, it is conserved during atmospheric displacements. Here we are dealing with the absolute vorticity. The theorem may be stated as

$$f + \zeta = \text{const} \tag{10-6}$$

We shall see later how this needs to be modified to take into consideration at least one additional effect. The time derivative of the absolute vorticity is

$$\frac{d}{dt}(f + \zeta) = \frac{df}{dt} + \frac{d\zeta}{dt} = 0 \tag{10-7}$$

In air moving over the rotating earth, latitude changes and therefore changes in $f$ occur. By writing

$$\frac{d\zeta}{dt} = -\frac{df}{d\varphi}\frac{d\varphi}{dt} = -\frac{df}{dy}\frac{dy}{dt} = -v\frac{df}{dy} \tag{10-8}$$

it can be seen that the relative vorticity will be increased in particles carried along in a north wind (negative $v$) and decreased in south winds.

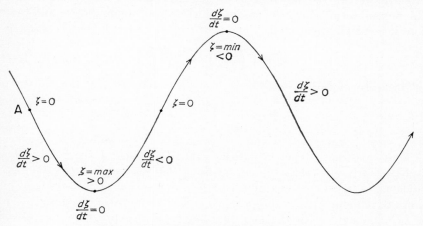

Fig. 10-2. Vorticity in sinusoidal trajectory.

Flow from the north generates cyclonic vorticity or decreases anticyclonic vorticity in the Northern Hemisphere while flow from the south generates anticyclonic vorticity or decreases cyclonic vorticity.

For forecasting purposes, future constant-vorticity trajectories can be computed. The simplest type of trajectory, shown in Fig. 10-2, can develop a sinusoidal wave form. Starting at $A$ the air moves southward with the relative vorticity increasing until the particles curve cyclonically so much that they turn back toward the north. Then the relative vorticity decreases through zero and becomes negative and anticyclonic to the extent that the air is turned back toward the south again to form a ridge.

A number of practical applications of the vorticity are based on the geostrophic vorticity, given in Eq. (10–5). In geostrophic motion on an isobaric surface, the velocity is given by the familiar relationship

$$c = \frac{1}{f}\left(\frac{\partial \Phi}{\partial n}\right)_p \tag{10–9}$$

Hence the geostrophic vorticity (in straight flow) on an isobaric surface is the partial derivative of $c$ in the direction $n$ normal to and to the right of the direction of $c$, taken on the isobaric surface.

$$\frac{\partial}{\partial n}\left[\frac{1}{f}\left(\frac{\partial \Phi}{\partial n}\right)_p\right] = \frac{f(\partial^2\Phi/\partial n^2)_p - (\partial\Phi/\partial n)_p(\partial f/\partial n)_p}{f^2}$$
$$= \frac{1}{f}\left(\frac{\partial^2\Phi}{\partial n^2}\right)_p - \frac{c}{f}\left(\frac{\partial f}{\partial n}\right)_p \tag{10–10}$$

the second term being obtained by substituting for $(\partial\Phi/\partial n)_p$ from Eq. (10–9). It can be shown that in the atmospheric range of conditions this second term is never more than one-tenth of the first term and therefore it is usually neglected. The geostrophic vorticity then is given as

$$\zeta_g = \frac{1}{f}\left(\frac{\partial^2\Phi}{\partial n^2}\right)_p = \frac{g}{f}\left(\frac{\partial^2 z}{\partial n^2}\right)_p \tag{10–11}$$

or, in vector notation,

$$\zeta_g = \frac{1}{f}\nabla_2{}^2\Phi_p = \frac{g}{f}\nabla_2{}^2 z_p \tag{10–12}$$

This second space derivative of a scalar quantity is called the Laplacian of that quantity. The second derivative in space of the height of an isobaric surface is really the curvature of that surface. A positive value (cyclonic vorticity) is characteristic of a depression of the surface while a negative value (anticylonic vorticity) is characteristic of a dome. This is in agreement with the fact that bulges and depressions on isobaric surfaces represent anticyclones and cyclones, respectively.

The absolute geostrophic vorticity much used in meteorological computations is, of course,

$$f + \zeta_g = f + \frac{1}{f}\left(\frac{\partial^2\Phi}{\partial n^2}\right)_p \tag{10–13}$$

**Streamline, Stream Function, and Velocity Potential.** A streamline is defined as a curve whose tangent at any point gives the direction of the velocity vector at that point. In Fig. 10–3, the curve $S$ represents a streamline in which the general sense of the motion is toward the northeastern part of the diagram. At the point 0, the tangent is in the direction of the velocity vector $c$ which characterizes the flow at that point. The $u$ and $v$ components of $c$ are as shown. The vector $c$ forms an angle $\beta$ with the $x$ axis.

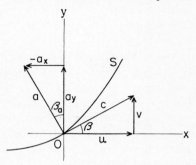

$$\tan \beta = \frac{v}{u} = \frac{dy/dt}{dx/dt} = \frac{dy}{dx} \quad (10\text{-}14)$$

$$v \, dx = u \, dy \quad (10\text{-}15)$$

$$v \, dx - u \, dy = 0 \quad (10\text{-}16)$$

$$\frac{dx}{u} = \frac{dv}{v} \quad (10\text{-}16a)$$

Fig. 10–3.

The latter expression is usually given as the mathematical definition (differential equation) of a streamline in two dimensions. When the streamlines retain the same shape at all times the motion is said to be *steady*. The particles will then have followed a path along a streamline. With changing streamlines, that is, with unsteady flow, the actual paths or *trajectories* have to be determined over small increments of time from the streamlines prevailing at those times.

Streamlines can be drawn on maps in such a way that their horizontal spacing, like the spacing of isobars or contours of a pressure surface, is proportional to the wind speed. A *stream function* $\psi$ is then defined such that

$$u = -\frac{\partial \psi}{\partial y} \qquad v = \frac{\partial \psi}{\partial x} \quad (10\text{-}17)$$

with streamlines labeled in arbitrary values of $\psi$, ascendant toward the right of the flow in the Northern Hemisphere, toward the left in the Southern Hemisphere. The streamlines and stream functions can be represented and computed on any desired surface—horizontal, isobaric, or isentropic. It is apparent that isobars are streamlines for gradient-equilibrium flow on a horizontal surface and that contours serve the same purpose on an isobaric surface.

Orthogonal to the streamlines is a set of lines represented in Fig. 10–3 by the vector $a$, perpendicular to and of the same magnitude as the vector $c$, and having the components $a_y$ and $-a_x$. Note that the two vector triangles are the same, so that in magnitudes $\beta_a = \beta$, $a_y = u$, and $a_x = v$. The slope of $a$ is

$$\tan (90 - \beta) = \cot \beta = \frac{dy}{dx} = -\frac{a_y}{a_x} = -\frac{u}{v} \quad (10\text{-}18)$$

and

$$u \, dx = -v \, dy \quad (10\text{-}19)$$

$$u \, dx + v \, dy = 0 \quad (10\text{-}20)$$

The number of these lines in a unit distance can also be made proportional to the wind speed to produce a *velocity potential* $\varphi$ defined by

$$u = -\frac{\partial \varphi}{\partial x} \qquad v = -\frac{\partial \varphi}{\partial y} \qquad (10\text{--}21)$$

The three-dimensional case can be considered by equating each of the two terms in Eq. (10–16a) to $dz/w$. In three dimensions, the flow is in streamline tubes bounded by streamlines. The velocity-potential lines become surfaces cutting the streamlines at right angles.

If a velocity potential exists, the flow must be *irrotational*, that is, the vorticity must be zero. This can be shown by obtaining $\partial v/\partial x$ and $\partial u/\partial y$ by differentiating Eq. (10–21).

$$\frac{\partial u}{\partial y} = -\frac{\partial \varphi}{\partial x\, \partial y} \qquad \frac{\partial v}{\partial x} = -\frac{\partial \varphi}{\partial x\, \partial y} \qquad (10\text{--}22)$$

$$\frac{\partial v}{\partial x} - \frac{\partial u}{\partial y} = 0 \qquad (10\text{--}23)$$

This result also is suggested by graphical investigation. Take, for example, the streamlines in Fig. 10–4a which show a wind shear by virtue of increasing crowding to the right, so that the stream function is increasing ($\partial \psi/\partial x > 0$). It is impossible to construct a set of lines representing velocity potential which would be orthogonal to the streamlines. If the velocity is to be proportional to $\partial \varphi/\partial x$, the lines of potential must become closer together toward the right, a requirement incompatible with orthogonality. In Fig. 10–4b the velocity is constant, as shown by equal spacing of the streamlines. The orthogonal lines are radial lines which separate as they extend outward from the center; thus the gradient of the potential cannot represent the velocity. These arguments substantiate the theorem that potential flow is irrotational. The

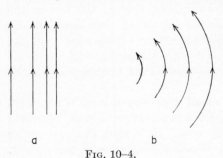

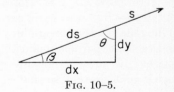

a                              b

Fig. 10–4.                              Fig. 10–5.

concept of potential flow, however, is useful in examining certain properties of vorticity and other flow problems.

**Circulation and Vorticity.** In Fig. 10–5, fluid is considered as flowing along the straight path $s$, an infinitesimal part of which is represented by

$ds$, with components $dx$ and $dy$. It is seen that

$$\frac{dx}{ds} = \cos \beta \qquad \frac{dy}{ds} = \cos \theta \qquad (10\text{–}24)$$

These may be designated as the directional cosines $l$ and $m$ of $s$.

$$dx = l \, ds \qquad dy = m \, ds$$

Equation (10–20) becomes

$$(ul + vm) \, ds = 0 \qquad (10\text{–}25)$$

Also

$$u = \frac{dx}{dt} = l \frac{ds}{dt} = lc \qquad (10\text{–}26)$$

$$v = \frac{dy}{dt} = m \frac{ds}{dt} = mc \qquad (10\text{–}27)$$

$$ul + vm = (l^2 + m^2)c \qquad (10\text{–}28)$$

$$m = \cos \theta = \sin \beta$$

$$\sin^2 \beta + \cos^2 \beta = 1$$

$$u \, dx + v \, dy = c \, ds \qquad (10\text{–}29)$$

where $c$ is the actual velocity $ds/dt$ along $s$. If the fluid flows at constant speed $c_0$ a distance $s$, the expression would be

$$c_0 s = c_0 \int_0^s ds \qquad (10\text{–}30)$$

The value of the integral

$$\int_{s_1}^{s_2} u \, dx + v \, dy = \int_{s_1}^{s_2} \left( u \frac{dx}{ds} + v \frac{dy}{ds} \right) ds = \int_{s_1}^{s_2} c \, ds \qquad (10\text{–}31)$$

is the *flow* of the fluid from $s_1$ to $s_2$. It has the dimensions cm$^2$ per sec or the product of speed and distance.

When the flow is not of the simple form described in Fig. 10–5 and in the last two equations, $u$ and $v$ may each be a function of both $x$ and $y$ in the fluid. In order to perform the integration, it is necessary to know what these functions are. They can be specified only along a given line of flow and the resulting integral along this line is called a *line integral*, since the $u$ and $v$ as functions of $x$ and $y$ are only valid along the chosen line. This can be a curved line, a line with angular turns in it, or a closed circuit (circular, square, rectangular, elliptical, or in any odd form).

The flow around a closed circuit, that is, the line integral of Eq. (10–31) around a closed path, is called the *circulation*, which we will designate by $C$.

$$C = \int_c (u\,dx + v\,dy) = \int_c \left( u\,\frac{dx}{ds} + v\,\frac{dy}{ds} \right) ds \qquad (10\text{–}32)$$

where the subscript $c$ of the integral sign indicates a line integral around a closed circuit.

The area $A$ of any surface, such as in Fig. 10–6, may be divided by a double series of lines crossing it into infinitely small elements, one of

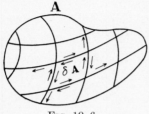

which is represented as $\delta A$ in the figure. The sum of the circulations around the boundaries of these elements, taken all in the same sense, is equal to the circulation around the boundary of the whole area. This is apparent when, in summing the circulations, the flow along each side common to two elements comes in twice, once for each element, but with opposite signs, and therefore disappears

FIG. 10–6.

from the result. There remain only the flows along those sides which are parts of the boundary of $A$. If $C$ represents the circulation around $A$ and $\delta C$ that around $\delta A$, we have

$$C = \int_A \delta C \qquad (10\text{–}33)$$

where the summation includes all the elements $\delta A$.

Consider the infinitesimal area, now assumed to be a rectangle $\delta A = \delta x\,\delta y$ shown in Fig. 10–7. On the opposite sides the $u$ and $v$ are not the same, since they are each functions of $x$ and $y$. Starting in the lower left corner, having the coordinates $x$, $y$, the flow is counterclockwise around the rectangle to $y$, $(x + \delta x)$, thence up to $(x + \delta x)$, $(y + \delta y)$, back to $x$, $(y + \delta y)$, and down to $x$, $y$ again. The velocities and flows are as follows:

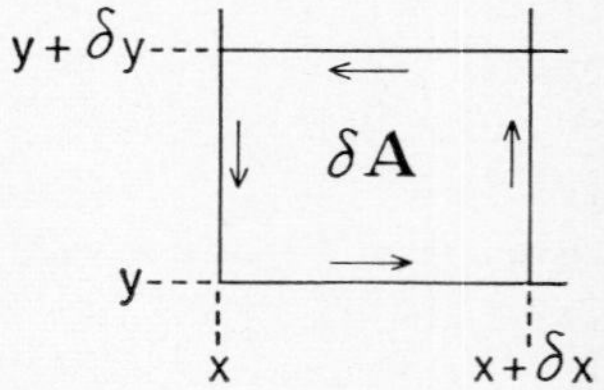

FIG. 10–7.

Along bottom, from $x$, $y$ to $(x + \delta x)$, $y$, velocity is $u$, flow is $u\,\delta x$.

Along right, from $(x + \delta x)$, $y$ to $(x + \delta x)$, $(y + \delta y)$, velocity is $v + \dfrac{\partial v}{\partial x}\,\delta x$, flow is $\left( v + \dfrac{\partial v}{\partial x}\,\delta x \right)\delta y$.

Along top, from $(x + \delta x)$, $(y + \delta y)$ to $x$, $(y + \delta y)$, velocity is $-\left( u + \dfrac{\partial u}{\partial y}\,\delta y \right)$, flow is $-\left( u + \dfrac{\partial u}{\partial y}\,\delta y \right)\delta x$.

Along left, from $x$, $(y + \delta y)$ to $x$, $y$, velocity is $-v$, flow is $-v\,\delta y$. The circulation around $\delta A$ is, then,

$$\delta C = u\,\delta x + \left(v + \frac{\partial v}{\partial x}\,\delta x\right)\delta y - \left(u + \frac{\partial u}{\partial y}\,\delta y\right)\delta x - v\,\delta y$$

$$= \frac{\partial v}{\partial x}\,\delta x\,\delta y - \frac{\partial u}{\partial y}\,\delta x\,\delta y \tag{10--34}$$

$$= \delta A\left(\frac{\partial v}{\partial x} - \frac{\partial u}{\partial y}\right)$$

$$\frac{\delta C}{\delta A} = \frac{\partial v}{\partial x} - \frac{\partial u}{\partial y} = \zeta \tag{10--35}$$

Thus it is seen that the vertical component of the vorticity is equivalent to the circulation around unit horizontal area. Checking dimensions, we see that the flow divided by area is in units of $\sec^{-1}$, appropriate to vorticity or angular velocity.

We can write

$$C = \int_A \zeta\,\delta A \tag{10--36}$$

by substituting (10–35) into (10–33) to eliminate $\delta C$. Equation (10–36) is an expression for Stokes' theorem: The circulation around the boundary of any finite horizontal area is equal to the integral of the vertical component of vorticity taken over the area.

**Circulation and Solenoids.** Circulations in the atmosphere which nearly everyone has observed on a local scale are those arising from local heat differences. Cold air sinks and flows along at the ground while warm air rises and moves aloft. Sea breezes, lake breezes, valley breezes, "drainage" winds, and various mountain air circulations are all driven by density and pressure differences associated with temperature differences. In terms of the basic forces driving it, the general circulation of the atmosphere which transports heat between low and high latitudes is of this type. The cold air surrounding the poles sinks and spreads toward the equator while the tropical air is forced upward, moving poleward aloft. The coriolis acceleration with the resulting tendency for geostrophic balance makes the meridional motions hard to detect, but this highly inefficient circulation is nevertheless driven by the heat differences.

In Chap. 7 the buoyancy acceleration arising from density differences was treated in one dimension in the atmosphere on the basis of an individual sounding. It was shown that the energy available for accelerating the motion can be represented on a $p,\alpha$ diagram, a $T \ln p$, or other thermodynamically related diagram. We are now required to consider a similar problem in the three dimensions of the atmosphere. However, the analysis will be aimed toward investigating the circulation through atmospheric space rather than processes represented on an energy diagram.

Just as pressure lines become surfaces in space, so also do other lines of state, such as specific volume, temperature, and potential temperature. Any two sets of surfaces may intersect to form a honeycomblike set of tubes, adjacent ones having common walls and appearing approximately as parallelograms in cross section. In Fig. 10–8 a schematic cross section in a vertical plane through a portion of the atmosphere shows some of the tubes formed by intersection of isobaric and *isosteric* (constant specific volume) surfaces. Other planes would intersect the tubes at a different angle, but normally we are interested only in vertical and horizontal planes. These tubes, formed by intersection of surfaces of pressure and specific volume or of surfaces of properties which bear a similar relationship to each other in a thermodynamic sense, are called *solenoids*. A *unit p,α solenoid* is bounded on two opposite sides by isobaric surfaces

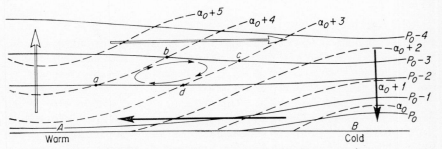

Fɪɢ. 10–8. Solenoidal field as viewed in vertical cross section.

corresponding to values differing from each other by one unit of pressure and on the other pair of opposite sides by isosteric surfaces representing two values of specific volume one unit apart.

Before going into a physical-mathematical discussion, it is useful to consider descriptively the relation of solenoids to the circulation. In the atmosphere, pressure decreases and specific volume increases with height. At any given pressure, the specific volume increases with increasing temperature. The pressure decreases more rapidly with height in cold air than in warm air at the same levels. These conditions are shown in Fig. 10–8 where the $p,α$ solenoids are represented schematically in a vertical cross section between a cold and warm region. This might be typical of the solenoidal field between the antarctic and the surrounding oceans.

The cold air is denser (has a smaller $α$) than the surrounding air and therefore sinks. The warm air, less dense (greater $α$) than its environment, rises. The circulation is completed by flow from cold to warm in the low levels and in the reverse sense aloft. Note that, since the isobars are expanded upward over the heat source, the isobaric slopes tend to fit the upper branch of the circulation. The high pressure at the surface, which is often characteristic of cold areas, produces a pressure gradient in keeping with the surface flow.

If a unit solenoid $abcd$ is taken, it is noted that the circulation must be in the sense associated with flow down the gradient of pressure and with the ascendant of specific volume, in other words, from $a$ to $b$ to $c$ to $d$.

For a physical-mathematical analysis, let us consider the development of circulation in a vertical or $y,z$ plane intersected by $p,\alpha$ solenoids. As defined in Eq. (10–32) the circulation is

$$C = \int_c (v\,dy + w\,dz)$$

The acceleration of the circulation is obtained by differentiating $C$ with respect to time, giving

$$\frac{dC}{dt} = \int_c \left(\frac{dv}{dt}\,dy + \frac{dw}{dt}\,dz\right) + \int_c \left(v\,\frac{d}{dt}(dy) + w\,\frac{d}{dt}(dz)\right) \quad (10\text{–}37)$$

But, since

$$\frac{dy}{dt} = v \quad \text{and} \quad \frac{dz}{dt} = w$$

the second integral becomes

$$\int_c (v\,dv + w\,dw)$$

Around a closed path this integral must be zero, for returning to the same point one reaches the same $v$ and the same $w$ and the integrals of $v\,dv$ and $w\,dw$ must both vanish.

The first integral can be evaluated by substituting for $dv/dt$ and $dw/dt$ in unbalanced flow. In terms of the absolute motion, without coriolis acceleration, the only other accelerations would be associated with the pressure-gradient force, the acceleration of gravity, and frictional forces. The latter can be neglected for the present in order to study the frictionless case and can be injected into the problem later, if desired.

The accelerations in the imbalance under investigation would be expressed, according to Eqs. (9–23b,c) and (9–26), as follows:

$$\frac{dv}{dt} = -\alpha\,\frac{\partial p}{\partial y} \quad\quad\quad (10\text{–}38)$$

$$\frac{dw}{dt} = -g - \alpha\,\frac{\partial p}{\partial z} \quad\quad\quad (10\text{–}39)$$

Upon substitution into (10–37) the acceleration of the circulation in the vertical $y,z$ plane becomes

$$\frac{dC}{dt} = - \int_c \alpha \left(\frac{\partial p}{\partial y}\, dy + \frac{\partial p}{\partial z}\, dz\right) - \int_c g\, dz \qquad (10\text{--}40)$$

Since, around a closed path, one returns to the same height $z$, the second integral is zero. As is characteristic of partial differentials of quantities that are continuous functions of space coordinates only,

$$\frac{\partial p}{\partial y}\, dy + \frac{\partial p}{\partial z}\, dz = dp$$

Thus the integral becomes

$$\frac{dC}{dt} = - \int_c \alpha\, dp \qquad (10\text{--}41)$$

The acceleration is positive in the expected sense of flow in the direction of the pressure gradient $-\partial p/\partial n$ and the specific-volume ascendant $+\partial \alpha/\partial n$. Its sign depends on these quantitites alone and is not determined by the sense of the coordinate axes $x$, $y$, $z$. It can be the same as or the opposite of the sense of circulation associated with the existing vorticity. The sense of the solenoids may be represented by a vector pointing in the direction of advance of a right-handed screw turning in the direction of the circulation accelerated by the solenoids. In Fig. 10–8 the sense would be inward toward the page.

Solenoids may also intersect a horizontal plane in the atmosphere, though at a very small angle. They may have an effect when the conservation of the vertical component of the absolute vorticity is considered. They may operate either to increase or decrease the vorticity. Ordinarily the effect is small, but it can be eliminated altogether if the vorticity is considered on a constant-pressure surface. A constant-pressure surface forms one wall of a family of solenoids and therefore solenoids cannot intersect it. This is another advantage of representation in pressure surfaces.

The acceleration in Eq. (10–41) around any closed curve is given by the number of unit solenoids enclosed by the curve. This can be demonstrated by projecting the curve on a $-p$, $\alpha$ diagram as in Fig. 10–9. The closed curve in Fig. 10–9a encloses the same number of unit solenoids as that in the $-p$, $\alpha$ diagram of Fig. 10–9b. Since the coordinates of the latter are in units of $-p$ and $\alpha$, the integral measures the actual area enclosed by the curve, and the unit solenoids each represent a unit of area. The area is the number of unit areas, therefore the number of unit solenoids. This is the same number of solenoids enclosed by the curve in Fig. 10–9a. In terms of $p$ and $\alpha$ the two integrals are the same, so the number of unit solenoids enclosed determines the value of the integral in each case. We may write

$$- \int_c \alpha \, dp = N \tag{10-42}$$

where $N$ is the number of unit solenoids of $-p$, $\alpha$ contained within the closed curve.

Two other practical forms of solenoids may be represented by transforming the integral into expressions involving other thermodynamic properties.

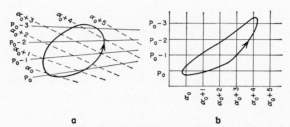

FIG. 10-9. Projection of solenoidal field on $p$, $\alpha$ diagram.

Since, from the equation of state, $\alpha = RT/mp$, we may write

$$- \int_c \alpha \, dp = - \frac{R}{m} \int_c T \, d(\ln p) \tag{10-43}$$

Thus solenoids of temperature[1] and natural logarithm of pressure may be used. These are indeed practical, since pressure and temperature are in greater use than any other set of properties in charting the atmosphere. The pressure surfaces have a $-\ln p$ distribution with height in the atmosphere, thus making this form quite convenient, and when the plotting of temperature is on constant-pressure surfaces, the $T$, $-\ln p$ solenoids are immediately obtained.

Another form of representation is in terms of temperature and potential temperature. The differential equation relating potential temperature to the temperature and pressure is, from Eq. (7-77),

$$C_p \frac{dT}{T} = C_p \frac{d\theta}{\theta} + \frac{R}{m} \frac{dp}{p}$$

$$C_p \, dT = C_p T \frac{d\theta}{\theta} + \frac{RT}{mp} \, dp$$

$$= C_p T \frac{d\theta}{\theta} + \alpha \, dp$$

$$\alpha \, dp = C_p \left( dT - T \frac{d\theta}{\theta} \right) \tag{10-44}$$

[1] More properly, virtual temperature should be used throughout, but we recall that this is a trivial matter which becomes even more trivial in affecting the count of solenoids.

The first term on the right, when integrated around a closed path, becomes zero, since the circuit comes back to the same temperature and no variable other than $T$ is involved. We have, therefore,

$$- \int_c \alpha \, dp = C_p \int_c T \, d(\ln \theta) \tag{10–45}$$

showing that temperature and the natural logarithm of potential temperature[1] can be used to construct solenoids. These are useful in working with isentropic charts and vertical cross sections through the atmosphere.

The axes of the three forms of solenoids are always parallel. Along a line of intersection of the isobaric and isosteric surfaces, pressure and specific volume are, by definition, constant. Temperature is determined from these two quantitites from the equation of state, so it is also constant along this line. The potential temperature, determined by temperature and pressure, must also be constant along this line. The walls of the first two forms of solenoids have the same orientation.

The relation between the number of solenoids of different kinds in a given cross-sectional area can be stated as follows:

$$N = \frac{R}{m} N' = C_p N'' \tag{10–46}$$

where $N$, $N'$, and $N''$ refer to the number, respectively, of pressure-specific volume, pressure-temperature, and temperature-potential temperature solenoids.

Before leaving this subject it should be stressed again that the coriolis acceleration and frictional effects cannot be neglected in applying the solenoidal circulation to actual motions. The coriolis acceleration is so strong in most situations that the solenoidal effect is an essentially undetectable influence on the geostrophic balance. In seeking to outline the main features of the general circulation of the atmosphere, meteorologists find great difficulty owing to the almost complete masking of the meridional circulation which must develop from the strong solenoidal field present in a north-south vertical plane.

In the local solenoidal circulations, such as those of the afternoon sea breezes, the closed circulation is almost never seen because of the widespread prevailing, essentially geostrophic winds which are present above the surface inflow. The return flow is dissipated, at least in part, by the frictional stress of the upper wind.

It is probable that a steady-state circulation can exist on a local scale in which the acceleration of the circulation is exactly balanced by the surface and internal frictional stresses. In the general circulation of the atmosphere, such a mean steady state involves a balance of the solenoidal

---

[1] Again, to be proper, based on virtual temperature.

acceleration against all accelerations acting on the air between the equator and the poles. Actually, as is quite apparent to residents outside the tropics, the exchange of air involved in the general circulation is anything but steady, but in the mean it is sometimes convenient to regard it as so.

It is assumed that even the beginning student of meteorology is acquainted with the concept of fronts as depicted in newspaper and television presentations. By definition, a front must be a zone in which solenoids are highly concentrated. Many of the violent features of cold fronts are developed from extreme density gradients producing accelerations measurable through solenoids. In general, intensifying storms have concentrated solenoidal fields associated with them. On a localized scale, thunderstorms represent continually changing circulations accompanied by intense solenoidal concentrations. They change so rapidly that geostrophic or gradient balance is not achieved and the air flows almost directly across the locally distorted isobars.

**Barotropic and Baroclinic Atmospheres.** A portion of the atmosphere in which the surfaces of pressure, specific volume (or density), temperature, or potential temperature are all parallel is called *barotropic*. In other words, a barotropic atmosphere is one without solenoids. The atmosphere is approximately barotropic in large regions in the tropics. As a first approximation for the solution of certain problems in meteorology, the atmosphere sometimes is assumed to be barotropic when it really is not. Such simplifications are common in theoretical studies in order to handle otherwise intractable problems and thus to gain incomplete yet important knowledge about intricate processes.

The opposite of barotropic is *baroclinic*, i.e., characterized by the presence of a solenoidal field. The natural atmosphere is mainly baroclinic, since horizontal temperature gradients are the rule and often have a direction opposite to that of the pressure gradients.

**Eulerian Expansion.** Fluid motion may be regarded in two different ways. One may investigate the motion and properties at all points in the fluid at various times or one may determine the changes in velocity and properties of a single particle. In the first case, the measurements are made at fixed points, while in the latter the measuring system must be able to follow the course of the particle. The equations of motion have different forms in the two methods, the first called the *Eulerian* (pronounced oil-air'-ian) form and the second the *Lagrangian* form.

Euler introduced the complete expression for the changes in velocity or properties involving both the moving particles and the distributions through the fluid space. To arrive at the so-called "Eulerian expansion," consider any quantity $Q$ which varies in space and in time in a moving particle. If the particle is moving with velocity $u$ in the $x$ axis starting at time $t$ from the point $x$, then at the time $t + \delta t$ (Fig. 10–10), its position would be at

$$x + \delta x = x + u \, \delta t$$

If the quantity $Q$ changes both in time and in space, the new value of $Q$ is

$$Q_{x+\delta x, t+\delta t} = Q_{x,t} + \delta Q$$
$$= Q_{x,t} + \frac{\partial Q}{\partial x} \, \delta x + \frac{\partial Q}{\partial t} \, \delta t = Q_{x,t} + u \, \delta t \frac{\partial Q}{\partial x} + \frac{\partial Q}{\partial t} \, \delta t \quad (10\text{–}47)$$

If, as previously, we introduce the symbol $D/Dt$ to denote differentiation following the motion of the particle, the new value of $Q$ is

$$Q_{x+\delta x, t+\delta t} = Q_{x,t} + \frac{DQ}{Dt} \, \delta t \quad (10\text{–}48)$$

and, from (10–47), the change of $Q$ in the $x$ direction with time would be

$$\left(\frac{DQ}{Dt}\right)_x = \frac{\partial Q}{\partial t} + u \frac{\partial Q}{\partial x} \quad (10\text{–}49)$$

or, considering motion with all three components,

$$\frac{DQ}{Dt} = \frac{\partial Q}{\partial t} + u \frac{\partial Q}{\partial x} + v \frac{\partial Q}{\partial y} + w \frac{\partial Q}{\partial z} \quad (10\text{–}50)$$

The derivative on the left in capital letters we will call the "individual change" and the first term on the right will be designated as the "local change," since it is the change that will be noted by an observer at a fixed point past which many particles are moving.

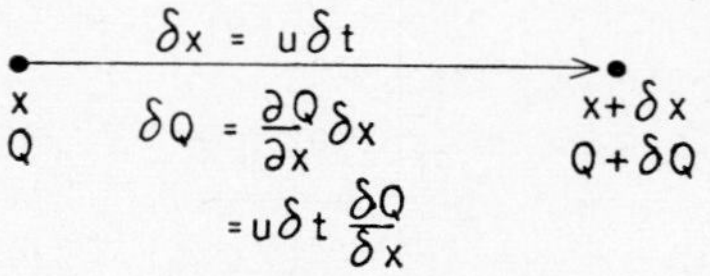

This distinction between individual and local change may best be illustrated by considering some property of the air such as temperature. If we carried a thermograph along with an air parcel, the temperature change recorded would be the individual change of temperature $DT/Dt$. If we had a thermograph at a fixed station, it would record the local change of temperature $\partial T/\partial t$. We should have

Fig. 10–10.

$$\frac{DT}{Dt} = \frac{\partial T}{\partial t} + u \frac{\partial T}{\partial x} + v \frac{\partial T}{\partial y} + w \frac{\partial T}{\partial z} \quad (10\text{–}51)$$

If the axis is taken normal to the isotherms, and $C_n$ is the wind component in this axis,

$$\frac{DT}{Dt} = \frac{\partial T}{\partial t} + C_n \frac{\partial T}{\partial n} \quad (10\text{–}52)$$

where $n$ refers to the normal direction.

The second term on the right is the *advective change* due to the movement of air particles of differing temperatures. The change observed at a given location, the local change, would be

$$\frac{\partial T}{\partial t} = \frac{DT}{Dt} - C_n \frac{\partial T}{\partial n} \tag{10-53}$$

In other words, it would be the change due to the advection of air of different temperature (movement of isotherms) corrected for the change of temperature within the air particles as they move along—the fact that the isotherms are not displaced with the same speed as the wind normal to them. If we had no individual change, the temperature would be conservative, i.e., the isotherms would move with the speed of the normal wind. Then the local change would be entirely due to advection and the first term on the right would be zero. If $C_n$ is toward increasing temperature, advection would cause the temperature to decrease locally. If the air parcels moved faster than the isotherms, $DT/Dt$ (within the parcels) would be positive. This would counteract to a certain extent the advective cooling.

The expression

$$\frac{DQ}{Dt} = \frac{\partial Q}{\partial t} + C_n \frac{\partial Q}{\partial n} = 0 \tag{10-54}$$

where $Q$ is any property of the air, expresses the condition of conservativeness of that property. A conservative property is one of which the individual change $DQ/Dt$ is zero.

The Eulerian expansion applied to the three components of velocity becomes

$$\frac{Du}{Dt} = \frac{\partial u}{\partial t} + u \frac{\partial u}{\partial x} + v \frac{\partial u}{\partial y} + w \frac{\partial u}{\partial z} \tag{10-55a}$$

$$\frac{Dv}{Dt} = \frac{\partial v}{\partial t} + u \frac{\partial v}{\partial x} + v \frac{\partial v}{\partial y} + w \frac{\partial v}{\partial z} \tag{10-55b}$$

$$\frac{Dw}{Dt} = \frac{\partial w}{\partial t} + u \frac{\partial w}{\partial x} + v \frac{\partial w}{\partial y} + w \frac{\partial w}{\partial z} \tag{10-55c}$$

In using isobaric surfaces for studying motions and properties, the $p$ coordinate normal to the pressure surface is substituted in the above equations for $z$, and $w_p = Dp/Dt$ is substituted for $w$. In all other respects the Eulerian expanded equations are the same.

**Continuity and Divergence.** A statement of the law of conservation of matter in the form of the "equation of continuity" is useful in meteorology. This equation indicates that, in a continuous fluid or gaseous medium, the mass of fluid material passing into a given volume must be equal to that coming out unless a density change has occurred in the volume.

Let us consider a volume in a 1-cm cube as in Fig. 10–11. In the $x$ direction, the air is moving through with a variable speed $u$, passing into the cube through the face $x_0$ and out of the cube through the face $x'$. The inflow of mass at the face $x_0$ is $\rho u$ while the mass outflow at the face $x'$ may be different from that coming in, expressible as $\rho u + \partial \rho u / \partial x$. The net accumulation (inflow) of mass through these two faces would be given by

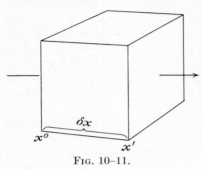

FIG. 10–11.

Inflow at $x_0$ − outflow at $x'$

$$\rho u - \left(\rho u + \frac{\partial \rho u}{\partial x}\right) = -\frac{\partial \rho u}{\partial x} \qquad (10\text{–}56)$$

If we go through the same reasoning for each of the other pairs of opposite sides, we obtain the total net inflow of mass in the cube, viz.,

$$-\left(\frac{\partial \rho u}{\partial x} + \frac{\partial \rho v}{\partial y} + \frac{\partial \rho w}{\partial z}\right)$$

This net inflow, or accumulation, must give rise to a local increase in the density in the cube, and therefore the above expression must be equal to $\partial \rho / \partial t$ or

$$\frac{\partial \rho}{\partial t} + \frac{\partial \rho u}{\partial x} + \frac{\partial \rho v}{\partial y} + \frac{\partial \rho w}{\partial z} = 0 \qquad (10\text{–}57a)$$

This may be expanded into

$$\frac{\partial \rho}{\partial t} + u\frac{\partial \rho}{\partial x} + v\frac{\partial \rho}{\partial y} + w\frac{\partial \rho}{\partial z} + \rho\frac{\partial u}{\partial x} + \rho\frac{\partial v}{\partial y} + \rho\frac{\partial w}{\partial z} = 0 \qquad (10\text{–}57b)$$

The first four terms give the expression for the individual change of the density. Therefore, using this individual change $D\rho/Dt$, we may write

$$\frac{D\rho}{Dt} + \rho\left(\frac{\partial u}{\partial x} + \frac{\partial v}{\partial y} + \frac{\partial w}{\partial z}\right) = 0 \qquad (10\text{–}58)$$

or

$$\frac{1}{\rho}\frac{D\rho}{Dt} + \frac{\partial u}{\partial x} + \frac{\partial v}{\partial y} + \frac{\partial w}{\partial z} = 0 \qquad (10\text{–}59)$$

This last expression is the equation of continuity as it is most often used in meteorology.

The partial derivatives $\partial u/\partial x$, $\partial v/\partial y$, $\partial w/\partial z$ express the divergence of the air. This may be seen by considering the speed $u$ to be greater at the $x'$ face than at the $x_0$ face of the cube in Fig. 10–11. Under this condition, $\partial u/\partial x$ would be positive. The air particles would be pulling or stretching farther apart. If the speed decreased between $x_0$ and $x'$, $\partial u/\partial x$ would be negative. The air particles would be pushing closer together. In the first case we would have divergence $(+\partial u/\partial x)$ and in the second case, convergence $(-\partial u/\partial x)$ in the direction of the $x$ axis. The sum of the three partial derivatives gives the total divergence out of the cube. If there is divergence, these terms are positive and we have

$$\frac{\partial u}{\partial x} + \frac{\partial v}{\partial y} + \frac{\partial w}{\partial z} = -\frac{1}{\rho}\frac{D\rho}{Dt} \tag{10–60}$$

showing that, if we have divergence, i.e., if more comes out than goes in, the density within the volume has to decrease. Conversely, if convergence occurs, we have

$$-\frac{\partial u}{\partial x} - \frac{\partial v}{\partial y} - \frac{\partial w}{\partial z} = \frac{1}{\rho}\frac{D\rho}{Dt} \tag{10–61}$$

or, we can say, if more goes in than comes out, the density must increase.

For the case of incompressibility or, more properly, for the case when compression is not favored, the divergence is zero, i.e.,

$$\frac{\partial u}{\partial x} + \frac{\partial v}{\partial y} + \frac{\partial w}{\partial z} = 0 \tag{10–62}$$

In meteorology, we are often concerned with the lateral divergence. In this case, without compressibility,

$$\frac{\partial u}{\partial x} + \frac{\partial v}{\partial y} = -\frac{\partial w}{\partial z} \tag{10–63}$$

This indicates that lateral divergence must be compensated by vertical shrinking or vertical convergence ($\partial w/\partial z$ negative) and lateral convergence must be accompanied by vertical stretching or vertical divergence ($\partial w/\partial z$ positive). Any wind component that is increasing downstream is divergent in that component. If it is decreasing downstream, it is convergent in that component.

In the pressure system, the equation of continuity can be developed for a unit rectangular parallelopiped, the lower surface coinciding with a pressure surface and with sides $x$, $y$, and $p$. For the case of no compression,

$$\left(\frac{\partial u}{\partial x} + \frac{\partial v}{\partial y}\right)_p = +\frac{\partial w_p}{\partial p} \tag{10–64}$$

Here the sign on the right is positive because $p$ increases downward.

The divergence is often written as div $c$, where $c$ is the total velocity, or, in vector notation, as $\nabla \cdot c$. In the $x$ and $y$ dimensions it is written as $\text{div}_2 \, c$ or $\nabla_2 \cdot c$, meaning the lateral divergence. In meteorology it is desirable to consider the horizontal component separately in order to get at the important vertical component. It is not revealing to take the three-dimensional divergence to find only that it is zero, as is usually the case in restricted volumes of the atmosphere. By computing the lateral divergence in the same situation, significant positive or negative values may be found which have a profound effect on the vertical motions, already known from Chap. 7 to be important for development of thermal instability. As will be shown later, the vertical motions are of great importance in causing pressure changes over large areas in the atmosphere.

From the divergence, one cannot determine the vertical velocity directly; only the change of that quantity with height or pressure is given. Conversely, one cannot infer that the existence of vertical velocity at any point in the atmosphere means divergence or convergence at that point. Since the atmosphere has a fixed lower boundary at the surface of the earth and also some indefinite upper layer beyond which vertical motions cannot exist, the presence of vertical motions always indicates horizontal divergence and convergence above and below to complete the continuity. Thus a region of steady upward motion would be maintained by convergence below and divergence above. A downward-moving component would require divergence below and convergence above.

At the surface of the earth the vertical velocity must be zero. With zero as a starting point, the direction of the vertical motion in convergent or divergent flow immediately above the surface is at once determined from the equation of continuity. Physically this means that if air converges along the ground there is no escape for the accumulating air except upward, and if divergence occurs the deficit can only be supplied by air coming down from above. In heat convection, especially in the building stage of thunderstorms, convergence is observed in the low levels and divergence in the upper parts.

The different possibilities in the free atmosphere and at the surface are represented schematically in Fig. 10–12. In the top row horizontal divergence is represented for the three types of vertical motion—upward, downward, and zero. The second row shows the same for nondivergent flow. Continuous vertical flow could occur between this row and the ones above and below it, considered as layers in the atmosphere, except in the last column of the second row which is boxed to indicate that zero vertical velocity would have to exist for some distance above and below in the box. The third row represents the convergent conditions. At the ground, indicated in the lowest row, there is only one possibility for each of the three different values of divergence. In this part of the diagram, the vertical velocities given for the various columns should be regarded as occurring immediately above the ground while at the air-earth boundary itself, $w$ is zero. These comments, of course, must be modified when one is considering a sloping terrain. For all of the situations it is to be noted that horizontal divergence is accompanied by vertical convergence and that horizontal convergence goes with vertical divergence.

A practical way of considering continuity is to state the condition of zero total divergence as one in which the mass of any given volume of air

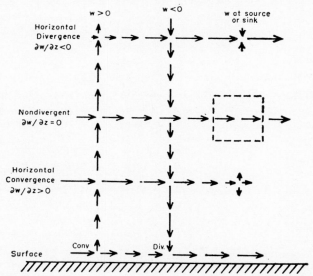

FIG. 10–12. Divergence-convergence patterns and vertical velocities in the atmosphere.

does not change. This is another way of saying that the density does not change. If neither the mass nor the density varies, the volume must also remain constant. While remaining constant, the volume may change its shape; for example, stretching horizontally while shrinking vertically by the same amount. In this case there would be horizontal divergence and vertical convergence of the air particles. It is not difficult to obtain a mathematical expression for these effects.

The mass $M$ of a given volume $V$, such as a cylinder or rectangular parallelopiped, is given by

$$M = \rho V = \rho A D = \text{const}$$

where $A$ and $D$ are the area and height (depth) of the volume, respectively. The constant indicates that there is no total divergence. If through the depth $D$ the pressure varies from $p_0$ to $p$, we have, from the hydrostatic equation,

$$M = \frac{\rho A}{\rho g} \int_p^{p_0} dp = \frac{A}{g} D_p = \text{const} \qquad (10\text{--}65)$$

where $D_p$ is the pressure-depth. The time derivative of the last expression is

$$\frac{dM}{dt} = \frac{A}{g} \frac{dD_p}{dt} + \frac{D_p}{g} \frac{dA}{dt} = 0 \qquad (10\text{--}66)$$

In multiplying through by $g/AD_p$, it is seen that

$$\frac{1}{A} \frac{dA}{dt} + \frac{1}{D_p} \frac{dD_p}{dt} = 0$$

$$\frac{1}{A} \frac{dA}{dt} = -\frac{1}{D_p} \frac{dD_p}{dt} \qquad (10\text{--}67)$$

On the left is the horizontal stretching and on the right the vertical shrinking of the volume. Since horizontal stretching is horizontal divergence, we may write

$$\text{div}_2\, c = \frac{\partial u}{\partial x} + \frac{\partial v}{\partial y} = \frac{1}{A} \frac{dA}{dt} = -\frac{1}{D_p} \frac{dD_p}{dt} \qquad (10\text{--}68)$$

The relationship states that the measurement of the fractional change per unit time of the area occupied by an identifiable body of air gives the horizontal divergence. It is also given in the negative sense by the fractional change per unit time of the depth. For the total divergence to be zero, horizontal stretching (divergence) must be compensated by vertical shrinking (convergence) and vice versa.

The area method of measuring horizontal divergence in the atmosphere can be accomplished by the use of carefully tracked balloons. Three or more balloons are released simultaneously so that, having the same free lift, they reach the different levels of the atmosphere at the same time. Three balloons will form the vertices of a triangular area and four or more balloons will form the corners of a figure of four or more sides. The area enclosed by the balloons is measured at frequent time intervals. If the area enlarges as the balloons pass through a layer of finite thickness, say from 300 to 500 m, horizontal divergence is given for that layer by the fractional change of the area. The fractional shrinkage of the area per unit of time as the balloons pass through a layer would measure the horizontal convergence in that layer.

The depth-change method of determining divergence or convergence can be applied in connection with isentropic surfaces. If vertical displacements are accomplished adiabatically (isentropically), then an isentropic surface is a *substantial* surface, that is, one which must move exactly up or down with the displacement of the air particles, or a surface through which air particles cannot move. The fractional variation with time of the pressure-depth contained between two given isentropic surfaces as the air is channeled between them gives a measure of the horizontal divergence and convergence.

A more conventional method of computing the horizontal divergence is based on an analysis of the wind field to obtain $\partial u/\partial x$ and $\partial v/\partial y$. A map is made of a region, such as the United States or Western Europe, containing isolines of values of $u$ and a similar map of the values of $v$. The number of unit isolines in a unit $x$ distance at a given location on the first map is $\partial u/\partial x$ and the number in a unit $y$ distance on the second map is $\partial v/\partial y$. The sum of these two values is plotted on a third map and the isolines constructed therefrom show the pattern of horizontal divergence and convergence.

It is also possible to evaluate the horizontal divergence by means of a streamline chart using the total velocity $c$. Two sets of lines are needed: the streamlines and the isolines of equal total wind speed, called *isotachs*. Over restricted areas, or if the velocity is irrotational, the isotachs, like lines of velocity potential, are orthogonal to the streamlines. However, this is not a requirement for application of the method. In Fig. 10–13 the two stream-lines and the two isotachs form an area $abcd$. The isotachs correspond to the magnitudes

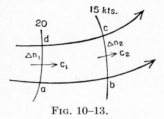

FIG. 10–13.

of the wind vectors $c_1$ and $c_2$ drawn in the middle of the streamline channel. These vectors represent the distance the air particles would be displaced in unit time, so if the streamlines remain fixed, the change in area in unit time would be given by $c_2\,\Delta n_2 - c_1\,\Delta n_1$. Dividing this by the area itself, we would have the horizontal divergence

$$\operatorname{div}_2 c = \frac{c_2\,\Delta n_2 - c_1\,\Delta n_1}{A} \tag{10–69}$$

This method is difficult to apply in the free air because of the difficulty of obtaining true streamlines from the sparse network of slightly inaccurate balloon wind measurements.

It should be noted that convergence of the streamlines does not in itself indicate convergence. As the separation $\Delta n$ becomes smaller, $c$ increases and often does so in the same proportion such that the divergence is zero.

**Continuity, Angular Momentum, and Vorticity.** Earlier in this chapter some consequences of the tendency for conservation of absolute vorticity in the atmosphere were suggested. Considerations of conservation of mass (continuity) and, indirectly, of the conservation of total angular momentum enter into the problem, as will now be shown.

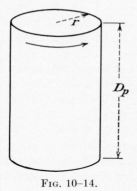

For a simple approach to the problem, a cylindrical mass of air with its base on the ground as in Fig. 10–14 is considered. It has the area $A = \pi r^2$ and the depth or height $D_p$, both of which may be permitted to vary together in such a way that the mass is preserved. It is assumed that the cylindrical column has vertical components of relative vorticity $\zeta$ and of angular velocity $\omega'$ superimposed on the local vertical components of the earth $f$, and $\omega$, respectively. The vertical component of the absolute vorticity is $f + \zeta$ and the vertical component of the absolute angular velocity is $\omega + \omega'$.

FIG. 10–14.

As stated in Eq. (9–7), the angular momentum is given in general terms by

$$M\omega r^2$$

where $M$ is the mass and $\omega$ is any angular velocity. According to the physical law of the conservation of momentum, rotating masses, in the absence of friction, conserve their angular momentum. In our example, we are dealing with the absolute angular momentum of the air column, so

$$M(\omega + \omega')r^2 = \text{const} \qquad (10\text{–}70)$$

The vertical component of the absolute vorticity is, according to Eq. (10–1),

$$f + \zeta = \tfrac{1}{2}(\omega + \omega')$$

so we may write Eq. (10–70) in the form

$$M(f + \zeta)r^2 = \text{const} \qquad (10\text{–}71)$$

Substituting the area of the cylinder $A$ for $\pi r^2$ and absorbing $1/\pi M$ in the constant, we have, for constant mass,

$$(f + \zeta)A = \text{const} \qquad (10\text{–}72)$$

as a statement of the conservation of absolute angular momentum. The derivative of this expression with respect to time is

$$(f + \zeta)\frac{dA}{dt} + A\frac{d}{dt}(f + \zeta) = 0 \qquad (10\text{–}73)$$

We divide through this equation by $(f + \zeta)A$ obtaining

$$\frac{1}{A} \frac{dA}{dt} + \frac{1}{f + \zeta} \frac{d}{dt} (f + \zeta) = 0 \tag{10-74}$$

The first term is recognized as the horizontal divergence. We substitute the pressure-depth for the area and obtain the meteorologically important equation

$$\frac{1}{f + \zeta} \frac{d}{dt} (f + \zeta) - \frac{1}{D_p} \frac{dD_p}{dt} = 0 \tag{10-75}$$

or

$$\frac{1}{f + \zeta} \frac{d}{dt} (f + \zeta) = \frac{1}{D_p} \frac{dD_p}{dt} = - \operatorname{div}_2 c \tag{10-76}$$

This shows that the change in absolute vorticity and the change in depth of an air column must go together and that the fractional change in the absolute vorticity is equal to the horizontal convergence.

To integrate this expression, we multiply through by $D_p(f + \zeta)/D_p{}^2$ and get

$$\frac{D_p (d/dt)(f + \zeta) - (f + \zeta) dD_p/dt}{D_p{}^2} = 0 \tag{10-77}$$

which has the form

$$\frac{d}{dt} \left( \frac{x}{y} \right) = \frac{y(dx/dt) - x(dy/dt)}{y^2}$$

So, the integral of Eq. (10–77) is

$$\frac{f + \zeta}{D_p} = \text{const} \tag{10-78}$$

This equation and its time derivative represent one of a handful of relations that have real value in predicting future atmospheric flow patterns. As air particles move from one latitude to another, $f$ must change. Compensating changes must occur in $\zeta$ and $D_p$ in order to meet the requirements expressed by these physical equations. Keeping in mind the fact that vorticity is positive in the cyclonic sense and that divergence is symbolized by decreasing depth of a layer, the student can recognize the following qualitative results:

1. In poleward displacements, $f$ increases, so either $\zeta$ decreases or $D_p$ increases (convergence) or both adjustments occur.

2. In equatorward displacements, $f$ decreases, so either $\zeta$ increases or $D_p$ decreases (divergence) or both adjustments occur.

3. In straight easterly or westerly flows, $f$ does not change, so divergence decreases the relative vorticity $\zeta$ and convergence increases it. The same is true in small circulations, such as thunderstorms, where

the motions take place at essentially one latitude and there is no appreciable change in $f$.

**The Tendency Equation.**  At this point it should be of interest to use concepts discussed in this chapter to illustrate some of the factors that determine the changes in atmospheric flows, that is, the departures from the steady state.  One application of these concepts, namely the computation of trajectories with constant absolute vorticity, neglecting the divergence term, has already been mentioned.  Another application of these concepts is in the development of the barometric tendency equation.  It shows how divergence and vertical motion contribute to the change in the pressure with time either at the surface or in the free atmosphere.

The pressure at any point at height $z$ is given by the total weight of a column of unit cross-sectional area extending from $z$ to the outer limit of the atmosphere.  Or, integrating the hydrostatic equation from $z$ to $\infty$ where the pressure goes from $p$ to $0$, we have

$$- \int_p^0 dp = \int_0^p dp = p = g \int_z^\infty \rho \, dz \qquad (10\text{--}79)$$

The pressure tendency recorded on a barograph at a fixed point at height $z$ would simply be the derivative of the above with respect to time, or

$$\left( \frac{\partial p}{\partial t} \right)_z = g \int_z^\infty \frac{\partial \rho}{\partial t} \, dz \qquad (10\text{--}80)$$

From the equation of continuity we have

$$\frac{\partial \rho}{\partial t} = - \frac{\partial(\rho u)}{\partial x} - \frac{\partial(\rho v)}{\partial y} - \frac{\partial(\rho w)}{\partial z}$$

This may be written as

$$\frac{\partial \rho}{\partial t} = - \frac{\partial(\rho c)}{\partial s} - \frac{\partial(\rho w)}{\partial z} = - \operatorname{div}_2 (\rho c) - \frac{\partial(\rho w)}{\partial z} \qquad (10\text{--}81)$$

where $c$ is the total horizontal velocity and $s$ is distance, positive downwind, on a streamline of that velocity.  When this is substituted in Eq. (10–80) the result is

$$\left( \frac{\partial p}{\partial t} \right)_z = -g \int_z^\infty \operatorname{div}_2 (\rho c) \, dz - g \int_z^\infty \frac{\partial(\rho w)}{\partial z}$$

$$= -g \int_z^\infty \operatorname{div}_2 (\rho c) \, dz + (g\rho w)_z \qquad (10\text{--}82)$$

the last term being zero at $z = \infty$ where $\rho = 0$ and at the ground where $w = 0$.

This equation, which is an explicit expression of the change in weight of the air column above $z$, shows that this change is contributed to in part by horizontal mass divergence above $z$ and in part by transport of air into or out of the column through the level $z$. If more air goes out of the column than into it, either by horizontal divergence (first term) or downflow through the bottom (second term) or by both processes, the pressure at $z$ will fall.

By itself the tendency equation is not very useful because standard synoptic-aerological observations cannot supply the values required for solution. In practice the tendency equation is useful as a guide to thinking about all pressure changes and it forms the starting point of approaches to numerical prediction. Numerical forecasting methods are discussed in Chap. 17.

**Comment.** In this chapter the student has been led through the equations of motion which are derived from fluid mechanics and applied to an atmosphere over a rotating, unequally heated planet. Since the laws of fluid flow are hardly touched upon in elementary college physics courses, the student has no doubt encountered much that is new and, perhaps, difficult.

At this point it must be apparent that meteorology is basically an exact science. Exact methods cannot be realized fully because all of the information necessary to apply the hydrodynamical and thermodynamical equations is not available. It is necessary to deal only with those data derived from the simple surface and aerological observations which can be made routinely and at a price the world economy can afford.

The development of high-speed electronic computing machines has made it possible to apply the equations to the atmosphere for purposes of prediction of the motion.

# CHAPTER 11

## THE GENERAL CIRCULATION

In discussing the general circulation of the atmosphere, one must keep in mind the fact that any system that purports to show the general movement of the air currents over the earth must be based on mean conditions. Since the daily weather charts show irregularities in the air flow, the mean circulation in many cases has little real significance. Nevertheless there is a general pattern of air transport over the earth, however complicated and inconstant it may be, which can be referred to as the general circulation of the atmosphere and which serves as the basis for explaining the distribution of various meteorological features. The climates of the earth are determined in large measure by location with respect to the main flows of the general circulation.

**The Thermal Driving Force.** A general circulation must arise by virtue of the fact that the surface and therefore the atmospheric envelope of the earth have strong poleward temperature gradients. A wide belt centered at the equator serves as a heat source while the high-latitude areas around the two poles act as heat sinks. The atmosphere is a gigantic, though inefficient, heat engine, transforming the potential energy represented by the heat differences into kinetic energy of the mean motion. Through this motion, called the general circulation, heat is transported from source to sink. It is a solenoidal circulation, as discussed in the preceding chapter, but one that is highly modified by the coriolis acceleration due to the earth's rotation.

It should be pointed out, parenthetically, that the rotation alone cannot produce planetary winds. Except for the effects of atmospheric tides, which produce relatively insignificant motions in the denser part of the atmosphere, the atmosphere is fixed to the earth in gravitational equilibrium and, in the absence of other forces, moves with it.

Over the half of the area of the earth that lies between lat 30°N and S, the earth gains by net radiation a total of more than $10^{15}$ g-cal per sec averaged throughout the year. Between 30° and the poles there is a net loss of heat at about the same rate. (Actually, the boundary between gaining and losing portions in the Northern Hemisphere occurs at about

35° lat.) If there were no circulation to carry heat from equatorial to polar regions the tropics would have to become very much hotter and the high-latitude regions very much colder than they are at the present time. Radiation equilibrium would then be the only limit on the temperatures. While over the earth as a whole, averaged through the year, the same amount of radiant energy goes out to space as is received from the sun, a point-to-point equilibrium of this kind would lead to fantastically high temperatures in low latitudes and unheard-of cold in more northerly and southerly places. It is difficult, if not senseless, to try to compute these hypothetical temperatures, since the whole structure of the atmosphere, including the cloudiness, evaporation, etc., would have to change under these circumstances.

The observed temperatures, which, averaged over many years short of periods involved in geological epochs, remain approximately unchanged, result from a more or less steady heat transport by the general circulation superimposed upon radiation equilibrium. From the radiation data discussed in Chap. 3 it is possible to compute the rates at which heat must be transported across the latitude circles in order to account for the observed mean conditions of temperature in the various latitude belts. The amount of energy thus transported is given in Table 3–3 of that chapter.

The energy is transported partly as sensible heat and partly as latent heat, the former far outweighing the latter. A very small but not quite negligible amount of heat is transported by the ocean currents of which the Gulf Stream in the North Atlantic is the most important.

In the absence of rotation and surface inhomogeneities, the solenoidal field of the atmosphere should produce a single meridional circulation cell in each hemisphere. Near the equator the heating causes the atmosphere to expand vertically (bulge upward) so that there is a greater portion of the atmosphere above a certain height in the middle troposphere in that area than elsewhere. Since the pressure is the weight on a unit area, the pressure would be higher at that level over the equatorial region than north or south of it. The cooling at the poles causes the air to shrink vertically so that the mass above a fixed middle-troposphere height would be less there than in surrounding areas and therefore the pressure would be less. We should then have high pressure at, let us say, 5 km over the equator and low pressure at the same height over the poles. In response to this pressure gradient the air, on a nonrotating earth, would flow from the equator toward the poles at this level. The poleward outflow aloft over the equatorial region reduces the total weight of the atmosphere observed at sea level, that is, the sea-level pressure. The inflow aloft over the poles increases the total weight or sea-level pressure there. Thus, in response to the pressure gradient, there would be an equatorward flow at the surface of the earth. The circulation is completed by the ascension of warm air in the equatorial region and the sinking of cold air in the vicinity of the poles. The solenoidal field and circulation shown in Fig. 10–9 is exactly the one described here.

**Rotation Effects and the Tricellular Circulation.** A direct solenoidal circulation between the equator and the poles cannot exist on the rotating earth because of the coriolis acceleration. The poleward flow aloft has to turn into a westerly wind and equatorward currents become easterlies. Actually, the situation is much more complicated than one having a simple distortion by the coriolis deflection.

As shown in the derivation of the coriolis acceleration in Chap. 9, a useful way of looking at the deflection problem is from the point of view of conservation of angular momentum. If a particle at the equator, having initially no zonal (easterly or westerly) component in its motion, goes poleward toward the polar axis, conserving its angular momentum, it is flung eastward, while a particle going equatorward from one of the poles would have a deficit of west-to-east momentum with respect to the earth and would have to curve toward the west. The resulting zonal linear speeds with respect to the earth's surface can be computed from Eq. (9–7) for the conservation of angular momentum of a unit mass

$$u_1 r_1 = u_2 r_2$$

where $r_1$ and $r_2$ are the distances from the axis of rotation at latitudes $\varphi_1$ and $\varphi_2$, respectively. If the radius of the earth is designated by $R$, then

$$r_1 = R \cos \varphi_1$$
$$r_2 = R \cos \varphi_2 \text{ etc.}$$

We have, then,

$$u_1 R \cos \varphi_1 = u_2 R \cos \varphi_2 \tag{11-1}$$

or

$$u_2 = u_1 \frac{\cos \varphi_1}{\cos \varphi_2} \tag{11-2}$$

The west-to-east speed of a point fixed on the surface of the earth is given by Eq. (9–3):

$$u = \Omega r = \Omega R \cos \varphi$$

For the particle described above starting from the equator, since $\cos 0 = 1$, $u_1 = \Omega R$. If we take $\varphi_2$ as $60°$, $\cos 60° = \frac{1}{2}$, $u_2 = \Omega R/2 = u_1/2$. The values are

$$u_1 = 7.29 \times 6.37 \times 10^8 = 46{,}500 \text{ cm per sec}$$

$$u_2 = \frac{u_1}{2} = 23{,}225 \text{ cm per sec or 232 m per sec or 519 mph}$$

For a particle displaced from the pole to lat 60°, we have

$$u_1 - u_2 = \Omega R(\cos \varphi_1 - \cos \varphi_2)$$

but at the pole $u_1$ and $\cos \varphi_1$ are zero, so

$$u_2 = -\frac{\Omega R}{2} = -232 \text{ m per sec or 519 mph from the east}$$

These speeds are so far from reality that one immediately realizes that something must happen to the wind system. The reduction of the winds

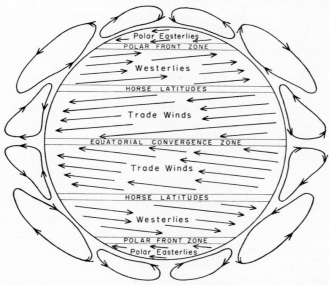

FIG. 11–1. Schematic representation of the general circulation, modified after Bergeron and Rossby.

from speeds calculated above to those that we normally observe cannot be accounted for by friction which, at least in the upper air, probably could reduce the speeds by only a few per cent.

What happens is that the meridional circulation breaks down into smaller circulations. Bergeron[1] depicted a system containing a meridional circulation of three cells. This system was modified by Rossby[2] and is shown in Fig. 11–1 with additional modifications. The net meridional circulation is represented in vertical cross section around the profile of the earth and the actual wind directions at the surface are

[1] Bergeron, T., Über die Dreidimensional Verknüpfende Wetteranalyse, *Geofys. Publikasjoner*, vol. 5, no. 6, 1928.

[2] Rossby, C.-G., The Scientific Basis of Modern Meteorology, in "Climate and Man," Yearbook of Agriculture, pp. 599–655, U.S. Department of Agriculture, 1941.

shown within the circumference. Throughout the atmosphere the meridional components are on the average less than one-tenth of the zonal components. Except for a belt of deep easterlies around the equator, the upper winds are prevailingly from the west. At the surface, three wind belts are noted in each hemisphere: the trade winds of low latitudes, the middle-latitude westerlies, and the polar easterlies.

The pressure-wind relationship applied to the surface circulation requires a belt of high pressure at about 30°N and S of the equator. This belt is called the "horse latitudes."[1] Low pressure is required between the westerlies and the polar easterlies.

Except for the easterlies of the trade-wind belt, the surface wind systems are quite variable. The continents develop thermally-induced wind and pressure systems, with relatively high pressures over the land areas in winter and lower pressures in summer. The wind systems pictured in Fig. 11–1 are best marked over the oceans, particularly in the Southern Hemisphere where the continental areas are small. The low-pressure area around the latitude of 60° is most inconstant. It is an average made up of the effects of all the moving cyclones of middle and high latitudes. The polar highs are also quite variable, especially in the Northern Hemisphere.

It is apparent from Fig. 11–1 that low-level convergence occurs in the meridional components at the equator between the trade winds of the two hemispheres and also between the middle-latitude westerlies and the polar easterlies. This latter convergence zone is in a strongly baroclinic part of the atmosphere. The meridional temperature advection tends to concentrate the solenoids and an average front, called the *polar front*, is developed there. As might be expected, however, the convergence is concentrated in certain parts of it where vorticity is generated. The cyclonic circulations pull the front away from any stationary position it may have and severe distortions are imposed. The equatorial convergence zone is in a barotropic atmosphere and in a latitude where the earth has no vertical component of vorticity. The absence of a coriolis force means that the air flows directly across the isobars and no cyclones can develop. At certain seasons the equatorial convergence zone is displaced 10 to 15° away from the equator. Under this circumstance cyclones can develop. Hurricanes and their Far Eastern counterparts, typhoons, sometimes develop in the displaced equatorial convergence zone.

As seen in Fig. 11–1, the polar and tropical meridional circulation cells

[1] It is thought that the name is derived from the numerous bodies of horses seen floating on the sea in these latitudes in the seventeenth century. It is related that sailing vessels transporting horses to the New World were becalmed in the high-pressure center and, running low on feed and water, reduced their cargoes in mid-ocean.

are in accordance with the expected circulation on a rotating planet with cold poles, but the middle cell cannot be explained easily. Bergeron's original picture has been modified by a number of investigators, as will be discussed on succeeding pages, so as to provide for a much smaller middle cell. The sinking in the horse latitudes has been explained as resulting from net heat losses by radiation at the upper levels. The

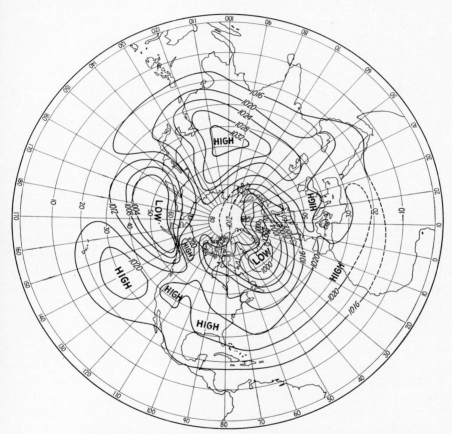

Fig. 11–2. January normal sea-level pressure, Northern Hemisphere.

magnitude of this effect can be estimated by examining Figs. 3–8 and 3–9 of Chap. 3. However, until more accurate data on the water-vapor and carbon dioxide absorptions and emissions at these levels have been obtained, this cooling cannot be specified with numerical certainty.

Charts of isobars at sea level or contours of the 1000-mb surface show considerable departures from the idealized flow pattern of the general circulation. The charts of Figs. 11–2 and 11–3 represent these distributions in midwinter and midsummer, respectively. The following departures from the idealized pattern should be noted in the Northern Hemisphere:

*Winter*

   *Polar anticyclone:* Missing.
   *Polar-front low-pressure belt:* Icelandic low and Aleutian low well developed; continents show high pressure, especially the Siberian high.

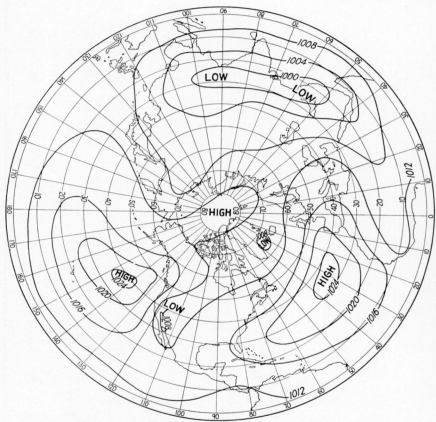

Fig. 11–3. July normal sea-level pressure, Northern Hemisphere.

   *Horse-latitude high-pressure belt:* Broken into cells over oceans, the Pacific anticyclone being the best defined; tendency for merging with continental highs in North America, Europe, and North Africa.
   *Trade-wind and equatorial regions:* Pushed southward but otherwise little modified.

*Summer*

   *Polar anticyclone:* Fairly well pronounced over Arctic Ocean.
   *Polar-front low-pressure belt:* Icelandic low present but weak; Aleutian low not discernible, but trough extends along Arctic Circle into Siberia.

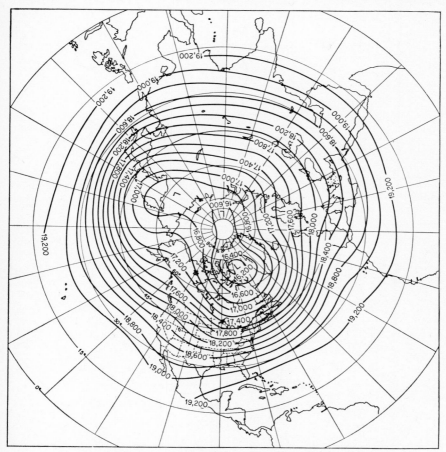

Fig. 11–4. January normal 500-mb chart, Northern Hemisphere.

   *Horse-latitude high-pressure belt:* Atlantic and Pacific high-pressure cells very well marked; continents in this belt are occupied by heat lows, especially in North Africa and Asia and the Arizona low.
   *Trade-wind and equatorial regions:* Trades interrupted by monsoon circulations in Indian Ocean, southern Asia, southwestern North Pacific Ocean areas, Gulf of Panama, and southern part of the bulge of Africa.
   In the Southern Hemisphere the circulation follows the idealized pattern more closely than in the Northern Hemisphere. Nevertheless

the horse-latitude high-pressure belt is broken up into cells and noticeable thermal effects of the continents are present. For example, over Australia there is a summer (January) heat low and a winter (July) continental high pressure.

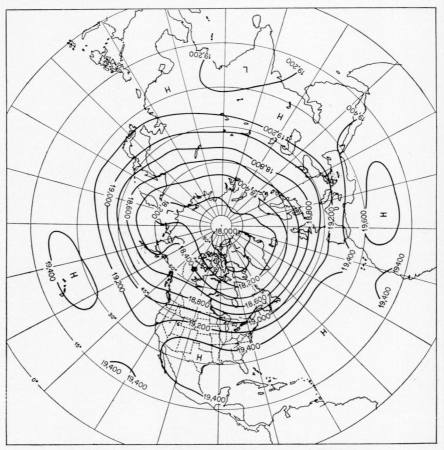

Fig. 11–5. July normal 500-mb chart, Northern Hemisphere.

The upper-air mean charts shown in Figs. 11–4 and 11–5 exhibit fewer departures from the idealized flow. Note the concentration of the westerlies in a relatively narrow band, to be discussed in a later section, and the asymmetrical character of the polar low.

In all charts the winds may be inferred from the isolines, which, according to the pressure-wind relationship, are approximate streamlines.

**Moving Cyclones and Anticyclones.** Persons living in middle to high latitudes are well aware that their weather represents anything but a steady state.   In general, westerly winds prevail, but the weather is characterized by the alternate passage of cyclones and anticlycones, accompanied by windshifts and sharp changes in temperature as well as by large, moving precipitation areas.   As pointed out by Bjerknes and Solberg[1] in 1922, the migrating cyclones and anticyclones furnish the most important mechanism by means of which the heat exchange

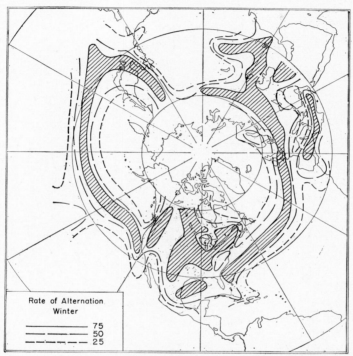

Rate of Alternation
Winter

————————————— 75
————  —  ——  — 50
——  — —  ——  — 25

Fig. 11–6. Rate of alternation (per cent) between cyclones and anticyclones in winter, after Petterssen.   Shaded areas have rates above 75 per cent.

between high and low latitudes occurs.   As a matter of fact, a meteorologist studying synoptic charts in the Northern Hemisphere in winter is much more aware of the heat exchange by means of these wheels within wheels than he is of the large wheels of the gross circulation.

A chart prepared by Petterssen[2] is reproduced in Fig. 11–6 showing the rate of alternation between cyclones and anticyclones in the Northern Hemisphere in winter.   From 40 years of weather maps the positions of all centers of cyclones and anticyclones were located to the nearest

[1] Bjerknes, J., and H. Solberg, Life Cycle of Cyclones and the Polar Front Theory of Atmospheric Circulation, *Geofys. Publikasjoner*, vol. 3, no. 1, 1922.

[2] Petterssen, S., *Roy. Meteorol. Soc. Centenary Proc.*, pp. 120–155, 1950.

degree of latitude and longitude, and were grouped for each 5° square. To correct for the difference in area of the various 5° squares, the frequencies were reduced to a standard area of 100,000 sq km, or approximately the area of such a square at 70°N. The numbers are the ratio of cyclone frequency to anticyclone frequency, or vice versa, expressed in percentages. The summer chart, not reproduced here, is similar.

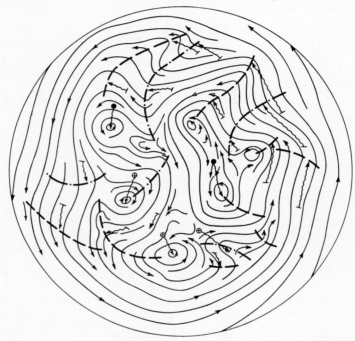

FIG. 11–7. Flow pattern represented in streamline analysis of rotating-pan experiment. (*After Fultz.*)

These charts demonstrate the importance of alternating cyclones and anticyclones and the various currents and air masses they bring with them in exchanging air across the latitudes.

How the atmospheric circulation breaks up into complicated flow patterns is demonstrable in fluid-model experiments. Fultz[1] has reproduced circulations remarkably similar to those of the atmosphere in the laboratory. A shallow cylindrical pan containing water and a tracer material is rotated at the center and heated below the rim. A flow pattern obtained in the case of a rotation at 3.86 rpm is shown in Fig. 11–7. And for comparison the 500-mb pressure-contour map for 0300 GMT on Feb. 17, 1952, is shown in Fig. 11–8.

[1] Fultz, D., *Proc. Midwest Conf. Fluid Dynamics*, pp. 297–304, 1950.

**Analysis of Meridional Exchange.** The preceding discussion points out the unreality of a model in which mean meridional flows account for the heat exchange. Measured winds and pressure distributions over the earth fail to show the necessary transport of heat by the *mean* winds. The next step is to determine quantitatively whether or not the superscale

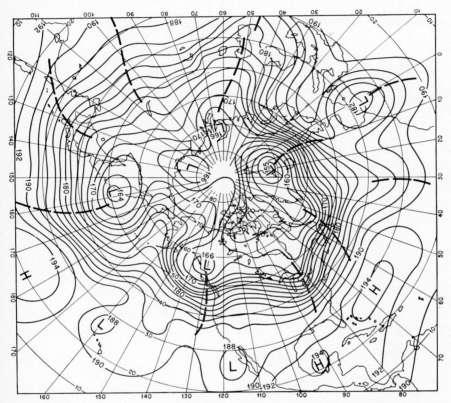

Fig. 11–8. Chart of contours of 500-mb surface in the Northern Hemisphere at 0300 GMT, Feb. 17, 1949, showing similarity to Fig. 11–7.

eddies of cyclonic and anticyclonic disturbances will bring the heat distribution into proper balance.

From a study of daily synoptic charts for the surface and free atmosphere it is possible to arrive at good estimates of the poleward transport by these superscale eddies of sensible and latent heat. These can then be compared with the values of the required transports given in Table 3–3. Estimates of this kind for the Northern Hemisphere have been made by a number of meteorologists. The estimates at the latitudes of maximum transport, i.e., at from 30 to 50°N, give values of about 9.5 to 11.1 × 10¹⁹

g-cal per day northward transport.    This accounts for nearly all of the
required amounts in these latitudes.    In the trade-wind belt, the exchange
by this method is far below that required, being close to zero at 20°N and
questionable from there to the equator.    It is suggested that there is a
direct mean transport in the tropics.

These studies lead to the conclusion that for the general circulation
as a whole the mean potential energy is not converted directly into the

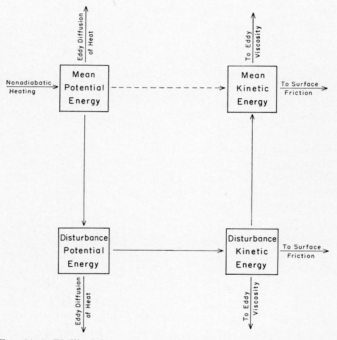

Fig. 11–9. Phillips' flow chart of energy in the general circulation.

mean kinetic energy, but operates through the transformation of energy
in disturbances.

Phillips[1] has summarized the transformations of energy by means of a
flow chart, as in Fig. 11–9.    Starting in the upper left, one sees that the
mean potential energy is supplied by the heating and cooling processes
over the earth, as indicated by the arrow coming into the box from the
left.    These are the nonadiabatic processes due mainly to net radiation
gains and losses.    This potential energy is contained in the solenoidal
field in a north-south vertical plane.    The outgoing arrow above the box

[1] Phillips, N. A., The General Circulation of the Atmosphere: A Numerical Experiment, Quart. J. Roy. Meteorol. Soc., vol. 82, pp. 123–164, 1956.

signifies the loss of some of the potential energy by diffusion which tends to smooth out the temperature gradients and thus to decrease the solenoidal concentration. From the mean potential energy the disturbances have been started, as the mean potential energy is transformed into disturbance potential energy by distorting the field of temperature and solenoids. While the mean potential energy is represented by a meridional solenoidal field, the disturbance potential energy is characterized by a zonal component of the solenoidal field. Again, some of this energy is lost by eddy diffusion of heat to weaken the field. The transformation of disturbance potential energy into disturbance kinetic energy, as shown by the lower horizontal line, represents the effect of the circulation accelerated by the zonal solenoidal field. Some of this kinetic energy is lost through internal eddy viscosity and surface friction, as signified by the two outgoing flows. Along the right-hand side of the chart it is seen that the kinetic energy of the disturbances goes into the kinetic energy of the mean zonal flow. Phillips has derived analytical expressions for each of these transformations from which it is found that the last-named transformation is favored by having the disturbances so arranged as to transport the high angular momentum of lower latitudes to higher latitudes where it becomes greater *relative* momentum.

While the classical theories assume that the greater part of the energy transformation is from the mean potential energy to the kinetic energy of the mean zonal motion, as indicated by the dashed arrow across the top of the diagram, more recent information suggests that the energy flow may be in the opposite direction. That is to say, the mean zonal circulation does not use up the mean potential energy but rather helps to create it. The mean flow seems to have a slight tendency to strengthen the meridional solenoidal field rather than to weaken it by using up the energy represented therein. Although the amount of energy transformed from kinetic to potential in this way must be small, it has been found to go in this direction by Starr[1], Phillips[2], and others. Riehl and Fultz,[3] however, have suggested that this result is found because the equator and other latitude and longitude circles are taken as the coordinate reference system for the flow of energy. By taking a reference system fixed along the center line of maximum wind in the upper troposphere, they find that the net energy flow is in the direct sense, from mean potential energy to mean kinetic energy. This line of maximum wind which meanders through each hemisphere in middle latitudes is the so-called

[1] Starr, V. P., Commentaries Concerning Research on the General Circulation, *Tellus*, vol. 6, pp. 268–272, 1954.

[2] Phillips, *loc. cit.*

[3] Riehl, H., and D. Fultz, The General Circulation in a Steady Rotating-Dishpan Experiment, *Quart. J. Roy. Meteorol. Soc.*, vol. 84, pp. 389–417, 1958.

*jet stream.* More information about it is given later in this chapter. It is significant as a reference line because it divides the upper meridional-vertical circulation into two parts—a warm part between the equator and middle latitudes and a cold part between middle latitudes and the poles. The temperature gradient is concentrated within the jet stream.

Hydrodynamic-model experiments, such as those shown in Fig. 11–7, as well as theoretical analyses demonstrate that the circulation of planetary atmospheres should break up into a number of perturbations and that these perturbations really characterize the flow. The theoretical equations are beyond the intended scope of this book. After developing the equations, Phillips applied them to an atmosphere initially at rest with heat being added but with no disturbances permitted. After the atmosphere was thus set in motion, a random perturbation was added and the resulting circulations noted. To do this, it was necessary to use a high-speed electronic computer. About five rotations, or five days, after the disturbance was introduced and lasting for about 20 more days, a wave developed having many of the characteristics of the large-scale eddies seen on actual weather charts. At the end of the 20-day period the errors caused by taking finite differences between a manageable number of points instead of actual gradients and curvatures from an infinite number of points became serious. The theory predicted the three principal surface wind belts, the existence of a concentrated west-to-east flow in upper levels (the jet stream), and the required net poleward transport of energy. For the 20-day period when the theoretical model was behaving naturally, the energy transformation processes were in agreement with available knowledge of these processes in the natural atmosphere.

The disturbances account for most of the required heat transport across middle latitude circles but produce virtually no effect in the tropics. The polar regions are also in the doubtful category, but the amount of air included in a latitude circle at, let us say, 80° is relatively too small to be very important. Where the transport by disturbances does not seem to apply, one seeks some other explanation. A useful way of getting at the problem is through an analysis of the meridional transport of momentum.

**Meridional Transport of Momentum.** In the rotating-pan experiment mentioned on page 270, one finds that the fluid, especially in a middle-latitude ring, rotates faster than the pan. It is obvious that angular momentum from the rim of the pan is being transported inward toward the center. In order to get a general expression for this transport, a ring of unit width can be taken running around the latitude $\varphi$ in the pan and through the depth $D$ of the water. Neglecting the difference in circumference of the outside and inside of the ring, which we certainly could do if we were considering something as big as the atmosphere, we can say that the mass of the ring is

$$M_\varphi = 2\pi r_\varphi \bar\rho D \tag{11-3}$$

where $\bar\rho$ is the mean density of the water in the ring. The absolute angular momentum of the water is made up of the angular momentum of a fixed ring plus the relative angular momentum of the water in that ring, or

$$\mu_\varphi = M_\varphi \Omega r_\varphi^2 + M_\varphi \bar u r_\varphi \tag{11-4}$$

where $\bar u$ is the average relative linear zonal speed in the ring. Substitution for $M_\varphi$ gives

$$\mu_\varphi = 2\pi r_\varphi^2 \bar\rho D(\Omega r_\varphi + \bar u) \tag{11-5}$$

The momentum would be transferred toward the center by the mean inward velocity component around the ring $-dr/dt$ which we choose to call $+\bar v$ as in the rectangular coordinates used in the actual atmosphere. The transport is the momentum multiplied by this velocity or

$$\mu_\varphi \bar v = 2\pi r_\varphi^2 D(\Omega r_\varphi \overline{\rho v} + \overline{\rho u v}) \tag{11-6}$$

For a ring in the atmosphere, we would have a similar expression, except that the values of the density and the velocity would vary with height and would have to be integrated through the height instead of being simply multiplied by $D$. At the surface, $r_\varphi = R \cos \varphi$, where $R$ is the radius of the earth. To be exact, we would have to consider that the distances from the center and from the axis $R$ and $r_\varphi$, respectively, vary between the bottom and top of the atmosphere, but the appreciable atmosphere is so thin compared with the radius of the earth that we are justified in assuming the same values all the way out from the surface. We have, then,

$$[\mu_\varphi \bar v]_{z_1}^{z_2} = 2\pi R^2 \cos^2 \varphi \left\{ \int_{z_1}^{z_2} \Omega R \cos \varphi \, \overline{\rho v} \, dz + \int_{z_1}^{z_2} \overline{\rho u v} \, dz \right. \tag{11-7}$$

Over a long time the mass of air north and south of latitude $\varphi$ is conserved; that is, there is neither a net accumulation nor a net deficit of air on either side of the ring. If the entire ring and the total depth of the atmosphere is considered, we note that

$$\int_0^\infty \overline{\rho v} \, dz = 0$$

So the first term vanishes and

$$[\mu_\varphi]_0^\infty = 2\pi R^2 \cos^2 \varphi \int_0^\infty \overline{\rho u v} \, dz \tag{11-8}$$

or, on pressure surfaces, since $dp = -\rho g\, dz$,

$$[\mu_\varphi]_{p_0}^0 = \frac{2\pi R^2 \cos^2 \varphi}{g} \int_0^{p_0} \overline{uv}\, dp \qquad (11\text{--}9)$$

where $p_0$ is the mean surface pressure at latitude $\varphi$. It is seen that north-ward transport of positive (west-to-east) relative momentum occurs when the $u$ and $v$ components of the mean flow around the ring are both positive. This is equivalent to the southward transport of negative (east-to-west) relative momentum when both components are negative. Thus the net meridional transfer of angular momentum depends on a correlation between these two components.

A correlation occurs in systems of troughs and ridges in the contours when the wind from the north has an easterly component (both components negative) and when the air from the south has a westerly component (both components positive). In a flow in the upper westerlies that is more or less sinusoidal, the winds on the east sides of the troughs would be from the southwest, thus with positive $\overline{uv}$, but on the west sides the winds would be from the northwest, hence with negative $\overline{uv}$. There would be no net momentum transport. "Tilted" troughs in the westerlies with streamlines from a northeasterly direction to the west of the troughs are required in order to produce a net northward transfer of momentum. This type of wind distribution occurs occasionally over limited areas of the westerlies.

Following the method of Priestley[1] and Palmén,[2] we can divide the last integral into two parts by considering $\overline{uv}$ to be made up the of mean values of the $u$ and $v$ components, designated $\bar{u}$ and $\bar{v}$, and of the fluctuations from the individual mean, designated $\overline{u'v'}$, so that $\overline{uv} = \bar{u}\bar{v} + \overline{u'v'}$. Equation (11–9) then becomes

$$[\mu_\varphi]_{p_0}^0 = \frac{2\pi R^2 \cos^2 \varphi}{g} \left( \int_0^{p_0} \bar{u}\bar{v}\, dp + \int_0^{p_0} \overline{u'v'}\, dp \right) \qquad (11\text{--}10)$$

The first term, called by Priestley the *drift term*, gives the net flux due to meridional flow. The second term gives the net flux due to fluctuations in the flow at latitude $\varphi$. Priestley calls it the *eddy-flux term*. It is the most important term for the exchange across middle latitudes because it represents the effects of the disturbances in the atmosphere of cyclonic and anticyclonic scale.

The drift term depends upon the existence of one or several circulation cells in the meridional plane. In going around a latitude circle, one must come back to the same pressure; therefore the mean value of the *geostrophic*

[1] Priestley, C. H. B., *Australian J. Sci. Research*, p. 1, 1950.
[2] Palmén, E., *Quart. J. Roy. Meteorol. Soc.*, vol. 77, p. 337, 1951.

meridional flow, which depends on this pressure distribution, must be zero. The mean drift is given by the mean value of the *ageostrophic* component $\overline{\Delta v}$. The drift term is positive if, through the vertical, there is a positive correlation between $\bar{u}$ and $\overline{\Delta v}$. Therefore, there is a poleward flux only if a poleward drift occurs, on the average, in layers with stronger west-wind components $\bar{u}$ than in layers of equatorward drift. The poleward drift would be most effective if it occurred at the tropopause, where $\bar{u}$ is strongest, and with an equatorward drift in the weaker winds above and below.

Since the poleward flux in the drift term depends on the integral through height of $\bar{u}\bar{v}$, the maximum must be where we have the strongest increase of $\bar{u}$ with height. Therefore this term gives the strongest contribution above the horse latitudes where calms exist at the surface and where a subtropical westerly jet stream is above.

Surface friction has the effect of injecting west-to-east angular momentum into the surface easterlies and extracting it from the westerlies. So the source of momentum is in the easterlies and the sink in the westerlies. It is therefore to be expected that the momentum transport will reach its maximum value at the horse-latitude high-pressure belt, which is the boundary zone between the easterly trades and the middle-latitude westerlies.

In middle to high latitudes the eddy-flux term predominates in transporting heat and momentum. It is in the $\overline{u'v'}$ term that the transfer of mean potential energy to mean kinetic energy is accomplished through the disturbance energy as outlined in the previous section.

In the tropics there appears to be a direct flux of heat and momentum through ageostrophic, direct circulations. Riehl,[1] after study of the tropical circulations, has shown that the exchange is a direct meridional one. The components are hard to identify because of seasonal variations. In the Northern Hemisphere part of the tropics, for example, the trade winds transport air toward the equator over the oceans. But over the continents the monsoon circulation transports air northward in summer. In winter, however, the outflows from the continents, especially into the Indian Ocean from Asia, transport air in the same meridional direction as do the trades.

**The Jet Stream and Its Perturbations.** Fluid model experiments agree with the observed motions in the atmosphere and in the oceans in showing a pronounced concentration of west-to-east motion in a narrow band. In the atmosphere, this concentrated current, called the *jet stream*, is centered just below the tropopause in middle latitudes around the earth; but it varies its position considerably, appearing as a fast-moving mean-

---

[1] Riehl, H., "Tropical Meteorology," McGraw-Hill Book Company, Inc., New York, 1954.

dering stream. These meanders are the perturbations in the upper westerlies, associated with the cyclones and anticyclones of the layers near the surface. Thus we find that from about 3 km upward into the lower stratosphere, westerlies prevail at all latitudes but tend to be concentrated in one or more jet streams. The perturbations appear on upper-air maps as troughs and ridges radiating from the great polar-cyclonic vortex. Mean contour charts of the 500-mb surface for winter and summer show the mean picture (Figs. 11–4 and 11–5). Vertical cross sections representing the meridional temperature and zonal wind distributions averaged for all the meridians of the Northern Hemisphere have

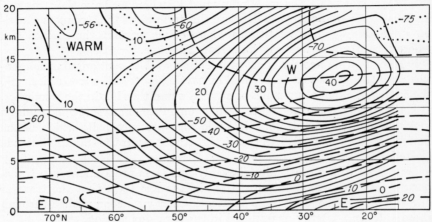

FIG. 11–10. Meridional cross section of mean zonal component of the geostrophic wind in m per sec (solid lines) and mean isotherms in °C (broken and dotted lines), both for winter season. Data are the means of all longitudes in the Northern Hemisphere. (*After Petterssen.*)

been prepared for winter and summer by Petterssen[1] and are shown in Figs. 11–10 and 11–11. As might be expected, the zones of strongest temperature gradient, the greatest slope of the isobaric surfaces, and the strongest zonal winds more or less coincide.

In the winter cross section it is noted that there is a mean speed in the jet stream of 40 m per sec (90 mph) and in summer, 15 m per sec (34 mph). This picture is somewhat misleading, however, for it does not show the speeds and positions attained at any given moment. The cross section in Fig. 11–12, taken from Riehl,[2] is more typical. It shows two jet streams; the one over southern Texas, which corresponds to the mean jet stream of Fig. 11–10, is the weaker of the two. The mean picture

[1] Petterssen, S., *Roy. Meteorol. Soc. Centenary Proc.*, pp. 120–155, 1950.

[2] Riehl, H., Jet Stream in the Upper Troposphere and Cyclone Formation, *Trans. Am. Geophys. Union*, vol. 29, pp. 175–186, 1948.

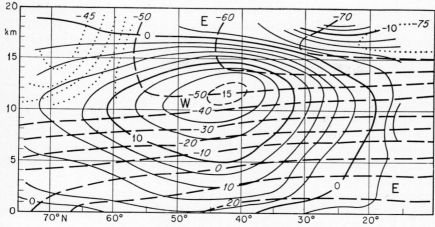

Fig. 11–11. Same as Fig. 11–10, for summer.

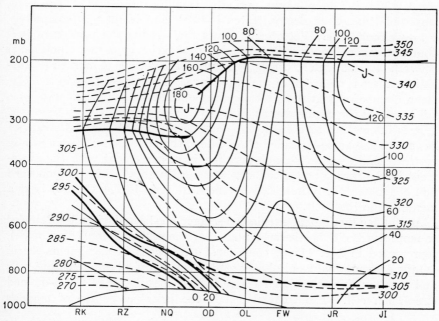

Fig. 11–12. Vertical cross section from Bismarck, North Dakota (*RK*) to Browns-ville, Texas (*JI*), Jan. 29, 1947, 03h, GMT.   Thin solid lines are lines of equal geostrophic zonal-wind speed (mph); broken lines are isotherms of potential tempera-ture; and heavy solid lines are tropopauses and boundaries of frontal layer.   The letter *J* represents regions of west-wind maximum.   (*From Riehl*, 1947.)

emphasizes this weaker jet because it is relatively stationary and therefore shows up repeatedly in the statistics.  The stronger jet to the north is constantly meandering and changing position and is the one associated with the middle-latitude perturbations.  This more northerly jet is associated with the polar front (see the cross section in Fig. 11–13).  Notice that the northern jet is in the vicinity of the strongest south-to-north temperature gradient where the heavy lines designate the polar front.  Notice also that the tropopause not only has its greatest slope but is actually broken at that point, permitting tropospheric air to flow more or less horizontally into the lower stratosphere.  The meanders or perturbations of the more northerly jet stream are associated with the perturbations of the polar front, where stormy conditions develop.  As air ascends upward along the slope of the front, condensation and precipitation occur.  This is therefore an important region for the transport of latent heat into the various levels of the troposphere.

As pointed out by Namias[1] and others, the atmosphere goes through periods of from perhaps a week to as much as two months in which the circulation over a large portion of the Northern Hemisphere is mainly zonal.  This is followed by a period of troughs and ridges of increasing amplitude, many, as demonstrated by Palmén,[2] leading to completely cut-off circulations.  Petterssen[3] shows that during the periods of predominantly zonal motion there is a deficit of exchange of mass (and heat) between low and high latitudes, and during the periods of marked perturbations there is an excess of such exchange.  Thus, we see again that the mean circulation statistics, by damping out the irregular perturbations, fail to reveal the required exchange.

It is interesting to note in the cross sections that the statistical jet lies above the horse-latitude belt of calms, thus producing there a strong vertical wind shear.  This observation is in agreement with the statement in the preceding section which states, in effect, that the poleward flux of momentum represented by the drift term in Eq. (11–10) is at a maximum in that belt.

A modified meridional circulation scheme has been devised by Palmén[4] to more nearly fit the observed facts.  His meridional circulation model, represented in Fig. 11–13, consists of three cells in each hemisphere: (1) the conventional tropical cell; (2) the extratropical or polar-front cell; and (3) the polar or subpolar region, which does not have a well-defined circulation cell.  The tropical cell is the principal source of angular

[1] Namias, J., General Aspects of Extended-range Forecasting, *Compendium of Meteorol.*, 1951, pp. 802–813.

[2] Palmén, E., *Tellus*, vol. 1, p. 22, 1949.

[3] Petterssen, S., *loc. cit.*

[4] Palmén, E., *Quart. J. Roy. Meteorol. Soc.*, vol. 77, p. 337, 1951.

momentum in the atmosphere. This cell has the subtropical jet at its poleward boundary. The polar front is given in dashed lines in the surface layer and in the upper troposphere to emphasize the necessity for exchange there in the form of intermittent "break-throughs." The polar front is not a continuous boundary. It should also be noted that there is a gap in the tropopause above the polar front, in agreement with observations. The polar front is given in its winter position. In summer it would be nearer the pole, but the general picture would be about the same.

Behind the polar front, former tropical air comes in aloft and is transformed as it converges with an upper-polar current, sinks, and then spreads out in the lower levels. The convergence shown around 60°N has been associated with the polar front in the older models, but according

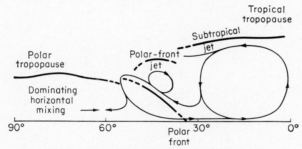

Fig. 11–13. Palmén's meridional circulation scheme.

to this picture that is incorrect. The mean polar front is not in that position. The stratosphere is not included in this representation, but it is to be expected that there is a weak poleward drift in the lower part and equatorward components above. The picture calls for large-scale horizontal mixing north of 60°.

In discussing perturbations linked with the jet stream there is some logic in working from the center of the vertical distribution of mass—the 500-mb surface—instead of from the level of the jet-stream maximum. From these levels upward into the stratosphere there is very little change in the location of the troughs and ridges. In the lower part of the atmosphere the axes of the troughs and ridges have a considerable slope, and at the surface of the earth the flow patterns are more complicated than those found in the free air. In the middle tropospheric layer, around 500 mb, the jet stream is a dominant feature of the circulation, although its core is at a higher level. Here one also finds, associated with the jet stream, the polar front existing all around the middle latitudes and, as Palmén[1]

[1] Palmén, E., Aerology of Extratropical Disturbances, *Compendium of Meteorol.*, 1951, pp. 599–620.

has pointed out, one finds the front more continuous and striking than it is at the surface of the earth.   Two schematic circumpolar charts for the 500-mb surface, showing the relation of this front to the perturbations on that surface as well as to the frontal systems at the ground, are reproduced from Palmén's paper in Figs. 11–14 and 11–15.   The first represents a simple four-wave pattern in the middle troposphere and the second, a highly-perturbed state with cut-off cyclonic centers.

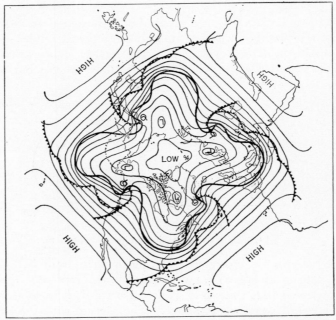

Fig. 11–14. Schematic circumpolar chart—four-wave pattern.   (*After Palmén.*)

It is apparent that with the meandering of the jet stream and the bulk of the upper westerlies there comes a series of wavelike displacements of the polar front and its accompanying tropopause perturbation. These wave disturbances in the upper westerlies are linked with the frontal waves, cyclones, and anticyclones observed at the surface of the earth.   The waves form troughs and ridges, and domes and basins in the constant-pressure surfaces such as the 500-mb surface.   Their action can be followed and understood most easily in these middle-troposphere levels.

One is naturally curious about the way in which these wavy perturbations get started.   Note that in starting a theoretical circulation from scratch as outlined on page 274, Phillips added a random perturbation after the atmosphere was set in motion.   In the rotating-pan experiments of Fultz the flow appears to go spontaneously into wavelike perturbations in the westerlies.   It is believed that disturbances inherent in the apparatus and its surroundings, too minor to be detected, start the waves going.   It is reasonable to conclude that it is not necessary to look for detectable causes in the baroclinic atmosphere.   The unrest of convection

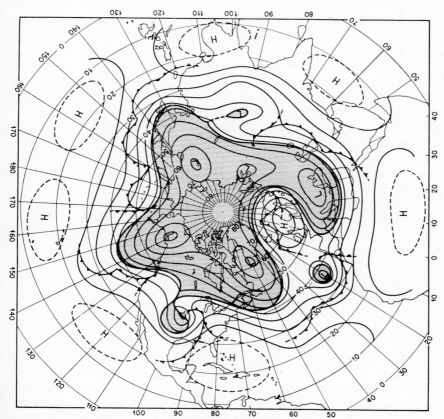

FIG. 11–15. Schematic circumpolar chart—highly perturbed state.   (*After Palmén.*)

and frictional turbulence may be enough to ensure that characteristic wave patterns develop.   There are at least two obvious large-scale initiating causes: (1) waves formed by flow over mountain barriers; and (2) disturbances of the general circulation by irregularly distributed heat sources, especially oceans (in winter) and continents (in summer).

From a study of synoptic charts, one gains the impression that extratropical cyclones are induced by moving disturbances already in existence. Every disturbance seems to be developed from or affected by a preexisting one.   In frontal zones there is a concentration of solenoids and therefore a concentration of potential energy.   A traveling middle-troposphere perturbation can induce there an irreversible process initiating the life cycle of a cyclone.

**Remarks on the Dynamics of the Jet Stream.**   As stated earlier in this chapter, the existence of a jet stream in the atmosphere of the planet Earth is predicted from a mathematically formulated model based on the hydrodynamic equations.   Phillips's mathematical-physical model, starting from an initial perturbation in an atmosphere at rest, was worked out on one of the giant electronic computers.

One can explain the existence of a jet stream by qualitative reasoning based on familiar concepts.   One might reason through the following steps:

1. From the law of conservation of angular momentum, the northward movement of tropical air required to balance the heat budget must produce zonal-wind speeds increasing with latitude, but this increase cannot continue all the way to the pole where an infinite speed would be approached.   The maximum zonal wind must occur at some intermediate latitude.

2. The cellular circulation is characterized by horizontal convergence in middle latitudes which brings the isotherms together and concentrates the temperature gradient there.   The solenoidal field is correspondingly concentrated.

3. The change of the geostrophic wind with height in a baroclinic atmosphere leads to the strongest upper winds in regions of maximum horizontal temperature gradient (maximum thermal-wind component).

4. The mutual adjustment of the wind and the pressure-density systems leads to a maximum wind at the belt where coincidence produces the most immediate adjustment.

5. Finally, from entirely empirical results in rotating hydrodynamic models, it can be shown that the rotation speed and the heating of the earth are right for the production of the kind of circulation observed, which includes a wavy middle-latitude jet stream.   Certain other rotation speeds and other heating rates in a properly scaled laboratory model do not produce a true jet stream or the kinds of circulation cells observed on the planet Earth.   It would be interesting if a way could be found for measuring the winds on other planets having other rates of rotation and heating.

**Monsoon Circulations.**   We return now to further consideration of the low levels and a direct thermal circulation of a seasonal nature which develops in those regions where thermally produced continental highs in winter or lows in summer dominate the circulation around a continent. Such circulations are called *monsoons*.   An ideal monsoon would be characterized by air flowing inward toward the thermal low of a continent in summer and outward from a continental high in winter. This flow produces heavy rains in the damp sea air, called *monsoon rains*. Some of the rain is caused by direct convection as the air comes in over the summer-heated land; but where the monsoon rains are most pronounced, e.g., in India, there is a convergence zone between the monsoon current and another wind system. In India this convergence takes place between the south and southwest monsoon current and a current from the northwest from the Arabian Sea. The effects are accentuated by mountains. What is reputed to be the rainiest place in the world, Cherrapunji, India, at 4455 ft on the south slope of the Khasi Hills in northeastern India, receives an average of $35\frac{1}{2}$ ft of rain annually, mostly in the summer monsoon.

In the winter monsoon, dry continental air is brought out from the continent. Usually, it is also very stable in the beginning and therefore does not produce rainfall until it travels out to sea. The warmth and high moisture content of the ocean, however, quickly modify the air. On the eastern coast of Asia the winter monsoon is quite generally felt, although it is interrupted at times by general storms. It deposits heavy rain on the Asiatic side of the Japanese islands, especially on Honshu, the largest and principal island, which is very mountainous. Farther south, in Taiwan and the Philippines, the winter monsoon appears as a pronounced northeast wind. It is sometimes said that the Indian monsoon is an ideal monsoon. However, the summer monsoon only is present in India. The Himalayas to the north and the mountains of Burma, Yunan, and Indo-China to the east prevent the winter monsoon from reaching India. The only region where both kinds of monsoon are felt in a pronounced way is in the vicinity of Taiwan and the East China Sea, with southerly winds in summer and northerly in winter.

No continents other than Asia show appreciable monsoon effects. In the Southern United States southerly winds predominate in summer, bringing air from the Gulf of Mexico, while northerly components prevail in winter. However, in both summer and winter the circulation is highly variable, and monsoon effects are noticeable only to the practiced eye. In India and southern Asia even the lowliest laborer in the rice fields is aware of the monsoon and depends on its regularity to save him from famine.

**The Oceanic Anticyclones.** The high-pressure cells over the oceans in the horse latitudes are the most permanent features of the general circulation. They are sometimes referred to as "centers of action," although they are characterized by inaction. The name comes from their importance as pivot areas around which storms circulate; i.e., when the center is displaced abnormally far to the north, storminess prevails farther north than usual, and when it is displaced to the south, the storms enter the continents in more southerly latitudes. Since these anticyclones are large and permanent and exist over the ocean where the greatest store of moisture is available, it is important to know their structure.

The Pacific and Azores anticyclones are great areas of subsiding air. The circulation is such that the subsidence effects are most noticeable in the eastern parts of these highs. In the western regions of the oceanic highs, convergence and ascent appear to be more prevalent. These differences produce differences in the thermal structure of the air. In the eastern portion, subsidence produces a strong inversion that usually lies at about 500 to 1500 m above sea level. The air above this inversion is very dry, and as a consequence of the dryness and thermal stability, the continents on the eastern sides of the oceans (west coasts) near lat 30°N and S are markedly deficient in rainfall. Some of the most arid regions of the world are found immediately on the ocean in these places, e.g., the Sahara Desert in North Africa, the Kalahari Desert in South Africa, the deserts of Western Australia, and the coastal deserts of northern Chile and Lower California. The western side of the oceanic highs is characterized by moist, conditionally unstable air and quite ample rains. Through the eastern part of the trade-wind belt the inversion is gradually carried to greater heights, often disappearing by the time the western part of the anticyclone is reached.

# CHAPTER 12

# VERTICAL STRUCTURE OF CYCLONES AND ANTICYCLONES

Rotating-pan experiments and aerological observations show the polar-front jet stream to be in a strongly baroclinic region. When wave-like perturbations develop in this meandering current, the frontal boundary is likewise displaced. At least in the upper and middle troposphere, the polar air is drawn equatorward in the troughs and the subtropical air is carried northward in the ridges. The tropopause is similarly displaced so that low tropopause conditions prevail in the troughs while the ridges have a high tropopause. Graphically speaking, one can say that the jet stream in its meanderings draws the isotherms with it. The strongest temperature gradients are observed across the jet, irrespective of the wave-like displacements.

In Fig. 12–1 a chart used by Bradbury and Palmén[1] is reproduced to illustrate the consistent pattern of the polar front extending all around the Northern Hemisphere at middle-troposphere levels (500 mb). Although the level represented here is considerably below the height of the core of the jet stream, the front is nevertheless associated with it and follows its meanderings.

By integrating the hydrostatic equation upward or downward from the core of the jet stream one would find that the pressure in the cold air occupying the troughs would increase rapidly downward. Upward it would decrease rapidly until the warm subpolar stratosphere is reached, after which it would decrease less rapidly than in the cool subtropical stratosphere. In the warm ridges, the rate of change with height would be relatively smaller, except in the stratosphere. At a level considerably below or above, the troughs and ridges could become completely smoothed, reversed, displaced, or otherwise modified because of the differences in hydrostatic weight between cold and warm air.

Since the air motion is approximately geostrophic, we can get at these

[1] Bradbury, D. L., and E. Palmén, On the Existence of a Polar-front Zone at the 500-mb Level, *Bull. Am. Meteorol. Soc.*, vol. 34, pp. 56–62, 1953.

changes in pressure pattern with height by applying the expressions for the change of the geostrophic wind with height.

**Vertical Structure as Shown by the Thermal Wind.** The thermal wind between any two pressure levels is defined from Eq. (9–62) as the vector

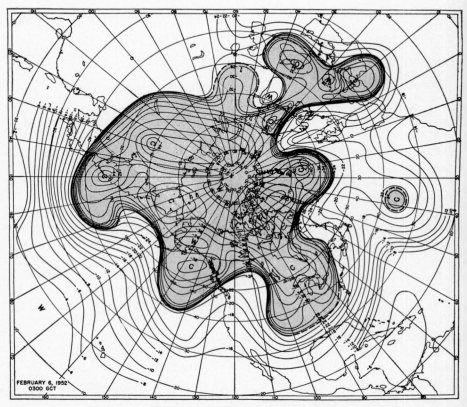

FIG. 12–1. Isotherms at 500 mb, Feb. 6, 1952, 0300 GCT for the Northern Hemisphere, showing front, *heavy line*, in vicinity of strongest temperature gradient. Shaded area represents polar air. Note cut-off cold air mass in middle Atlantic.

difference of the geostrophic wind at the upper level minus that at the lower level, given by the horizontal gradient of the thicknesses between the two pressure surfaces.

$$\vec{c_T} = -\frac{g}{f}\frac{\partial Z}{\partial n} = \vec{c_2} - \vec{c_1}$$

where $Z$ represents the thickness.

It has already been indicated that lines of thickness are likely to coincide with contour lines of the pressure surfaces in the vicinity of the jet stream, such as at the 300-mb surface. One also finds that when the entire layer between 300 mb and 1000 mb is considered, the gradient of the thicknesses is often about the same as the slope of the 300-mb contours. This would mean that the thermal wind for this very thick layer would

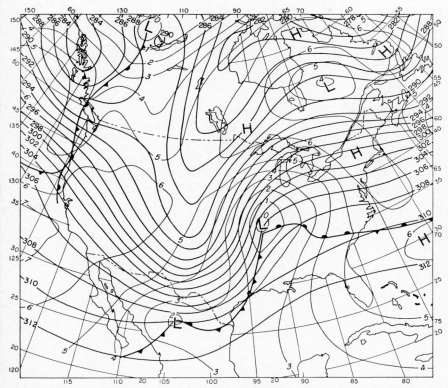

Fig. 12–2. Contours of the 1000-mb surface (light lines), thickness isolines 1000 to 300 mb (heavy lines) for 1200 GCT, Nov. 18, 1957, over North America. Values are given in hundreds of feet (5 is 500 ft, 312 is 31,200 ft, etc.).

not be very different from the 300-mb wind. In magnitude, the wind in the jet core may be several times the geostrophic wind at 1000 mb, in agreement with approximate similarity in magnitude between the thermal wind and upper wind. The thickness lines often have a slightly different orientation from the 300-mb contours, so that, even though it is of about the same magnitude as the 300-mb wind, the thermal wind has a slightly different direction. The vector difference between the two fits a 1000-mb wind vector with a direction quite different from that of the 300-mb wind.

A common case is that in which polar easterlies are observed at the ground under a westerly jet. Under these circumstances the thermal wind vector would exceed in magnitude the wind in the jet core.

The two charts in Figs. 12–2 and 12–3 illustrate the normal situation in which the 300-mb contours and the thickness lines between 1000 and 300 mb do not quite coincide. The difference between the pressure-contour patterns of the two surfaces represented separately in the two

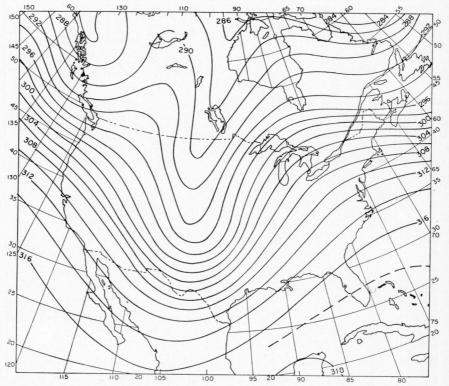

Fig. 12–3. Contours of the 300-mb surface corresponding to chart of Fig. 12–2.

figures is characteristic. It may be of interest to the student to use the three sets of lines (300-mb and 1000-mb contours and thickness lines) to construct the corresponding vector triangles at a few points of the maps.

The change in the geostrophic wind going upward in the stratosphere smooths out the perturbations. This should be apparent when one considers that warm stratospheric conditions overlie the cold troughs of the troposphere and that the warm tropospheric ridges have a high, cold stratosphere above. The pressure decreases slowly with height in the polar stratosphere and falls off rapidly with height in the cold subtropical stratosphere. As this tendency continues upward, the pressure slopes can approach zero and finally reverse. The increase of temperature with height in the subtropical stratosphere results in a diminution of the meridional temperature gradient at a certain height, so reversals of the flow pattern are not commonly observed. One cannot carry this line of thought upward too far, for reasons that become apparent in studies of the physics of the outer atmosphere.

**Temperature-pressure Statistics.** Formerly it was thought that high-pressure regions were due to the weight of cold air in the entire troposphere and that low pressures were caused by warm tropospheric air. This seemed to be in agreement with the fact that, at the ground, cold weather is associated with highs and warm weather with lows. It was somewhat of a surprise when in 1912 Schedler[1] and Dines[2] showed from statistical studies of European ballonsondes that high pressure is correlated with a predominantly warm troposphere and low pressure with a predominantly cold one. This is compensated by a high cold stratosphere over the highs and a low warm stratosphere over the lows.

Instead of considering the distributions directly over the highs and lows, it is more enlightening to consider the whole temperature and pressure field. We have already done this in our remarks about the relationship between the displacements with altitude of highs and lows and the distribution of the thickness lines or thermal wind. It is found from observation that the highest troposphere temperatures are found over the rear portion of surface highs and the lowest temperatures over the rear portion of surface lows. In the stratosphere, this temperature relationship is the reverse, i.e., cold stratosphere air is above the rear portion of surface highs and warm stratosphere air is above the rear portion of surface lows. These results are borne out by observations in North America by Haurwitz and Haurwitz[3] and by Penner.[4]

Penner's data, taken from the radiosonde observations of the U.S. Weather Bureau at Sault Sainte Marie, Michigan, are shown in Figs. 12–4 and 12–5. Penner divided the highs and lows passing the station into three regions each: the east side, the center, and the west side. Since the movement is from west to east most of the time, these regions become

[1] Schedler, A., Über den Einfluss der Lufttemperatur in verschiedenen Höhen auf die Luftdruckschwankungen am Erdboden, *Beitr. z. Phys. d. freien Atm.*, vol. 7, pp. 88–101, 1915.

[2] Dines, W. H., The Statical Changes of Pressure and Temperature in a Column of Air That Accompany Changes of Pressure at the Bottom, *J. Roy. Meteorol. Soc.*, vol. 38, pp. 41–50, 1912.

[3] Haurwitz, B., and E. Haurwitz, Pressure and Temperature Variations in the Free Atmosphere over Boston, *Harvard Meteorol. Studies*, no. 3, 1939.

[4] Penner, C. M., The Effects of Troposphere and Stratosphere Advection on Pressure and Temperature Variations, *Can. J. Research*, vol. 19, pp. 1–20, 1941.

the forward portion, center portion, and rear portion, thus indicating the order in which they pass over the station.   There were then six groups into which the available soundings at the station were arranged.   These are abbreviated in the figures as $L_f$, $L_c$, and $L_r$ for front, center, and rear of a low and by $H_f$, $H_c$, and $H_r$ for front, center, and rear of a high.

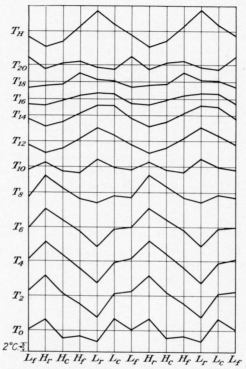

FIG. 12–4. Temperature profiles at various levels through highs and lows, based on mean annual conditions at Sault Sainte Marie, Michigan, as analyzed by Penner. $T_H$ is the temperature of the tropopause.

The temperature distribution at the various heights in Fig. 12–4 is for all seasons of the year.   It shows rather uniformly low temperatures at the ground extending from the rear of lows to the center of highs, then relatively warm conditions through the rear of highs to the center of the lows.   At all heights between 2 and 8 km, the points above the rear portion of surface highs show markedly higher temperatures than elsewhere, and the points above the rear portion of surface lows exhibit the lowest temperatures.   At the 10-km level, the temperature curve is highly irregular, as a result of mixed observations above and below the tropopause and a general transition from the characteristics of the troposphere to those of the stratosphere.   At 12 km, the temperature curves are completely reversed, the warmest air lying above the rear of lows and the coldest air above the rear of highs.   The temperature at the tropopause itself, represented by the curve $T_H$, shows the effects in a pronounced manner.

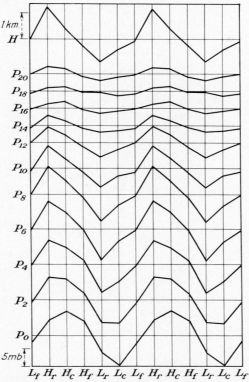

Fig. 12–5. Pressure profiles at various levels through highs and lows, from the same observations as in Fig. 12–4.   The curve $H$ gives the height of the tropopause.

The pressure distribution corresponding to these data is shown in Fig. 12–5.   The sea-level pressure $p_0$ furnishes the data on which the diagram is constructed.   At 2 km it is noted that the pressure to the rear of highs and lows is about the same as that at their centers and at 4 km the rear portion of each represents the highest or lowest pressure.   This condition exists throughout the troposphere and into the stratosphere. The height of the tropopause, represented by the top curve $H$, is greatest over the rear of the highs and least over the rear of the lows.

By combining the results of the two diagrams, one sees that through most of the troposphere the points above the rear portions of highs have the highest temperature and the highest pressure, while in the stratosphere this highest pressure still exists, but with the coldest temperature conditions and a high tropopause. The points above the rear portion of lows have, through most of the troposphere, the lowest temperatures and the lowest pressures, whereas this same lowest pressure exists in the stratosphere with the highest temperature and the lowest tropopause.

It is noted that the temperature or pressure condition does not change materially with height except near the ground and in the vicinity of the tropopause. The relative horizontal distribution of temperature is essentially the same at 6 as at 2 km. On the diagram of the pressures, it is seen that the pressure distribution is the same at all levels above 2 to 4 km. This is highly significant, since it suggests that, if a pressure map is drawn for a level such as 3 km, the troughs and ridges will, on the average, be found in the same longitudes at all levels up to about 14 km.

**Reflections on Pressure and Temperature Distributions.** The hydrostatic equation points directly to the fact that the pressure changes more rapidly with height in cold air than in warm air. Since pressure centers, troughs, ridges, etc., are only identifiable relative to their surroundings, that is, only by virtue of the fact that the pressure is higher or lower than at other nearby places at the same level, they can disappear, intensify, or change position relative to their surroundings if the weights or thicknesses vary horizontally. With a little reflection or application of the hydrostatic equation to the various situations, one can arrive at the following rules:

1. A surface warm-core cyclone disappears quickly with height.

2. A cyclone aloft in a warm-air column increases in intensity downward.

3. A cold-core cyclone increases in intensity with height.

4. A cyclone aloft in a cold-air column diminishes in intensity or disappears toward the ground.

5. A warm-core anticyclone increases in intensity with height.

6. An anticyclone aloft in a warm-air column diminishes in intensity or disappears toward the ground.

7. A cold-core anticyclone disappears quickly with height.

8. An anticyclone aloft in a cold-air column increases in intensity downward.

9. Low-pressure centers are displaced with height toward the colder air.

10. A low-pressure center aloft is found in lower levels in the direction of the warmer air.

11. High-pressure centers are displaced with height toward the warmer air.

12. A high-pressure center aloft is found in lower levels in the direction of the colder air.

13. At the surface of the earth, high pressure is favored in cold regions and low pressure in warm regions.

**The Nature of Fronts.** Fronts were first studied from the point of view of an observer on the ground. It is easy to make measurements and observations concerning fronts at the surface of the earth for obvious reasons of accessibility; hence a great deal of detail is known about them as they occur at the bottom of the atmosphere. This is fortunate, because their structure and behavior appear to be more complicated there than in the free atmosphere.

The picture of the continuous polar front at 500 mb, as represented in Fig. 12–1 at the beginning of this chapter, is quite different from that found at the ground. From the remarks on the preceding pages about the changes in wind and pressure distributions between the 300- or 500- and 1000-mb surfaces, one would also expect to find a difference in frontal distributions. The change in frontal patterns between the two surfaces is greater, however, than can be accounted for in terms of the change in pressure and wind distributions. Several reasons can be given for this situation. One condition that appears frequently in the low levels, particularly over and near continents in winter, is the tendency for solenoidal concentrations to develop or to disappear somewhat independently of the upper jet-stream concentration. Layers of temperature inversion, which are quite common in the low levels, can become frontal zones under some circumstances.

In Fig. 12–6, reproduced from a paper by Palmén and Newton,[1] a vertical cross section along the meridian 80°W shows the mean temperature and geostrophic west-wind component from twelve polar-front cases in December, 1946. This cross section represents the most simple, ideal situation in which a single frontal zone, associated with the polar-front jet stream, extends from the tropopause to the surface of the earth. In Chap. 15 a case is shown in which there appears to be no real connection between the upper-troposphere front and frontal zones near the surface. The student will encounter many such situations as he delves into synoptic analysis.

In the simplest sense, fronts may be defined as the boundary surfaces separating air masses of differing densities. While the air masses may exhibit changes in their properties measured over considerable distances, these changes are negligible when compared with those occurring across a front. To maintain this situation, the winds cannot be divergent in the vicinity of the front. If they were, they would cause the density or

[1] Palmén, E., and C. W. Newton, A Study of the Mean Wind and Temperature Distribution in the Vicinity of the Polar Front in Winter, *J. Meteorol.*, vol. 5, pp. 220–226, 1948.

specific volume lines to diverge away from each other rather than to concentrate as required.

In the idealized case it is convenient to think of a front as a mathematical discontinuity in property. Actually there is always a transition zone of a certain width, perhaps from 10 to 15 miles, where the air is of neither one kind nor another. However, in the scale of the usual synoptic map, 1:5,000,000 to 1:20,000,000, we are justified in marking the front as a broad pencil line, as is customary.

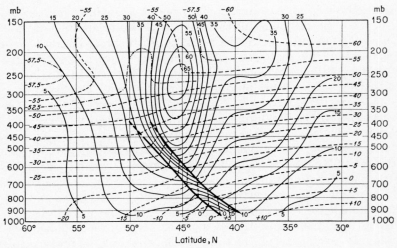

FIG. 12–6. Mean temperature and zonal component of geostrophic wind, computed from 12 cases in December, 1946. The cross section lies along the meridian 80°W. Heavy lines indicate mean positions of frontal boundaries. Thin dashed lines are isotherms (°C, slanting numbers) and solid lines are isolines of the westerly component of the wind (m per sec, upright numbers). Means were computed with respect to the polar front.

The front represents a temperature discontinuity, for it is only by differences in temperature that differences in density at any given level (or pressure) can be preserved, except for the slight effect on densities caused by varying amounts of water vapor. Since the air follows the ordinary laws of fluid statics and dynamics, it would be expected that the surface of separation would be horizontal, just as in the case of two fluids of different density, e.g., oil and water in a tank. However, the air masses can have a sloping boundary separating them and still be in equilibrium with respect to each other. This is because there are other forces besides that due to gravity which come into play where atmospheric motion is concerned. Most important of these forces is the coriolis force.

Under the conditions in the atmosphere, the denser air tends to force itself underneath the warmer, lighter air, just as in the case of laboratory fluid tests. But the colder air underlies the warm in a wedgelike fashion, the colder current resting on the ground with the warm air above its sloping upper surface. The representation of fronts on any surface amounts simply to a charting of the line of intersection of the fronts with the surface.

From given wind and temperature conditions in two air masses at a given latitude, it is possible to compute the slope of the front between them. This was first done by Margules[1] from methods developed previously by Helmholtz. A simple derivation of the equation for the equilibrium slope can be obtained from a consideration of the horizontal pressure gradient and static relationship above and below the front shown in vertical cross section in Fig. 12–7. In this figure, we may consider the rectangle

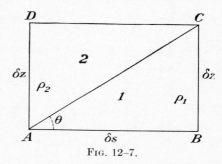

FIG. 12–7.

$ABCD$ to be of infinitesimal size, having vertical and horizontal sides $\delta z$ and $\delta s$. The slope of the front from $A$ to $C$ would be $\tan \theta$ or $\delta z / \delta s$.

Our problem first is to find the pressure gradient along $AB$ and along $CD$ in terms of the density of the two air masses and the slope of the surface, using the fact that the pressure gradient along $AC$ is common to both air masses. The lower colder air mass is designated by the subscript 1 and the upper warmer mass by the subscript 2. $P$ with appropriate subscripts denotes the pressure at points in question.

Remembering that $dP = -\rho g\, dz$, where $dP$ is measured vertically, we may set up the following expressions for the pressures at the corners of the rectangle:

$$P_B = P_C + \rho_1 g\, \delta z \tag{12–1}$$
$$P_D = P_A - \rho_2 g\, \delta z \tag{12–2}$$

Then, introducing the horizontal pressure gradients and substituting the above two expressions for $P_B$ and $P_D$, we have

$$\frac{P_B - P_A}{\overline{AB}} = \left(\frac{\delta P}{\delta s}\right)_1 = \frac{P_C - P_A}{\delta s} + \rho_1 g\, \frac{\delta z}{\delta s} \tag{12–3}$$

$$\frac{P_C - P_D}{\overline{DC}} = \left(\frac{\delta P}{\delta s}\right)_2 = \frac{P_C - P_A}{\delta s} + \rho_2 g\, \frac{\delta z}{\delta s} \tag{12–4}$$

[1] Margules, M., Über Temperaturschichtung in stationär bewegter und in ruhender Luft, Meteorol. Zeits., Hann-Band, p. 243, 1906.

Subtracting Eq. (12–4) from Eq. (12–3) gives

$$\left(\frac{\delta P}{\delta s}\right)_1 - \left(\frac{\delta P}{\delta s}\right)_2 = (\rho_1 - \rho_2)g\,\frac{\delta z}{\delta s} \qquad (12\text{–}5)$$

in which $(P_C - P_A)/\delta s$, which is a function of the pressure gradient along the frontal surface, has been eliminated. We then write

$$\frac{\delta z}{\delta s} = \tan\theta = \frac{\left(\dfrac{\delta P}{\delta s}\right)_1 - \left(\dfrac{\delta P}{\delta s}\right)_2}{g(\rho_1 - \rho_2)} \qquad (12\text{–}6)$$

According to the gradient wind equation,

$$\left(\frac{\delta P}{\delta s}\right)_1 = \rho_1\left(fv_1 \pm \frac{v_1{}^2}{r_1}\right)$$

with a similar expression for $(\delta P/\delta s)_2$, in which $r$ is the radius of curvature and $v$ is the component of the wind in a direction along the front. By substitution, Eq. (12–6) becomes

$$\tan\theta = \frac{\rho_1\left(fv_1 \pm \dfrac{v_1{}^2}{r_1}\right) - \rho_2\left(fv_2 \pm \dfrac{v_2{}^2}{r_2}\right)}{g(\rho_1 - \rho_2)} \qquad (12\text{–}7)$$

Experience has shown that the centrifugal term may be neglected in most determinations and that the wind may be considered as geostrophic. It is noteworthy, however, that in a cyclonic wind circulation $v^2/r$ is positive and thus may contribute to a steeper slope of the front, while an anticyclonic circulation would make this term negative and the slope would be less steep than for straight-line motion. For geostrophic conditions, we have

$$\tan\theta = \frac{f(\rho_1 v_1 - \rho_2 v_2)}{g(\rho_1 - \rho_2)} \qquad (12\text{–}8)$$

From the equation of state, $\rho_1 = p_1 m/RT_1$ and $\rho_2 = p_2 m/RT_2$, but, at any point on the frontal discontinuity surface, $p_1 = p_2$, so Eq. (12–8) becomes

$$\tan\theta = f\,\frac{(T_2 v_1 - T_1 v_2)}{g(T_2 - T_1)} \qquad (12\text{–}9)$$

If the temperature difference $T_2 - T_1$ is not too large and the wind difference is appreciable, we may neglect the difference in the two temperatures in the numerator of Eq. (12–9), and write

$$\tan\theta = \frac{fT_m}{g}\frac{(v_1 - v_2)}{T_2 - T_1} \qquad (12\text{–}10)$$

where $T_m$ is the mean of the two temperatures.    Ordinarily this expression is entirely suitable and sufficiently accurate.

In these equations the nature of the discontinuity under the assumed conditions of gradient balance [Eq. (12–7)] or geostrophic balance [Eqs. (12–8), (12–9), and (12–10)] and complete hydrostatic balance (no vertical accelerations other than gravity) is shown.    It is seen that the discontinuity, or front, can be sloping and still be in equilibrium with no net forces tending to rotate the front.    It is also possible for the front to be horizontal (tan $\theta$ = 0) if $v_1 = v_2$.    Under actual conditions in the atmosphere, any value of the slope from 0 to $\frac{1}{25}$ is observed.    It is probable that a mean value for actual fronts would be somewhere in the vicinity of $\frac{1}{100}$.    When the slope becomes less than $\frac{1}{500}$, the front intersects the ground so diffusely that it is no longer recognizable as a front.    Since the coriolis parameter at the equator is zero, no discontinuity of this nature can intersect the level ground, since then tan $\theta$ = 0.

Upon examination of the equations, it is seen that the following factors favor a steep slope of the front:

1. Large wind difference.
2. Small temperature difference.
3. High latitude.
4. High mean temperature (small effect).

As an example of a computation of the equilibrium slope, consider a case at lat 45° with east wind 5 m per sec in the cold air and west wind 5 m per sec in the warm air, temperature 277°K in the warm air and 273°K in the cold.    To simplify the computation, we shall use Eq. (12–10) and assume, as is approximately the case, that $f = 10^{-4}$ sec$^{-1}$ and that $g = 980$ cm sec$^{-2}$.    The wind difference is 10 m per sec, or $10^3$ cm per sec, while the temperature difference is 4°.

$$\text{Slope} = \tan \theta = \frac{10^{-4} \times 275 \times 10^3}{980 \times 4} = \frac{27.5}{3920} = \frac{1}{140} \text{ (approx)}$$

It is unwise, owing to the nature of the assumptions made in the derivation of the original equations, to attempt to compute the slope except approximately, especially since the fronts or other similar discontinuities are seldom of constant slope anyway.    The computed slope is reasonable for the latitude in question.    An ascent of 1 mile in 140 does not appear to the layman to be important, but such a slope can easily produce rain in the warm air moving upward along the front.    If a cloud or haze layer existed on the frontal surface as a distinguishing mark, an observer above it would, under conditions of excellent visibility, barely be able to notice a slope of this magnitude.    Actually the clouds have a greater vertical development above the high parts of the front and therefore present a steeper slope of their upper surfaces than the slope of the front itself; hence the too-frequent report by pilots that they can "see the slope."

In the derivation of the equations two fluids or air masses were considered, one having one temperature and the other having a higher temperature. In the normal atmosphere the temperature is decreasing with height in each air mass, and no single temperature will describe all of them. Actually the mean temperature of the upper so-called "warmer air mass" is lower than that of the so-called "colder air mass." There may be an inversion such that the air immediately above the discontinuity has a higher temperature than that immediately below. It can be shown, however, that if the upper air mass has a higher *potential* temperature than the lower air mass and the rate of increase of potential temperature is discontinuous or very sudden at the frontal surface, the air masses will arrange themselves in the described distribution with the potentially colder one underneath. For, if the air masses are brought to the same level without adding or removing heat, i.e., by an adiabatic process, the upper air mass will be warmer and will not be in equilibrium. In practice, a method of determining the values of temperature that works satisfactorily is to use the temperature at the base of the inversion for the temperature of the lower colder air mass and the temperature at the top of the inversion reduced adiabatically to the pressure of the base of the inversion for the temperature of the upper warmer air. The method is shown graphically in Fig. 12–8.

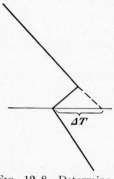

FIG. 12–8. Determination of air-mass temperature differences.

**Effects of Wind Shear.** It is possible to consider the horizontal component of the wind shear across the front from the point of view of the Margules formula (12–10). Since the subscript 2 always refers to the upper warmer air mass, the denominator is always positive, as also are the terms $T_m$, $g$, and $f$ (in the Southern Hemisphere $f$ would be considered negative). The sign of the velocity difference $v_1 - v_2$ will therefore determine the direction of slope of the discontinuity. However, the slope must be in such a direction that the warmer air mass, labeled 2, is above the colder air mass, labeled 1. A horizontal wind shear across a front that is incompatible with the required arrangement of the two air masses would not represent an equilibrium condition and could not support a front.

A series of possible and impossible situations for the Northern Hemisphere is shown in horizontal plan in Fig. 12–9. It will be noted that the possible cases all show a cyclonic wind shear across the front and the

impossible cases show an anticyclonic wind shear across the front. A
north wind would be negative, and a slope of the discontinuity upward
toward the east would be positive. From static-equilibrium conditions
it is obvious that the front must slope upward on the side that has the
coldest air. In the first case, $a$, with the colder air to the west and a
cyclonic shear in a north wind, let us suppose that the wind velocities
are $-10$ for $v_1$ and $-5$ for $v_2$. The sign of the slope in Eq. (12–10) will be
determined by the sign of the difference $v_1 - v_2$. In this case the
difference is $-5$, which means that the front will slope upward toward the
west and that 1 will be under 2. With the same situation and anticyclonic shear, $v_1 - v_2 = +5$, which means an upward slope toward
the east, which is statically impossible because it puts warm air under the

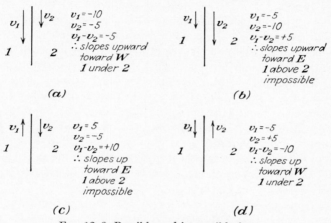

Fig. 12–9. Possible and impossible fronts.

cold. The proof of the other situations, including those involving east-
west lying fronts, is left to the student.

It should be noted that only the components of the wind along, i.e.,
parallel to, the front enter into the slope determinations. The cyclonic
wind shear necessary for a front refers only to these components. The
actual winds may be different in direction on the two sides, and this is
usually the case. The only way in which streamlines and therefore
isobars can show this is for the front to be in a low-pressure trough, i.e.,
the isobars at the front must make an angle of less than 180° on the
side toward low pressure. A front cannot exist in a ridge line of high
pressure.

Also shown in Fig. 12–9 is a case where the component along the front
shifts to the opposite direction as the front is crossed. This is a true
windshift, although the term is often applied to any change of wind,
regardless of whether there are any opposing components or not. Here

again there are possible and impossible cases.   A front cannot exist with
an anticyclonic windshift, as a study of the illustrated examples in conjunction with the Margules equation will indicate.

We have, then, the following rules:

*Fronts are possible only where there is a cyclonic windshift or a cyclonic
wind shear.*

*Fronts occur mostly along low-pressure troughs, although they are possible
anywhere if there is a cyclonic wind shear and not possible along a ridge
line or in an anticyclonic shear zone.*

*Isobars drawn across a front in which there is a wind discontinuity
must make an angle of less than 180° on the side toward low pressure, i.e.,
the isobars must be kinked or pointed away from the low pressure.*

**Moving Fronts.**   If a front has a component of the wind normal
to it, it should, in the ideal case, move with the speed of and in the same
sense as that component.   If gradient conditions prevailed, a front would
move whenever and wherever it was crossed by isobars, and the spacing
of the isobars along the front would give the rate of movement in accordance with the gradient-wind equation.   Owing to the effects of friction,
fronts move with a speed slightly less than that of the normal gradient-
wind component.   Since pressure is continuous across a front, the normal
component of the wind immediately ahead of the front must be the same
as that immediately behind.   Fronts may be considered as separating
walls in the moving air streams through which the air particles cannot
move but which must move along at the same speed as the normal
component of the air particles.

When a front moves toward the warmer air, i.e., with the cold air
occupying territory formerly covered by warm air, it is called a *cold front.*
If it is moving toward the colder air, with warm air occupying territory
formerly covered by cold air, it is called a *warm front.*   A front may be
moving in one direction at one portion of its length and another direction
at another sector; therefore it may be partly a warm front and partly a
cold front.

In a cold front, the wedge of cold air is moving actively forward, and
the effect of surface friction is to hold back the part near the ground so
that it tends to steepen the front.   Sometimes this frictional steepening
produces an action like that produced on a wave reaching a beach,
causing the upper part to tumble over the lower part in an unstable,
top-heavy interaction and mixing of the air masses.   The normal condition is shown in Fig. 12-10.   The average slope of cold fronts is between
$\frac{1}{50}$ and $\frac{1}{150}$.   In the illustration, the vertical dimension is exaggerated
some five hundred times with respect to the horizontal.

In a warm front, the cold-air wedge is receding and the effect of
surface friction is to hold back the front near the ground so that it trails

with a small slope, as shown in Fig. 12–11, also exaggerated some five hundred times in the vertical. The average slope of warm fronts is between $\frac{1}{100}$ and $\frac{1}{300}$ with occasional fronts with lesser slopes still discernible at the ground. Sometimes the portion of a warm front near the ground is drawn out such a great distance that some cold air may remain in a shallow layer near the surface after the effective warm front has passed a station. This often makes the exact location of the front difficult to trace on the surface chart. At times this shallow layer is heated by solar radiation or mixes by mechanical turbulence with the upper air in such a way as to cause an apparent movement of the surface position of the warm front that is much faster than the actual movement

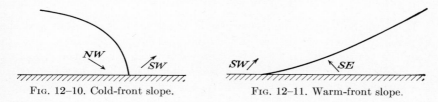

FIG. 12–10. Cold-front slope.          FIG. 12–11. Warm-front slope.

of the air masses. This effect is especially noticeable in the lee of mountains where the warm air does not readily come down to sweep out the cool shielding layer.

Since at least a kink in the isobars in the form of a cyclonic trough occurs at a front, one observes at a station with a front passage one of the following pressure changes:

1. Falling, then rising.
2. Falling, then falling less rapidly.
3. Rising, then rising more rapidly.

The pressure change before or after a front may be zero, in which case the change on the other side is different in relatively the same sense as the above.

The windshift observed at a station in the Northern Hemisphere with the passage of a front is always such that the wind should veer (turn clockwise) with time. This must always be the case in a trough that is moving with the wind. The fronts must move around the lows in a counterclockwise rotation, and a few graphical considerations on a synoptic chart will prove that as the fronts pass a station the wind must turn in a clockwise direction (veer) with time. A veering wind does not always mean a front passage. The wind also veers with the passage of a high-pressure wedge from the west with the anticyclonic center to the north. In an anticyclonic condition, a long period of calm occurs with the change in wind, while in fronts the wind may change almost instantaneously with a very short period of calm or no calm at all.

# CHAPTER 13

## DEVELOPMENT AND LIFE CYCLE OF CYCLONES

It is apparent from the discussions in the preceding chapters that the upper-troposphere waves are associated with surface cyclones. Except near the ground, the troughs are occupied by cold air and the ridges by warm air. Thus, from hydrostatic reasoning, it has been explained that the surface troughs or cyclones may not lie directly under the upper troughs. Statistically, they tend to lie below the forward or eastern portion of these eastward-moving upper troughs. This characteristic is found in the hydrodynamic model experiments as well as in the natural

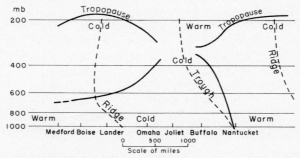

Fig. 13–1. Vertical distribution of troughs and ridges with reference to warm and cold air as shown in transcontinental cross section approximately along the 42nd parallel. The cold and warm fronts are represented by the heavy lines in the troposphere. The chart represents conditions at 1500 GCT, March 1, 1950.

atmosphere. One might ask why there is not an equal likelihood of the surface cyclones' occurrence immediately behind the upper troughs.

The explanation of the preferred position of the cyclones east of the trough is to be found in an asymmetry of the cold mass of air. The cold front ahead of the upper trough has a much steeper slope than the following warm front in the typical situation, such as that represented in Fig. 13–1. The cold air is spread out over most of the surface high-pressure area west of the trough. The highest pressure at the surface in this cross section is under the shallow western part of the cold air mass. On the eastern side, the cold front does not spread over the preceding high-pressure area because this is the warmest part of that high-pressure area. The air circulates around the high in such a way as to bring warm air around its western side from low latitudes. If there were a regular succession of major troposphere waves, the pattern of this cross section would be repeated to the west with a new cold front to the west of the trailing warm front.

Because the upper-troposphere waves are a striking feature of upper-air charts, are somewhat predictable, and are the first perturbations noticed in hydrodynamic model experiments, meteorologists quite naturally associate surface cyclones with energy transformations initiated by these waves. In some cases, however, there is clear evidence, both in the atmosphere and in models, of disturbances building upward from the surface of the earth and apparently causing the development of the upper waves or centers. Historically, the lower disturbances were studied first. After many years of observation and experience, a great deal is known about them, so it is convenient to study fronts and cyclones as they have been noted near the surface of the earth.

**Fronts and the Life Cycle of Cyclones.** The existence of approximate discontinuities in the atmosphere and to some extent the association of these with extratropical cyclones were vaguely known to meteorologists in the nineteenth century. The systematic relationship between fronts and cyclones and the application of these concepts to daily synoptic analysis were developed by meteorologists working at the Geophysical Institute in Bergen, Norway, during and shortly after World War I. The names of V. Bjerknes, J. Bjerknes, H. Solberg, and T. Bergeron[1] are associated with these early discoveries. During the war years 1914–1918 the Norwegians were cut off from weather reports from surrounding areas, especially the oceans. In order to make up for this deficiency their government established in Norway itself a dense network of observing stations, located every few miles. Through the preparation of synoptic charts for this region the details of extratropical cyclones and fronts were obtained. The so-called "polar-front theory" of cyclones was evolved. This theory recognizes that extratropical cyclones develop on the "polar front" separating the westerlies from the polar winds. Later it was discovered that several fronts may exist, each with cyclone-forming possibilities. Several other complications soon became apparent, but

[1] Bjerknes, J., On the Structure of Moving Cyclones, *Geofys. Publikasjoner*, vol. 1, no. 2, 1918. Bjerknes, J., and H. Solberg, Meteorological Conditions for the Formation of Rain, *ibid.*, vol. 2, no. 3, 1920. Bjerknes, J., and H. Solberg, The Life Cycle of Cyclones and the Polar Front Theory, *ibid.*, vol. 3, no. 1, 1922. Bergeron, T., Über die dreidimensional verknüpfende Wetteranalyse, *ibid.*, vol. 5, no. 6, 1928.

the main substance of the theory is today an accepted part of meteorological thought and practice.

**Wave Theory of Cyclones.**    The method recognizes that extratropical cyclones form along fronts, a fact that has been verified by countless synoptic studies.    They form at a wavelike twist or perturbation on the front.    They go through a cycle in which either (1) the amplitude of the wave increases until great sweeps of arctic, polar, or tropical air are carried away from the source regions, eventually to become modified and mixed together; or (2) the wave may remain about the same without noticeable further development, eventually dying out without having participated in any great meridional mass exchange.    Waves of the first type are called *unstable* waves, i.e., they grow in amplitude until they appear to "break" like waves in a confused sea.    The second type is the *stable* wave, having a tendency to be damped out.

Waves on the discontinuity surface separating two fluids of different density can be studied in the laboratory by filling a large horizontal glass tube with two suitable fluids, such as carbon tetrachloride and glycerin.    By giving the tube an initial tilt, a wave can be set up on the boundary between the two fluids and can be observed in vertical cross sections.    The waves on fronts are on sloping discontinuity surfaces that intersect the ground.    Therefore they appear both on horizontal maps and in vertical cross sections.

The life cycle of an unstable wave is shown in map plan in Fig. 13–2. On the front separating westerlies from the easterlies, a small wavelike indentation is formed.    As this develops more of a wave character, a cyclone of increasing intensity forms around it.    The air, in adjusting itself toward equilibrium, pushes in toward this weak point in the front and, under the combined gradient and frictional conditions, develops a cyclonic circulation, centered at the wave crest.    In the figure, a Northern Hemisphere development is depicted, and it is noted that the westerlies turn into a southwest gradient wind which pushes the eastern part of the front northward as a warm front and the western part southward as a cold front.    Each of these fronts is convex in the direction toward which it is moving, like a sail on a ship.

The cold front moves faster than the warm front and closes the warm sector to form a combined front, indicated by the heavy broken line in the figure.    This process is called *occlusion*, and the front thus formed is called an *occluded front*.    It represents a folding of the discontinuity surface by the action of the warm and cold fronts in such a way that the warm sector is shut off from the surface and occurs only aloft.    As the occlusion process continues, the warm sector is displaced more and more aloft and the cyclone becomes completely surrounded by cold air in the low levels.    It is then that the air masses are either completely modified or mixed and the cyclone decreases in intensity until it dies out completely. The cyclone generally reaches its greatest intensity just as occlusion is beginning, or just after reaching "maturity."

Similar conditions for the Southern Hemisphere are depicted in Fig. 13–3. In both hemispheres, the cyclones are carried along in the westerlies, with the cold air in high latitudes and the warm air in the direction of the equator. Over the great Northern Hemisphere continents in winter, the warmer air may be to the west over the oceans, producing wave cyclones that move from northwest to southeast.

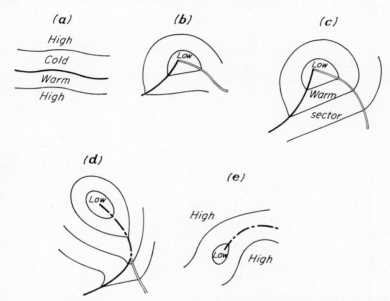

Fig. 13–2. Life cycle of extratropical cyclone of Northern Hemisphere.

In terms of the life cycle, it may be said that an unstable wave is one that develops and goes to occlusion, whereas a stable wave is one that does not develop or go to occlusion.

Nothing has been said as to how a wave can be started originally on an unperturbed front. It is likely that mountains, land and sea temperature contrasts, and ocean-current contrasts can affect the air flow and divert it sufficiently to create a wave. It has also been found that many waves are started by some nearby disturbance. Thus in North America in winter, waves are frequently formed on the arctic front by occluded polar-front cyclones coming in from the Pacific and disturbing the westerlies in such a way that they make inroads against the arctic air. Experience has shown that a very important effect comes from the appearance of an upper-level trough which superimposes a horizontal oscillation at an angle to the surface front.

**Cyclogenesis.** In the preceding chapter it was shown that a front can exist only when there is a cyclonic windshift or wind shear across it. If the flow of air about the front is disturbed in such a way as to form a wave, a cyclonic circulation must arise. An anticyclonic wind would not push against the front, but rather would move the air away from it and no wave disturbance would be developed. Figure 12–9 represents these conditions for the Northern Hemisphere. An anticyclonic circulation turning the air against the front can be conceived in theory, but it would

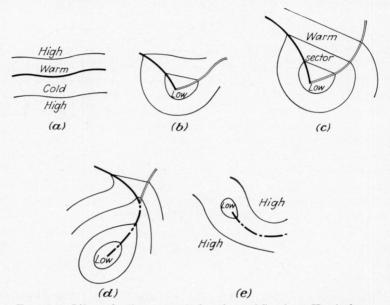

Fig. 13–3. Life cycle of extratropical cyclone of Southern Hemisphere.

require an initial anticyclonic shear across the front, which we have already shown to be impossible.

Accordingly, the formation of a wave disturbance on a front is a means of generating a new cyclone—called *cyclogenesis*. The Norwegian concept is based on the idea that the moving extratropical cyclones all form in this way, and this is fairly well verified by hundreds or possibly thousands of synoptic charts. In a few cases other factors enter into extratropical cyclogenesis. These factors will be discussed presently.

The picture of the life cycle of cyclones in Fig. 13–2 shows increasing amplitude of the wave. This is accompanied by a circulation of the air that accentuates the cyclonic nature of the disturbance. Since there is a mutual adjustment between the wind and the isobars, a low-pressure center occurs at the center of the cyclonic circulation. By constructing the streamlines and their corresponding isobars one can show that the center must be at the crest of the wave, i.e., at the pivot point between the warm and cold air, at least until occlusion starts. After occlusion, the lowest pressure follows the outer part of the occluded front, although there is nothing about the surface circulation that requires this. However, if the center of low pressure remains at the wave crest after an occluded front is formed, the latter will be swung counterclockwise around the center, perhaps folding back toward the cold front and disappearing, or forming a secondary cold front. The exact behavior of the occluded front and center in relation to each other is usually determined by conditions in the upper air.

A complete explanation of cyclogenesis cannot be given simply by stating that it occurs at waves on fronts. It is also necessary to explain why waves form, or why they form at a given time at one place and not at another. Nearby disturbances in the westerlies have already been mentioned as a cause of the wave perturbations. The more one examines synoptic charts, the more one is led to the view that there is no really primary cyclone that forms entirely independently of any nearby disturbances. Throughout middle latitudes the secondary circulations are in evidence as much as, if not more than, the primary general circulation, so that wind irregularities are the rule rather than the exception. These irregularities bring about the wave disturbances on nearby fronts.

Another factor in creating wind perturbations and therefore waves is entirely geographical. At coast lines, sudden changes in the frictional component acting on the wind result in an alteration of the wind in both magnitude and direction. Mountain ranges likewise deflect the air flow. Owing to land and sea temperature contrasts, the solenoidal field near the coasts has a slight horizontal component that can generate a cyclonic curvature. This appears to be a real effect along the Atlantic Coast of the United States in winter and along the Pacific Coast in summer, at least in the upper-air winds.

Sometimes extratropical cyclogenesis occurs in a region where there is no front. If the formation is large enough and if it moves, it will have the same characteristics as a frontal cyclone and may eventually draw fronts into its circulation.

Another type of cyclone is the so-called "heat low." Over continental regions in summer, particularly over the deserts, there is intense heating. The heated atmosphere expands vertically. This vertical expansion is compensated by a lateral outflow or divergence aloft. This reduces the total weight of the air column, thus reducing the pressure and forming a low center. These thermally produced lows usually do not move and are usually found in areas that are almost entirely free of fronts in summer. In the United States there is one low centered more or less permanently during the warm part of the year in southwestern Arizona and southeastern California. The most pronounced summer heat low is found in the region of the Persian Gulf, affecting the winds over a large part of Asia and the Levant.

Cyclones sometimes develop in the lee of mountain ranges. In the United States, a region of frequent cyclogenesis is just east of the Rockies, in eastern Colorado and the Texas Panhandle. These cyclones often become important traveling extratropical disturbances, drawing fronts into their circulations after cyclogenesis has occurred and after the circulation has existed for some time. Most explanations of this formation are somewhat vague. It is possible that a back eddy is set up east of the mountains as the westerlies flow over the sharp edge of the mountains. This eddy could develop a cyclonic circulation. Another possible explanation is found in the tendency of the ascending air on the western part of the plateau to develop an anticyclonic circulation for reasons that will be shown later. This gives the air, particularly aloft, a perturbation so that over the southern Rockies the wind is coming down from the north. It thus has increasing cyclonic vorticity.

Low-pressure troughs aloft have an important bearing on cyclogenesis in the low levels. Often what has been mistaken for cyclogenesis of an entirely surface character has been found to be the building downward of a high-level trough.

**Simplified Vertical Structure.** If a vertical cross section is made through a "mature" idealized cyclone at the stage indicated in Fig. 13–2c, the structure south of the cyclone center through both the cold and warm front would appear in the ideal case in accordance with Fig. 13–4. Here the fronts slope in such a manner as to give a wedgelike shape to the cold air. The smaller slope of the warm front in comparison with the cold front is to be noted; also the greater tendency for ascending motion in the air above the warm-front surface. The prevailing westerlies aloft above the frontal surfaces are downslope winds above the cold front, the upward movement being confined mainly to an upward and outward pushing of the lower warm-sector air by the advancing cold-air wedge.

The main cloudiness and precipitation occurs in the lifted warm-sector air. Clouds may form in the lower cold-air wedge, but these are generally not rain-producing and often form by reevaporation of the water that has fallen from the overrunning air. The precipitation is to be explained as resulting from the decreasing temperature with lifting due to the adiabatic expansion against the decreasing pressures with height as the warm-sector air is lifted at the fronts.

*The Warm Front.* In view of the prevailing west-to-east direction of movement of the extratropical cyclone and the arrangement of the fronts about it, it is evident that the warm-front effects should be the first events heralding the approach of one of these storms. These usually make their appearance just as the clear skies and calm winds associated with the preceding anticyclone are being replaced by the return current of polar air moving from the southeast or east on the southwestern side of that anticyclone. The front is a sloping surface of discontinuity, or temperature and moisture inversion, between this returning mass of polar air and the warm moist current which overruns it from the west.

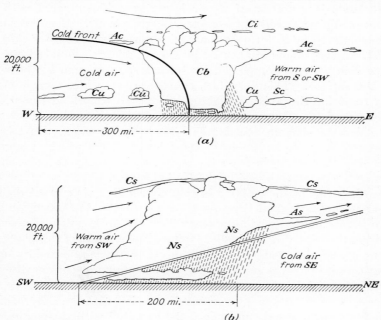

Fig. 13–4. Idealized cross section through a cold front (a) and a warm front (b) in a mature cyclone.

The upward decrease of pressure as this air slides up over the cold wedge ahead of it causes the cooling by adiabatic expansion necessary to produce clouds and precipitation.

The first sign of a warm front coming toward any particular place is the appearance of the clouds that have been caused by the air forced well up the slope to where the cold air is from 15,000 to 20,000 ft deep. These clouds, of course, are the types characteristic of these and greater heights. First the cirrus appear, becoming cirrostratus in a continually denser sheet. If the overrunning air is unstable and turbulent, cirrocumulus will be noted, forming the so-called "mackerel sky" recognized for its import by the old-time sailors. The nearer approach of the front brings the warm air lower, and the intermediately high clouds are noted —altostratus and altocumulus—then finally stratocumulus, nimbostratus and stratus, and occasionally cumulonimbus. Rain or snow usually begins from the altostratus clouds as they approach their greatest density and continues until the front has passed at the surface. In many cases, particularly in maritime locations, lower clouds are present in the cold air so that the sequence of clouds as given above cannot be noted by an observer on the ground. In any event, the precipitation from these lower clouds is generally of minor importance if compared with the amount precipitating out of the overrunning warm air. Even over land, lower clouds begin to form in the cold air usually soon after rain has started. These clouds are caused by the evaporation of raindrops and surface rain water accompanied by turbulent convection in the winds near the surface. This very fact constitutes the chief danger of the warm front for the aviator. The suddenness with which these lower clouds may form where previously only precipitating altostratus were observed is a phenomenon familiar to every experienced pilot and meteorologist. The formation of these lower clouds will be favored if the cold air is moving in from the ocean, as is usually the case in the storms of the Atlantic Coast of the United States.

The character of the activity in the overrunning air current depends in a large measure upon the conditions existing in the warm air mass before it was lifted. Furthermore, in view of the slow rate of ascent of the air up the relatively gradually sloping surface, much of the heavy rain that we observe in warm-front conditions cannot be accounted for unless strong convection is present within the overrunning current itself on account of its inherent instability.

The sequence of events at a particular station with the approach of a warm front is the usual condition to be expected with the coming of a cyclone; for the warm front is the first unit of the advancing low. Obviously, then, a fall in pressure, which becomes more rapid as the front nears, is observed. The increase in cloudiness and precipitation as well as in the humidity is a characteristic feature. Generally, the temperature is constant or slowly rising until the surface front reaches the station, at which time there is a sharp increase, depending for its sharpness on the degree of contrast existing between the two air masses on either side of the front. With the passage of the front, there is a decrease in cloudiness, or a complete clearing, as the station now is in the warm sector. The cloudiness then depends on the general properties of the air mass that occupies the warm sector, in accordance with temperature, moisture, and lapse-rate conditions for air masses. In the warm sector, the temperature remains relatively high, and the barometer is steady or shows only a slight falling tendency, unless another front, the cold front, is approaching.

*The Cold Front.*   The greater steepness of the cold front makes it act more violently in producing clouds and precipitation when displacing warm moist air.   The squall line, with its sudden showers and vigorous windshift, is a manifestation of the cold front when interacting with moist unstable air.   It is generally characterized by heavy clouds, usually of the cumulonimbus type, gusty turbulent winds, heavy rain, and sometimes thunderstorms.   Since it produces within a very short distance the same amount of lifting as occurs over a much broader zone in advance of the warm front, and since its direction of motion is such that the warm air generally retreats from it instead of sliding actively up over it, the cold front is accompanied by a much narrower band of cloudiness and precipitation than is found in the case of the warm front.   In other words, the precipitation and cloud phenomena of a well-marked cold front are usually brief and violent.

The sequence of events in a pronounced cold-front passage begins with the observance of a general increase in the southerly winds of the warm sector and the appearance of high cumuliform clouds, such as alto-cumulus, darkening on the horizon to the west or north.   A fall in the barometer is often noted at about the same time, but this is usually not so pronounced as the marked rise in pressure which occurs immediately following the passage of the front.   The lowering of clouds to cumulonimbus with rain of increasing intensity marks the approach of the front.   The most vigorous squall condition occurs with the actual passage of the front and the shifting of the wind to a westerly or northerly direction.   Normally this is followed by a fairly rapid clearing, unless in a mountainous or moist region, where cumulus or stratocumulus in the following cold air mass may linger for a long time.   As in the case of the warm sector, the cloud conditions in the cold air mass depend on the stability and moisture relationships inherent in the mass.   The presence of the dry superior air mass above the front has a marked effect in limiting the vigor of the frontal interaction with regard to clouds and precipitation, and the existence of subsidence inversions within the cold air mass has a prominent influence on conditions there.

*The Occluded Front.*   The occluded front as an individual phenomenon adheres less to type than do cold and warm fronts.   Consequently, there are several different kinds of conditions to be expected.   From a study of the general process of occlusion as outlined previously in this chapter, it appears that the occluded front is formed near the center of the disturbance in the cold air mass, thus separating the latter into two sections.   Theoretically, these represent two parts of the identical air mass.   In actuality, however, the circulation about the front brings in air from opposing directions; and although originally these oppositely moving currents consisted of the same air mass, their difference in path, or trajectory, has given them different modifications. Therefore, contrasts develop between them. Thus, after a certain length of time following its initial formation, every occluded front shows not only a contrast in wind direction but also in most cases temperature differences.

Regardless of the temperature and other differences occurring in the cold air, the definition of the occluded front requires that it consist of a trough of warm air pushed aloft from the warm sector, as illustrated in Fig. 13–5. In other words, an occluded front means that there is a warm sector at upper levels. Clouds and precipitation will occur in this warm air above as the cold air squeezes it upward.

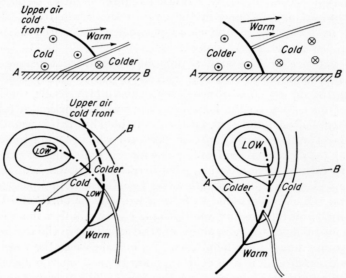

Fig. 13–5. The two types of occlusions: (a) warm type and (b) cold type.

The temperature contrasts within the cold air below the warm sector and on either side of the windshift line determine whether the front is (1) a cold occluded front or (2) a warm occluded front. If the colder of the two cold currents is advancing, then it is a cold type of occluded front. If the less cold of the two is gaining ground, it is a warm occluded front. The two types are represented in vertical cross section in Fig. 13–5, where it is assumed that in each case the movement of the front is from west to east. It will be noted that the intersection of the front with the ground, which is the part represented on the weather map, is ahead of the upper warm sector in the case of the cold type and lags far behind in the warm type. On many occasions the lower cold-acting or warm-acting front will itself produce clouds and precipitation and otherwise behave as a regular cold or warm front.

The type of weather associated with the occluded front cannot be described definitely because of the variability of its structure and action. In general, it would be expected that the warm type of occluded front would be preceded by the same sequence of events that comes with the approach of a warm front, except that in some cases the clouds and precipitation may cease before the passage of the surface front. Under such circumstances, one might justifiably conclude that the warm sector aloft was the only part of the system capable of producing rain or snow and that the front at the ground, which for the warm type of occlusion trails behind the lifted warm trough, represented an interaction between air masses too dry or too stable to produce significant weather phenomena. The cold type of occluded front should have no forerunning clouds and precipitation. If these were confined solely to the lifted warm sector, then rain or snow would not be observed until after the passage of the surface front, i.e., after the windshift. In many cases, however, the interaction between the two cold surface air masses produces clouds and precipitation in the lower levels accompanying the windshift line. It is conceivable, and is occasionally supported by actual observation, that two definite zones of clouds and rain or snow will follow each other, the one representing the lifted air of the warm sector and the other the interaction of the colder surface air masses.

As the process of occlusion continues, the cold air deepens as it crowds the warm sector upward until the latter has reached a height sufficient for it to spread out over the domes of cold air that have occluded it. It then ceases to be lifted farther and becomes inactive as a cloud- and rain-producing air mass. It is then that the contrasting properties of the two parts of the lower cold air on either side of the occluded front become more important than the interactions with the lifted warm sector. When such a stage is reached, it is good practice to regard only the lower masses of air and to consider the lower discontinuity as being either a warm or a cold front depending on the type represented by the occluded front. Such old occluded fronts often will act as "secondary" cold fronts or as separate warm fronts.

**Bergeron's Model of Occluded Cyclones.** On weather charts of Western Europe and the North Atlantic, Bergeron[1] has noted that the most frequently observed cyclonic structure is that of the warm-front-type occlusion. His model is shown in Fig. 13–6. The first impression one obtains is that the structure is very complicated. As the details are studied in relation to the legend, a systematic pattern emerges. Bergeron designates the model as a three-dimensional model of main disturbances (two separate cyclone series) in the system of polar front and jet, including

[1] Bergeron, T., Paper presented at the Rome Assembly of the International Union of Geodesy and Geophysics, 1954.

the weather systems. The conditions depicted are most typical of autumn. It is noted that in the vertical cross section the positions of the jet are shown, but since it is a zonal cross section, the meridional components of the meandering jet are the ones shown, with northerly winds (toward the viewer) over the cold fronts and southerly winds (toward the page) above the warm front.

In addition to the symbols given in the legend, Roman numerals appear on the map to represent the weather regions related to the main fronts and air masses. Their meanings are as follows:

*I.* Cloudless in tropical air.

*II.* Stratocumulus-stratus fog in tropical air.

*III.* Drizzle (or rain) in tropical air.

*IIIb.* Showers or convective systems in tropical air, which are especially common in North America.

*IV.* Nimbostratus in polar air.

*V.* Altostratus in polar air.

*VI.* Subsidence in polar air.

*VII.* Showers in polar air.

*VIII.* Stratocumulus-stratus fog in polar air.

The suffix *A* refers to weather regions in relation to the arctic front, such that near that front the *A* refers to polar air for the numbers *I* to *III* and arctic air for *IV* to *VIII*.

According to Bergeron, the chief aim of the model is to show the average connection between the weather regions and the three-dimensional front and air-mass structure, including temperature and flow pattern aloft. The model comprises two whole cyclone series or cyclone "families" and therefore two whole long waves in the upper westerlies. Thus it may cover, for instance, all the area from Eastern Europe to North America. For the sake of simplicity, each cyclone series is represented essentially by one major occlusion. The two occlusions are purposely shown in different stages of development.

The difference between the deep excursions of the polar air, with its vigorous occlusions, and the relatively flat, nonoccluded waves of the arctic front is strongly emphasized. The two arctic domes have been shown with different structures. In the eastern or European one, where the arctic air has traveled partly over the sea, the arctic front is penetrated and partly dissolved by the cumulonimbus forming from below. Over the North American continent the conditions in the western arctic dome are typified.

Bergeron points out that the arctic front may also have a secondary jet associated with it, and mentions the possibility of multiple arctic-front and jet structures. Typically the arctic front overtakes the polar front near the rear of the low-pressure centers, but the two fronts are

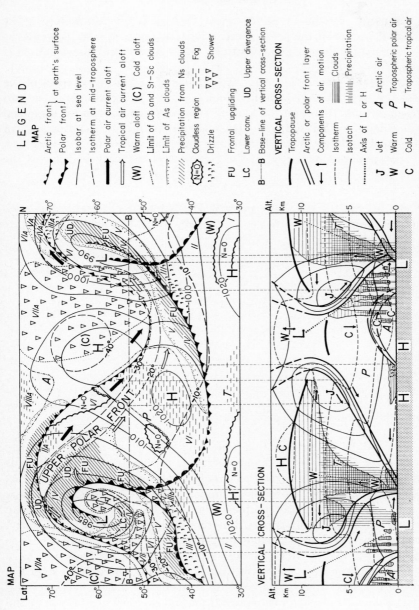

FIG. 13–6. Bergeron's model of two cyclone systems such as might extend across the North Atlantic.

317

kept separate in the model to show their different characters. The broken character of the polar front in its southwestern part between the two cyclones indicates the "venting" of polar air into the trade-wind region.

**Flow in the Overrunning Air.**  The effects of ascent and descent of the warm air over shallow cold-air domes in producing convergence and divergence and therefore influencing the vorticity have been discussed in some detail by J. Bjerknes.[1]  It is shown that the air ascending a warm front must undergo vertical shrinking and therefore lateral divergence. This comes about by virtue of the fact that at the very high levels the

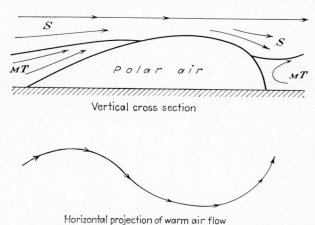

Vertical cross section

Horizontal projection of warm air flow

Fig. 13–7. Vertical and horizontal flow of warm air over a cold dome in the troposphere.  $mT$—maritime-tropical air; $S$—superior (dry) air.

air does not participate in this ascending motion, so that the vertical thickness of the ascending layer decreases during the ascent.  This is shown graphically in the vertical cross section over a cold dome in Fig. 13–7.  Note that the arrows in the upper part of the ascending air mass show only a slight vertical component and, at the height represented by the long horizontal arrow, upward motion is entirely lacking.  Similarly, in the air moving down the cold-front slope, vertical stretching occurs as suggested by the vertical spreading of the arrows.  Thus we have lateral divergence over the warm front and lateral convergence over the cold front.  According to the vorticity relationship, these effects develop anticyclonic vorticity over the warm front and cyclonic vorticity over the cold front.

[1] Bjerknes, J., Explorations de quelques perturbations atmosphériques, *Geofys. Publikasjoner*, vol. 9, no. 9, 1933.  Also, Bjerknes et al., "Physikalische Hydrodynamik," 1933.

In the lower part of Fig. 13–7 is shown a horizontal map plan of the circulation developing over the cold-air domes from these causes.   The southwest wind of the warm sector turns anticyclonically as it ascends over the warm front until it changes into a northwest wind.   Then, in the descent along the cold-front slope, the wind turns cyclonically to become a southwest wind again in the warm sector.   Large mountain masses produce the same effects on the air flowing over them as do cold-air domes.

Fronts are sometimes masked at the surface, appearing as upper-air fronts.   In the warm type of occluded-front system there is a cold front aloft.   Cold air acts against warm air, but the action occurs above a third still colder air mass which lies in wedge fashion at the ground underneath the occluded front.   Synoptic practice has shown that such activity of cold fronts can occur aloft above an essentially horizontal, nonfrontal inversion.   In the United States and Canada, such fronts, not directly connected with a warm type occlusion, move for considerable distances across the continent.   This type of structure is of the greatest frequency in winter when a shallow layer of continental-arctic air covers much of the land.   Cold fronts from the Pacific will move across the continent above this cold-air cushion and will have pronounced effects on the weather.   The direction of motion is sometimes quite inconsistent with the surface currents, e.g., in the case of east winds in the arctic air mass and west winds carrying the front along in a contrary direction above.

Upper-air cold fronts are frequently found extending northward from the centers of cyclones, where easterly winds prevail at the ground. Many of them are so near the ground that they produce changes that may be mistaken for the passage of a surface front.   However, any front that appears to move from west to east north of a low must be an upper-air front, because the gradient winds north of a cyclonic center would oppose such movement of a surface front.   Occasionally, when strong frictional and other nongradient influences are at work, the actual surface air may be moving in such a direction as to be favorable for west-to-east motion despite unfavorable gradient indications.   In such cases, the gradient simply does not represent the actual air flow.

Upper-air warm fronts are also important.   They are noticeable where a nearly horizontal warm front or other discontinuity surface becomes abruptly steeper.   The line along which this change in slope occurs shows many signs of an actual warm-front passage and is called an upper-air warm front.   Owing to the steepness of the slope, the advection of warm air is more rapid than in the region of lesser slope. Therefore the pressure falls rapidly in advance of an upper-air warm front and tends to level off underneath the nearly horizontal portion of the front.   Also precipitation may develop just ahead of the upper-air warm front, owing to the rapid ascent of the damp air along this portion of the frontal surface. Occasionally these fronts work down to the surface. As a warm front crosses a mountain range, it may encounter colder air to the east and may therefore move along as a warm front aloft above the shielding layer of cold air. This is a common observation in warm fronts that cross the Appalachian Mountains in winter.

Another important effect demonstrable from potential-temperature cross sections is the advection of cool air aloft ahead of a surface cold front. Bjerknes[1] calls this air "cool tropical air" to emphasize that it is not the air under the cold front that is "overrunning" warmer air. It should be noted that this upper air still has a higher potential temperature than the lower air, but a lower potential temperature than the air formerly at its upper level. Figure 13–8 illustrates the effect in terms of isentropic

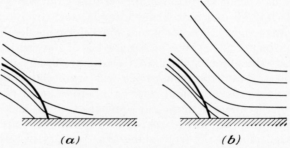

*(a)*                          *(b)*

Fig. 13–8. Distribution of isentropic surfaces ahead of a cold front.

surfaces. It is noted that in this case, where the vertical spacing of the isentropic surfaces above and ahead of the cold front is approximately the same, the slope of the upper isentropic surfaces begins at some distance ahead of the surface position of the front. If the vertical spacing of the surfaces is greater ahead of than above the front, the upper-air cooling will precede the cold front by a lesser amount. The case represented in Fig. 13–8b will cause the cooling aloft to proceed at a greater distance ahead of the front.

**Energy of Cyclones.** The important part played by extratropical cyclones in transforming energy in the atmosphere has already been mentioned in the chapter on the general circulation. Cyclones are areas of concentration of kinetic energy, which is equivalent to saying that cyclones are regions of strong winds. This is a very pronounced characteristic of cyclones in the low levels. It is appropriate at this point to consider the transformations of energy somewhat along the lines taken up in Chap. 11, but with particular reference to the concentration of kinetic energy in cyclones.

[1] *Ibid.*

From the point of view of the fronts and frontal waves, cyclones may be considered as deriving their kinetic energy from the potential energy of distribution of mass—the existence in nonequilibrium juxtaposition of air masses of contrasting densities. This is what was called disturbance potential energy in Chap. 11. The concentrated solenoidal field is distorted in the region of the developing cyclone so that the solenoidal gradients have a marked zonal component. The solenoids are tilted so as to accelerate the circulation both in the vertical and in the horizontal. The acceleration of the circulation must continue as long as the favorable solenoidal field exists; thus the cyclone increases in energy until it reaches its maximum intensity at occlusion.

From the larger point of view, the upper-troposphere waves may be considered as the sources of the cyclone developments. As shown by experiments in rotating fluids, these waves must occur in the atmosphere merely because it is unequally heated and is rotating. These waves distort the jet-stream polar front. Because of the connection, either direct or indirect, between the polar front in the upper troposphere and surface fronts, the latter are also distorted, giving rise to the process described in the preceding paragraph. In certain situations it has been observed that frontal-wave cyclones have developed near the ground and have built upward to become intense cyclones without the presence of a preexisting upper-troposphere wave in the region. Apparently in these cases, strong low-level fronts become distorted without any related disturbance of the upper jet-stream front. Although experience shows that the low-level disturbances are much more frequently associated with upper troughs than not, it suggests that the principal source of energy can come from any level in the atmosphere.

Much of the energy seen in cyclones may have been concentrated there by what might be considered random coincidences. It is normal for the atmosphere to be in a highly disturbed state. The waves and related systems at upper levels normally move at a speed different from that of the low-level disturbances, thereby providing an opportunity for superpositions of upper and lower systems. Thus when two systems of cyclonic vorticity too weak to be noticed as cyclones are superimposed in such a way as to combine their kinetic energies, a vigorous cyclone may develop. The principal effects of superposition upon the development of vorticity at the ground are taken up in a later chapter.

Heat of condensation is irreversibly added to the atmosphere in a cyclone where rain falls to the earth. This source of energy should also be considered. In parts of the cyclones of middle latitudes the lapse rate is favorable for pseudoadiabatic ascent of moist air. Ascending motion induces low-level convergence and the heat of condensation increases the temperature of the air. Both of these effects are favorable for cyclonic development.   In the development equation referred to in Chap. 17, the latent heat is included in the stability term.   In analyzing the magnitudes of the different quantities, Petterssen concludes that the latent heat has a small effect in most extratropical cylones.   The thermal stratification is stable in most of the cyclonic area, and such instabilities as occur as a result of saturation are not enough to overcome the net stability effect in the cyclone as a whole.   What has been said in this paragraph does not apply to tropical cyclones (hurricanes and typhoons) which derive their principal energy from the buoyancy in pseudoadiabatic ascent.

**Frontogenesis.**   Chapter 12 indicated that it is possible for fronts to develop near the surface of the earth somewhat independently of the upper-troposphere polar front.   The term "frontogenesis" has been applied by Bergeron[1] to the formation of new fronts.   The definition may be broadened to include the regeneration of old fronts.   Conversely, the degeneration of fronts is called *frontolysis*.

Bergeron showed that wind streams forming what is known in hydrodynamics as a deformation field can be responsible for frontogenesis. The simple type of deformation field which he studied is shown in Fig. 13–9.   Petterssen[2] elaborated on this system in giving a quantitative theory of frontogenesis.   The streamlines in Fig. 13–9 are rectangular hyperbolas representing a possible flow around two highs and two lows of the Northern Hemisphere, with the origin of coordinates taken at the "neutral point" between them.   Such a neutral point and wind system could develop, for example, between a Canadian high to the northwest, the Azores-Bermuda high to the southeast, the Icelandic low to the northeast, and a Mexican low to the southwest.   It could also develop on a much smaller scale between two small highs and two small lows.

In the figure, the axis along which the particles are carried away from the neutral point, i.e., the $x$ axis, is called the *axis of dilatation*, and that along which they are transported toward the neutral point, the $y$ axis, is known as the *axis of contraction*.   It is easier to visualize how a velocity distribution of this nature can bring particles together by separating it into its two components.   This has been done in Fig. 13–10, which gives the $x$ and $y$ components of the motion separately.   In each case the length of the arrow is proportional to the wind velocity.   The two components, added together, give the hyperbolic streamlines of Fig. 13–9. The slowing motion as the particles near the $x$ axis in the $y$ component and the speeding up in the $x$ component as they leave the $y$ axis mean that there must be a crowding as the $x$ axis is approached, because there

[1] Bergeron, T., Über die dreidimensionale verknüpfende Wetteranalyse, *Geofys. Publikasjoner*, vol. 5, no. 6, 1928.

[2] Petterssen, S., Contribution to the Theory of Frontogenesis, *Geofys. Publikasjoner*, vol. 9, no. 6, 1936.

will always be particles coming in from the rear at higher speeds— contraction. In the $x$ direction, the particles speed up as they move outward from the center; hence they are carried far from each other— dilatation.

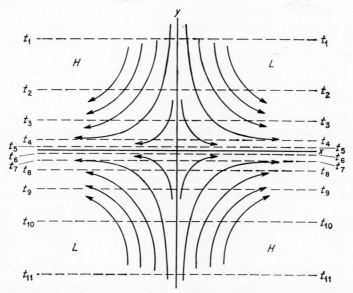

FIG. 13–9. Simplified deformation field, showing how isotherms (broken lines) become concentrated along the axis of dilatation.

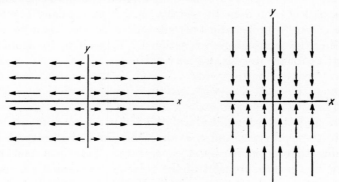

FIG. 13–10. Components of deformation field.

If the elements of air carried along in this circulation preserve their temperature, which is often approximately the case, then the isotherms, unless they parallel the streamlines, will also be carried along. If the distribution of isotherms is such that they are perpendicular to the axis of dilatation, frontolysis will result, for then the isotherms will be more and more widely separated. On the other hand, isotherms forming a high angle with the axis of contraction will be carried toward each other, and the necessary conditions for the formation of a front—the concentration of isotherms and therefore also of solenoids—will be fulfilled. In Fig. 13–9 the isotherms are drawn parallel to the axis of dilatation, a perfect condition for frontogenesis, especially along that axis.

For a neutral point in which the axes are at right angles, Petterssen has shown that an angle of less than 45° between the isotherms and the axis of dilatation is necessary for frontogenesis; if they cut this axis at a greater angle, frontolysis occurs. For nonperpendicular axes, the critical angle is altered correspondingly. In most cases, the line of frontogenesis will fall along the axis of dilatation.

It is not necessary to have a deformation field like that in Fig. 13–9 to have frontogenesis. Any wind and temperature distribution that brings isotherms together and keeps them there is frontogenetic. The only requirement is that the winds shall have a cross-isotherm component and that this component shall decrease downwind. This assumes, of course, that temperatures are at least partially conserved and that the temperature gradient maintains the same approximate direction throughout the region considered; for example, frontogenesis could not occur along a cold zone surrounded by warm air or along a warm zone surrounded by cold air. If the component of the wind normal to the isotherms changes sign (reverses itself) downstream, it will be in many cases the same as a diminution. This is sometimes the case in fronts along windshift lines.

It is possible to express these statements in the form of a mathematical equation, as has been done by Petterssen. A numerical measure of the intensity of the frontogenetic or frontolytic effect can then be obtained. Designating the frontogenetic function by $F$, positive for frontogenesis and negative for frontolysis, we may write

$$F = - \left| \frac{\partial T}{\partial n} \right| \frac{\partial c_n}{\partial n}$$

where $|\partial T/\partial n|$ is the magnitude of the temperature gradient, $n$ is the normal to the isotherms, and $c_n$ is the wind along that normal, positive in the direction of increasing temperature. This is a mathematical statement and a measurement of the rule: *If the wind has a component across the isotherms that decreases in its downstream direction, frontogensis is to be expected.* If any of these conditions fail, that is if there is no temperature gradient or no cross-isotherm wind component or if this component increases in its downstream direction, no frontogenesis will occur. The intensity of frontogenesis will be greatest with a large temperature gradient, a strong component of wind across the isotherms, and a sharp decrease in this wind downstream.

# CHAPTER 14

# AIR MASSES AND THEIR STRUCTURE

The existence of a zone of sharp temperature changes at fronts requires that other parts of the atmosphere have lesser horizontal gradients. In their studies in the 1920s the Scandinavian meteorologists found that for purposes of synoptic (large-scale, instantaneous) analysis, it was advantageous to make the simplification that fronts are discontinuities in the field of atmospheric properties and that the areas between the fronts are occupied by horizontally homogeneous *air masses*. In this view the baroclinicity of the atmosphere is concentrated in the frontal zones and the rest of the atmosphere is barotropic. While this model of the atmosphere is not precisely correct, its adoption represents one of the great forward steps in meteorology. The concept of fronts and air masses and the charting of their distributions forms an important part of practical meteorology today.

**Source Regions of Air Masses.** A simplified picture of the general circulation of the atmosphere shows a single front, the polar front, with two air masses, polar and tropical, on the two sides. This distribution is found in the middle and upper troposphere with only slight modifications, as is shown in Fig. 12–1. In the lower troposphere the picture is more complicated for two reasons: (1) the perturbations (cyclones, anticyclones) are more complex and hence are capable of creating transitional air-mass types through circuitous passages of air and of forming intermediate, detached fronts; (2) the continents and oceans impart different properties to the overlying atmosphere and thus create contrasting air masses.

Different air masses are created because certain sections of the atmosphere are acted upon for long periods of time (days to weeks) by the radiation, convection, turbulent-exchange, and evaporation-condensation processes characteristic of a certain region of the earth. In the simplest picture described in the preceding paragraph, the polar air north of the polar front acquires properties characteristic of high latitudes and the air to the south has tropical or subtropical properties. The concentration of momentum in the jet stream is accompanied by a concentration of gradient at the front.　Perturbations cause breaks in the front through which the air masses are mixed.

Regions in which air masses attain characteristic properties are called air-mass source regions.　Air masses are given names according to their source.　For example, in the United States east of the Rockies, Canadian air is a distinct air mass of winter, recognized by every school child. In dealing with large sections of the earth, however, it is not possible in synoptic practice to cling to the source name very long.　Long trajectories of air masses over different parts of the earth, which are to be expected as a consequence of the air exchange of the normal circulation, subject the air masses to new source regions.　Thus the source name refers only to the recent history of the air mass.

In the lower troposphere the continental and maritime source regions stand in sharp contrast and during the extreme seasons of the year, summer and winter, produce air-mass contrasts equal to or greater than the latitudinal effects.　Another feature of the lower troposphere is the appearance of a third air mass, arctic or antarctic air behind a second front.

With the combined effects of latitude and continents versus oceans, the general classification of air masses is as follows: maritime tropical $(mT)$; continental tropical $(cT)$; maritime polar $(mP)$; continental polar $(cP)$; maritime arctic $(mA)$; continental arctic $(cA)$.　Another air mass, not having a surface source but often appearing at the surface is superior $(S)$ air.　It is dry, often very warm air, characteristic of the westerlies of the middle and lower troposphere equatorward from the jet stream and often consists of air that has subsided in the horse-latitude anticyclones.　Some meteorologists simply call it continental tropical air when it appears at the surface.

In synoptic practice the air masses are identified, not only by the characteristic properties which they carry with them from the source region and which show up quite well in the aerological soundings, but also by the contrasts which appear between them along the fronts on the synoptic charts.　Continuity in time between successive synoptic charts reveals the recent histories of the air masses.

**Processes Determining Air-mass Characteristics.**　As already implied, the air masses obtain their characteristics by radiation fluxes and by heat and water-vapor fluxes through the air-earth boundary layers.　The latitude and the nature of the underlying surface determine the relative importance of the various processes.

The thermal stability of the air limits the vertical transport of heat and property, since the vertical exchange must be accomplished in air parcels carried by vertical eddies or convective currents.　If the temperature lapse rate is very stable, such as in the case of a temperature inversion, the radiation heat flux will exceed the eddy flux.  In the case of a moderate lapse rate, mechanical friction in the wind blowing across the surface of the earth can set up eddies which will transport heat and properties vertically.  With superadiabatic or nearly adiabatic lapse rates the mixing is aided by thermally driven convection currents.

When air masses lie over a cold surface, the cooling from below creates a stable lapse rate virtually cutting off vertical eddy exchange.  The air mass is cooled almost entirely by radiation fluxes.  Over a warm surface the heating from below creates a steep lapse rate in the low levels so that turbulent eddy exchange and convection carry the heat and water vapor quickly through a considerable depth of the air mass.

Cold air over a warm ocean will have heat and moisture transported quickly through a great height.  On the contrary, warm air over a cold surface may cool a few degrees until a strong temperature inversion is established at the ground, after which it must depend on radiation fluxes to cool it further.  Numerical comparisons show that radiation processes proceed much more slowly than do the changes brought about by internal vertical motions over a warm surface.  This difference accounts for the observation that it may take weeks for maritime-polar air from the North Pacific in winter to be transformed into continental-arctic air over northern Alaska and Canada, while it may take only a day or two for the continental arctic to be changed to maritime polar again after streaming out over the Atlantic beyond Newfoundland.

The pronounced effects apparent in air masses warmer or colder than the surface over which they are passing led Bergeron[1] to devise a subclassification of air masses based on air-earth temperature differences. The air is labeled as colder than the surface over which it is passing or warmer than the surface ($k$ or $w$).  This "differential" classification produces the combinations:

$$cAw \qquad cPw \qquad cTw$$
$$cAk \qquad cPk \qquad cTk$$
$$mAw \qquad mPw \qquad mTw$$
$$mAk \qquad mPk \qquad mTk$$

A typical $k$ air mass has convective cloud types, good visibilities (except in dust storms which occur mostly in $k$ air masses), and turbulent, gusty winds.  Typical of a $w$ air mass are stratus clouds or fog, poor visibilities (smoke, haze, etc.), and steady winds or dead calms.  These two widely different states result from steep temperature lapse rates on the one hand and very stable lapse rates on the other.  In the first case vertical eddy and convective transports are favored, while the stable atmosphere of

---

[1] Bergeron, T., Rechtlinien einer dynamischen Klimatologie, *Meteorol. Z.*, vol. 47, pp. 246–262, 1930.

the $w$ air mass inhibits vertical motions, in some instances causing smoke, haze, and fog to be held at the ground under low temperature inversions.

It is found, however, that surface conditions alone do not determine the effects that will be produced on an air mass. As pointed out on page 155, effects of convergence, divergence, and subsidence are important in determining the lapse rates. In areas of strong cyclones and anticyclones, such as in the eastern United States, these dynamic processes may act more prominently than the thermal ones.

**Ocean Heat Exchange and Evaporation.** By comparison with the land, ocean surfaces respond very little to seasonal change. Thus the oceans are warm in winter and cold in summer, relative to the land. The main reasons for the differences in heating and cooling of continents and oceans are, in descending order of importance, the following:

1. The oceans have a mixed or homogeneous layer extending for a number of meters below the surface. Heated or cooled water parcels at the surface are mixed to considerable depth and replaced by other water from below. Thus a mass of water a number of meters deep is involved in the heating or cooling. On the solid earth only the top few centimeters participate in the heating or cooling so only a relatively small mass is involved. From the relation

$$dQ = M_w s_w \, dT_w = M_e s_e \, dT_e \qquad (14\text{--}1)$$

where the subscript $w$ refers to water and $e$ to solid earth, we see that if the specific heats $s_w$ and $s_e$ are of the same order of magnitude and if $M_w$, the mass of water involved, is ten times the mass of earth involved $M_e$ (both per unit area), then the increment of heat $dQ$ added or removed from the land would raise or reduce its temperature 10° to every 1° for the same amount of heating or cooling over the ocean.

2. The specific heat of the sea water is about three times that of most types of land surface. This would make $s_w = 3s_e$ and, if $M_w = 10M_e$, then $dT_e/dT_w = 30$. These are only approximate figures, useful in indicating magnitudes of the effects. It is obvious that not all of the indicated temperature change would occur in the surface itself since some of it would be transmitted to the atmosphere. The air, through eddies and convection, provides a "ventilation" effect which, combined with radiation fluxes, serves to limit the temperature extremes that any exposed surface can attain.

3. The ocean is a continuous source of evaporating water, while soil and vegetation are highly variable in this respect. The more the sun heats the surface layers, the greater the evaporation. Since each gram of water evaporated removes nearly 600 calories of heat from the evaporating surface, this process is very effective in preventing the oceans from getting very warm in summer.

4. The sun's rays penetrate to some few meters of depth in the ocean with appreciable intensity. Thus the solar energy is not entirely absorbed at the surface as it is in the case of the soil. The internal absorption helps preserve the homogeneity and therefore the mixed state of the upper layers of the ocean.

Differences in reflectivity might at first glance appear to be important, but they are not. Impressions of high reflectivity of water are gained from looking toward the sun at low angles of incidence. At normal angles the oceans have lower reflectivity than most land surfaces.

Evaporation at the earth-air boundary is more complicated than in a closed system such as is studied in the laboratory. The evaporation of a liquid in a partially filled, closed container proceeds at a rate proportional to the difference between the vapor tension of the liquid and the vapor pressure in the space above it. As vapor is added to the space by the evaporation, the rate must decrease until it reaches zero when the space is saturated with the vapor.

In the open atmosphere it is possible for the water vapor to be carried away from the evaporating surface in the eddies or in the convection currents. The vapor pressure in the air above the water and therefore the evaporation rate for a given water temperature will be determined by the vertical flux of vapor, that is, the amount of water vapor flowing upward through a unit horizontal area in unit time. The eddy diffusivity, which varies with the temperature lapse rate, can have values several orders of magnitude greater than the ordinary (molecular) diffusivity of water vapor in air.

It is apparent that the same air-mass characteristics that favor the upward spread of water vapor through the atmosphere also enhance its evaporation from the surface.

Seasonal and annual charts of evaporation from the oceans prepared by Jacobs[1] show that the highest rates of evaporation occur in winter over the ocean near Japan where the water is warm and where the cold Siberian winter-monsoon air is pouring off the continent. In summer, this region has relatively little evaporation because the summer-monsoon air is warmer than the water and is laden with moisture. Condensation in the form of fog is prevalent in the early summer over the Japan Sea and the ocean areas to the northeast. On an annual basis, the greatest evaporation is from the tropical ocean regions. Evaporation involves a transfer of *latent* heat from the ocean to the atmosphere. Charts similar to those for evaporation show that the *sensible* heat taken up by the atmosphere is also, in general, at a maximum in regions of greatest evaporation.

[1] Jacobs, W. C., *Ann. N.Y. Acad. Sci.*, vol. 44, pp. 19–40, 1943.

**General Expressions for Vertical Transport.** The equations for the vertical flux of heat or property (such as water vapor) are, in their classical form, similar to the expression for the conduction of heat in a solid. The flux of heat in the $x$ direction, that is, across a square-centimeter area in the $y,z$ plane in one second in a solid, is given by

$$H = -k\frac{\partial T}{\partial x} \tag{14-2}$$

The coefficient $k$, called the *thermal conductivity*, is constant through a wide range of temperature for any given solid. The expression indicates that the flux of heat by conduction in a specified direction is proportional to the temperature gradient in that direction.

The diffusion of one gas in another, e.g., the diffusion of water vapor in air, is expressed similarly. If $\rho_w$ is the density or concentration of the diffusing gas, the vertical flux by diffusion is given by

$$E = -D\frac{\partial \rho_w}{\partial z} \tag{14-3}$$

where the coefficient $D$ is the *diffusivity* of the gas in air. $D$, with the dimensions $cm^2\ sec^{-1}$ $(L^2T^{-1})$, varies from 0.20 to 0.29 $cm^2\ sec^{-1}$ in a temperature range from $-20$ to $+40°C$ at 1000 mb. At lower pressures if is greater by a factor $p_0/p$.

If eddies are present, as in the case of the natural atmosphere, the flux may be several orders of magnitude greater than that given by this expression. To satisfy the relation, the *eddy diffusivity* must be used. It ranges in value from about $10^3\ cm^2$ per sec under conditions of great thermal stability to about $10^6\ cm^2$ per sec in unstable lapse rates. The wide range of values leads to great difficulties in solving the turbulent transfer problem. In Chap. 21 turbulence is discussed in some detail and ways are shown for taking these variations into account.

A convenient form of the equation can be obtained by expressing the concentration in gravimetric terms, that is, in grams of the substance per gram of air. In the case of water vapor, such an expression would be the specific humidity $q = \rho_w/\rho$. Equation (14-3) then becomes

$$E = -D\frac{\partial(\rho q)}{\partial z} \tag{14-4}$$

If the eddy diffusivity is used in either of the two equations, $E$ will be the eddy flux. If humidity measurements are made within a meter or two of the surface at two or more heights to obtain the vertical gradient of humidity, $E$ will give the actual evaporation from that surface in grams of water vapor per square centimeter per second. In such low-level measurements the vertical gradient of density is negligible compared to the humidity gradient and can go outside the derivative.

A more useful form of the flux equation can be obtained for conservative properties like specific humidity. Such properties will be transported unchanged by the eddy motions regardless of the air density. Another coefficient, the *exchange* coefficient $D'$, can be used in the simple form

$$E = -D' \frac{\partial q}{\partial z} \tag{14-5}$$

$D'$ has the dimensions g cm$^{-1}$ sec$^{-1}$ = poise. This is an advantage because frictional and viscosity coefficients are often expressed in poises.

These relations confirm the expected result that the eddy flux of water vapor is along the gradient toward lower values which, in the normal atmosphere, means that water vapor is transported upward. As the rate of decrease of specific humidity with height becomes greater, the upward flux increases. The same may be said for the evaporation. The flux also depends on the exchange coefficient. This coefficient increases rapidly as the lapse rate increases. It also varies with the strength of the wind and the roughness of the surface. Thus when cold air passes over a warm-water surface, all factors combine to give a maximum evaporation and vertical flux of water vapor. In warm air over a cold surface, $D'$ is small because of the inherent stability and the vapor gradient may be very small or even directed downward.

**Eddy Flux of Heat.** To express the heat flux in the atmosphere it is necessary to take into account the adiabatic changes in the vertically moving eddy currents. This effect can be handled by using the potential temperature, which remains constant during an adiabatic process just as $q$ does. Heat added per unit mass is given by $c_p \, dT = c_p \, d\theta$ at constant pressure. We can treat the heat content per unit mass in the same way as we did $q$ [Eq. (14–4)] and write for the upward heat flux

$$H = -K\rho c_p \frac{\partial \theta}{\partial z} \tag{14-6}$$

where $K$ is the *eddy conductivity* which has, like the eddy diffusivity, the dimensions cm$^2$ sec$^{-1}$. Theoretically $K$ should be the same as the eddy diffusivity and, in fact, the latter is sometimes substituted for it.

Equation (14–6) shows that if the potential temperature increases with height, as is normal in most of the atmosphere, heat is transported downward by turbulence. Neglect of the vertical gradient of density as in this equation is not usually serious close to the ground. A superadiabatic lapse rate with potential temperature decreasing with height is necessary in order for heat to be transported upward. This criterion, however, does not take into consideration heat released by condensation. In clouds, the vertical gradient of wet-bulb-potential temperature or equivalent-potential temperature should be used, although entrainment effects in convective clouds will modify the equilibrium.

*Energy-balance Method.* Another approach to the problem of eddy flux from a surface is through a determination of the entire heat balance at the surface. The insolation $S$ is balanced as follows:

$$S = R + H - H_s + H_E \qquad (14\text{--}7)$$

where $R$ is the outgoing reflected and radiated heat, $H$ is the flux of sensible heat from the surface, $H_E$ the heat used in evaporation, and $H_S$ the heat going into the surface. I. S. Bowen[1] introduced the use of the ratio $H/H_E$, now known as the *Bowen ratio*, as a convenient way of handling the balance equation. We can rearrange the equation to the form

$$H_E + H = S - R + H_s \qquad (14\text{--}8)$$

then divide through by $H_E$

$$1 + \frac{H}{H_E} = \frac{S - R + H_s}{H_E} \qquad (14\text{--}9)$$

and, designating the Bowen ratio $H/H_E$ by $B$, we obtain

$$H_E = \frac{S - R + H_s}{1 + B} \qquad (14\text{--}10)$$

Also, since $H_E = LE$, where $L$ is the latent heat of vaporization and $E$ is the evaporation from a unit surface area in unit time, we can write

$$E = \frac{S - R + H_s}{L(1 + B)} \qquad (14\text{--}11)$$

The ratio of the two fluxes comprising the Bowen ratio must be proportional to the ratios of the two vertical gradients, that is, $-\partial T/\partial z$ for $H$ and $-\partial q/\partial z$ for $H_E$. In practice, especially over the oceans, Bowen found that these gradients could be obtained by taking measurements of temperature of the evaporating surface and temperature and humidity measurements in the air at some convenient height such as on the deck of a ship. He gave the practical value

$$B = 6.1 \times 10^{-4} p \left( \frac{T_s - T_a}{e_s - e_a} \right) \qquad (14\text{--}12)$$

where $T_s$ and $T_a$ are temperatures in the surface and in the air, respectively, $e_s$ is the vapor tension of the surface, and $e_a$ is the vapor pressure in the air.

[1] Bowen, I. S., *Phys. Rev.*, vol. 27, p. 779, 1926.

The energy-balance method involves measuring the radiation fluxes and ascribing what is left to vertical transport. The Bowen ratio or its equivalent gives us a method of using simple measurements for obtaining the evaporation, especially at sea. For climatological purposes, such as in obtaining seasonal and annual values, the system is quite useful. Thus from crude ships' observations and reasonable values of the radiation balance, a good idea of evaporation rates over the oceans can be obtained. The method avoids the difficult problem of determining the coefficient of eddy diffusivity.

*Transfer of Momentum.* Horizontal momentum is a property of the air that also is conserved in parcels of air forced up or down from their "mother" layers. In fact the viscosity of the air arising from vertical wind shear is derived from these eddies. Called the *eddy viscosity*, it is several orders of magnitude larger than the ordinary, or molecular, viscosity. The upward flux of momentum is given by the following expression, which is the same type of expression as that used for flux of heat and matter:

$$\tau_x = -\kappa\rho\,\frac{\partial u}{\partial z} \tag{14–13a}$$

$$\tau_y = -\kappa\rho\,\frac{\partial v}{\partial z} \tag{14–13b}$$

The two separate components enter because of the directional (vector) nature of the wind. The flux $\tau$ is in units of gm cm$^{-1}$ sec$^{-2}$, so $\kappa$ has the dimensions cm$^2$ sec$^{-1}$ as does the coefficient $K$ in the heat diffusion equation. The product $\kappa\rho$ is in units of dynamic viscosity

$$(\text{g cm}^{-1}\text{ sec}^{-1} = \text{poise})$$

but $\kappa$ itself is in units of kinematic viscosity, which is the dynamic viscosity divided by the density. We call $\kappa$ the eddy viscosity. It is interesting to note that $\tau$ has the dimensions of a stress, or force, per unit area. The stress is exerted on neighboring layers or on the surface. The frictional force per unit mass caused by the eddies is given by

$$\frac{1}{\rho}\frac{\partial}{\partial z}\tau_x = \kappa\,\frac{\partial^2 u}{\partial z^2} \tag{14–14a}$$

and
$$\frac{1}{\rho}\frac{\partial}{\partial z}\tau_y = \kappa\,\frac{\partial^2 v}{\partial z^2} \tag{14–14b}$$

This frictional force is customarily added to the equations of motion as given on page 212. The student may verify that it has the dimensions of a force per unit mass.

Like the other eddy coefficients, $\kappa$ varies with the lapse rate. Since normally the wind increases with height, the eddies transfer momentum downward. The diurnal change in the wind at the ground is accounted for by these circumstances. During the day the lapse rate increases and $\kappa$ increases so that the high momentum aloft is transported downward by the eddies. The wind at the ground reaches its maximum value in the afternoon when the lapse rates are greatest. In the night, the lapse rate becomes stable, $\kappa$ diminishes, and there is little exchange of momentum. Thus the winds die down at the ground. At the Eiffel Tower in Paris, the wind at the top of the tower is strongest at night and weakest in the daytime, which is just the opposite from the diurnal variation measured at the base of the tower. The transfer of momentum downward by the daytime eddies accounts for the difference in trend.

It is now perhaps a little clearer why a $k$ (colder than surface) air mass has gusty winds at the ground and a $w$ air mass does not. The gusts are the manifestations of the large eddies transporting downward puffs of high momentum.

**Effects of Radiation Flux.** In cases of very strong cooling of air masses, such as over the arctic and antarctic continental regions, the air becomes so stable that eddy exchange practically disappears and only radiation fluxes are left to accomplish heat exchange.

Wexler[1] has demonstrated the mechanism whereby air from warmer regions, such as the North Pacific, is cooled by radiation over the northern continent forming $cAw$ air. The process involves considerations of the radiation equilibrium between the snow surface and the overlying water-vapor atmosphere, taking into account the partial transparency of the water vapor to the radiation from the surface.

The radiation going outward from the snow surface is made up of two parts, that which is not absorbed by the atmosphere, i.e., the radiation in the so-called "transparent wavelengths," and that which is absorbed by the water vapor, i.e., the so-called "opaque radiation." Since the water vapor does not absorb in the transparent bands, it also, in compliance with Kirchhoff's law, does not emit radiation of that wavelength. Therefore, under similar conditions of temperature, the ground surface can emit more radiant energy than the atmosphere. However, since the emission is approximately proportional to the fourth power of the absolute temperature, it is possible for the atmosphere to overcome this deficiency in emissive power by having a considerably higher temperature than the snow surface. Thus, if the snow surface continues to cool, its emissive power over its entire black-body spectrum may become less than that of the warmer atmosphere, which is emitting only in the opaque bands. Then the atmosphere would lose heat energy to the snow surface, and that heat would be utilized to check the decrease in temperature going on

[1] Wexler, H., Cooling in the Lower Atmosphere and the Structure of Polar Continental Air, *Monthly Weather Rev.*, vol. 64, pp. 122–136, 1936.

at the surface.   For a given water-vapor (and, as a matter of fact, carbon dioxide) content of the atmosphere, the condition of equilibrium between the atmospheric radiation in the opaque bands and the ground radiation in all bands depends on the temperature relationship of the atmosphere and the surface.   This relationship is shown graphically in Fig. 14–1.   The curve $a$ gives the total black-body radiation as the ordinate for the various temperatures represented on the abscissa.   This may be considered as representing the radiation from the snow surface at various temperatures, since a snow surface, according to numerous determinations, radiates for all practical purposes as a black body.   The curve $b$ represents the radiation from the water-vapor and carbon dioxide atmosphere at the various temperatures but, of course, only in the opaque bands.   By following along horizontally from the curve $a$ to the curve $b$,

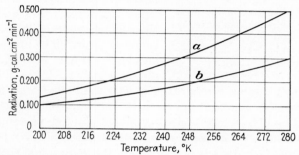

Fig. 14–1. Wexler's graphical representation of radiation balance between snow surface and air aloft during the arctic night.

one can determine how much warmer than the ground the air must be for the atmospheric radiation to balance the ground radiation.

The atmosphere does not absorb all the energy radiated from the ground, because the radiation in the transparent portion of the spectrum escapes to space.   Thus the atmospheric layer is emitting more energy than it absorbs.   The air cools, and with it also the snow surface, in such a way that each is emitting the same amount of energy as the other. Further cooling is possible because of the energy escape through the transparent bands.   The atmosphere therefore cools by way of the snow surface through the medium of the transparent bands.   The only requirement is that the ordinate of the two curves in Fig. 14–1 shall be the same.   The temperature relationship is then obtained from the abscissa. For example, with a snow-surface temperature of 240°K, the atmosphere must have a temperature of 275°K.

The question may well be asked: What part of the overlying atmosphere acquires the specified temperature?   Actual soundings show that at first a ground inversion is formed when the warm air moves over the snow surface. As soon as the ground has become the required number of degrees colder than the air at the top of the ground inversion, the latter cools off in such a way that an approximately isothermal layer is formed above the inversion. The air higher up is undisturbed. As the temperature at the ground goes lower and the atmosphere and ground cool together, this isothermal layer gets thicker, as determined by the temperature conditions aloft. It is the temperature of this approximately isothermal layer that determines the balance. Apparently the air above, which is more or less unaffected by the cooling, would still be called maritime-polar air. The process is shown graphically on a temperature-height diagram in Fig. 14–2.

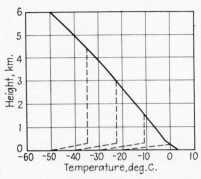

Fig. 14–2. Modification of the lapse rate owing to radiation cooling in the arctic continental regions. Original lapse rate shown by heavy line, subsequent stages by dashed lines.

The effect of cooling rarely extends 3000 m in the *cA* air masses that reach the United States, but cases of the approximately isothermal layer extending above 4000 m are occasionally noted, particularly in the interior of Canada. The lapse rate above the stable layer continues in about the same form that it was in before the radiational cooling began. There is a slight loss of heat at the upper levels apparently due to radiation so that the temperatures at the high levels are 2 or 3° lower than before the cooling. This is of course a very slight amount of cooling compared with the cooling of 30 or 40°C occurring near the ground. The air above the stable region should properly be called *mP*, since most of the time the original source of the air is the North Pacific.

In the extremely cold continents of Siberia and Antarctica, the cooling may include the entire troposphere, in which case the stratosphere disappears as an entity.

**Summary of Air-mass Processes.** The processes which create or modify air masses at the source and in their travels are fairly numerous. At a given locality, especially in middle latitudes far removed from the arctic and tropical sources, the characteristic properties found in an air mass depend not only on the nature of its source region but also on the modifications of the source properties which the air mass has undergone en route to the place of observation. The modifications have a marked effect on the type of weather that will occur within the air mass.

It is helpful to make a list of the predominating types of modifying influences the air mass undergoes. These may be classified as follows:

A. Thermodynamic

    1. Heating from below
        *a.* By passing from a cold to a warm surface
        *b.* By solar heating of the ground
    2. Cooling from below
        *a.* By passing from a warm to a cold surface
        *b.* By radiation cooling of the earth's surface
    3. Addition of moisture by evaporation
        *a.* From a water or ice and snow surface or from moist ground
        *b.* From raindrops or other precipitation forms which fall through the air mass out of an overrunning saturated air current
    4. Removal of moisture by condensation and precipitation

B. Mechanical

    1. Turbulent mixing (eddies and convection)
    2. Large-scale dynamic effects on lapse rate
        *a.* Divergence or outflow
        *b.* Convergence (cyclones, etc.)
    3. Sinking
        *a.* In subsidence and lateral spreading
        *b.* Movement down from above colder air masses
        *c.* Descent from high elevations to lowlands
    4. Lifting
        *a.* Over colder air masses
        *b.* To compensate for horizontal convergence
        *c.* Over elevations of the land
    5. Advection of new properties aloft due to shearing action of the wind

These modifying influences seldom occur singly; usually two or more of the processes are combined, resulting in a change of the air-mass characteristics that sometimes can become fairly complicated. Consider, for example, an air mass moving from the Bering Sea out over the Pacific Ocean. It will be heated from below by passing from a cold to a warm surface; the resulting steep temperature lapse rate will cause considerable turbulent-convective mixing, and this combination will favor a rapid addition of moisture to the air by evaporation from the ocean. If it is winter, the air mass will be cooled from below by ground radiation as it moves inland over the North American continent, and furthermore it will undergo mixing and lifting over the western mountain ranges which will cause condensation and precipitation of a large part of its moisture, so that it reaches the Middle West as a warm, dry air mass. The dryness may be accentuated by descent from the intermontane plateau, sometimes with the added effect of subsidence. During its travel from the source, the air has undergone the following types of modification: heating from below, lifting over mountains, more turbulent mixing, removal of moisture by condensation and precipitation, and then sinking.   This is perhaps an extreme case of air-mass modification, but it happens regularly in maritime-polar air masses from the Pacific Ocean.

**Temperature Inversions.**   One of the most important characteristics of air masses is the development within them of temperature inversions. Their occurrence is so widespread that it is the rule rather than the exception to find them somewhere in the atmosphere.

For convenience, inversions may be classified as either thermally or mechanically produced, with the frontal inversions (observed in the transition layer between a cold air mass and a warm one lying above it) forming a third group.   Listed according to the processes that cause them, the inversion types are as follows:

1. Thermally produced
   *a.* Radiation or contact cooling at the surface
   *b.* Radiation cooling at high levels
2. Mechanically produced
   *a.* Turbulence or convection
   *b.* Subsidence
3. Frontal inversions

The ground-radiation type is best exemplified by the well-known nocturnal inversion observed during the night and early morning, especially at land stations in light winds.   It is caused by the rapid cooling of the earth's surface by radiation during the hours of darkness. This cooling does not affect the air above the first few hundred feet, and so aloft the temperatures remain moderately high.   The result is an increase of temperature with altitude in the layer next to the ground—in other words, a temperature inversion.

The gases of the atmosphere lose relatively little heat by radiation, and therefore radiation cooling at high levels is a relatively unimportant process.   Water vapor, clouds, and atmospheric impurities (dust, smoke, haze, etc.) sometimes form a fairly effective radiation surface when concentrated in a well-defined layer.   However, such stratification into definite haze and smoke lines depends on a preexisting inversion, so that radiation cooling in the free air is unimportant in forming a temperature inversion but may intensify one that has already developed from another cause.

Mechanical processes are contributing causes of temperature inversions at altitudes above the surface.   Turbulence and convection, if continued long enough, result in a thorough mixing of the atmosphere through the layers where the turbulence exists.   There is always a limiting height above which the turbulent or convective mixing does not penetrate, and it is at this altitude that temperature inversions are produced. In the turbulence layers, air is brought downward from this maximum height of penetration to lower levels, and air from below is carried upward in the general vertical mixing process. We know that air moving downward is heated by adiabatic compression and that when carried upward it cools at the adiabatic rate due to expansion. Since the air at high levels in the atmosphere is nearly always potentially warmer, i.e., has a higher potential temperature than at low altitudes, the turbulence elements of air carried downward arrive at their new position with a higher temperature than the air that they replaced, while those lifted upward are cooler than the rest of the air at the new level. After this mixing has continued for some time, all the air in the turbulence layer will be air that has undergone adiabatic expansion and compression due to change of level, so that an adia-

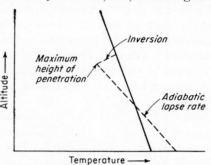

FIG. 14-3. Development of turbulence inversion.

batic lapse rate will develop in which the air at the bottom of the turbulence layer will be warmer than formerly; and that at the maximum height of turbulent penetration, colder than before. The transition from this cold upper part of the turbulence zone to the air above with its temperature unaffected by adiabatic cooling will comprise a temperature inversion. The process is shown in Fig. 14-3 where the solid line represents the temperature distribution existing before the development of the turbulence, and the broken line after it has continued for some time. The approximate mid-point of the turbulence layer undergoes no temperature change, as is also the case in the warm air above the layer.

If clouds form in this type of condition, they will usually be of the stratus or stratocumulus variety. If the turbulence is accompanied by an addition of heat from the ground, then cumulus or cumulonimbus may form. If it is an ordinary turbulence inversion near the ground, smoke, haze, and the lighter dust particles will be carried by turbulence up to the inversion where they will spread laterally under the inversion to form a well-marked haze and smoke line, in the absence of clouds at that level.

The anvil-shaped tops of thunderstorm clouds are due to a temperature inversion at very high altitudes through which the thunderstorm convection cannot penetrate because of the pronounced stability in the inversion layer. Sometimes cumulonimbus clouds have sufficient convective energy to penetrate through inversions, and these inversions are usually marked by a layer of altostratus forming a narrow girdle or appearing in bands around the cloud. Experience has shown that whenever stratiform clouds appear in the atmosphere, one can be certain that they have some sort of temperature inversion above them. Sometimes cumulus clouds take on a stunted appearance due to an inversion that limits their vertical growth.

Subsidence, or slow sinking of the air in a high-pressure area, is an important air-mass modification and accounts for the development of a great many of the temperature inversions observed in the atmosphere, especially in regions where anticyclones remain stationary for long periods of time. The process of subsidence was outlined in its physical aspects in Chap. 7 where it was shown that sinking makes the air layers more stable than they were at their original higher levels. Furthermore, it was stated that, in its slow movement downward, the air heats at the rapid adiabatic rate due to compression. The air near the ground does not participate in the subsidence, because only the slightest degree of turbulence, which is nearly always present at low levels, can completely counteract the slow sinking. The lower atmosphere, then, acts as a sort of shield against the subsidence and shows no appreciable temperature increase, while above, the temperature at any level will slowly rise with the bringing down of potentially warmer air from greater heights. Between the shielding layer and the adiabatically heated air above, there will then be observed a temperature inversion. The greater the amount of turbulence or vertical convection in the shielding layer, the higher in the atmosphere will the inversion be found.

Subsidence is well developed in the Pacific anticyclone, the Azores anticyclone, and the stationary highs over the continents in winter. Often the combined process of a marked turbulence condition in the shielding layer and subsidence above produces an especially sharp temperature inversion, with radiation cooling of the cloud and dust and smoke-laden stratum just below the inversion to intensify it further.

The subject of frontal inversions will be taken up in a later chapter. It will suffice here to point out that, whereas the ordinary inversions in an air mass have a rapid decrease in moisture content accompanying the temperature rise, the frontal types usually show an increasing specific humidity in the inversion.

**"Characteristic Curves" of Air Masses.** In Chap. 8 it was shown that conservative air-mass properties can be used to identify air masses from soundings made through them. The Rossby diagram, with mixing ratio and potential temperature of the dry air as coordinates, is used for plotting the soundings. Each of the principal air masses has a certain "characteristic curve," shown in these plots, which serves for identification. The characteristic curve also reveals features of the air-mass structure and suggests the processes involved in producing this structure. For example, maritime air masses have deep layers of nearly constant equivalent-potential temperature, indicating a thoroughly mixed equilibrium for air over a warm, moist surface.

In practice, it is convenient to plot the curves on the same thermodynamic diagram on which the soundings are plotted originally. On one of these diagrams the curve, which is essentially the same as the Rossby-diagram curve, is obtained by plotting the isentropic-condensation points corresponding to all of the significant points of the original temperature

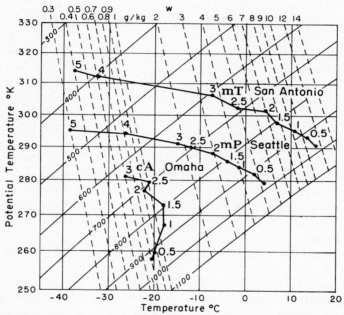

Fig. 14–4. Characteristic curves on tephigram for winter air masses in North America.

plot. These points are obtained simply by going dry-adiabatically from each significant point to the intersection with the mixing-ratio line corresponding to the humidity at the significant point.

Plots of some characteristic curves on a tephigram are shown in Figs. 14–4 and 14–5. The soundings are first plotted as $T,p$ curves, with straight-line segments connecting the significant points. The characteristic curves are formed by line segments connecting the corresponding isentropic-condensation points. The curves for the three principal American winter air masses should be compared with those of Fig. 8–7 in Chap. 8.

On the tephigram the ordinate is the potential temperature and not the potential temperature of the dry air as in the Rossby diagram, but this is a minor difference. The mixing-ratio lines are not vertical and linearly spaced as on the Rossby diagram. The effect of this difference is to separate the curves for the different air masses more widely at low values on the tephigram.

In day-to-day synoptic work, the entering of these curves on the basic thermodynamic chart is preferred to plotting them on the separate

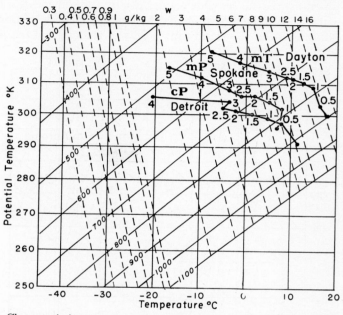

Fig. 14–5. Characteristic curves on tephigram for summer air masses in North America.

Rossby diagram. This is done not to save paper but to save time, the most precious commodity in the forecast room. It is advantageous to be able to study the basic sounding for temperature, humidity, and stability conditions without the distraction of a separate chart. In practice, it is regarded as sufficiently correct to use plots of dew points rather than condensation points as characteristic curves. This is a matter of personal preference.

# CHAPTER 15

# OUTLINE OF SYNOPTIC ANALYSIS

Synoptic analysis can be learned only by laboratory practice. The purpose of this chapter is to point out the general character of the problem of representing the atmosphere and its processes on charts, diagrams, and other sheets of paper. The intricate craftsmanship required to construct a three-dimensional model of the fleeting structure of the atmosphere at a given instant is not worth the effort; therefore the representation is accomplished on various surfaces cutting through the atmosphere. These may be horizontal surfaces at various heights; vertical surfaces or cross sections; isobaric, isentropic, or frontal surfaces; and of course, the surface of the earth. The earth is represented on a map projection, preferably one that comes close to preserving angles and distances.

The task of analysis is essentially one of representing scalar fields by means of lines on the surfaces, and the recognition of discontinuities, maxima, and minima in these scalar fields. The lines are the intersections of one or more sets of surfaces with the surface represented on the chart. Thus a chart of an isobaric surface has lines corresponding to the intersections of various level surfaces, of temperature surfaces, of surfaces of equal humidity, and of other properties. Some vector fields, such as the wind field and the vorticity field, may be represented.

The various lines or surfaces each represent equal values of the scalar quantities. The general term for such a line or surface is *isogram* or *isopleth*, from the Greek *isos* meaning equal, *gramma* meaning weight, and *plethes* meaning quantity. The word *isoline*, a linguistic hybrid, is sometimes used. An incomplete list of isograms or isopleths, together with the quantities they represent, includes the following:

*isobars*—pressure

*isotherms*—temperature

*isentropes*—entropy or potential
    temperature

*isotachs*—speed

*isokinetics*—speed

*isohypses*—height

*isohyets*—precipitation amount

*isochrones*—time of arrival

*isosteres*—specific volume

*isopycnics*—density

*isogons*—angle

In the following sections some of the principal ways of analyzing atmospheric structure and motions will be summarized. Not all of them are used in daily charting and forecasting, but all have an important

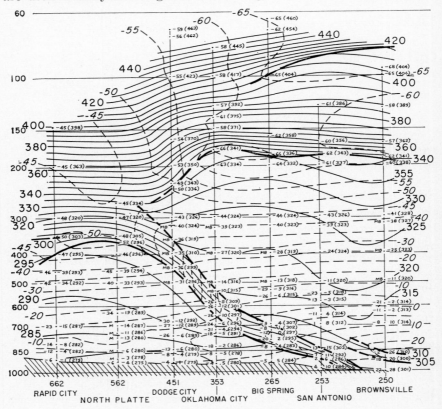

4 APRIL 1950, 1500 GCT

FIG. 15–1. Example of vertical cross section in a north-south direction. At each station is entered, at each characteristic level, the temperature (°C) and the potential temperature (°K) on the right and the dew-point temperature (°C) on the left. *MB* means "motor-boating," the sound heard in the radiosonde signal when the humidity is too low to be recorded. *M* alone means data missing for some other reason. Isotherms for the actual temperature are dashed lines, while the light solid lines are for potential temperature. Heavy lines represent frontal and tropopause surfaces.

place in study and research concerning atmospheric characteristics and behavior.

**Cross-section Analysis.** The beginner who has had some practice in examining vertical soundings in detail will find little difficulty in going to the study of vertical cross sections. They form a logical introduction to the importance of the vertical structure of the atmosphere.

The usual cross-section chart is quite simple, having as its base a graph of horizontal distance against height, or, preferably, against the more or less equivalent $-\ln p$. The vertical scale is exaggerated to about

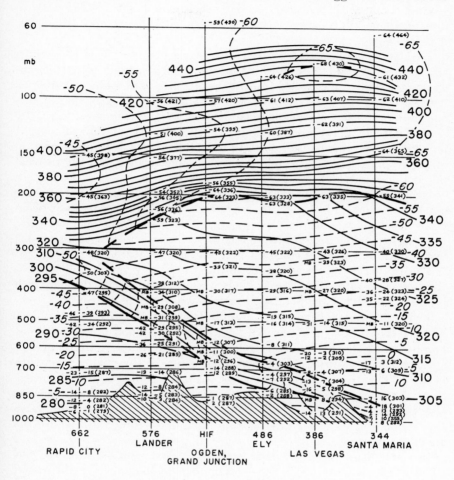

4 APRIL 1950, 1500 GCT

Fig. 15–2. East-west cross section for same time as Fig. 15–1.

two hundred fifty times the horizontal scale, but the user is free to lay off any horizontal scale he wishes. The cross section lies along an approximately straight line of aerological stations (they almost never lie exactly in a straight line) and the significant points of each sounding are entered in their proper places over the locations of each station (see Figs. 15–1 and 15–2).

Inversions or other stable layers are usually easily identified from one station to another. They ordinarily extend along isentropic surfaces and if the individual plots of soundings on thermodynamic diagrams are studied along with the cross section, there should be no difficulty in locating them. The greater the separation of the isentropes, the lesser is the stability.

The tropopause is best located on cross sections. Since it is characterized by a sudden diminishing or ending of the lapse rate, the isentropes are suddenly crowded from that height upward and the isotherms rise vertically or become very widely spread. The tropopause discontinuity at each station can be located precisely in most cases by studying the individual sounding. In the vicinity of the polar-front jet stream the tropopause is broken and ill-defined. The polar portion of the tropopause tends to follow an isentropic surface, but the tropical portion does not.

Isentropic surfaces are *substantial* surfaces for unsaturated air, so the air moves on them but not through them. Since the air does not penetrate stable layers, these layers correspond with isentropic surfaces. Most atmospheric discontinuities appear in vertical cross section as stable layers and tend to have constant potential temperature.

The isotherms of actual temperature cut sharply through all discontinuities, and must of necessity show a kink as they pass through such layers. Through a temperature inversion they are, of course, inverted.

The water-vapor distribution is represented by the mixing-ratio lines. These follow a fairly complicated pattern, with dry and moist centers at various places. The stable layers corresponding to active fronts exhibit an increase, or at least a fairly constant value, of the mixing ratio with height. This is one of the sure ways of distinguishing a frontal surface from an inversion surface within an air mass. Subsidence inversions always show a marked dryness aloft. On the isentropic surfaces above the fronts, tongues of high moisture are found intruding into the dry ($S$) air of the upper westerlies.

In some situations fronts follow closely the isentropic surfaces, but widespread condensation in the ascending air makes substantial surfaces of the equivalent-potential temperature or wet-bulb-potential temperature surfaces. These nearly always slope in the same direction as but more steeply than the isentropic surfaces; however, in air masses or layers where $\theta_E$ or $\theta_w$ decreases with height, the lines are inverted and slope upward in the opposite direction from the $\theta$ lines. Cross-section analysis reveals that fronts need not remain fixed on a thermodynamically defined substantial surface, but due to latent heat releases and the patterns of the vertical wind shear they make their own way.

The representation of solenoids in vertical cross section has been discussed in preceding chapters. If the ordinate of the cross section is in terms of pressure, as in the accompanying illustrations, one set of solenoid walls is already built into the chart. Isosteres delineate the other set of walls to make up the projection on this cross section of the $p,\alpha$ solenoidal field and isotherms can be used for $p,T$ solenoids. The actual acceleration of the vertical circulation and the baroclinity can be measured if the cross section is chosen to lie along the gradient of specific volume. This is difficult to accomplish since the gradient may change direction both with horizontal distance and with height, requiring a twisted cross section.

**The $D$ System.** A system useful for analysing the vertical distribution of highs, lows, ridges, and troughs has been devised by J. C. Bellamy.[1] It provides for the charting of the departure of the pressure at a given height from that of a standard atmosphere at that height, or, conversely, the height departure for a given pressure. Called the $D$ system, it is based on the height departure $D = Z - Z_s$, where $Z$ is the true height and $Z_s$ is the height for the corresponding pressure in the standard atmosphere. Bellamy chose the aeronautical standard atmosphere upon which altimeter readings are based; therefore $D$ is the altimeter correction at the given height and pressure.

Airplanes flying over the sea and equipped with both radio altimeters and pressure altimeters provide $D$ directly as the difference between the readings of the two instruments. From ordinary upper-air soundings the meteorologist obtains $Z$ and finds $Z_s$ from a table or graph usually printed on his thermodynamic chart.

If an attempt were made to represent height profiles in a cross section in the $x,p$ or $y,p$ plane or pressure profiles in the $x,z$ or $y,z$ plane it would be necessary to have the vertical scale expanded to many thousand times the horizontal scale. In the vertical exaggeration of some hundreds used in this chapter, the surfaces or lines would depart only slightly from the horizontal. With the $D$ system, the high and low centers, ridges, and troughs are sharply revealed.

By definition, $Z_s$ is constant on an isobaric surface, so

$$\left(\frac{\partial D}{\partial n}\right)_p = \left(\frac{\partial Z}{\partial n}\right)_p$$

While the $Z$ surfaces cut the isobaric surface with the same spacing as the $D$ surfaces, the former always intersect at a very low angle while the latter may intersect vertically. An appreciation of this fact can be gained from examining Fig. 15–3. The equality of the gradients on an

[1] Bellamy, J. C., The Use of Pressure Altitude and Altimeter Corrections in Meteorology, *J. Meteorol.*, vol. 2, pp. 1–79, 1945.

isobaric surface permits the computation of the geostrophic wind, geostrophic vorticity, and related features by either system.

The $D$ lines are useful for showing the vertical tilt of troughs and ridges and for indicating the extent to which the disturbances may be derived

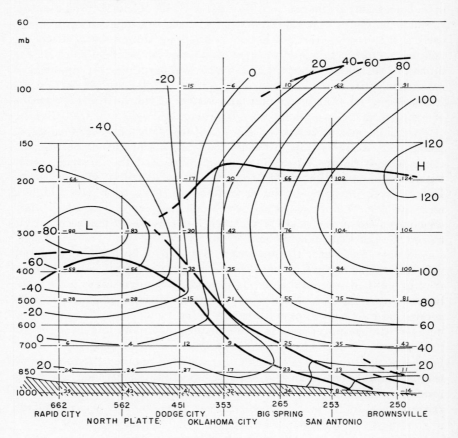

4 APRIL 1950, 1500 GCT

Fig. 15–3. Cross section represented in the $D$ system corresponding to Fig. 15–1. Values are in feet. The speed of the wind component normal to the cross section at any point is given by the gradient of the $D$ values at that point. At all points except in the low levels south of Big Spring, this component would be from the reader into the page, i.e., westerly.

from conditions at the tropopause or higher. They are also useful in showing the presence of weak disturbances, such as are frequently found in the tropics. In cross sections, the horizontal gradient of $D$, or gradient along an isobaric surface, gives the geostrophic wind component normal to the section.  Thus, on a north-south cross section the zonal wind components can be studied in detail for a chosen meridian.

**Isobaric Analysis.**  Isobars drawn on maps for fixed levels or height contours on constant-pressure maps produce identical patterns.  The use of isobaric surfaces has some advantages over the use of level surfaces in weather mapping, as was pointed out in Chap. 9.  At the surface of the earth it is common practice to analyze the pressure field reduced to sea level, although some analysts prefer to transform these values into heights of the 1000-mb surface.  In the free atmosphere isobaric surfaces are represented.  By international agreement, the teletypewriter reports from aerological stations contain data for the standard isobaric surfaces of 850, 700, 500, 300 mb, and sometimes higher.

The analysis can take in the entire Northern Hemisphere (the Southern Hemisphere is partially an aerological void because of the great expanse of ocean and the impoverished state of some of the national meteorological services) or it can comprise only a small portion of a continent. In forecasting practice the analyzed area for the usual one-day to two-day forecast should be about the size of North America and adjacent ocean areas or larger, if practical.  For forecasting more than two days ahead the entire Northern Hemisphere should be considered.  This statement should not imply that the patterns of highs, lows, troughs, ridges, etc., maintain their identities around the hemisphere.  Today's flow patterns may be hard to recognize three days hence.  Changes only in the very broad features, such as total hemispheric wave number, major blocking actions, and total jet-stream energy are carefully followed in the analyses directed toward extended forecasting.

In Fig. 15–4 the surface synoptic chart, with fronts and sea-level isobars, is shown for the Northern Hemisphere for the same situation that is represented at 500 mb in Fig. 12–1 of Chap. 12.  Note that the surface isobaric configurations are much more complex than at 500 mb and that the fronts are detached in a very complicated system difficult to relate to the simple jet-stream polar front at the 500-mb surface.

Analysis over the oceans and in other areas of sparse data can be accomplished by taking into consideration certain details of properties other than the scalar field being analysed.  For example, historical continuity in the systems must be observed to give a consistent change from one region to another and from one time to the next.  In many cases wind data are available but pressure measurements have not been made.  The geostrophic wind scale can be applied to the map to get the direction and spacing of the isobars or contours.

Perhaps the most important check for consistency to be made in the preparation of an isobaric chart is the relating of the thickness patterns to the contour patterns.  The thickness can be obtained from the aero-

logical reporting stations by simple subtraction of the heights of the two
standard isobaric surfaces being considered.   One can then draw lines
for this quantity on a map by the usual methods of scalar analysis.
From charts for two isobaric surfaces, superimposed on a light table, the
thicknesses can be obtained immediately for any desired points.   One or

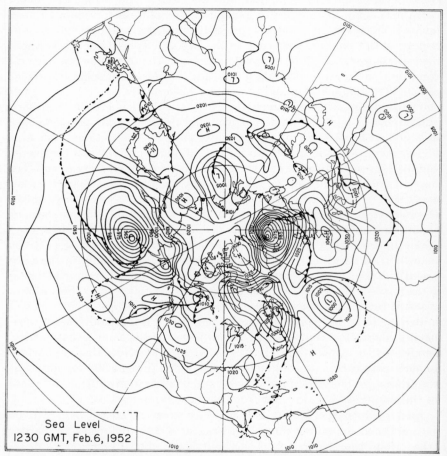

FIG. 15–4. Surface synoptic chart corresponding with the 500-mb chart of Fig. 12–1.

both of the analyses of isobaric surface must be changed if they are not
consistent with a reasonable thickness pattern.   The thickness pattern
must also be consistent with the pattern of virtual temperature, since
thickness between two isobaric levels depends only on the mean virtual
temperature of the layer through which the thickness is measured.
Furthermore, the thickness pattern must be consistent with the thermal

wind pattern, since the gradient of virtual temperature and therefore of thickness determines the thermal wind. In general, all surfaces in the atmosphere have fairly smooth contours and the gradients do not change sharply or vacillate widely. If any of the sets of lines have to be strained into peculiar contortions or odd gradients in order to satisfy internal consistency, some part of the analysis has to be changed.

Isotherms are usually drawn on the isobaric surfaces. Since, as was pointed out in Chap. 9, these have the same distribution on an isobaric surface as isosteres, isopycnics, or isentropes, the baroclinity or solenoidal field at that surface is shown. On the lower isobaric surfaces, such as 850 mb, it is useful to draw lines representing the water-vapor distribution. The tongues of moisture commonly found in summer weather show up well on this surface.

Beginners and also, to some extent, experienced meteorologists have difficulty locating fronts on the surface map. It would not be profitable to enter into a discussion of this technique here. A weather map with completely ideal frontal situations is virtually nonexistent and the methods of dealing with frontal analysis can only be learned by hard experience. As in all features of analysis, the fitting together of numerous factors in such a way that they will be consistent with each other establishes the work on a firm foundation.

One starts with a logical and consistent historical sequence of movement and frontogenesis (frontolysis). The isobaric analysis locates the troughs in which major fronts often lie, but no rule requires that fronts be located in troughs. All that is required is that there be a cyclonic wind shear *or* curvature in the vicinity of the front and that isobars crossing it have a cyclonic kink (often imperceptible in the coarse synoptic network). Next, the various discontinuities are looked for—discontinuities in the wind, the temperature, the moisture, and the 3-hr pressure tendency as plotted at each station. Clouds and precipitation areas and conditions at the 850-mb surface and lower help to confirm the locations of surface fronts.

**Isentropic Analysis.** In preparing an isentropic chart for an area it is well to choose an isentropic surface which extends quite low in the warmer part of the area but which does not intersect the ground. For North American isentropic charts the elevated lands around the northern border of Mexico are in the critical area; they have high surface potential temperatures and cannot be included on isentropic surfaces with lower $\theta$ values. One should not go to the other extreme of selecting an isentropic surface that is too high, for then the influx of low-level moisture from the south cannot be studied and the northern portion is likely to be in the stratosphere. The lowest usable potential temperatures for the entire United States are about 290°K in winter and 310°K in summer.

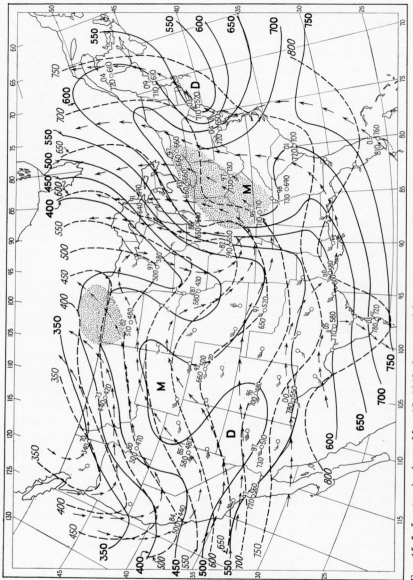

FIG. 15-5. Isentropic chart, May 15, 1942, for potential-temperature surface of 307°K. Solid lines are for isentropic-condensation pressure; dashed lines for actual pressure; lines of arrows are streamlines. Shaded areas show saturation at this surface.

The two principal sets of lines drawn on the isentropic chart are those for pressure and those for isentropic-condensation pressure. The first show essentially the heights and slopes of the surface. The isentropic-condensation pressures give the moisture distribution. For a given isentropic surface the mixing ratio is uniquely determined by the isentropic-condensation pressure. Furthermore, the separation of these lines from the pressure lines measures the pressure interval through which the air must ascend to reach condensation. Corresponding values of the two sets of lines intersect at points which outline the area of saturation on the isentropic surface. Since appreciable supersaturation does not occur in the atmosphere, the lines do not cross. The saturation areas contain only the lines of actual pressure and are usually shaded on the chart.

The tongues of moisture maxima, labeled $M$ in Fig. 15–5, are typically seen on isentropic charts, with dry areas, marked $D$ in the figure, around them. If the isentropic surface does not intersect the ground outside of the tropics, these circulations may usually be considered as occurring above the fronts. Since isentropic-condensation pressure is a conservative property before saturation, the moist and dry tongues might be expected to show the trajectories of the air, and this they do. The moisture lines advance at a speed somewhat less than the wind speed at the isentropic surface, and this is believed to be due to loss of moisture by lateral mixing with the surrounding drier air. This process, on a broad horizontal scale, is similar to entrainment on the convective scale.

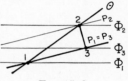

Fig. 15–6.

It is possible to represent geostrophic or gradient winds on an isentropic surface by means of a stream function $\psi$, which can be developed from the geostrophic wind relations for an isobaric surface or a level surface. Consider the isentropic surface shown in cross section in Fig. 15–6 running throught points 1 and 2. Isobaric surfaces and level surfaces, the latter in terms of geopotential $\Phi$, are shown. We can write the difference in geopotential along the isentropic surface between 1 and 2 as

$$\Phi_2 - \Phi_1 = (\Phi_3 - \Phi_1) + (\Phi_2 - \Phi_3) \tag{15–1}$$

If the differences are infinitesimal, we can write

$$\left(\frac{\partial \Phi}{\partial x}\right)_\theta \delta x = \left(\frac{\partial \Phi}{\partial x}\right)_p \delta x + \frac{\partial \Phi}{\partial p}(p_2 - p_1) \tag{15–2}$$

Since $\partial \Phi / \partial p$ is the same along an isentropic surface as along any other surface in this cross section, we may write, after substituting from the hydrostatic equation $\partial\Phi/\partial p = -\alpha$,

$$\left(\frac{\partial\Phi}{\partial x}\right)_p \delta x = \left(\frac{\partial\Phi}{\partial x}\right)_\theta \delta x + \alpha \left(\frac{\partial p}{\partial x}\right)_\theta \delta x \tag{15-3}$$

In an adiabatic process, that is, along an isentropic surface,

$$dq = c_p\, dT - \alpha\, dp = 0$$

and $\alpha\, dp = c_p\, dT$. This can be substituted in the last term, so that, after dividing through by $\delta x$, we have

$$\left(\frac{\partial\Phi}{\partial x}\right)_p = \left(\frac{\partial\Phi}{\partial x}\right)_\theta + c_p \left(\frac{\partial T}{\partial x}\right)_\theta \tag{15-4}$$

$$\left(\frac{\partial\Phi}{\partial x}\right)_p = \left[\frac{\partial(c_p T + \Phi)}{\partial x}\right]_\theta = \frac{\partial\psi}{\partial x} = fv \tag{15-5}$$

The stream function is $c_p T + \Phi = \psi$. We have, then, on an isentropic surface,

$$\frac{\partial\psi}{\partial x} = fv \tag{15-6}$$

$$\frac{\partial\psi}{\partial y} = -fu \tag{15-7}$$

Both terms in $\psi$ have the dimensions of ergs per gram. The value of $c_p$ is $0.24 \times 4.187 \times 10^7$ ergs g$^{-1}$°K$^{-1}$, and since $T$ ranges roughly between 200 and 300°K in the atmosphere, $c_p T$ ordinarily lies between 2 and $3 \times 10^9$ ergs per g. $\Phi$ is $9.8 \times 10^7$ ergs per g at 1 km and $9.8 \times 10^8$ at 10 km. The values of $\psi$ usually found in the usable isentropic surfaces range from about 2.9 to $3.2 \times 10^9$ ergs per g. The first term dominates, of course, in the low levels, but the second approaches it in magnitude near the tropopause. Normally the one term is an inverse function of the other.

The streamlines in Fig. 15–5 are drawn for intervals of $10^7$ ergs per g. As might be expected, they follow the isentropic isobars to a considerable extent. This relationship is in agreement with the fact that $p$ on an isentropic surface uniquely determines $T$ on that surface; also, $\Phi$ and $p$ are related through the integral involving virtual temperature and pressure from sea level to the point in question, and $T$ on the isentropic surface bears a relation, although a varying one, to the virtual temperature of the underlying column. The variations from place to place of sea-level pressure, temperature, and lapse rate in the underlying atmosphere cause the lack of coincidence of pressure and stream-function lines on isentropic surfaces.

The concept of air-mass movements and modifications implies that patterns of distribution of atmospheric properties are continually changing and being transported (advected) with the air currents. Although isentropic motion of air particles means that their potential temperature is conserved and that they must remain on the isentropic surface, their paths may not follow the contours of the isentropic surface because the surfaces themselves are usually displaced. Thus if a streamline intersects an isobar in the upslope sense it does not necessarily follow that the air particles are ascending; the isobars may retreat at the same speed as the motion. *Relative* motion must be considered.

Another type of relative motion—the geostrophic motion of air particles on an isentropic surface relative to that of air particles on a lower isentropic surface—was introduced by Starr.[1] If the upper particles are moving relative to the lower ones and in an upslope direction, it is reasonable to assume that ascent is occurring. The relative geostrophic velocities between the two have the components

$$u_2 - u_1 = -\frac{1}{f}\frac{\partial}{\partial y}(\psi_2 - \psi_1) \qquad (15\text{–}8)$$

$$v_2 - v_1 = \frac{1}{f}\frac{\partial}{\partial x}(\psi_2 - \psi_1) \qquad (15\text{–}9)$$

The quantity $\Delta\psi = \psi_2 - \psi_1$ is plotted on the lower of the two charts. The quantity is the stream function of the geostrophic motion on the upper chart relative to that on the lower one. The isopleths are streamlines of this relative motion.

The geostrophic wind scale as used on isobaric charts can be used in the same way on isentropic charts to obtain geostrophic winds, or the relative winds just described, from the spacing of the $\psi$ lines.

**Kinematic Analysis.** Up to this point the wind field has been considered as derived from the pattern of a scalar field, such as from heights on an isobaric surface or from stream function on an isentropic surface. For a picture of the broad synoptic features this type of analysis, supplemented with plotted wind observations, is sufficient in many cases. In studying smaller scale details, in analyzing weather in relatively inactive areas such as the tropics, and in making the transition from the analysis to the forecast certain analytical aids obtained from the field of motion are necessary. Analyses of streamlines, trajectories, divergence, and vorticity are derived from a study of the winds themselves or, in some instances, these properties can be investigated from the geostrophic values derived from the conventional scalar analysis.

Wind speed is itself a scalar and can be represented on charts by means of *isotachs*. These can be based on the observed winds or the geostrophic values or a combination of the two. Streamlines, as defined in Chap. 10,

---

[1] Starr, V. P., Construction of Isentropic Relative Motion Charts, *Bull. Am. Meteorol. Soc.*, vol. 21, pp. 236–239, 1940.

can be used to represent the wind field as to direction.  They are especially useful in the tropics where, owing to the relatively small value of the coriolis parameter, they are more revealing of the flow than the pressure analysis.  The wind arrows or vectors plotted on the map are the tangent vectors which define the streamlines.

Two different types of streamlines are in use.  One type, which we may call *directional* streamlines, consists of a set of lines drawn in such a way that the only requirement is that the wind be tangent to them throughout.  The wind speed does not necessarily correspond with the spacing of these streamlines.  At the windward edge of the map the spacing might be chosen to correspond with the speeds, but unless all changes in speed are accounted for in a nondivergent manner, a situation which is seldom the case over a large area, the relation of streamline spacing to speed is not preserved.  In the second type, which we may call *flux* streamlines, the spacing is made to correspond with the wind speed.  Each streamline can be labeled in terms of a stream function $\psi$ and the wind will then be proportional to the gradient of this function.  The relation of wind to this streamline pattern would be analogous to the geostrophic relationship to isobars.

The directional streamlines have a characteristic not found in the scalar lines representing flow.  They can branch, one from the other, join together, originate, or terminate at various places on the map.  As long as they are not assigned stream-function values, they can begin or terminate at lines along which the wind is discontinuous, such as at fronts.  They may spread outward or converge into a line of divergence or convergence.  They diverge outward from the calm centers of anticyclones and converge spirally inward to centers of low pressure.  The definition of such streamlines requires that where they join or separate they must do so at an infinitesimal angle.  Some of these features are shown on the streamline chart of Fig. 15–7.

The flux streamlines can be made to represent divergence and convergence by the beginning and termination of the lines, although this requires that some liberties be taken with the definition of flux streamlines.  The technique is illustrated in Fig. 15–8.  Where new streamlines originate, the flow is characterized by horizontal divergence and where they terminate, the flow is convergent.  The method is more pictorial than exact, for there are regions, designated by the dashed portions of the streamlines in the figure, where the spacing does not represent the speed.  It will be shown presently that gradients of stream function, as well as the geostrophic relationship, are only valid for representing nondivergent flow.

It is sometimes useful to construct a map of *isogons*, that is, of lines of equal wind direction, expressed in scalar values of compass degrees.

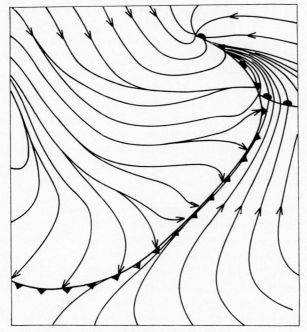

FIG. 15–7. Directional streamlines.

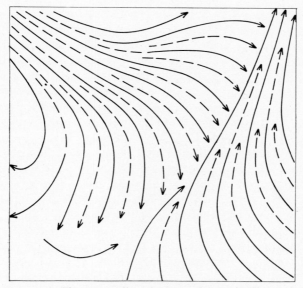

FIG. 15–8. Flux streamlines for same flow as in Fig. 15–7.

These are somewhat easier to analyze after the data have been plotted than are streamlines directly, and they aid in the construction of the streamlines. Isotachs may be drawn on the streamline chart to represent speeds. They are also useful in making certain computations of divergence, to be described presently.

In some forecasting and analytical applications it is desirable to determine the *trajectories* of the air. These are the actual paths followed by the air particles with respect to the surface of the earth. Streamlines give the instantaneous motion, but if the streamline pattern is changing or being displaced, the particles are subjected to a continually changing wind field and follow trajectories which may be quite different from the streamlines. The air acquires properties which depend on the type of surface over which it has been passing, that is, on the nature of the terrain covered by its past trajectory. For example, the study of trajectory will show whether the air has been over a body of water or not. Estimates of future trajectory are used in temperature and fog forecasting.

A reasonably accurate air trajectory for at least the last 24 hr may be constructed from surface synoptic charts for 6-hr intervals. It has been found that the surface winds over land areas are not reliable for this purpose owing to the variations in exposure between the different stations. The geostrophic wind, corrected for friction, is better for these computations. Experience shows what speed reductions and cross-isobar components are produced by friction over the average terrain being considered. In the graphical method illustrated in Fig.

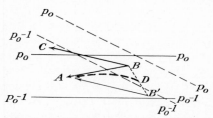

Fig. 15–9. Trajectory method for changing isobars. The dashed lines represent the isobars 6 hr previous to those represented by the solid lines.

15–9, a reduction of the geostrophic speed of 25 per cent and a cross-isobar angle of 15° is applied.

In Fig. 15–9 the point $A$ represents the station in question on the current map. The two solid isobars $p_0$ and $p_0 - 1$ indicate, for the Northern Hemisphere, a geostrophic wind from the east of 20 mph. Going backward 6 hr, one draws a vector for the displacement, corrected for friction. This displacement is found to be 90 miles in the 6 hr ($20 \times 6 \times 0.75$), and the vector is drawn with an angle of 15° across the isobars giving $B$ as the position 6 hr ago. However, this may not have represented the wind throughout the past 6 hr, so we study the wind on the map of 6 hr earlier. The point $B$ is located on the earlier map, and the wind is projected forward to the time of our present map. Since the isobars were placed differently at that time and at that place, we obtain a gradient wind of 30 mph and a displacement represented by the vector $BC$ of $30 \times 6 \times 0.75 = 135$ miles. This vector from the earlier chart is then placed on the current map with its head at $A$, giving us point $B'$ as a tentative position 6 hr ago. We then take the mean of the two positions $B$ and $B'$ which is $D$, as the correct previous position. We then construct the path from $D$ to correspond with the isobars of the earlier map in the first part of its trajectory and those of the present map at the end. Now, using $D$ as the station in question, we continue on back with the process using previous maps for as long an interval as is desired.

To construct the future estimated trajectory is, of course, more difficult. The corrected geostrophic wind on the present map is used to fit an appropriate vector heading at the station in question, and representing the displacement during the next 6 hr. However, the pressure distribution may be expected to change during the next 6 hr. From the pressure change in the 3 hr preceding the observation, transmitted by all stations, *isallobars*, lines of equal pressure change, can be drawn. By extrapolating these changes into the next 6 hr, the new pressure distribution can be estimated. Along coast lines it would be necessary to correct for the diurnal distortion of the pressure field, but ordinarily it would not be necessary to correct for the diurnal tendencies because they would have the same effect on all pressures in a region of the size in question, and we are interested only in the gradient of pressure, not in its absolute values. The extrapolated pressures, the "future past" trajectory for the station in question, can then be obtained, and the mean of the two trajectory vectors will be the approximate true path. Under certain conditions, future trajectories for 12 hr hence are obtainable with useful accuracy.

*Analysis of Divergence.* Since the divergence in the $x,y$ plane is given by $\partial u/\partial x + \partial v/\partial y$, the most obvious way of analyzing for divergence on a map is to obtain these derivatives graphically. On one map the $x$ component of the observed wind $u$ is plotted and on another map for the same time the $y$ component $v$ is plotted. Isotachs of these respective components are then constructed on each map. By finite differences, the variation of $u$ in the $x$ direction and of $v$ in the $y$ direction are determined for as many points as are necessary to describe the field, and these two values are added together and plotted on corresponding points on a third map. Isopleths are then drawn to show the field of divergence.

In Eq. (10–68) it was shown that the horizontal divergence is also given by $1/A\ dA/dt$, where $A$ is the area covered by the portion of air under study. $A$ can be defined as the area outlined by straight lines connecting any three or more identifiable particles. Since balloons move as air particles, three or more balloons released simultaneously from three or more different points can be followed to obtain the variations in area between them.

Divergence measurements made from synoptic charts can best be understood by considering the flow in streamline tubes, as defined in Chap. 10, which are capable of changing their vertical and horizontal dimensions by expanding in one dimension while contracting in the other; that is to say, by horizontal divergence compensated by vertical convergence and vice versa. In the derivation in Chap. 10 of the equation of continuity and the expression for divergence resulting therefrom, a cube of constant unit volume was considered. Let us now consider a section of a streamline tube which is not a cube and whose cross-sectional dimensions vary in the distance $\delta s = s_2 - s_1$ along the streamlines. Only the horizontal velocity $c$ along the streamlines is considered. Then, after the manner of Eq. (10–56), we write

$$\text{Mass accumulation} = \text{inflow at } s_1 - \text{outflow at } s_2$$

$$\frac{dM}{dt} = \rho c \ \delta n \ \delta z - \left[ \rho c \ \delta n \ \delta z + \frac{\partial(\rho c \ \delta n \ \delta z)}{\partial s} \ \delta s \right]$$

$$= -\frac{\partial}{\partial s} (\rho c \ \delta n \ \delta z) \ \delta s \tag{15–10}$$

where $\delta n$ and $\delta z$ are the horizontal and vertical cross-stream dimensions, respectively. In expanded form this expression becomes

$$\frac{dM}{dt} = -\rho c \ \delta n \ \frac{\partial(\delta z)}{\partial s} \ \delta s - \rho c \ \delta z \ \frac{\partial(\delta n)}{\partial s} \ \delta s - \rho \ \delta n \ \delta z \ \frac{\partial c}{\partial s} \ \delta s - c \ \delta n \ \delta z \ \frac{\partial \rho}{\partial s} \ \delta s$$

$$\tag{15–11}$$

If the density is not changed and if vertical and horizontal shrinking and stretching compensate each other, the mass does not change. We separate the horizontal and vertical changes after setting $dM/dt = 0$ and $\partial \rho/\partial s = 0$, and write

$$\rho c \ \delta z \ \frac{\partial(\delta n)}{\partial s} \ \delta s + \rho \ \delta n \ \delta z \ \frac{\partial c}{\partial s} \ \delta s = -\rho c \ \delta n \ \frac{\partial(\delta z)}{\partial s} \ \delta s \tag{15–12}$$

This expression indicates that any contribution toward increase in mass which would come from horizontal stretching would be compensated by vertical shrinking.

Note that all the terms are in units of change in mass per unit time. If we divide by $\rho$, which is already assumed to be constant, we have the rate of change in volume and if, in addition, we divide by $\delta z$, we have on the left-hand side of the last equation the rate of change in area of the floor (or ceiling) of the section of the tube, or

$$c \frac{\partial(\delta n)}{\partial s} \delta s + \delta n \frac{\partial c}{\partial s} \delta s = \frac{dA}{dt} = \frac{\partial(c\,\delta n)}{\partial s} \delta s$$
$$= c_2\,\delta n_2 - c_1\,\delta n_1 \qquad (15\text{–}13)$$

The horizontal divergence is expressed by $1/A\ dA/dt$, so the above expression divided by the area gives the horizontal divergence. Note that Eq. (15–13) divided by the area is precisely the same as Eq. (10–69).

The method of computation on a map was shown in Fig. 10–13. The $\delta n$s are measured along a set of lines orthogonal to the streamlines. In obtaining $A$ to divide into Eq. (15–13) one can set off equal downstream increments $\delta s$ and multiply this constant number by the $\delta n$ of the midpoint of $\delta s$.

It should be noted that if the velocity increases as $\delta n$ becomes smaller, $c\,\delta n$ can remain constant ($c_2\,\delta n_2 = c_1\,\delta n_1$) and the wind is nondivergent. In the case of potential flow, $c\,\delta n = -\delta\psi =$ constant ($\psi$ lines drawn for constant $\psi$ interval), and the divergence is zero. Similarly, in geostrophic flow, $fc\,\delta n = -\alpha\,\delta p$, and if $f$ and $\alpha$ do not change, the velocity is determined only by the closeness of the isobars. Therefore divergence may be expected only if the wind is *ageostrophic*.

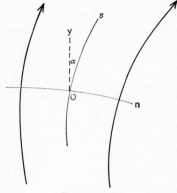

Fig. 15–10.

Strong divergence or convergence is found only where winds depart markedly from the geostrophic, such as in thunderstorms, in sea breezes, at some fronts, and in developing cyclones.

Another graphical method based on streamlines was presented by Saucier.[1] It is illustrated in Fig. 15–10. From an origin at $O$ on an intermediate streamline of the figure, two axes are drawn —one, the $s$ axis, along the streamline and the other, the $n$ axis, orthogonal to the streamlines. Both axes are curved. Their relationship to straight, rectangular axes $x$ and $y$ through $O$ is determined, and from that the horizontal divergence at $O$, expressed as $\partial u/\partial x + \partial v/\partial y$, is put into the new coordinates.

At a point near $O$ the streamline makes an angle $\alpha$ with the $y$ axis. If the velocity along the streamline is $c$, then the $x$ component of the velocity is

$$u = c \sin \alpha$$

[1] Saucier, W. J., "Principles of Meteorological Analysis," p. 323, University of Chicago Press, Chicago, 1955.

Near $O$, $\delta x = \delta n$ and

$$\frac{\partial u}{\partial x} = \frac{\partial u}{\partial n} = \frac{\partial}{\partial n}(c \sin \alpha)$$

$$= c \cos \alpha \frac{\partial \alpha}{\partial n} + \sin \alpha \frac{\partial c}{\partial n} \qquad (15\text{–}14)$$

At the infinitesimal distance $\delta n$ and $\delta x$, $\cos \alpha = 1$ and $\sin \alpha = 0$, so

$$\frac{\partial u}{\partial x} = c \frac{\partial \alpha}{\partial n} \qquad (15\text{–}15)$$

Also, at $O$,

$$\frac{\partial v}{\partial y} = \frac{\partial c}{\partial s} \qquad (15\text{–}16)$$

Thus, the horizontal divergence is

$$\mathrm{div}_2\, c = \frac{\partial u}{\partial x} + \frac{\partial v}{\partial y} = \frac{\partial c}{\partial s} + \frac{\partial u}{\partial n} = \frac{\partial c}{\partial s} + c\frac{\partial \alpha}{\partial n} \qquad (15\text{–}17)$$

Saucier called the first term the stretching term and the second one the spreading term. For measuring $\partial \alpha/\partial n$ he recommended using an isogon analysis. One obtains the difference in isogon values at both ends of the finite distance $\delta n$, multiplies by $\delta n$, and, if isogons are in degrees, multiplies also by $\pi/180$ rad per deg.

As might be expected, the two terms tend to cancel each other in normal conditions, for a spreading of the streamlines downstream is normally accompanied by a downstream decrease in velocity. In potential or geostrophic flow, the two terms are of equal value and opposite sign. Other methods of computing the divergence are described in Chap. 10.

As first pointed out by Panofsky,[1] the values of divergence obtained in the atmosphere are highly sensitive to scale of distance or area over which the measurements are made. Panofsky found that regardless of the scale used the change in wind was of the order of 1 to 10 m per sec, tending to give very little variation in the value of the numerator in the divergence expressions. The denominator depends on the scale chosen and the choice depends on the size of the phenomena considered. Thus, for an entire cyclone the divergence is of the order of $-10^{-5}$ per sec (convergence) in the low levels while for a thunderstorm cell which may have a diameter $\frac{1}{100}$ of that of a cyclone, the value is of the order of $\pm 10^{-3}$ per sec. It is wise when quoting values of divergence to specify the size of the area considered.

[1] Panofsky, H. A., Large-scale Vertical Velocity and Divergence, *Compendium of Meteorol.*, 1951, p. 639.

*Analysis of Vorticity.* The analysis of the wind field for vorticity is done in essentially the same way as for divergence; in fact the two are related, as already pointed out in Chap. 10. On a streamline chart with orthogonal lines drawn, and perhaps with isotachs and isogons included, the necessary information is available for vorticity analysis. For example, the same method that is employed for divergence measurement in Fig. 15–10 can be applied to vorticity computation. It can be shown, or by analogy with Eq. (15–17), it can be stated, that

$$\frac{\partial v}{\partial x} - \frac{\partial u}{\partial y} = \frac{\partial c}{\partial n} - c\frac{\partial \alpha}{\partial s} \tag{15–18}$$

It is seen that the vorticity is thus expressed as the sum of a shear term $\partial c/\partial n$ and a curvature term $c(\partial \alpha/\partial s)$.

Another method is illustrated in Fig. 15–11. A vector $c'$ is taken 90° to the right of the wind vector $c$, the two vectors having the components $u'$, $v'$ and $u$, $v$, as shown. It is noted that $u = -v'$ and $v = u'$ and it follows that

$$\frac{\partial u}{\partial y} = -\frac{\partial v'}{\partial y}, \qquad \frac{\partial v}{\partial x} = \frac{\partial u'}{\partial x} \tag{15–19}$$

The vorticity is given by

$$\frac{\partial v}{\partial x} - \frac{\partial u}{\partial y} = \frac{\partial u'}{\partial x} + \frac{\partial v'}{\partial y} \tag{15–20}$$

Hence the vertical component of the vorticity is given by the horizontal divergence of the wind vectors rotated 90° to the right.

In Chap. 10 it was shown that the vorticity of the geostrophic wind is given by the curvature of the isobaric surface, such that it is positive (cyclonic) in curving portions of depressions and anticyclonic or negative around domes. The curvature of the surface can be computed from a large number of grid points. This may be done by an electronic computer as part of the forecasting problem. It can be estimated as to sign almost at a glance by taking a small square of four grid points with a fifth in the center of the square.

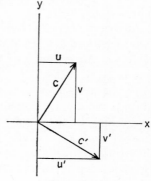

FIG 15–11.

If the center point is lower than the four corners the vorticity is positive; if it is higher the vorticity is negative.

**Mesometeorology.** Some weather systems are too small to be followed in the standard synoptic network yet produce profound effects.

Such organized systems as squall lines, masses of thunderstorms, sea-breeze systems, and large precipitation cells are in this category. They are said to be on a *mesosynoptic* scale. As a rough classification based on scale we may list *micrometeorology*, which covers turbulence, diffusion, evaporation, and heat fluxes, especially in the layer next to the ground; *mesometeorology*, which is concerned with small-scale weather patterns over distances of perhaps 10 to 1000 miles; standard *synoptic meteorology*, which covers those phenomena observed in networks of stations 50 to 500 miles apart; and *macrometeorology*, in which the atmosphere is viewed on a hemispheric scale, with only the major waves, blocking actions, and broad circulation features considered. A fifth scale, called *cosmic meteorology*, might be added, concerned with the relation of the atmosphere to its interplanetary environment. All of these scales require somewhat different analysis techniques.

Mesosynoptic analyses can best be accomplished where special, dense station networks have been established for that or similar purposes. There are also a number of special airway and cooperative stations which are not included in the regular synoptic reports. Many of the special network stations are unmanned, since the cost of automatically transmitting the records to the analysis center is less than the cost of manpower. Either way the job is done, the communication load is such that most of the data have to be collected hours or days after the event from the autographic records. Thus the starting point of mesoanalysis is nearly always the autographic records—the barograph, thermograph, hygrograph, rain gauge, wind, and other traces. These, of course, are supplemented by any visual, direct-reading, or upper-air observations made at manned stations.

An event such as a squall line or mass of thunderstorms leaves an unmistakable record at each station as it blusters in and works its way past the station. An example of the pronounced changes produced by a squall line is given in Fig. 15–12. Note that time increases from right to left in the figure. This reversal of the time scale when reproducing the autographic records is commonly practiced outside the tropics so that a time graph may be fitted with a space graph. The systems move from west to east and west is always to the left. The conditions preceding the disturbance are those conditions found to the east of it, therefore to the right in map representation, so we find it convenient to have the prior events to the right and the later time to the left.

The time of arrival of the disturbance at each station can be recognized on the traces, and isochrones can be drawn on the map. Over short distances and short periods of time it can be assumed that the individual changes in properties of the disturbance are negligible, and that, taking

$p$ as an example,

$$\frac{Dp}{Dt} = \frac{\partial p}{\partial t} + c \cdot \nabla p = 0 \qquad (15\text{–}21)$$

$$\frac{\partial p}{\partial t} = -c \cdot \nabla p \qquad (15\text{–}22)$$

In other words, the local change, as indicated on the autographic records, may be regarded as being entirely due to advection. Through this relationship it is possible to extrapolate and interpolate in short intervals of time and space. Time changes at a point can be substituted for space gradients through a knowledge of the rate-of-displacement vector $c$.

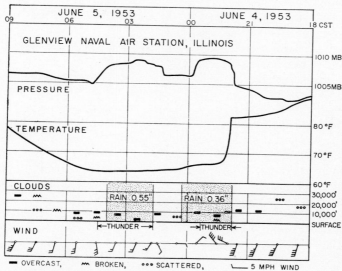

FIG. 15–12. Autographic records during passage of a squall line. (*After Fujita.*)

A variety of graphical methods, which will not be dwelt upon here, are employed to reveal features of the disturbances. One such method consists of obtaining from the surrounding, undisturbed stations the undisturbed pressure trace. In the disturbed areas only the pressure excess or pressure deficit as compared with the undisturbed field is treated in order to give a more striking picture of the important features. Other properties can be similarly represented.

Mesometeorological techniques were first directed toward an improved understanding of the mechanism of squall lines, that is, the lines of thunderstorms that do not occur along fronts. These disturbances are large enough to affect the analysis and forecasting on the standard synoptic scale, but not much more can be done on that scale than to indicate their presence. Fujita[1] showed that these lines, which may be several hundred miles long and may be accompanied by disturbed areas of as much as 100,000 square miles, have a humble beginning in a single shower or thunderstorm. This growth from a point on the map is illustrated in Fig. 15–13. The squall line and accompanying thunderstorm area are shown in their 0300 CST position. The isochrones, represented somewhat like arcs centered on the point of origin, show the

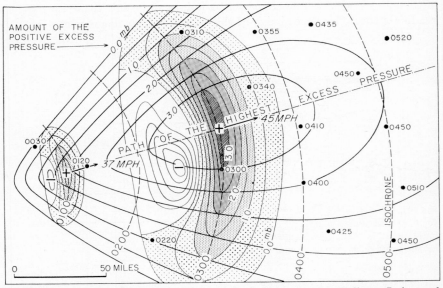

FIG. 15–13. Spread of thunderstorm area with advancing squall line. Isobars of excess of pressure are drawn for two times, 0100 and 0300, with hourly isochrones and envelopes of the various pressure values. (*After Fujita.*)

position of the squall front at other times. The radial lines at the ends of these isochrones envelop the maximum lengths attained by the squall system. Thus from the time of its beginning at 0030 CST to the time of the last isochrone represented here, the system has swept out an area bounded by the last isochrone and the outer radial lines.

Fujita's 1955 model of a squall line is shown in Fig. 15–14. Three main features are present on the map—the *thunderstorm high*, the *wake depression*, and the *pressure-surge line*, the latter being identified by the characteristics of an intense cold front, sometimes called a pseudo-front.

[1] Fujita, T., Results of Detailed Synoptic Studies of Squall Lines, *Tellus*, vol. 7, pp. 405–436, 1955.

Some of the features of thunderstorms and squall lines will be considered in greater detail in Chap. 19.

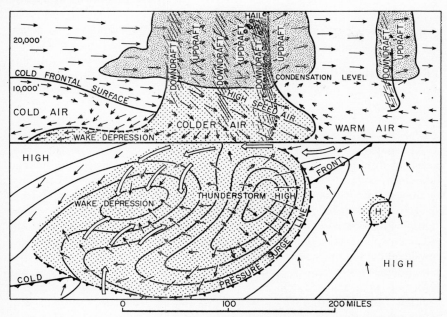

FIG. 15–14. Fujita's model of a squall line, in vertical cross section (upper) and in surface map plan (lower). Lines on surface map are isobars. Wind vectors are indicated by small arrows; upper motion relative to the moving system is represented by the large open arrows on the surface map.

Radar has its greatest usefulness in mesometeorology. Thunderstorms and squall lines show up markedly on the radarscopes and in this type of analysis much use is made of photographs of the radarscope presentations.

# CHAPTER 16

# TROPICAL METEOROLOGY

As we view the daily weather maps we note that the perturbation activity diminishes rapidly toward the tropical borders of the charts. The impression is obtained that, except for the rare appearance of tropical cyclones (hurricanes or typhoons), the tropical atmosphere is characterized by monotonous inactivity. In terms of fronts, cyclones, and major wave disturbances this impression is correct. However, the tropical atmosphere is so heavily charged with water vapor that any slight low-level convergence will produce rain and squalls. Some of the smaller convergence areas cannot be detected on the standard synoptic scale, but many of them can. Tropical analysis and forecasting consist mainly in looking for minor disturbances and predicting their development and movement, especially with reference to the major rainstorms which they produce. In addition, of course, tropical cyclones are a major concern during the season and in the regions of their occurrence. Tropical meteorology also involves a variety of studies concerning heat and momentum transfers, meridional circulation components, monsoons, and other features of importance in the broad-scale flow patterns and in the general circulation.

**Zones of Convergence.** There are two principal convergence zones in the tropics—the *equatorial convergence zone* and the *monsoon convergence zone.* The former is the zone of convergence of the trade-wind systems of the two hemispheres. Unlike the polar-front zone, it has no significant, persistent temperature differences across it. The zone is one of weak air currents and, from nautical terminology, sometimes is called the *doldrums* or belt of calms. A net upward motion and therefore heavy clouds and rain are formed there. The equatorial convergence zone migrates seasonally as far as 15° or more north and south of the equator in some places, reaching its northernmost point in September and southernmost in March, corresponding to the seasons of highest temperatures in the oceans. These two extreme monthly mean positions are illustrated in Fig. 16–1. The reverse coriolis effect on trade-wind air from one hemisphere moving into the other accentuates the conflict in wind direc-

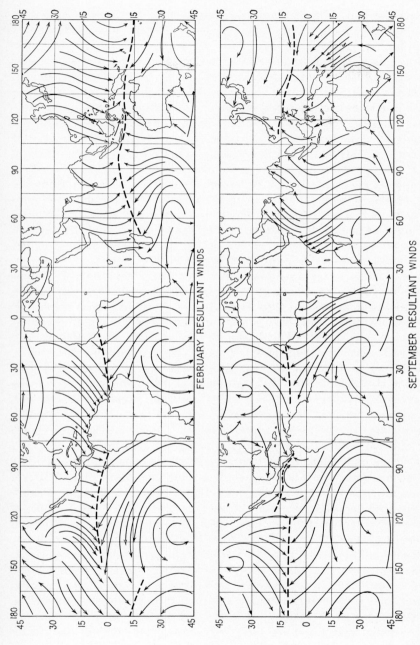

FEBRUARY RESULTANT WINDS

SEPTEMBER RESULTANT WINDS

Fig. 16–1. Resultant winds over the oceans at the height of the northern and southern hurricane seasons, showing positions of convergence zones over the oceans.

369

tion on the two sides of the zone. When it is at or near its seasonal maximum displacement, the equatorial convergence zone plays a part in the formation of tropical cyclones.

Monsoon-wind systems have convergence zones associated with them. Although monsoons are usually defined merely as winds that come in from the sea during summer and from the land during winter, the true monsoon amounts to more than that. In the Indian monsoon there is convergence between the very humid air from the Indian Ocean and the westerlies coming from the Mediterranean across the Arabian Desert and the Arabian Sea, and the heaviest monsoon rains occur in this convergence zone. Farther east, the monsoon is linked with the equatorial convergence zone, the monsoon air being Southern Hemisphere air from the South Indian Ocean. Again, along the China coast, the monsoon converges with the westerlies. In Central America a weak summer monsoon on the Pacific side converges against the trade winds of the Atlantic and Caribbean. A similar situation, where the monsoon and equatorial convergence zones are tied together, occurs in West Africa.

Rather than having directional convergence, the equatorial and monsoon convergence zones may be of the shear-line type at some points. Cyclonic shear in straight flow means positive vorticity, and, if the flow is essentially zonal and the vorticity not decreasing, it must be accompanied by convergence. In addition to the equatorial convergence zone, other east-west shear lines of lesser magnitude are found in the tropics. Often they are the remnants of polar fronts swept into the tropics with the flow still exhibiting a shear although density differences have disappeared. In other cases they result from some peculiar configuration of the flow imposed by crowding of the subtropical highs by extratropical disturbances. Even in the mean picture other convergence zones appear. Reihl[1] computed the divergence field from January and July charts of the mean resultant surface winds over the oceans. The results, reproduced in Fig. 16–2, show a somewhat complicated pattern. For example, in both the January and July charts there is a convergence zone in each hemisphere in the western part of the Pacific with a zone of divergence between them. The weak convergence zones north and northeast of Australia also depart from the simplified picture.

The often-dramatized rainy seasons at tropical locations are associated with the seasonal displacements of these convergence zones. Some tropical stations have two distinct rainy seasons, one when the equatorial convergence zone crosses the area going northward and the other when it passes going south again. The dry seasons between these periods can be as dramatic as the rains. Contrary to popular opinion, the greater

[1] Riehl, H., On the Role of the Tropics in the General Circulation of the Atmosphere, *Tellus*, vol. 2, pp. 1–25, 1950.

part of the land areas of the tropics are grassy or only sparsely tree-covered because of the climatic stress of long dry periods each year.

Temporary moving convergence zones associated with moving disturbances will be taken up in the sections describing these disturbances.

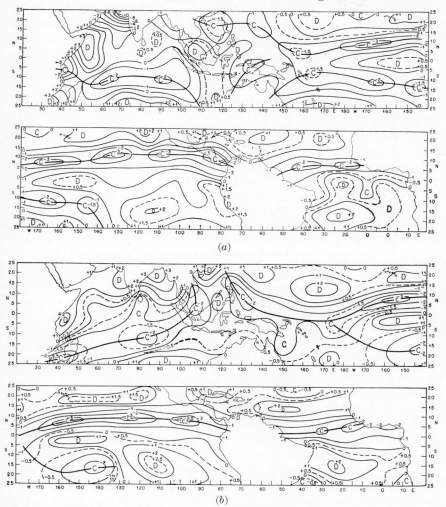

FIG. 16–2. Divergence charts as computed by Riehl for (a) January and (b) July. Values are given in units of $10^{-6}$ sec$^{-1}$.

**Vertical Structure of the Winds.** In the discussion of the general circulation in Chap. 11 the tropics were characterized as a region of easterlies at all heights. This picture is essentially correct, although somewhat simplified. The subtropical (horse-latitude) ridges of high pressure are displaced equatorward with height, leading to a corresponding tilt in the boundary between the westerlies and the easterlies.   The boundary may have a slope of about $\frac{1}{600}$ in the low levels so that a station in the easterlies 10° of latitude from the surface ridge line will have westerlies beginning at a height of about 6000 ft.   The slope increases with height and distance from the surface ridge line to such an extent that throughout the troposphere easterlies are found within about 20° of the surface position. The seasonal shifting of the entire system toward the warmer hemisphere results in wide annual variations in depth of the easterlies, at least at stations 15° or more from the equator.

Across large areas of the deep tropics *equatorial westerlies* are found seasonally or intermittently.   These are most pronounced on the average across the Indian Ocean and into the western Pacific on both sides of the

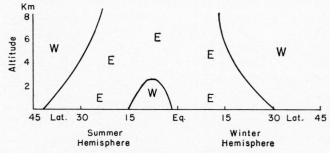

FIG. 16–3. Wind regimes of the tropics.

equator, but they have been observed on occasions in many tropical locations.   Except where mountains affect the circulation, these westerlies are nearly always confined to the lower levels; they are thus quite distinct from the upper westerlies that are beyond the subtropical ridge, and from which they are separated by a broad and deep mass of easterlies. The equatorial westerlies may reach as high as from 20,000 to 30,000 ft in some areas, such as between India and the Phillippines, but elsewhere they seldom extend above 10,000 ft.   As might be expected, they are often observed to have a direct connection with monsoon circulations, and to occur on the equatorward side of the equatorial convergence zone.

Figure 16–3 shows in vertical cross section the wind regimes of the tropics, with the positions of the boundaries indicated for the two extreme seasons.   It should be realized that the boundary between the circumpolar westerlies and the easterlies of the trade-wind region is the horse-latitude high-pressure belt, characterized by divergence, while the boundaries of the equatorial westerlies are cyclonic shear lines and therefore lines of low pressure, characterized by convergence.

The easterlies or trade winds have an equatorward component in the low levels usually explained by friction. Winter monsoon effects in the cold hemisphere, especially in the Northern Hemisphere in the vicinity of Asia, account for an appreciable meridional exchange of heat.

Since the tropical atmosphere is essentially barotropic, thermal-wind components are negligible in the deep easterlies. Near the outer limits of the trades the winds often decrease with height above the friction layer, but this does not seem to be true in the deep easterlies. As the coriolis effect disappears near the equator the thermal wind component no longer has a real meaning, since it is based on the geostrophic assumption.

**Characteristics of Trade-wind and Monsoon Air.** In the brief discussion of the oceanic anticyclones in Chap. 11 it was pointed out that the air which they feed into the trade winds has undergone strong subsidence and is therefore dry aloft and has an inversion of temperature in the low levels. The temperature inversion is accentuated in the eastern parts of the oceans by cooling from below over cold ocean currents. Through the trade-wind belt the transition is made from a low and very strong inversion with stratus clouds or fog in the eastern part of the ocean to a disappearance of the inversion in the western part. Subsidence is likely to continue in the trade-wind region despite the addition of heat from below as the air moves over the warm tropical waters, so the effects of the inversion are seldom completely obliterated. Over the Caribbean, for example, a stable layer is usually found at about 2000 to 2500 m above the sea. Above it the air is remarkably dry. The depth of the moist layer varies with changes in the low-level divergence-convergence pattern. This stable layer is well within the easterlies and does not correspond with the boundary of the westerlies; in fact there is seldom much change in wind through it.

Where no large-scale convergence has taken place in the low levels, a characteristic type of convective cloud known as the *trade-wind cumulus* occurs. It has its base at about 2000 ft and top at 5000 to 8000 ft. Characteristically about one-third to one-half of the ocean area is covered by these clouds. The convection currents in them are weak, but nevertheless they are capable of producing showers of fine rain. In areas of convergence and over islands in the daytime they mass together to produce large towering clouds and copious downpours of rain.

The monsoon air and the air of the equatorial westerlies is generally more moist aloft than the typical trade-wind air, although there are some striking exceptions. In Fig. 16–4 two soundings are plotted to illustrate the difference between monsoon air and trade-wind air. The monsoon sounding for the Indian station shows higher temperatures and moistures than the mean Caribbean atmosphere, characteristic of the trade-wind region.

**Transverse Waves.** Transverse waves, with axes across the trade-wind current, are nearly always found moving through the tropics. They are essentially of two types: (1) waves in the deep easterlies or (2) waves in the upper westerlies over shallow easterlies. While neither of these looks impressive on isobaric or streamline charts, the high moisture content of their medium results in the production of copious rains. The troughs of these waves appear only as poleward bulges of the isobars or streamlines. In this sense the two types have the same appearance at the surface. Their differences are found aloft and also in their direction of movement. The waves in the deep easterlies exhibit only perturbed easterlies at all heights. The waves in the upper westerlies are found where westerlies extend aloft equatorward over the easterlies, and they progress from west to east, against the low-level winds.

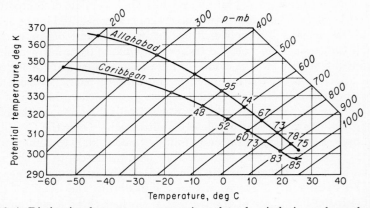

FIG. 16–4. Distinction between monsoon air and trade-wind air as shown by mean monsoon soundings at Allahabad, India, and mean soundings in the Caribbean.

The transverse waves cresting away from the equator establish patterns of convergence and divergence depending on the meridional component of the disturbed flow. This effect can be shown by considering the relationship of the vertical component of absolute vorticity and the horizontal convergence as given in Eq. (10–76), or

$$\frac{1}{f + \zeta} \frac{d}{dt} (f + \zeta) = - \operatorname{div}_2 c = K \tag{16-1}$$

where $K$ is the convergence. We will consider Northern Hemisphere conditions, but with suitable interpretation of signs the equations will be applicable to the Southern Hemisphere. The variation of the coriolis parameter may be written as

$$\frac{df}{dt} = \frac{df}{dy} \frac{dy}{dt} = \beta v \tag{16-2}$$

where $\beta$ is the increase in $f$ with linear distance northward.    This substitution and a rearrangement of terms produce

$$K = \frac{1}{f + \zeta}\frac{d\zeta}{dt} + \frac{\beta v}{f + \zeta} \qquad (16\text{–}3)$$

The term $\beta$ is always positive; $f$ is positive, and near the equator, quite small.    The denominator of the two right-hand terms can be negative only if the relative vorticity $\zeta$ is anticyclonic (negative) and greater in absolute value than $f$, which is usually not the case in these waves.    It turns out that if the wave is not moving too rapidly, all of the terms are positive to the east of the wave axis.    This can be seen from the typical example of such a wave in Fig. 16–5.    Where the winds have a southerly

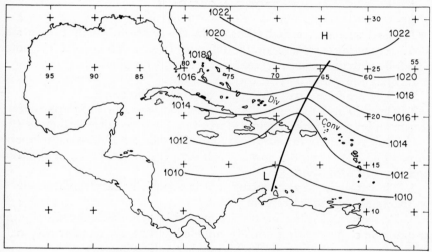

Fig. 16–5. Transverse wave in the easterlies.

component, that is, where $\beta v$ is positive, $\zeta$ is increasing.    On the western side, $\zeta$ is decreasing as the air moves back southward again, so both terms are negative, indicating divergence.

The weather connected with the waves reflects the field of horizontal divergence, exhibiting large, massive clouds and showers or continuous rain to the east and in the center.    To the west, divergence and subsidence suppress the convection, the moist air is shallow, and the stable layer characteristic of the trade-wind region is quite well marked.

Over the tropical oceans, at least in their western parts, there is a more or less continual succession of these waves, producing alternate periods of bright days and heavy rains.    Over land masses and larger islands they are difficult to detect because of the overpowering orographical and diurnal effects.    The differences in weather during their passage are accentuated at places on the southern sides of mountainous islands.   The protection of the mountains makes the air unusually hot, dry, and clear in the current from the north, but in the southerly winds the convective activity is accentuated as the air piles up against the mountains.

The waves in the deep easterlies progress westward at a speed of less than that of the basic current.   The troughs usually tilt slightly toward the east with height and most often have their maximum intensity somewhere between 5000 and 15,000 ft above sea level.   As shown by Riehl[1] these disturbances often show up in a marked manner even on the 200-mb surface, roughly at 35,000 ft.

## TROPICAL CYCLONES

Tropical cyclones, called *typhoons* in the western North Pacific and *hurricanes* elsewhere, are quite different from extratropical cyclones. The following distinguishing features are most prominent:

1. They are found only at certain seasons.

2. They are found only in certain regions of the tropics.

3. They do not form with any regularity, even in their appropriate season and region, which suggests fortuitous circumstances in their origin.

4. They form only in those ocean areas having a high surface temperature, 26 or 27°C being the lowest such temperature observed at the time and place of formation.

5. They form in an atmosphere that is essentially barotropic, and have no fronts associated with them.

6. Pressure and other properties are fairly symmetrically distributed around the center, with gradually rounded and nearly circular isobars.

7. They are not associated with moving anticyclones.

8. They derive their energy from the latent heat of condensation.

9. They are usually about one-third the diameter of extratropical cyclones.

10. They are many times more intense than extratropical cyclones, occasionally having a central sea-level pressure of 900 mb or lower and surface winds often exceeding 100 knots.

11. They can exist only over the oceans and die out rapidly on land.

12. They have a central core of calm or very light winds.   This central region, called the *eye*, has a diameter, on the average, of about 20 km and is largely free of heavy clouds.

13. They are seldom observed within 5° of the equator, thus indicating the importance of the coriolis force in their development and maintenance.

[1] Riehl, H., On the Formation of Typhoons, *J. Meteorol.*, vol. 5, pp. 247–267, 1948.

14. The centrifugal effect in the balanced wind is of great importance; the cyclostrophic term is about thirty times the geostrophic term at a radius of 25 miles from the center at lat 15° with a 100-mph wind.

**Geographical and Seasonal Distribution.** The distribution of tropical cyclones throughout the world and their seasons of occurrence are given in Table 16–1. The map in Fig. 16–6 shows the tropical-cyclone regions of the world and the principal paths of the storms. It will be noted that there are eight regions of tropical cyclones: one in the North Atlantic, two in the North Pacific, two in the region of India, one in the South Pacific, and two in the South Indian Ocean. There are great areas of the tropical seas, notably the entire South Atlantic and the eastern South Pacific, that are entirely free of tropical cyclones.

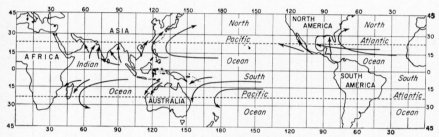

Fig. 16–6. Paths of tropical cyclones.

Of all the regions of the earth, the southwestern North Pacific has by far the greatest number of tropical cyclones. The western North Atlantic and Caribbean Sea is perhaps the best known hurricane region of the world. The hurricanes of this region, although surpassed by the tropical storms of the Far East in intensity, have attracted a great deal of attention because of the damage they have caused in the West Indies and on the highly developed Atlantic Coast of North America. The South Indian Ocean and the South Pacific have frequent, long-lived tropical cyclones. The frequency in the South Indian Ocean is exceeded only by that of the western North Pacific.

Late summer and early autumn is the time of greatest tropical-cyclone activity. In the Far East the season is longer; also, off-season hurricanes are sometimes encountered in mid-ocean in the tropical North Atlantic. The peak frequency corresponds to the period of highest ocean-surface temperatures and also to the time of maximum poleward displacement of the equatorial convergence zone.

**Formation of Tropical Cyclones.** The processes bringing about the formation of tropical cyclones are not well known, although several plausible theories have been presented. Since the regions of formation

**TABLE 16-1. WORLD DISTRIBUTION OF TROPICAL CYCLONES**

| | Ocean | General region | Places of origin | Principal paths | Months of greatest frequency | Cyclone-free months (tropical) |
|---|---|---|---|---|---|---|
| Northern Hemisphere | Atlantic | West Indies | Cape Verde Islands and westward; Western Caribbean | Through West Indies and northward to United States or Atlantic or into Mexico, Honduras, etc. | August, September, October | December to May, inclusive |
| | Pacific | Southwestern North Pacific | Marshall Islands; Philippine Region; South China Sea | Through or near Philippines and northward toward China, Japan, etc. | July, August, September, October | February to April, inclusive |
| | | West coast of Central America | Gulf of Tehuantepec to Revillagigedo Islands | Northwestward to Lower California or halfway to Hawaiian Islands | September, October | December to May, inclusive |
| | Indian | Bay of Bengal | Southwestern part; other parts of Bay | Clockwise path into India or Burma | June to November, inclusive | January to March, inclusive |
| | | Arabian Sea | Laccadive—Maldive Islands Ceylon region (?) | Clockwise into India or Gulf of Oman; other doubtful paths | June, October, November | January, February, March, August (?) |
| Southern Hemisphere | Atlantic | None | None | None | None | All months |
| | Pacific | Northwestern South Pacific | West of Tuamotu Islands; Coral Sea | Westward to Coral Sea, counterclockwise along Australian coast or toward New Zealand | January, February, March | July, August, September |
| | Indian | Madagascar-Mauritius | Cocos Islands and westward | Westward, then counterclockwise southward near Madagascar | January, February, March | July, August, September |
| | | Northwestern Australia | Timor Sea | Counterclockwise along Australian coast | January to March, inclusive | July to September, inclusive |

are fairly well fixed, it is obvious that some peculiarity of circulation or thermodynamic processes in those regions must be associated with their development. These regions are characterized by high temperature and water-vapor content, but it has been shown that this in itself is not sufficient to start a hurricane going, although the heat of condensation supports the process once it is started.

Riehl[1] has described the synoptic conditions during storm formation as follows:

Storms never develop spontaneously in the undisturbed tropical currents but always in a pre-existing disturbance. Such a disturbance may be of the shear-line type (equatorial convergence zone) or it may have the character of a transverse wave. Intensification of the bad weather zone attending such a disturbance and formation of a closed depression generally takes place when two or more disturbances meet. Considerable synoptic evidence supports this statement. The combination or superposition of disturbances usually results from motion in different directions or at different rates. Among many possibilities, a common type is westward travel of a wave trough in the easterlies that intersects an equatorial convergence zone extending east-west. At other times such wave troughs become coupled with the southern extensions of eastward-moving troughs in the upper westerlies. . . . The superpositions, therefore, can be horizontal and/or vertical.

. . . It is certain that most tropical depressions form in consequence of superposition. Yet the great majority of these circulations do not develop beyond a weak wind field with maximum speeds of about Beaufort 6. Sometimes such weak centers will persist in steady state up to a week and then suddenly deepen.

The purpose of the last two sentences is to point out that similar synoptic pictures do not indicate similar dynamic processes. One dynamic requirement, unquestionably the most important one, is that upper-air divergence must exceed low-level convergence. Superposition in the vertical also occurs outside the tropics. In Chap. 17 it will be shown that an important term in development is provided by the vorticity advection at the level of nondivergence. Presumably convergence would prevail below this level in a preexisting depression but this could only accumulate mass and thereby increase the pressure. Important for further development is a divergence above that level stronger than the convergence below.

The statistical information that tropical cyclones develop over very warm oceans and the knowledge of frequent superpositions of the kind described above should not be construed to indicate that the tropical atmosphere, since it is in labile equilibrium, can be "triggered" into forming hurricanes by superpositions, strong heating, or thermonuclear explosions. A closer look at the problem shows that a combination

---

[1] Riehl, H., Aerology of Tropical Storms, *Compendium of Meteorol.*, 1951, p. 908.

of divergence and convergence maintained over a considerable period of time on a *proper scale* is necessary. The marked selectivity of the tropical cyclone concerning the scale on which it will operate can only be partially explained theoretically. In its initial stages, the disturbance seems to need a divergence pattern producing a suitable vertical circulation over a distance of the order of 100 miles. It is probable that the so-called "minor" disturbances, those which have well-defined centers of low pressure but never develop hurricane winds, do not have the right patterns of divergence or if the patterns are suitable, they are either too large or too small in scale.

The difference between a minor disturbance and a tropical cyclone also often appears in the vertical temperature distribution. The minor disturbances may have temperatures in their active centers lower than in the surrounding tropical environment, whereas the tropical cyclone is nearly everywhere warmer than the surrounding, undisturbed tropical air. In the former, the convection, with entrainment, is so cellular in character that there may be no total net upward flow of heat. In the tropical cyclone, there is so much *organized* ascent of air throughout the system that, in terms of temperature, it seems to be one giant parcel of air ascending through the typical conditionally unstable or labile tropical atmosphere. Once established, the hurricane derives its energy from the instability resulting from release of heat of condensation. The question is, how does such a thermoconvective system get organized?

The upper-air divergence effects may be assessed by referring to Eq. (16–3) which may be written as

$$\text{div}_2\, c = -\frac{1}{f + \zeta}\left(\frac{d\zeta}{dt} + \beta v\right)$$

We may accept Riehl's observation that $f + \zeta$ does not become negative in the latitudes of cyclone formation, that is to say that when $\zeta$ is anticyclonic (negative) it does not exceed $f$ in absolute value. The term $\beta v$ is positive in winds having components from the south and negative for northerly components. (All considerations are for the Northern Hemisphere.) The sign of the divergence will be determined in zonal flow by the sign of $d\zeta/dt$ in the negative sense. For meridional components, the circumstances determining the sign are the following:

1. $\text{div}_2\, c > 0$ if

    *a.* In northerly wind $\dfrac{d\zeta}{dt} < +|\beta v|$, including all values of $\dfrac{d\zeta}{dt} < 0$

    *b.* In southerly wind $\dfrac{d\zeta}{dt} < -\beta v$

2. $\text{div}_2\, c < 0$ if

    *a.* In northerly wind $\dfrac{d\zeta}{dt} > +|\beta v|$

    *b.* In southerly wind $\dfrac{d\zeta}{dt} > -\beta v$, including all values of $\dfrac{d\zeta}{dt} > 0$

These relations are shown graphically in Fig. 16–7. In the natural atmosphere $d\zeta/dt$ usually does not reach values appreciably beyond $+\beta v$, at least in low latitudes where $\beta$ is large. The figure then illustrates that divergence is most likely in regions where the flow is from the north and convergence is to be expected in southerly flow. When $d\zeta/dt$ and $\beta v$ exactly balance each other, the flow is nondivergent.

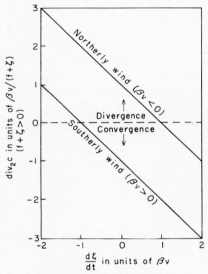

In Fig. 16–8, distributions of these effects are represented in the vicinity of a southern extension of a trough in the upper westerlies which we may consider to be superimposed on a lower trough in the easterlies. A quasistationary pattern of flow is assumed, in which the streamlines represent essentially the trajectories of the air. The points labeled 1a, 1b, 2a, and 2b are the places where the conditions listed in the preceding paragraph with the corresponding numbers are the most pronounced.

FIG. 16–7. Convergence related to generation of vorticity.

At 1a the streamlines show a downstream tendency for the air to curve anticyclonically, thus making the vorticity decrease as the air traces out the existing bend. At 1b the vorticity is decreasing downstream, and if this rate of decrease exceeds $\beta v$ in the negative sense, divergence is present there also. Convergence will occur at 2a if the vorticity increases downstream (therefore with time) at a rate greater than the absolute value of $\beta v$. At 2b convergence is to be expected for any value of $d\zeta/dt$ greater than $-\beta v$.

Since transverse waves in the easterlies normally tilt upward toward the east, the upper trough of Fig. 16–8 might be expected to be connected with a surface disturbance in the vicinity of 1a. Riehl,[1] in a discussion essentially of this model, pointed out the observed fact that a southward

[1] Riehl, H., *J. Appl. Phys.*, vol. 21, p. 917, 1950.

flow of modified polar air to the east of the surface depression and therefore in the vicinity of the upper trough location is to be expected in this type of situation. The eastward-upward tilt of the trough is thus in agreement with hydrostatic equilibrium. Riehl found that the conditions in the northerly winds to the west of the upper trough are the most favorable. He also pointed out that the coldness and southward spread of

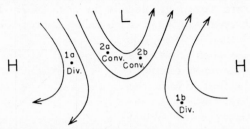

FIG. 16–8. Effects of Fig. 16–7 in trough in upper westerlies in the tropics.

the extratropical air near the upper trough favors subsidence which requires convergence at the upper level. Following Riehl's example, we may assume that the surface disturbance is at 1a and that the vertical circulation is between 1a and 2a.

Riehl's picture of the vertical circulation in a west-to-east vertical cross section is reproduced in Fig. 16–9. Whereas in an ordinary disturbance the small-scale convective circulation cells initiated at random in the

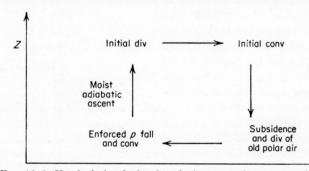

FIG. 16–9. Vertical circulation in relation to cyclone generation.

system have upward and downward motions that tend to cancel each other, the larger-scale circulation cell pictured in Fig. 16–9 produces a system of convection with a net upward motion in the disturbance. Through the moist adiabatic ascent and release of latent heat, part of it irreversibly through precipitation, a solenoidal field is created which further accelerates the circulation. The air that rises in the zone of convection does not sink again until it has been removed to a considerable distance. The solenoidal field accelerates a direct circulation, which transforms potential into kinetic energy. The old polar air also supplies energy to the system but not in the manner that it does for extratropical cyclones, for it does not enter the storm. Its contribution is through subsidence which helps create and maintain the organized circulation cell.

The possibility of generating a tropical cyclone to the east of the upper trough in a circulation developed between 1b and 2b is also of importance. In this case, if extratropical air is in the upper trough, the upward tilt would be toward the west and the disturbance presumably would take off toward the northeast after forming. This type of path is common in the late seasons when the upper westerlies begin to dip deeply into the tropics.

**Thermal Structure of Tropical Cyclones.** Soundings in the rain areas which comprise the major part of a tropical cyclone show that the values of temperature and the temperature lapse rate are close to those expected from the ascent of a parcel from the surface. In the eye of the storm much higher temperatures are observed which can be accounted for only by a certain amount of dry-adiabatic descent. The simplified thermal picture of the cyclone can be depicted by three temperature curves; one representing the tropical environment, one representing the conditions in the ascending air of the rain area, and another taken in the eye.

Actual measurements usually show that the rain area can be represented by several curves of temperature, indicating temperatures near the center higher than in the outer part of the rain area. As the air spirals inward, it is subjected to sea-level pressure reductions that could lower the surface temperature by 3°C or more if the process were adiabatic. The ocean is such a great heat reservoir that it is able to preserve the temperature of the air above it, so the pressure is reduced isothermally. The heat added is equal to the work done by the air in expanding. This added heat is reflected in the soundings. Furthermore, the capacity of the surface air for water vapor is greater at the lower pressure. Thus the wet-bulb-potential temperature is increased, prescribing higher-valued pseudoadiabatic ascent curves and accordingly greater buoyancy.

Some typical sounding data for tropical cyclones are presented in Fig. 16–10. In addition to the temperature distributions, the differences in tropopause heights should be noted.

The model of a mature tropical cyclone as represented by Palmén[1] is shown in Fig. 16–11. It is seen that the temperature increases gradually inward toward the eye, then jumps to very high values in the eye itself. The potential temperatures increase inward more rapidly than the temperatures because of the decrease of pressure inward. The boundary of the eye is funnel-shaped, spreading out and becoming diffuse at the tropical tropopause. The tropopause itself is diffuse and discontinuous

[1] Palmén, E., On the Formation and Structure of Tropical Hurricanes, *Geophysica*, vol. 3, pp. 26–38, 1948.

in this region. Over the eye, the tropopause is unusually high. The warm subsiding air of the eye corresponds with a vertically expanded troposphere. The shape of the eye boundary and the temperatures indicated through the eye and in the ascending air are in agreement with a hydrostatic balance corresponding to the observed sea-level pressures. It was found by Palmén in putting the data together for the model of Fig. 16–11 that the radial temperature gradients are stronger in the high levels than near the surface. Differences become largely smoothed out at 100 mb.

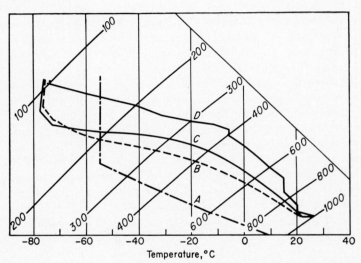

Fig. 16–10. Soundings in and around a tropical cyclone. *A*, standard atmosphere; *B*, mean tropical atmosphere; *C*, sounding in rain area of cyclone; *D*, sounding in eye. (*After Riehl.*)

The air in the eye subsides to a shielding layer where an inversion or at least a stable layer is produced. Jordan[1] found that the height of the base of this stable layer is correlated with the central sea-level pressure. This finding is in accord with hydrostatic relations, since the lower the pressure the greater must be the section of the overlying column occupied by warm air and therefore the lower down it must come. Jordan's study showed that the inversion height varied from 500 m for a central pressure of 920 mb to 1200 m for 980 mb central pressure.

**Wind Field in Tropical Cyclones.** The maximum speeds attainable in tropical cyclones have not been measured. Anemometers have blown away after recording speeds of from 120 to 150 mph with the wind still increasing. The strong surface winds prevent the launching of balloons

[1] Jordan, C. L., *J. Meteorol.*, vol. 9, p. 285, 1952.

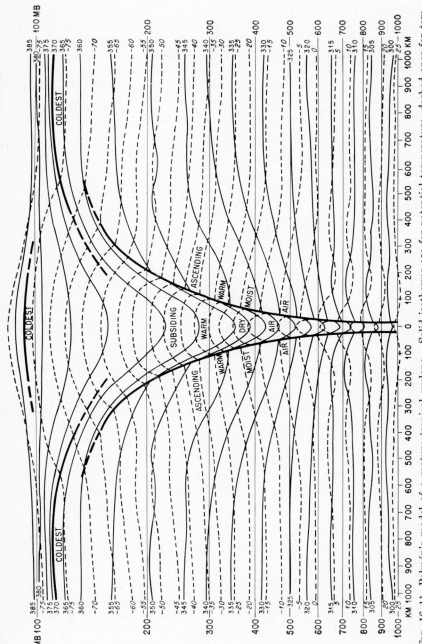

FIG. 16–11. Palmén's model of a mature tropical cyclone. Solid isotherms are for potential temperature, dashed ones for temperature. Tropopauses and eye boundaries are shown by heavy lines.

385

except in the weaker parts of the storm, so the winds in the area of maximum intensity cannot be obtained by that method. Electronic positioning and course-computing systems for airplanes have provided some information from weather-reconnaissance or research flights in tropical cyclones. Winds in the neighborhood of 200 knots seem to be the extremes in many hurricanes and typhoons. The highest values are

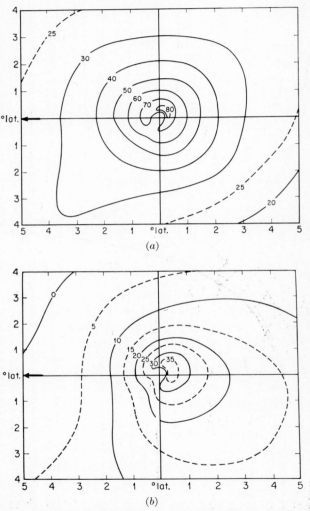

Fig. 16–12. Winds computed from Navy low-level flights, given as speeds in knots in (a) the tangential component, (b) the radial component, and (c) the total. Arrow at left indicates direction of storm movement. Distances expressed in latitude degrees from center.

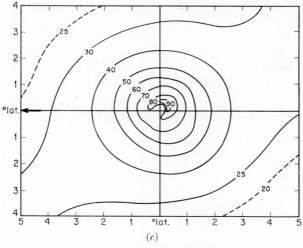

FIG. 16–12.    (*Continued*)

found near the center, but outside the eye, at heights of 1 to 3 km over the open sea.

In part the wind distribution in a tropical cyclone resembles that of a simple type of vortex often treated in fluid mechanics, that is, one in which the angular momentum is conserved throughout, or

$$\omega r^2 = cr = \text{const}$$

On the rotating earth, the absolute angular momentum is involved. The eye is then regarded as the region of breakdown of this distribution, eliminating the infinite speed at the center. In flow with a radial component inward, this type of vortex would require convergence at a point in the center. Observations show that the increase in wind speed toward the center is much less than that imposed by constant angular momentum.

The diagrams in Figs. 16–12 and 16–13 show horizontal profiles through hurricanes prepared by L. A. Hughes[1] from wind data taken from course computations of low-level Navy hurricane reconnaissance flights, made mainly at or below 1000 ft. Figure 16-12 shows the wind speed in the tangential component, the radial component, and the total, the latter being given as the square root of the sum of the squares of the components. It is noted that the *cr* product decreases inward. The patterns of horizontal divergence and of the vertical component of the relative vorticity produced by this wind field, shown in Fig. 16–13, may be taken as typical of a tropical cyclone. The convergence and

[1] Hughes, L. A., *J. Meteorol.*, vol. 9, p. 422, 1952.

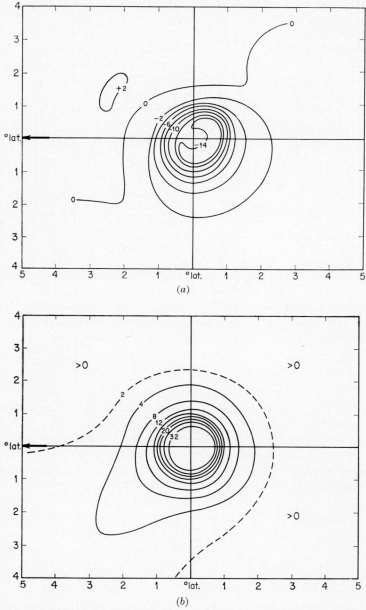

FIG. 16–13. Components of horizontal divergence (*a*) and of vertical component of the relative vorticity (*b*) produced by the wind field in Fig. 16–12.   Units are $10^{-5}$ sec$^{-1}$. In these units (*a*) also represents vertical velocity in cm per sec at 1 km if divergence is the mean from 0 to 1 km, since 1 km is $10^5$ cm and div$_2 c = -w$.   (*After Hughes.*)

cyclonic vorticity exceed $10^{-5}$ by an appreciable amount only within $1\frac{1}{2}°$ (90 nautical miles) of the center.

It is interesting to compare the magnitudes of the coriolis and centripetal accelerations in tropical cyclones. Such a comparison is given graphically in Fig. 16–14. For a wind speed of 100 mph, for example, the centripetal term is fifteen times the coriolis term at a distance of 50 miles

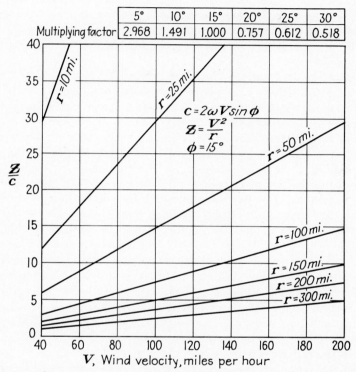

| Multiplying factor | 5° | 10° | 15° | 20° | 25° | 30° |
|---|---|---|---|---|---|---|
| | 2.968 | 1.491 | 1.000 | 0.757 | 0.612 | 0.518 |

$$c = 2\omega V \sin\phi$$
$$Z = \frac{V^2}{r}$$
$$\phi = 15°$$

$\frac{Z}{c}$

$V$, Wind velocity, miles per hour

FIG. 16–14. Ratio of centripetal force ($Z$) to coriolis force $c$ expressed as ordinate against wind velocity as abscissa for various radii of curvature at lat 15°. The ratios should be multiplied by the factor given in the table at the top of the chart for other latitudes.

from the center at lat 15°. For the same conditions at lat 20° the ratio would be 11.4 to 1, obtained by applying the multiplying factor appearing at the top of the diagram.

Persons experiencing a tropical cyclone find it hard to resist the temptation to go about "cleaning up" during the passage of the eye. The serenely calm, though sultry, air gives false assurance, for as the eye leaves, a new wall of cloud and rain moves in and the winds lash with renewed fury to lay siege to the region for many more devastating hours.

Perhaps the worst effect of the winds is in piling up water to inundate low-lying coasts.    In 1876 a storm in the Bay of Bengal inundated Backergunge, at the Mouths of the Ganges, covering the lowlands to a depth of from 10 to 40 ft.    It was estimated that 100,000 lives were lost by drowning and subsequently another 100,000 died of disease.    In the hurricane of Sept. 8, 1900, the sea swept over the entire town of Galveston, Texas, causing more than 6000 deaths and millions of dollars of property damage. A combination of critical wind conditions and peculiar configurations of the shore line has in all cases been responsible for the most serious inundations.    In some instances the highest water occurs during the passage of the eye.

**Precipitation in Tropical Cyclones.**    Some of the heaviest rains of record in low-latitude land areas have been experienced with slowly moving tropical cyclones; fast motion reduces the duration and therefore the accumulation at a station.

From radar observations it first became quite clear that the rain is distributed in bands in tropical storms.    Between the bands the rain is either missing or of light intensity.    The tendency for convection to occur in bands or lines, often called *squall lines*, is noted in other situations, such as in prefrontal or warm-sector squall lines in middle latitudes.    In these middle-latitude situations the lines cross the streamlines in which they are embedded at an angle of perhaps 20° to the left; that is, if the streamlines run from WNW to ENE, the squall lines are likely to be oriented from SW to NE.    The same situation occurs in tropical cyclones but since the streamlines are curved, the precipitation bands are even more sharply curved and have a form that spirals inward toward the center, terminating at the boundary of the eye.    Since the eye is free of precipitation echoes, the radar pattern of the storm greatly facilitates the location of the center when it is within range of the radar.    An example is seen in the radarscope photograph of Fig. 16–15.

There is no complete theoretical explanation as to why the atmosphere has a preference for an arrangement of convective precipitation in bands. It seems to be easier for a convective system to extend itself in a crosswind direction than upwind or downwind.    This characteristic is seen in many types of wave phenomena.

**Late Stages and Dissipation.**    As long as a tropical cyclone exists over warm waters it has the possibility of increasing in intensity, at least up to a certain theoretical maximum when the frictional forces and work against the surrounding atmosphere use up all the energy the storm can muster.    Many tropical cyclones follow the wind circulations of the upper atmosphere and break out of the tropics into the middle-latitude westerlies at the western ends of the oceanic high-pressure cells.    As they do this, they are said to *recurve* at the moment in their life histories when they cross the horse-latitude ridge of high pressure.  It so happens that the warm ocean currents are also driven into high latitudes on the western sides of the high-pressure cells, so the storms after recurvature may still follow a path over warm water.  Thus in the North Atlantic, for example, they can still maintain hurricane intensity as far north as New England and the principal northern steamer tracks.  In passing

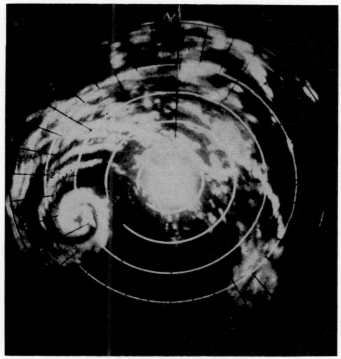

FIG. 16–15. Rain bands in tropical cyclone revealed by radar at Cape Hatteras, North Carolina, for hurricane "Connie—1955" at 1100 EST, Aug. 12, 1955.  Concentric circles are for range intervals of 20 nautical miles.  The eye is at about 243° 62 nautical miles.  (*U.S. Weather Bureau photograph.*)

over the cold waters near Newfoundland they decrease rapidly in intensity.

Tropical cyclones dissipate quickly when they move over large land masses, even in the tropics.  As shown in the examples of mesometeorological analysis in the preceding chapter, convective rains cool the air in the low levels.  The rain water, which arrives at the ground with about the same temperature as the cool air, covers the ground and holds the temperature down while the cloud cover prevents heating by the sun. Over the warm ocean, of course, the amount of rain water is infinitesimal when compared with the sea water and therefore does not cause a measurable lowering of the ocean temperature. (A further explanation of the relatively cool air under showers will be given in the chapter on thunderstorms.) Thus, over land, the hurricane loses the heat source necessary to keep the air buoyant and the thermo-convective driving mechanism disappears. The added surface friction over the land also has a considerable effect.

While still quite intense over warm ocean currents of middle latitudes, tropical cyclones frequently draw fronts into their circulations. There is evidence that this event causes a brief increase in intensity as a new source of potential energy is added, but in the cool air outside the newly created warm sector, conditions are no longer favorable for convective ascent. The storm gradually takes on more of the character of an extratropical cyclone, becoming larger but less intense. The advent of fronts in the system is usually accompanied by the superposition of a polar trough to the west which also helps the intensification. Such a situation existed in the New England hurricane of Sept. 21, 1938, and in hurricane "Hazel" of 1955.[1,2,3]

Very intense extratropical cyclones, such as are sometimes observed in the North Sea, are occasionally referred to as hurricanes, although they appear to be cold-core systems. Sometimes their history can be traced back to tropical hurricanes in the Caribbean or the tropical Atlantic.

[1] The custom of applying girls' names to tropical cyclones was started in World War II, apparently suggested by George Stewart's novel "Storm" in which the junior meteorologist at the San Francisco office of the U.S. Weather Bureau had the whimsey of applying girls' names to storms in the Pacific. He was dealing with extratropical cyclones, however.

[2] Pierce, C. H., The Meteorological History of the New England Hurricane of Sept. 21, 1938, *Monthly Weather Rev.*, vol. 67, pp. 237–285, 1939.

[3] Hughes, L. A., F. Baer, G. E. Birchfield, and R. E. Kaylor, Hurricane Hazel and a Long-wave Outlook, *Bull. Am. Meteorol. Soc.*, vol. 36, pp. 528–533, 1955.

# CHAPTER 17

# QUANTITATIVE APPROACHES
# TO FORECASTING

In this chapter only the quantitative approaches to the general fore-casting problem will be treated, and these only in outline form. The qualitative or semiquantitative forecasting methods can best be under-stood through direct contact with synoptic-aerologic charts and through experience. The discussion of this methodology is not suitable for a general textbook.

Before describing the quantitative methods used in forecasting, it is appropriate to consider some of the reasons why progress in this important area of meteorology is so difficult. A large part of the atmospheric circulation is made up of perturbations going through complete or aborted cycles of development and dissipation, giving a character of randomness and instability to the flow, sometimes looked upon as hemispheric-scale turbulence. The movement and development of the perturbations (cyclones, anticyclones, troughs, and ridges) can be extrapolated from a series of current synoptic charts with considerable success, but accelera-tions and intensifications are difficult to detect. For example, net diver-gence effects or deepening, computed by the tendency equation of Chap. 10, come out as a very small difference between very large quantities which themselves may not be determined within an accuracy of 10 per cent.

The generation of heavy cloud and precipitation systems depends on the concentration of upward motion in certain parts of the atmosphere in which motions are seldom measured. Or, rain may be associated with a meso-scale system inadequately detected on the regular synoptic scale available to the forecaster.

Despite these difficulties, meteorologists produce forecasts which governments and businesses consider to be economically valuable. An important ingredient in this partial success has been the subjective judgment of the forecaster based on his experience. A great forward step was made with the application of high-speed electronic computers to the forecasting problem. The thousands of integrations required to describe and predict the flow pattern over a large area can be done handily by these machines in a few minutes. Such computations were out of the question before the advent of the machines.

Forecasting can be considered in two steps: (1) the prediction of the flow pattern (isobar-contour pattern) and (2) the determination of the quantities in which the users are interested, such as times and places of precipitation, temperature changes, wind storms, and the like. The first step lends itself more easily to quantitative treatment than does the second. It is feasible to develop a system which combines the two steps, especially for those elements of the forecast most directly derived from the predicted field of motion, such as upper-air winds, precipitation areas resulting from vertical motions, and temperature changes caused by advection.

**Kinematics of the Surface Chart.** Surface synoptic observations include the pressure tendency as revealed by the barograph trace for the 3 hr immediately preceding the observations. This quantity, considered in connection with the pressure gradient, provides essentially current information concerning the rate of displacement of pressure systems. The methods for computing these displacements were devised largely by Petterssen,[1] whose name is usually associated with the formulas and computations. The formulas can be arrived at by rather elementary mathematics.

Station pressure tendencies always represent some form of movement or deformation of isobars. The pressure change in 3 hr at a station is the number of unit isobars crossing the station in that period. The number of any series of evenly-spaced things passing a point in 3 hr is the speed of these things in miles per 3 hr multiplied by the number of these things per mile. For isobars, the 3-hr tendency is

$$T = UN \tag{17-1}$$

where $U$ is the speed of the isobars in 3 hr and $N$ is the number of unit isobars in unit distance. In these units the speed of the isobars is

$$U = \frac{T}{N} \tag{17-2}$$

If $T$ is negative, the movement of the isobars is toward higher pressure regions (lower pressure moving in). If it is positive, the movement is toward lower pressure (higher pressure moving in). If this rule is kept in mind, the sign of the tendency should be easily interpreted. Another method is to consider that $N = -\Delta p/\Delta L$, where $L$ is the distance unit in the direction normal to the isobars, chosen positive in the indicated

[1] Petterssen, S., Kinematical and Dynamical Properties of the Field of Pressure with Application to Weather Forecasting, *Geofys. Publikasjoner*, vol. 10, no. 2, 1933.

sense of the motion.   If this system is followed, $U$ will be positive when $T$ and $N$ have the same sign.

*Troughs and Ridges.*   To obtain the speed of a trough or ridge, the equation could be applied to any set of isobars in the vicinity, except that deepening or filling effects would then be neglected.   Deepening or filling of an isobar has no meaning and therefore does not enter into the isobar calculation.   For a trough or ridge, filling and deepening sometimes have important effects on the displacement.

Consider the trough in the sketch map in Fig. 17–1a which, for simplicity, is constructed in a V shape.   Let us suppose that the system is deepening.   Then, at the point $B$, the pressure would be falling more rapidly than would be the case without deepening; therefore the isobar

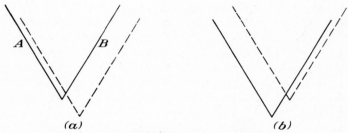

FIG. 17–1. Trough deepening (a) and filling (b).

would be moving more rapidly.   At the point $A$, the pressure would be rising more slowly than would be the case with no deepening, and therefore the isobar would be moving more slowly.   This also means that the isobar ahead of the trough is moving faster than the isobar behind the trough.   The new isobar positions are shown by the broken lines.   From the construction, it is seen that deepening means that the isobars progress with time along the trough line outward from the center of low pressure.

The case for filling in a trough is shown in Fig. 17–1b.   Filling of a trough means that the isobars in the rear are moving faster than those in advance of the trough.   The isobars progress along the trough line toward the lowest pressure.   From similar reasoning, one may treat the case of a ridge, and the following rules may be formulated:

1.  In a trough, deepening is indicated if the isobars ahead of the trough move faster than those behind, and filling is indicated if the isobars ahead of the trough move slower than those behind.

2.  In a ridge, deepening is indicated if the isobars ahead of the ridge move less rapidly than those behind, and filling if they move faster than those behind.

3. In addition, deepening or filling will occur if the two sets of isobars are moving in opposite directions.

Our problem is to take into consideration the possibility of deepening and filling effects in order to obtain a general expression for the speed of troughs and ridges. An obvious way of doing this is to determine the displacements of the isobars on each side, fit them into their new positions, and determine the location of the trough or ridge line by construction. It is necessary to assume that the systems retain their shapes, that is, that the angle between the prevailing isobars on the two sides is preserved. As yet, no one has devised a simple practical velocity formula that will

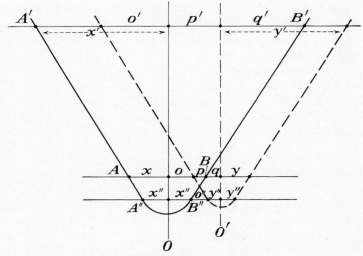

Fig. 17–2. Symmetrical trough.

consider changes in shape, and it is probable that such refinements are unnecessary for short-period extrapolations (up to 24 hr).

It is more convenient to have a combined formula that will give directly the speed of the trough or ridge without individual consideration of the isobars on the two sides. In arriving at such a combined expression, we shall consider first a trough (or ridge) in which the isobars, if extended as straight lines, would make a V-shaped intersection, and the trough line would bisect this angle, as in Fig. 17–2.

First, it must be agreed that, with no deepening or filling, such a symmetrical trough or ridge will be characterized by the same rate of motion of isobars on either side, which will also be the speed of the trough or ridge line. In this case, it would only be necessary to apply the isobar formula along the normal ahead of or behind the line, whichever is more convenient, or we can say

$$U = \frac{U_B + U_A}{2} = \frac{1}{2}\left(\frac{T_B}{N_B} + \frac{T_A}{N_A}\right) \qquad (17\text{–}3)$$

where the subscript $B$ refers to conditions on one side (point $B$ of Fig. 17–2) and $A$ to conditions on the other side (point $A$ of Fig. 17–2). This equation, of course, is trivial when $U_B = U_A$, but it will be shown now that this is the form that will also apply in the case of deepening or filling, when $U_B \neq U_A$. If that is true, then in Eq. (17–3) we have a simple expression applicable in all cases.

To show that Eq. (17–3) is thus applicable to displacements accompanied by deepening or filling, let us consider the trough in Fig. 17–2, in which the motion is accompanied by filling, i.e., the isobar behind the trough is moving more rapidly than ahead of the trough line. It is axiomatic that the movement of such a line can be defined only along its normal. Along the normal $AB$, the displacement in unit time of the rear isobar is $x + o$, while that of the forward isobar is $y + q$. The trough line, meanwhile, has been displaced from $O$ to $O'$, or $o + p + q$. Representing the displacements in unit time of the forward isobar, the rear isobar, and the trough by $U_B$, $U_A$, and $U$, respectively, we have

$$\begin{aligned}
U_A &= x + o = 2o + p \qquad \text{since} \qquad x = o + p \\
U_B &= y + q = 2q + p \qquad \text{since} \qquad y = p + q \\
U_A + U_B &= 2o + 2p + 2q \\
U &= o + p + q = \frac{U_B + U_A}{2} \qquad (17\text{–}4)
\end{aligned}$$

The expression for the velocity of a trough is therefore given by Eq. (17–3). This leads to the following simple rule:

*The speed of a symmetrical trough or ridge is the arithmetical average of the speed along the normal to the ridge or trough line of the isobars in advance of and behind the line.*

The proof of this rule by considering displacements along other normals in Fig. 17–2 such as $A'B'$ and $A''B''$ is equally simple. For example, along $A'B'$

$$\begin{aligned}
U_A &= x' - o' = p' + q' - o' \\
U_B &= y' - q' = o' + p' - q' \\
U_B + U_A &= 2p' \\
U &= p' = \frac{U_B + U_A}{2} \qquad (17\text{–}5)
\end{aligned}$$

The solution along $A''B''$ as well as along a line passing through the point of intersection of the old position of the forward isobar with the new position of the rear isobar is left to the student.

In some cases, the isobars on the two sides may be moving in opposite directions. This would be possible only when $T_B$ has the same sign as $T_A$. Then $U_B$ and $U_A$ are of opposite sign, since $N_B$ and $N_A$ are always

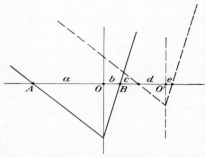

of opposite sign through a trough or ridge. When $T_B$ and $T_A$ are of opposite sign, only their absolute values need be considered and the velocity $U$ will be in the direction of falling pressure for a trough and in the direction of rising pressure for a ridge. This is the normal case.

The case of an asymmetrical trough or ridge, i.e., one in which the trough or ridge line does not bisect the angle made by the isobars, leads to a slightly different treat-

FIG. 17–3. Displacement of asymmetrical trough.

ment. In Fig. 17–3 the trough is displaced from $O$ to $O'$ without changing its asymmetrical shape.

$$U_A = a + b + c$$
$$U_B = c + d + e$$

Since we are dealing with similar triangles, the ratios $r$ of the distances from the isobars to the trough line are such that

$$\frac{b}{a} = \frac{e}{d} = r$$

$$e = rd \qquad a = \frac{b}{r}$$

$$U_A = b + c + \frac{b}{r}$$

$$rU_A = b(1 + r) + rc$$

$$U_B = c + d(1 + r)$$

$$rU_A + U_B = (1 + r)(b + c + d) = (1 + r)U$$

$$U = \frac{U_B + rU_A}{1 + r} \qquad\qquad (17\text{–}6)$$

But, since $r = b/a$ and $1 + r = (a + b)/a$, this last expression (17–6) may also be written

$$U = \left(U_B + \frac{b}{a} U_A\right)\frac{a}{a + b} = \frac{aU_B + bU_A}{a + b} \qquad\qquad (17\text{–}7)$$

The expression for the speed of an asymmetrical trough or ridge as shown by Eq. (17–6) differs from that of a purely symmetrical one in that it contains a term $r$, which is a measure of the asymmetry. The symmetrical trough may be considered a special case of Eq. (17–6) in which $r = 1$. If $b > a$ in a trough similar to Fig. 17–3, then $r > 1$, but the equation still holds in the same form.

The effects of $r$ usually are very slight. If $U_B = U_A$, $r$ has no effect, for then

$$U = \frac{U_B + rU_B}{1 + r} = \frac{U_B(1 + r)}{1 + r} = U_B \qquad (17\text{–}8)$$

which is the same result as for a symmetrical trough. In order for the asymmetry to have appreciable effect, $U_B$ and $U_A$ must be markedly different and $r$ must be considerably less than 1. To take an extreme case with $r = \frac{1}{2}$, $U_B = 50$, and $U_A = 25$, $U = 41.6$, whereas with these same values but $r = 1$, $U = 37.5$. The difference is about 10 per cent in this case. In general, it can be stated that an error of less than 10 per cent will be introduced through neglect of asymmetry. Only in very pronounced cases will one have to consider it.

To summarize, it may be stated that the following are the velocity formulas for troughs and ridges:

$$U = \frac{U_B + U_A}{2} = \frac{1}{2}\left(\frac{T_B}{N_B} + \frac{T_A}{N_A}\right) \qquad (17\text{–}9)$$

for a symmetrical system of isobars, and

$$U = \frac{aU_B + bU_A}{a + b} = \frac{1}{a + b}\left(\frac{aT_B}{N_B} + \frac{bT_A}{N_A}\right) \qquad (17\text{–}10)$$

for an asymmetrical system of isobars. Equation (17–9) is simply a special case of the more general relationship Eq. (17–10), in which $a = b$. Ordinarily Eq. (17–9) is preferable because of its greater simplicity and because it is accurate enough except in extreme cases of asymmetry.

Referring to Fig. 17–3, one sees that it is only necessary to take the tendency $T$ at $A$ and at $B$ and measure the isobar density $N$ along the axis in the vicinity of these two points.

It is of interest to compare Eqs. (17–9) and (17–10) with the equation arrived at by Petterssen through the numerical application of the calculus and advanced kinematics to the field of pressure. The Petterssen trough or ridge formula is, in our notation

$$U = \frac{1}{2}\left(\frac{T_A + T_B}{N_a + N_b}\right) \qquad (17\text{–}11)$$

where $N_a$ and $N_b$ are averaged over the distances $AO$ ($a$) and $OB$ ($b$), respectively (Fig. 17–3) or

$$U = \frac{T_a + T_b}{N_a + N_b} \qquad (17\text{–}12)$$

where $T_a$ and $T_b$ are taken in the middle of the segments $a$ and $b$ (Fig. 17-3) through which $N_a$ and $N_b$, respectively, are measured. It happens that ordinarily the part enclosed by parentheses in Eq. (17-9) is about twice the numerical value of Eq. (17-12). The factor of $\frac{1}{2}$ outside the parentheses in Eq. (17-9) makes the two equations about equal. It is not possible to say anything about the relative accuracy of these two expressions without investigating the manner in which they are applied.

In the application of the Petterssen formula, it is necessary to measure tendencies and isobar densities near the trough or ridge line, since the theory calls for values at these points. It is necessary to measure continuously along the axis through $O$. From the manner in which we have obtained Eqs. (17-9) and (17-10), no such necessity appears. In fact, the velocities can be obtained by measurements at rather widely separated points along the axis. Furthermore, by considering separately the velocities ahead of and behind the trough or ridge line, as is done in the two parts of Eqs. (17-9) and (17-10), information concerning deepening and filling is obtained at the same time.

It is possible to obtain the Petterssen formula (17-12) from Eq. (17-7) by considering in place of points $A$ and $B$, the mid-points of $AO$ and $OB$ (Fig. 17-3). Let $\Delta p$ be the number of unit isobars between $A$ or $B$ and $O$. We may consider the isobar density as averaged over the distances $a$ and $b$. Then

$$N_a = \frac{\Delta p}{a} \qquad N_b = \frac{\Delta p}{b}$$

and

$$U_a = a\,\frac{T_a}{\Delta p} \qquad U_b = b\,\frac{T_b}{\Delta p}$$

When this is introduced into Eq. (17-7),

$$U = \frac{ab(T_a + T_b)}{(a + b)\,\Delta p} = \frac{T_a + T_b}{\Delta p/a + \Delta p/b} = \frac{T_a + T_b}{N_a + N_b} \qquad (17\text{-}13)$$

which is Petterssen's formula (17-12). Many meteorologists may prefer to use this formula, since it was established earlier in forecasting practice.

**Choice of Length Unit.** As suggested by Petterssen, we use the simple device of setting off on the map a convenient distance $L$ over which $N$ is measured. The speed will then be in units of $L$ in 3 hr, and no attention need be paid to the scale of the map. While $L$ is chosen for convenience, it is not chosen arbitrarily. It must be a distance along which a *representative* value of the pressure gradient $N$ can be obtained, and it must have a representative tendency in the middle point.

In the application of the method developed by Petterssen, the length unit is laid out with one end at the trough or ridge line. In the computation developed here, this does not appear to be necessary, although it is probably desirable in many cases. In the use of Eqs. (17–9) and (17–10), $A$ and $B$ should be in the middle of the length unit $L$, as shown in Fig. 17–4a. To use Eq. (17–12), the length unit should be such that

$$L = AO = OB = \frac{AB}{2} \qquad (17\text{–}14)$$

(Fig. 17–4b). Equations (17–9) and (17–10) could also apply in Fig. 17–4b if $A$ and $B$ were in the mid-points of $a$ and $b$. Petterssen demonstrates from his derivation that a large length unit is desirable in order to suppress possible inaccuracies in the reported tendencies. In general, it is best to state that the length unit should be long enough so that a representative value of the pressure gradient can be read conveniently,

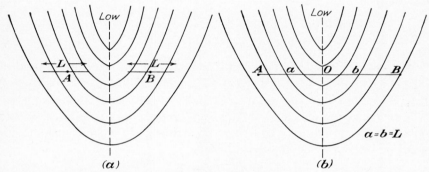

FIG. 17–4. Illustrating selection of length unit (a) for method of Eqs. (17–9) and (17–10) and (b) for Eq. (17–12).

but not so long that it runs into the surrounding regions having a substantially different gradient. This unit of length should also have its middle point of the rear portion far enough back so that it is not in a region through which the trough or ridge line has passed in the tendency interval (3 hr).

**Speed of Centers.** The same formula applies to centers of high and low pressure as applies to troughs and ridges. While we can define motion of troughs and ridges only in the normal direction, centers can exhibit motion in any direction, and computations must be made in two components. The $y$ component $v$ is calculated in the same manner as $u$. After obtaining the components of the displacement in $x$ and $y$, the actual displacement is obtained by constructing perpendiculars from the computed points on the two axes and by locating the point of intersection of these perpendiculars, as shown in Fig. 17–5, where $P_x$ is the displacement point computed along $x$ and $P_y$ is that along $y$. The actual movement of the center would be from $O$ to $P$.

**Speed of Fronts.** The derivation by Petterssen of the velocity formula for fronts as well as for troughs, ridges, and centers makes use of the slope of the tendency profile. In the case of a front, the profile is more or less discontinuous at the front, characterized by falling pressure ahead of the front and a sudden rise behind, so that, at least in the scale of synoptic charts, continuous isallobars cannot be drawn. A slight change in the Petterssen trough formula is introduced in order to take this into account. In the formula for a trough introduced above, no modification is necessary in order to make it applicable to fronts. Therefore we have in Eqs. (17–9) or (17–10) formulas of general utility in all types of computation of displacement.

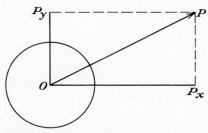

FIG. 17–5. Components of displacement of a center.

**Example of Computation.** The map of Oct. 9, 1941, 0100 EST, is reproduced in Fig. 17–6 to illustrate the computation method. On this map, in addition to the usual lines and symbols, the isallobars for the 3-hr tendency are also drawn. The map represents a computation both of a trough containing a front and of a ridge. It is convenient to use Eq. (17–12) in the computation, i.e.,

$$U = \frac{T_a + T_b}{N_a + N_b}$$

where $T_a$ and $T_b$ are the pressure tendencies taken at the mid-points of the two length units $L$, which extend an equal distance on the two sides from the trough or ridge line. For example, on the axis through the main trough just north of the Canadian border, $L = AB/2$.

To predict the 24-hr movement of the cold front and trough, we compute at several places, limiting the length units to representative regions. At the north, across $AB$, where $L = AB/2$, we note that the tendency in the middle of the length unit ahead of the trough is $T_b = 3.0$ mb per 3 hr and that the isobar density $N_b$ over the distance $L$ is 4 mb per unit $L$. Behind the trough, the tendency in the middle of the length unit is $T_a = 0.2$ mb per 3 hr and $N_a$ is 7.4 mb per unit $L$. Since we desire a 24-hr movement, we multiply by 8 because the tendency is for a 3-hr period and there are 8 such periods in 24 hr. We also compute along $CD$, $EF$, and $GJ$ so that the approximate position of the front 24 hr hence may be obtained. The computations, easily inter-

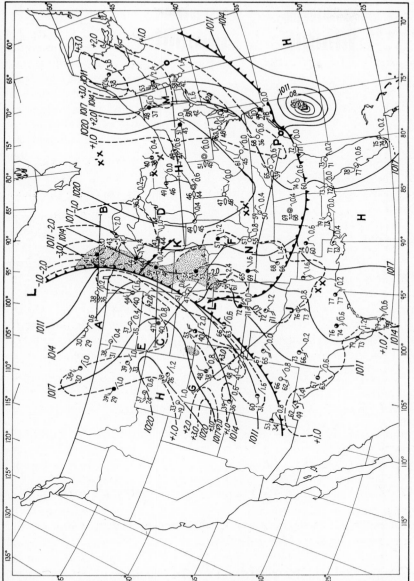

Fig. 17-6. Synoptic chart for 0100 EST, Oct. 9, 1941. Isallobars are entered as broken lines.

preted on the map, are as follows:

Along $AB$         $U = \dfrac{3.0 + 0.2}{7.4 + 4.0} \times 8 = 2.2$ units

Along $CD$         $U = \dfrac{0.8 + 1.8}{7.6 + 5.0} \times 8 = 1.6$ units

Along $EF$         $U = \dfrac{1.4 + 1.0}{5.0 + 7.0} \times 8 = 1.6$ units

Along $GJ$         $U = \dfrac{0.6 + 2.4}{4.5 + 11.0} \times 8 = 1.5$ units

The various projected positions are shown by the heavy $X$ marks.

On the basis of Eq. (17–9), applied with the tendencies taken at the same points and the isobar densities measured over the same distances, we have

Along $AB$         $U = 8 \times \dfrac{1}{2}\left(\dfrac{3.0}{7.4} + \dfrac{0.2}{4.0}\right) = 2.0$ units

Along $CD$         $U = 8 \times \dfrac{1}{2}\left(\dfrac{0.8}{7.6} + \dfrac{1.8}{5.0}\right) = 1.9$ units

Along $EF$         $U = 8 \times \dfrac{1}{2}\left(\dfrac{1.4}{5.0} + \dfrac{1.0}{7.0}\right) = 1.7$ units

Along $GJ$         $U = 8 \times \dfrac{1}{2}\left(\dfrac{0.6}{4.5} + \dfrac{2.4}{11.0}\right) = 1.4$ units

The future positions of the trough based on this formula are shown by heavy marks of $X'$.

Considering now the displacement of the ridge, we make computations as follows, from Eq. (17–12):

Along $KM$         $U = \dfrac{1.2 + 0.6}{4.6 + 4.4} \times 8 = 1.6$ units

Along $NP$         $U = \dfrac{0.4 + 0.4}{3.0 + 2.0} \times 8 = 1.3$ units

The future positions thus computed are shown by heavy circles.

On the basis of Eq. (17–9), we have

Along $KM$         $U = 8 \times \dfrac{1}{2}\left(\dfrac{1.2}{4.6} + \dfrac{0.6}{4.4}\right) = 1.6$ units

Along $NP$         $U = 8 \times \dfrac{1}{2}\left(\dfrac{0.4}{3.0} + \dfrac{0.4}{2.0}\right) = 1.3$ units

It is noted that the two formulas give the same result here.

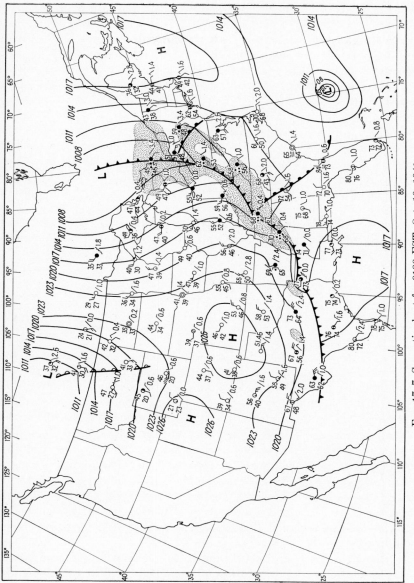

FIG. 17–7. Synoptic chart for 0100 EST, Oct. 10, 1941.

405

The verification of the computed positions is contained on the map for 24 hr later, 0100 EST on Oct. 10, 1941 (Fig. 17–7). It will be noted that the front is approximately in the predicted positions and that for the most part the positions using Eq. (17–9) are more nearly correct. This should not be taken as evidence of the superiority of one form of the equation over the other. The differences are probably within the range of error resulting from the difficulty of selecting representative tendency values.

The ridge was also displaced approximately in accordance with the computations. This was an extremely important computation, since it indicated that the tropical hurricane that was menacing the Cape Hatteras region would remain at sea.

**Tendencies in the Upper Air.** The height tendencies of the 500-mb surface, obtained by a method described by Hughes,[1] have been useful in forecasting. The change of the 500-mb surface in terms of height above the ground can be obtained from the time derivative of the hypsometric formula, Eq. (7–67). The expression is

$$\frac{\partial}{\partial t}(Z_{500}) = \frac{\partial}{\partial t}\left[\frac{R}{mg}\int_{5\times10^5}^{p_s} \bar{T}^* \frac{dp}{p}\right]$$
$$= \frac{R}{mg}\int_{5\times10^5}^{p_s} \frac{\partial\bar{T}^*}{\partial t}\frac{dp}{p} + \frac{R}{mg}\frac{T_s^*}{p_s}\frac{\partial p_s}{\partial t} \qquad (17\text{–}15)$$

where $p_s$ is the pressure at the ground. The changes involved in the expression are the change in the mean virtual temperature of the air column between the ground and 500 mb as expressed in the first term on the right-hand side and the pressure tendency at the bottom, as given in the second term on the right. All of the quantities are known from the observations except $\partial\bar{T}^*/\partial t$. The mean virtual temperature $\bar{T}^*$ is proportional to the thickness between the ground and 500 mb. On synoptic-aerologic charts the thicknesses between 1000 and 500 mb are normally drawn, so that in order to use them in the application of Eq. (17–15), a term for the artificial "thickness" between the station and the 1000-mb surface needs to be added. This term is usually small enough to be neglected or to be assigned a constant value for a wide range of terrain elevations.

The change in the mean virtual temperature is caused to a large extent by advection, but vertical motions and nonadiabatic heat exchanges are also effective. The effect of vertical motions was shown in the tendency equation (10–82) of Chap. 10. The advective contribution can be obtained by moving the thickness (mean-virtual-temperature) lines with

[1] Hughes, L. A., On the Determination of 500-mb Height Tendencies, *Bull. Am. Meteorol. Soc.*, vol. 38, pp. 221–225, 1957.

the wind.    It will be recalled from the discussion of Fig. 9–22 concerning the wind hodograph that for a smooth and continuous hodograph the advection is given by the wind component normal to the thermal-wind vector, taken at any level.    Such a component also would be normal to the lines of thickness or of mean virtual temperature.

In practice, forecasters compute the advective effect from the wind field and multiply it by a reducing factor $K$ which is determined empirically for different locations and seasons to cover the effects of vertical motions and nonadiabatic heat exchanges.

In summary, it may be stated that the computation of the 500-mb height tendency is based on the surface isallobaric field, the sea-level, 1000-mb or 500-mb geostrophic wind field, the field of thickness between 500 mb and 1000 mb, or equivalent, and an empirically determined factor for the nonadvective changes.

The 500-mb tendency field is useful in indicating deepening of troughs on that surface.    Surface pressure tendencies frequently compensate the advection effects in the equation.    Computation of the 500-mb tendency brings sharply to light those cases where this compensating effect is absent.    When this happens, profound changes and the development of unstable upper waves are indicated.

**Movement of the Upper Waves.**    The waves in the upper westerlies, such as those appearing on the 500-mb chart, can be treated by simplified equations which are of forecasting value.    The formulas were developed by Rossby[1] and bear his name; the long waves themselves are sometimes referred to as "Rossby waves."

The following simplified assumptions are made: that the wave is sinusoidal in shape and does not change its speed, shape, or amplitude during the period under consideration; that the streamlines coincide approximately with the contours of the isobaric surface; that the motion is horizontal, adiabatic, at constant speed, and nondivergent; that the wave and air motion may be represented in a system of rectangular coordinates and are essentially one-dimensional in character; that the axes of the troughs and ridges lie in the north-south direction; and that $\beta = df/dy$ is a constant through the relatively small latitude range included in the amplitude of any given wave.

These simplified assumptions are desirable if the relations are to be useful in the rush of making a forecast and, surprisingly enough, it is

[1] Rossby, C.-G., and Collaborators, Relation between Variations in the Intensity of the Zonal Circulation of the Atmosphere and Displacement of the Semipermanent Centers of Action, *J. Marine Research*, vol. 2, pp. 38–55, 1939.

Rossby, C.-G., Planetary Flow Patterns in the Atmosphere, *Quart. J. Roy. Meteorol. Soc.*, vol. 66 (Supplement), pp. 68–87, 1940.    Kinematic and Hydrostatic Properties of Certain Long Waves in the Westerlies, *Univ. Chicago Dep. Meteorol. Misc. Repts.*, no. 5, 1942.

found in practice that serious errors are usually not introduced as a result of the simplifications. Fortunately the 500-mb surface is commonly near the "level of nondivergence," between the upper and lower compensating divergent-convergent flows, but appreciable errors due to departure from this assumed condition are not infrequent.

The equation of a sine curve in $x,y$ coordinates is

$$y = A \sin \frac{2\pi}{L} x \qquad (17\text{--}16)$$

where $A$ is the amplitude and $L$ is the wavelength. From elementary mechanics it is shown that at any time $t$, the equation of the curve for a sinusoidal wave (such as in a rope) moving in the $x$ direction with speed $C$, is

$$y = A \sin \frac{2\pi}{L} (x - Ct) \qquad (17\text{--}17)$$

or, for sinusoidal streamlines,

$$Y_s = A_s \sin \frac{2\pi}{L} (x - Ct) \qquad (17\text{--}18)$$

Unlike the case of a wave in a rope, the streamlines represent air motion through the sinusoidal course. In Chap. 10 the equation of a streamline [Eq. (10–14)] was found to be

$$v \, dx = u \, dy \qquad \text{or} \qquad \frac{dx}{u} = \frac{dy}{v}$$

Then

$$v = u \frac{dy}{dx} \qquad (17\text{--}19)$$

Using the capital $U$ to represent the prevailing zonal (westerly) current, and taking the partial derivative, we may write

$$v = U \frac{\partial Y_s}{\partial x} = U \frac{2\pi}{L} A_s \cos \frac{2\pi}{L} (x - Ct) \qquad (17\text{--}20)$$

In a system of coordinates moving with the wave, the wave would be stationary and the wind components would be $U - C$ and $v$. If $Y_r$ is the ordinate of the *relative* streamlines in this system, we may write, in the manner of Eq. (17–19),

$$v = (U - C) \frac{\partial Y_r}{\partial x} \qquad (17\text{--}21)$$

Then

$$\frac{\partial Y_r}{\partial x} = \frac{v}{U - C} = \frac{U}{U - C} \frac{\partial Y_s}{\partial x} \qquad (17\text{--}22)$$

Since $U$ and $C$ do not vary with $x$,

$$Y_r = \frac{U}{U - C} Y_s \qquad (17\text{--}23)$$

The amplitudes $A_s$ and $A_r$ are the extreme values of $Y_s$ and $Y_r$, respectively, so they bear the same relationship to each other as do $Y_s$ and $Y_r$, and

$$A_r = A_s \frac{U}{U - C}$$

Solving for $C$, we obtain the wave speed as

$$C = U \left( 1 - \frac{A_s}{A_r} \right) \qquad (17\text{--}24)$$

By definition, the individual change of a conservative property is zero, so the local change is due to advection (considering horizontal motion only). As an approximation in the free atmosphere, we may regard the temperature as conservative. We have, for the local change,

$$\frac{\partial T}{\partial t} = -c \frac{\partial T}{\partial s} = -U \frac{\partial T}{\partial x} - v \frac{\partial T}{\partial y} \qquad (17\text{--}25)$$

With respect to a system of coordinates moving with the wave, the temperature along a streamline will be given as

$$T = T_0 + \frac{\partial T}{\partial y} y + F(x - Ct) \qquad (17\text{--}26)$$

where $T_0$ is the mean temperature at $y = 0$ and $F(x - Ct)$ is some function of the variables in the parenthesis. For fixed coordinates, the function would be of $x$ only, but in the moving system the $x$ distance would have to be reduced by the distance $Ct$ traveled by the system in time $t$.

We may assume, with Rossby, that the meridional temperature gradient is uniform in the vicinity of the streamline and therefore that $\partial T/\partial y = \text{const}$. We may then take the partial derivative with respect to $t$ of this expression, obtaining

$$\frac{\partial T}{\partial t} = \frac{\partial}{\partial t} [F(x - Ct)] \doteq F' \left( \frac{\partial x}{\partial t} - t \frac{\partial C}{\partial t} \right) = 0 \qquad (17\text{--}27)$$

Thus the local change vanishes in the moving system, the isotherms coincide with the relative streamlines, and the amplitude $A_r$ can be determined from the amplitude of the isotherms. $C$ can then be obtained from the amplitudes of the streamlines (contours) and isotherms applied to Eq. (17–24).

This method of obtaining the wave speed is inaccurate because of some of the assumptions made. In particular, in a normally stable atmosphere the temperature can be altered markedly by subsidence and other vertical motions, so the assumption of changes by horizontal advection only is not valid. Furthermore, the streamlines and isotherms

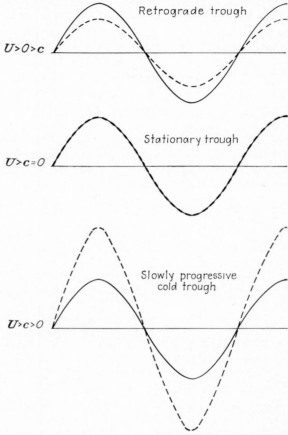

Fig. 17–8. Arrangement of streamlines (solid lines) and isotherms (broken lines) in special types of waves in the westerlies, according to Rossby.

are seldom of such a character that their amplitudes can be determined quantitatively. The relation is quite useful in a qualitative sense, since, on a map, the two amplitudes can be judged as to whether they are equal or whether one is greater or less than the other. Retrograde motion of the wave can immediately be recognized if the amplitude of the isotherms is less than that of the streamlines, for then $C$ must be negative. If the two amplitudes are essentially the same, the wave will be practically stationary. In a normally progressing wave, the isotherm amplitude is greater than that of the streamlines. The three cases, as illustrated by Rossby, are shown in Fig. 17–8.

A more useful quantitative method was derived by Rossby from the concept of the conservation of vorticity in a nondivergent field of wave motion.

If the absolute vorticity is conserved and the divergence is zero, the individual change in the relative vorticity balances the local vorticity of the earth, that is,

$$f + \zeta = \text{const}$$
$$\frac{D\zeta}{Dt} + \frac{Df}{Dt} = 0$$

following along with the particles, and

$$\frac{D\zeta}{Dt} = -\frac{Df}{Dt}$$
$$\frac{Df}{Dt} = v\frac{df}{dy} = \beta v \tag{17–28}$$

where $\beta = df/dy = df/R \, d\varphi = 2\Omega \cos \varphi / R$

$$\frac{D\zeta}{Dt} = -\beta v \tag{17–29}$$

Consider the mean zonal current $U$ constant in $x$, $y$, and $t$, and introduce perturbation velocities $u'$, $v'$ so that the actual wind components are $u = U + u'$ and $v = v'$. It is apparent that $U$ does not contribute to the vorticity. The expression for the relative vorticity is

$$\zeta = \frac{\partial v}{\partial x} - \frac{\partial u}{\partial y} = \zeta' = \frac{\partial v'}{\partial x} - \frac{\partial u'}{\partial y} \tag{17–30}$$

The individual change of relative vorticity, in expanded form, is

$$\frac{D\zeta}{Dt} = \frac{\partial \zeta}{\partial t} + u\frac{\partial \zeta}{\partial x} + v\frac{\partial \zeta}{\partial y} = -\beta v$$
$$= \frac{\partial \zeta}{\partial t} + U\frac{\partial \zeta}{\partial x} + \left[ u'\frac{\partial \zeta}{\partial x} + v'\frac{\partial \zeta}{\partial y} \right] = -\beta v' \tag{17–31}$$

According to Rossby the terms in the brackets in this equation are small terms of the first order, so we may neglect them and write

$$\frac{\partial \zeta}{\partial t} + U\frac{\partial \zeta}{\partial x} = -\beta v' \tag{17–32}$$

As shown previously, the local change vanishes in a stationary wave or in terms of coordinates moving with the wave, so the local change at a fixed point must be due to the advection of the wave motion only, or

$$\frac{\partial \zeta}{\partial t} = -C \frac{\partial \zeta}{\partial x} \tag{17-33}$$

Eq. (17–32) then becomes

$$(U - C) \frac{\partial \zeta}{\partial x} = -\beta v' \tag{17-34}$$

In the case of perturbations that are independent of $y$ (no $\partial u'/\partial y$ term),

$$\zeta = \frac{\partial v'}{\partial x} \tag{17-35}$$

so (17–34) becomes

$$(U - C) \frac{\partial^2 v'}{\partial x^2} = -\beta v' \tag{17-36}$$

The perturbation velocity of a sinusoidal wave has the form, as in Eq. (17–17),

$$v' \approx \sin \frac{2\pi}{L} (x - Ct) \tag{17-37}$$

The second derivative of this with respect to $x$ is

$$\frac{\partial^2 v'}{\partial x^2} = -\frac{4\pi^2}{L^2} \sin \frac{2\pi}{L} (x - Ct)$$
$$= -\frac{4\pi^2}{L^2} v' \tag{17-38}$$

which may be substituted in (17–36) to give

$$U - C = \frac{\beta L^2}{4\pi^2} \tag{17-39}$$

$$C = U - \frac{\beta L^2}{4\pi^2} \tag{17-40}$$

Thus the wave speed can be determined from the wind speed and wavelength. Since $\beta$ and $L$ are always positive, it is apparent that $C$ cannot exceed $U$. It is interesting to note that $C = 0$ when $U = \beta L^2/4\pi^2$. The stationary wavelength ($C = 0$) is seen to be

$$L_s = \sqrt{\frac{4\pi^2 U}{\beta}} = 2\pi \sqrt{\frac{U}{\beta}} \tag{17-41}$$

The graph in Fig. 17–9 is a convenient one for computing the various relationships. From the wavelength and the latitude, $U - C$ is obtained immediately, as at $B$. Since $U$ is measured by upper-air soundings, $C$ is then found as $U - (U - C)$. The stationary wavelength for any given

$U$ and latitude ($\beta$) is that in which $U = U - C$, so by using the scale $U - C$ for $U$, one can read the value of $L_s$, as at $A$ (72 deg for $U$ of 13 deg per day at lat 47°).    $C$ is the difference between points $A$ and $B$, or 5 deg per day.

**CAV Trajectories.**  It is possible with the simplifying assumptions made by Rossby to predict the trajectories air would follow with constant absolute vorticity (CAV).   The computation is useful in indicating movement and changes in the upper waves.

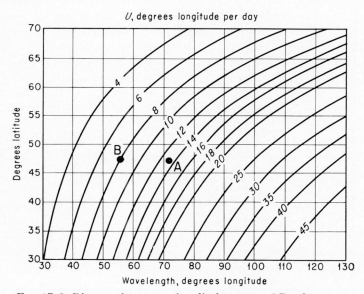

Fig. 17–9. Diagram for computing displacement of Rossby waves.

The trajectory is computed from an inflection point which, for a sinusoidal wave, would be halfway between a trough and a ridge, at $y = 0$, where the flow would be straight.   If there is no horizontal shear at this point of straight flow, the relative vorticity is zero and the absolute vorticity is given by the coriolis parameter at this starting point $f_0$.   If the flow continues without shear, the air will develop relative vorticity only from increasing curvature after it leaves this point.   Then, according to Eq. (10–4), the relative vorticity is given by

$$\zeta = \frac{c}{R_T} \tag{17–42}$$

where $c$ is the total wind and $R_T$ is the radius of curvature of the trajectory.   If the absolute vorticity is to be conserved from the starting point on,

$$f + \frac{c}{R_T} = f_0 \qquad (17\text{-}43)$$

If $df/dy = \beta$ is considered constant over the range of latitude of the path,

$$f_0 - f = -\beta y = \frac{c}{R_T} \qquad (17\text{-}44)$$

From this expression an equation of the trajectory as a function of the radius of curvature can be applied, but a more direct way of getting at the problem is using the Rossby relationships for trajectory. As demonstrated earlier in this chapter, trajectories, like isotherms, coincide with streamlines in a stationary wave. Therefore the wavelength of the trajectory in Rossby waves would be the stationary wavelength

$$L_T = 2\pi \sqrt{\frac{c}{\beta}} \qquad (17\text{-}45)$$

except that the actual velocity $c$ is substituted for the mean zonal velocity $U$. The use of $c$ in this way is permissible only in relatively flat waves in which $c$ has mainly a $u$ component.

The sine curve for this trajectory is

$$y = A_T \sin \frac{2\pi}{L_T} x = A_T \sin x \sqrt{\frac{\beta}{c}} \qquad (17\text{-}46)$$

If the angle of intersection with the $x$ axis at the inflection point is $\psi_0$, the slope of the path in $x$ and $y$ at that point is

$$\left(\frac{dy}{dx}\right)_0 = \tan \psi_0 = A_T \cos x \sqrt{\frac{\beta}{c}} = A_T \sqrt{\frac{\beta}{c}} \qquad (17\text{-}47)$$

and the amplitude is then

$$A_T = \tan \psi_0 \sqrt{\frac{c}{\beta}} \qquad (17\text{-}48)$$

When $c$ has an appreciable $v$ component such that $\psi_0$ is greater than about 25°, its substitution for $U$ in this relation leads to an important error in $A_T$ and $L_T$. For greater angles Petterssen[1] uses a relation obtained in part from Platzman[2] which will not be derived here. It is

$$y^2 = \frac{c}{\beta} 2(\cos \psi - \cos \psi_0) \qquad (17\text{-}49)$$

---

[1] Petterssen, S., "Weather Analysis and Forecasting," McGraw-Hill Book Company, Inc., New York, 1956.

[2] Platzman, G. W., Some Remarks on the Measurement of Curvature and Vorticity, *J. Meteorol.*, vol. 4, pp. 58–62, 1947.

The amplitude $A_T$ is $y_{max}$ at which point $\psi = 0$, so

$$A_T = y_{max} = \frac{2c(1 - \cos \psi_0)}{\beta} \qquad (17\text{–}50)$$

The wavelength in terms of $A_T$ and $\psi_0$ can be found by differentiating the equation for the sine curve (17–17) to obtain

$$\frac{dy}{dx} = A_T \frac{2\pi}{L_T} \cos \frac{2\pi}{L_T} x \qquad (17\text{–}51)$$

and noting that at $x = L_T$, that is, at one wavelength along the $x$ axis,

$$\left(\frac{dy}{dx}\right)_{L_T} = A_T \frac{2\pi}{L_T} = \left(\frac{dy}{dx}\right)_0 = \tan \psi_0 \qquad (17\text{–}52)$$

and therefore that

$$L_T = \frac{2\pi A_T}{\tan \psi_0} \qquad (17\text{–}53)$$

Platzman showed that when the spherical earth is considered, the trajectories are not symmetrical sine curves, but the amplitude of the poleward part is less than that on the equatorward side of the axis.

In practice, the CAV trajectories are computed from graphs or tables, such as the tables in the appendix of Volume 1 of Petterssen's book, which include the Platzman correction. The method is especially useful when the regular equations for wave speed cannot be applied, e.g., when the wavelength of the long waves is not clear, or when there is a complicated combination of long and short waves.

**Numerical Forecasting.** A computation of the future state of the atmosphere from a given initial state by the application of the laws of motion was first attempted in 1922 by Richardson.[1] As might be expected, he found that the computational work was so time-consuming that the job could not be completed until long after the predicted weather had occurred. This difficulty has been overcome by high-speed electronic computers. Richardson also found that all changes in pressure and motion resulted from small differences between very large values, and since his equations were oversensitive to certain effects, some types of minor influences and errors were magnified to produce spurious results. As a result of the work of Charney[2] and others the equations have been

---

[1] Richardson, L. F., "Weather Prediction by Numerical Processes," Cambridge University Press, London, 1922.

[2] Charney, J. G., *J. Meteorol.*, vol. 6, 1949; Charney, J. G., and N. A. Phillips, *J. Meteorol.*, vol. 10, 1953; Charney, J. G., R. Fjörtoft, and J. von Neumann, *Tellus*, vol. 2, 1950.

improved by using more crude approximations to make them less sensitive to small effects. Only those effects which are of critical importance are incorporated into the equations.

The methods introduced in the early 1950s involve a quasigeostrophic assumption based on the relation between the divergence and changes in the absolute vorticity. The assumption is called *quasigeostrophic* because the vorticity is measured and advected by the geostrophic wind, but divergence, a nongeostrophic condition, is taken into consideration. The relation expressed in Eq. (10–76) may be expanded into the individual, local, and advective changes and written as

$$\frac{D}{Dt}(f + \zeta) = \frac{\partial}{\partial t}(f + \zeta) + c\frac{\partial}{\partial s}(f + \zeta) = -(f + \zeta)\operatorname{div}_2 c \quad (17\text{--}54)$$

The advection is along the streamlines, so only the component of the vorticity gradient along $s$ is involved. We will designate the geostrophic absolute vorticity $f + \zeta_g$ as $Q_g$, but in the divergence term on the right we will regard $\zeta$ as negligible in comparison with $f$, and write

$$\frac{\partial Q_g}{\partial t} + c_g\frac{\partial Q_g}{\partial s} = -f\operatorname{div}_2 c = f\frac{\partial w_p}{\partial p} \quad (17\text{--}55)$$

the last expression on the right being in accord with Eq. (10–64).

On an isobaric surface the geostrophic wind components are

$$u_g = -\frac{g}{f}\frac{\partial Z}{\partial y} \qquad v_g = \frac{g}{f}\frac{\partial Z}{\partial x}$$

The advection of the vorticity may be divided into components:

$$\begin{aligned}
c_g\frac{\partial Q_g}{\partial s} &= v_g\frac{\partial Q_g}{\partial y} + u_g\frac{\partial Q_g}{\partial x} \\
&= \frac{g}{f}\left(\frac{\partial Z}{\partial x}\frac{\partial Q_g}{\partial y} - \frac{\partial Z}{\partial y}\frac{\partial Q_g}{\partial x}\right)
\end{aligned} \quad (17\text{--}56)$$

and since

$$Q_g = \zeta_g + f = \left(\frac{\partial v_g}{\partial x} - \frac{\partial u_g}{\partial y}\right) + f$$

we can substitute for $u_g$ and $v_g$ and carry out the differentiation to obtain

$$Q_g = \frac{g}{f}\left(\frac{\partial^2 Z}{\partial x^2} + \frac{\partial^2 Z}{\partial y^2}\right) + f = \frac{g}{f}\nabla^2 Z + f \quad (17\text{--}57)$$

From this we find

$$\frac{\partial Q_g}{\partial t} = \frac{g}{f}\left(\frac{\partial^2}{\partial x^2} + \frac{\partial^2}{\partial y^2}\right)\frac{\partial Z}{\partial t} + \frac{\partial f}{\partial t} \quad (17\text{--}58)$$

but $\partial f/\partial t = 0$ locally (remembering that this is only the equation for the local change). We then substitute the expressions (17–58) and (17–56) into Eq. (17–55) with the result that

$$\frac{g}{f}\left(\frac{\partial^2}{\partial x^2} + \frac{\partial^2}{\partial y^2}\right)\frac{\partial Z}{\partial t} + \frac{g}{f}\left(\frac{\partial Z}{\partial x}\frac{\partial Q_g}{\partial y} - \frac{\partial Z}{\partial y}\frac{\partial Q_g}{\partial x}\right) = f\frac{\partial w_p}{\partial p} \qquad (17–59)$$

or, after multiplying both sides by $f/g$ and rearranging,

$$\left(\frac{\partial^2}{\partial x^2} + \frac{\partial^2}{\partial y^2}\right)\frac{\partial Z}{\partial t} - \frac{f^2}{g}\frac{\partial w_p}{\partial p} = \frac{\partial Z}{\partial y}\frac{\partial Q_g}{\partial x} - \frac{\partial Z}{\partial x}\frac{\partial Q_g}{\partial y} \qquad (17–60)$$

While the terms on the right can be obtained from the isobaric contour chart, those on the left, namely, the height tendency $\partial Z/\partial t$ and the vertical-velocity gradient are both considered as unknowns, so an additional equation is required. This equation is obtained from thermodynamics and hydrostatics. It is assumed that all changes are adiabatic and hence that potential temperature is conserved. From the expression

$$\frac{1}{\theta}\frac{D\theta}{Dt} = \frac{1}{\theta}\frac{\partial\theta}{\partial t} + \frac{1}{\theta}c\cdot\nabla\theta = 0 \qquad (17–61)$$

we may divide the transport term into vertical- and horizontal-geostrophic components to obtain

$$\frac{1}{\theta}\frac{D\theta}{Dt} = \frac{1}{\theta}\frac{\partial\theta}{\partial t} + \frac{1}{\theta}c_g\frac{\partial\theta}{\partial s} + \frac{1}{\theta}w_p\frac{\partial\theta}{\partial p} = 0 \qquad (17–62)$$

On an isobaric surface, $1/\theta\ \partial\theta/\partial t = 1/\alpha\ \partial\alpha/\partial t$ and $1/\theta\ \partial\theta/\partial s = 1/\alpha\ \partial\alpha/\partial s$. From the hydrostatic equation

$$\alpha = -g\frac{\partial Z}{\partial p}$$

Thus

$$\frac{1}{\theta}\frac{\partial\theta}{\partial t} = \frac{1}{\alpha}\frac{\partial\alpha}{\partial t} = \frac{1}{\alpha}\frac{\partial}{\partial t}\left(-g\frac{\partial Z}{\partial p}\right) = -\frac{g}{\alpha}\frac{\partial}{\partial t}\left(\frac{Z}{p}\right) = -\frac{g}{\alpha}\frac{\partial}{\partial p}\left(\frac{\partial Z}{\partial t}\right) \qquad (17–63)$$

$$\frac{1}{\theta}\frac{\partial\theta}{\partial s} = \frac{1}{\alpha}\frac{\partial\alpha}{\partial s}$$

$$\frac{1}{\theta}c_g\frac{\partial\theta}{\partial s} = \frac{1}{\alpha}c_g\frac{\partial\alpha}{\partial s} = \frac{1}{\alpha}c_g\frac{\partial}{\partial s}\left(-g\frac{\partial Z}{\partial p}\right) = -\frac{g}{\alpha}c_g\frac{\partial}{\partial s}\left(\frac{\partial Z}{\partial p}\right) \qquad (17–64)$$

The substitution in Eq. (17–62) results in

$$-\frac{g}{\alpha}\frac{\partial}{\partial p}\left(\frac{\partial Z}{\partial t}\right) + \frac{1}{\alpha}c_g\frac{\partial}{\partial s}\left(-g\frac{\partial Z}{\partial p}\right) + \frac{1}{\theta}w_p\frac{\partial\theta}{\partial p} = 0 \qquad (17–65)$$

We then multiply through by $\alpha/g$ and reverse signs, so that

$$\frac{\partial}{\partial p}\left(\frac{\partial Z}{\partial t}\right) - \frac{\alpha}{g\theta} w_p \frac{\partial \theta}{\partial p} = -c_g \frac{\partial}{\partial s}\left(\frac{\partial Z}{\partial p}\right) \qquad (17\text{--}66)$$

Then, with the $u_g$, $v_g$, $x$, and $y$ components substituted on the right, the equation is

$$\frac{\partial}{\partial p}\left(\frac{\partial Z}{\partial t}\right) - \frac{\alpha}{g\theta} w_p \frac{\partial \theta}{\partial p} = -\frac{g}{f}\left[\frac{\partial Z}{\partial y}\frac{\partial}{\partial x}\left(\frac{\partial Z}{\partial p}\right) - \frac{\partial Z}{\partial x}\frac{\partial}{\partial y}\left(\frac{\partial Z}{\partial p}\right)\right] \qquad (17\text{--}67)$$

The coefficient of $w_p$ is a measure of the vertical stability of the air. It can be obtained from the thickness pattern or it can be given a standard value.

The two equations to be used are (17–60) and (17–67), and from them the two unknowns $\partial Z/\partial t$ and $w_p$ are determined. To do this, we introduce the conditions at the boundaries. One condition is that $w_p = 0$ at $p = 0$ and at $p = 1000$ mb. (Actually $w_p = 0$ at sea level instead of at 1000 mb, but it is more practical, yet accurate enough, to use the latter.) At the boundaries of the weather map, arbitrary but reasonable values of the height tendencies and of the vorticity transport are assigned. Large errors thus are likely to be introduced, but in practice it is found that they are rapidly suppressed with distance inward from the boundaries, becoming insignificant in about 1000 km. The map is constructed for an area much larger than the area of forecasting responsibility, so the uncertainties at the boundaries will not affect the users.

In the forecasting procedure, the initial values of the contours are obtained either from a manual or a machine analysis and from this the initial values of the terms on the right of Eqs. (17–60) and (17–67) are obtained for a large number of grid points. After putting in the boundary conditions, the operator lets the machine solve the equations and determine the height-tendency field. In the machine, the height increments $\delta Z$ are added to the initial height field to produce the height at the end of a short time interval $\delta t$. The computation of height increments for small time intervals continues and the values are accumulated in the machine for as long a forecast period as is practical.

Usually the end product is a series of charts printed by the machine in the form of typewriter "art" showing the computed contours of the pressure surface for 12, 24, 36, etc., hours from the initial observations. From a chart of computed vertical velocities $w_p$ and a consideration of water-vapor distribution, areas of probable precipitation can be delineated.

*The Barotropic Model.* In a barotropic atmosphere there is no conversion of potential and internal energy into kinetic energy, hence no divergence-convergence and no development of cyclones and anticyclones.

Nevertheless, a simple barotropic model was used in the 1950s with some success in northwestern Europe, perhaps because it is a region of occluding cyclones.

The equation

$$\frac{\partial Q}{\partial t} + c\,\frac{\partial Q}{\partial s} = -f\,\mathrm{div}_2\,c = 0$$

is valid in a barotropic atmosphere. The justification for using it in middle latitudes can be made on the basis that (1) the net divergence averaged through all layers of the atmosphere is negligible, or (2) the computation is made at the level of nondivergence which itself does not change with time.

At the level of nondivergence, Eq. (17–60) becomes

$$\left(\frac{\partial^2}{\partial x^2} + \frac{\partial^2}{\partial y^2}\right)\frac{\partial Z}{\partial t} = \frac{\partial Z}{\partial y}\frac{\partial Q_g}{\partial x} - \frac{\partial Z}{\partial x}\frac{\partial Q_g}{\partial y} \tag{17–68}$$

The terms on the right can be determined for every grid point from the contour analysis and the machine solves for the field of height tendency $\partial Z/\partial t$, accumulating the increments $\delta Z$ in successive $\delta t$ intervals to the end of the forecast period.

*Multilevel Models.* During the early years of numerical prediction, models involving related computations for several levels were put into practice. One method is to consider the atmosphere in two isobaric surfaces, e.g., 250 and 750 mb, and to apply the quasigeostrophic equation (17–60) to these surfaces. The value of $\partial w_p/\partial p$ of Eq. (17–60) is measured through a thickness of 500 mb straddling the isobaric surface in question, so that

$$\left(\frac{\partial w_p}{\partial p}\right)_{250} \approx \frac{w_{p500} - w_{p\text{top}}}{500} = \frac{w_{p500}}{500} \tag{17–69a}$$

$$\left(\frac{\partial w_p}{\partial p}\right)_{750} \approx \frac{w_{p1000} - w_{p500}}{500} = -\frac{w_{p500}}{500} \tag{17–69b}$$

since $w_{p\text{top}} = w_{p1000} = 0$.

The equations are

$$\left(\frac{\partial^2}{\partial x^2} + \frac{\partial^2}{\partial y^2}\right)\frac{\partial Z_{250}}{\partial t} - \frac{f^2}{g}\frac{w_{p500}}{500} = \frac{\partial Z_{250}}{\partial y}\frac{\partial Q_{g250}}{\partial x} - \frac{\partial Z_{250}}{\partial x}\frac{\partial Q_{g250}}{\partial y} \tag{17–70a}$$

$$\left(\frac{\partial^2}{\partial x^2} + \frac{\partial^2}{\partial y^2}\right)\frac{\partial Z_{750}}{\partial t} + \frac{f^2}{g}\frac{w_{p500}}{500} = \frac{\partial Z_{750}}{\partial y}\frac{\partial Q_{g750}}{\partial x} - \frac{\partial Z_{750}}{\partial x}\frac{\partial Q_{g750}}{\partial y} \tag{17–70b}$$

The opposite signs of the terms of vertical velocity indicate that with subsidence at 500 mb (positive $w_{p500}$), convergence, and therefore local increase of vorticity is indicated at 250 mb with divergence and local decrease of vorticity at 750 mb.

Since there are in these two equations three unknowns, namely the height tendencies at 250 and at 750 mb and the vertical velocity at 500 mb, a third equation derived from thermodynamics and statics is introduced. It is Eq. (17–67) for the 500-mb level with finite differences used for the derivative $\partial/\partial p$ of the height tendency and contour gradient. The expression is

$$\frac{1}{500}\left(\frac{\partial Z_{750}}{\partial t} - \frac{\partial Z_{250}}{\partial t}\right) - \frac{\alpha}{g\theta}\frac{\partial\theta}{\partial p}\, w_{p500}$$
$$= \frac{g}{f\cdot 1000}\left[\frac{\partial(Z_{750} - Z_{250})}{\partial y}\frac{\partial(Z_{750} - Z_{250})}{\partial x} - \frac{\partial(Z_{750} + Z_{250})}{\partial x}\frac{\partial(Z_{750} - Z_{250})}{\partial y}\right]$$
$$(17–71)$$

A standard value is used for $\alpha/g\theta \cdot \partial\theta/\partial p$.

The solutions of Eqs. (17–70a and b) and (17–71) are obtained from initial distributions of the 250-mb and 750-mb heights with the aid of suitable lateral-boundary conditions. An equation without the unknown of the vertical velocity can be obtained by adding Eqs. (17–70a and b). The machine computes and accumulates the height tendencies in small increments during the forecasting period.

It should be noted that $Z_{250} - Z_{750}$ is the thickness of the layer between the two isobaric surfaces, and that the horizontal gradient of it is proportional to the thermal wind and is a measure of the baroclinity. Thus the multilevel model is a baroclinic model and allows for conversions of potential and internal energy into kinetic energy.

*Comments on Computation.* In all of the equations for numerical prediction it is necessary to correct for the use of cartesian coordinates on the spherical earth. The use of these coordinates is favored over spherical representation for reasons of simplicity. The equations are transformed so as to apply directly to the quantities measured on the conformal projections which are in general use in meteorology.

The computation procedure involves a finite number of grid points and in place of the differential equations, finite-difference equations have to be used. These approximations lead to what are termed *truncation* errors, referring to the fact that linear slopes are substituted for curved gradients within the finite distances.

*Graphical Methods.* Graphical methods of applying the numerical-prediction relations to synoptic charts to produce prognostic charts have been developed by Fjörtoft,[1] Petterssen,[2] and others. The method involves details associated with synoptic analysis which can best be

[1] Fjörtoft, R., Integration of the Barotropic Vorticity Equation, *Tellus*, vol. 4, pp. 179–194, 1952.

[2] Petterssen, S., M. A. Estoque, and L. A. Hughes, An Experiment in Prognostication, *J. Meteorol.*, vol. 14, pp. 191–205, 1957.

grasped by work in the laboratory; hence no discussion of the system will be attempted here.

With proper systematization it is possible to perform the graphical computations in time to be useful within the ordinary forecast period. The charts must be plotted and analyzed in a manner suitable for performing the vorticity advection and analysis of the tendency fields.

The method is particularly valuable for research purposes, because as the various steps are performed, a fairly good insight into the reasons behind difficulties is obtained in the process. Models can thus be tested with more detail than is possible on the machines and subjective judgment, and experience of the forecaster can be applied to discover deficiencies as they appear. New models have been suggested as a result of these studies. The graphical method performs a useful check on what is going on in the machine, especially in discovering errors or details to which the equations are oversensitive. For example, by the graphical method, it is possible to see to what extent the pressure reductions to sea level in plateau areas under unusual temperature conditions are affecting the results, or the extent to which nongeostrophic effects in mountain areas are responsible for errors.

**Development.** A promising way of anticipating pressure or height changes is through the application of vorticity advection and generation. The mutual adjustment of pressure gradient and wind results in changing pressure with changing vorticity. The vorticity effects on deepening at the ground or other levels have been incorporated in the so-called development equation introduced by Sutcliffe[1] and elaborated upon by Petterssen[2] and others. It makes use of the vorticity-generating properties of convergence as expressed in Eq. (17–54), that is,

$$\frac{D}{Dt}(f + \zeta) = -(f + \zeta) \, \mathrm{div}_2 \, c$$

To simplify the notation, the absolute vorticity will be designated by $Q$ and the convergence $(- \, \mathrm{div}_2 \, c)$ will be signified by $K$. The expression then becomes

$$\frac{DQ}{Dt} = KQ \tag{17-72}$$

This may be expanded to

$$\frac{DQ}{Dt} = \frac{\partial Q}{\partial t} + c \, \frac{\partial Q}{\partial s} = KQ \tag{17-73}$$

[1] Sutcliffe, R. C., *Quart. J. Roy. Meteorol. Soc.*, vol. 73, 1947.

[2] Petterssen, S., "Weather Analysis and Forecasting," pp. 320–325, McGraw-Hill Book Company, Inc., New York, 1956.

to divide the individual change into the local change and the advective change.

The generation of vorticity as observed at the ground can be the result of convergences and divergences and of advection of vorticities at all levels through the atmosphere over the area in question. Experience has shown that vorticity advection occurs in a more or less uniform manner from the lower and middle troposphere upward. To arrive at an applicable relationship, only the lower part of the atmosphere is considered, up to the first level of nondivergence (700 to 400 mb in the usual situation). One can take the vorticity advected at that level and assume that any changes of vorticity in the moving air will be generated below that level. The advection at any other height, especially at the surface, can be added.

The geostrophic assumption is used as a starting point from which to measure the imbalance leading to the development. It is desired to obtain the development at the surface, where the absolute vorticity is $Q_0$ and the wind velocity is $c_0$. At the level of nondivergence the velocity is $c$ and the absolute vorticity is $Q$.

The geostrophic-vector wind difference between the two levels is the thermal wind $\vec{c_T} = \vec{c} - \vec{c_0}$. Since the vorticity at these two levels is derived from these same winds,

$$Q = f + \zeta = f + (\zeta_0 + \zeta_T) = Q_0 + \zeta_T \qquad (17\text{--}74)$$

At the level of nondivergence, $K$ by definition is zero, so

$$\frac{\partial Q}{\partial t} = -c\frac{\partial Q}{\partial s}$$

This expression is substituted in the partial derivative of Eq. (17–74) to obtain

$$\frac{\partial Q_0}{\partial t} = -\frac{\partial \zeta_T}{\partial t} - c\frac{\partial Q}{\partial s} \qquad (17\text{--}75)$$

The quantity $\partial Q_0/\partial t$, which is the increase in vorticity with time at a fixed point on the surface of the earth, is thus given by the advection of the vorticity at the level of nondivergence and the change of the vorticity of the thermal wind. The negative sign in the advective term means that positive-vorticity advection is associated with increasing vorticity upstream, but $s$ has been taken positive downstream. The thermal-wind-vorticity term is not easily interpreted.

The thermal wind is given by

$$c_T = \frac{1}{f}\frac{\partial}{\partial n}(\Phi - \Phi_0) = -\frac{g}{f}\frac{\partial Z}{\partial n} \qquad (17\text{--}76)$$

and its relative vorticity, neglecting curvature, is

$$\zeta_T = \frac{\partial c_T}{\partial n} \tag{17-77}$$

and

$$\frac{\partial \zeta_T}{\partial t} = -\frac{g}{f}\frac{\partial}{\partial t}\left(\frac{\partial^2 Z}{\partial n^2}\right) \tag{17-78}$$

where $Z$ is the thickness up to the level of nondivergence. The first term in Eq. (17-75) therefore is proportional to the rate of change with time of the La Placian of thickness.

Equations (17-75) and (17-78) can be combined to give the local increase of the absolute vorticity at the surface as

$$\frac{\partial Q_0}{\partial t} = -\frac{g}{f}\frac{\partial}{\partial t}\left(\frac{\partial^2 Z}{\partial n^2}\right) - c\frac{\partial Q}{\partial s} \tag{17-79}$$

where the second or advective term on the right refers to the level of nondivergence and the first term refers to the local change with time of the La Placian of thickness between the surface and that level, or, let us say, between 1000 mb and 500 mb.

After the manner of Eq. (15–18), the relative vorticity may be written

$$\zeta = \frac{\partial c}{\partial n} - c\frac{\partial \alpha}{\partial s} \tag{17-80}$$

where $\alpha$ is the angle between the streamline and the $y$ axis and $n$ is the direction orthogonal to the streamlines. [Note that $n$ here is not in the same direction as in Eq. (17–79), thus emphasizing the value of vector notation, that is, of $\nabla_2 Z$ for $\partial Z/\partial n$.] The absolute vorticity is, then,

$$Q = \zeta + f = \frac{\partial c}{\partial n} - c\frac{\partial \alpha}{\partial s} + f \tag{17-81}$$

The vorticity advection $-c\,\partial Q/\partial s$ is then the speed times the variation along the streamline of the horizontal shear $\partial c/\partial n$, of the coriolis parameter, and of $c\,\partial\alpha/\partial s$. In most cases neither the shear nor the coriolis parameter varies appreciably with distance along the streamline, at least not in predominantly zonal flow, so we may write the vorticity advection simply as

$$c\frac{\partial Q}{\partial s} = c\frac{\partial}{\partial s}\left(c\frac{\partial \alpha}{\partial s}\right) = c^2\frac{\partial^2 \alpha}{\partial s^2} + c\frac{\partial \alpha}{\partial s}\frac{\partial c}{\partial s} \tag{17-82}$$

If the flow is not too far from geostrophic, we may assume that, as related in connection with Eq. (15–17), a downstream increase in speed is exactly balanced by a downstream confluence, so that

$$\frac{\partial c}{\partial s} = -c \frac{\partial \alpha}{\partial n} \qquad (17\text{–}83)$$

and
$$c \frac{\partial Q}{\partial s} = c^2 \left( \frac{\partial^2 \alpha}{\partial s^2} - \frac{\partial \alpha}{\partial s} \frac{\partial \alpha}{\partial n} \right) \qquad (17\text{–}84)$$

the latter being the vorticity advection, positive if the vorticity decreases downstream.

It is not difficult to determine this vorticity advection from streamline (or contour) patterns. Before discussing the first term of Eq. (17–79)

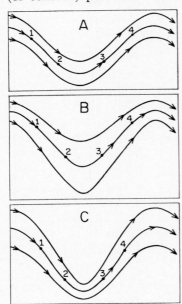

FIG. 17–10. Vorticity advection in three typical situations.

the vorticity advection term might be tried qualitatively in the three situations represented in Fig. 17–10. In diagram $A$ where the streamlines run essentially parallel to each other, $\partial \alpha / \partial n = 0$, so only the first term in Eq. (17–84) is relevant. From the left of the diagram to 1, $\partial \alpha / \partial s$ is positive, from 1 to 2 it is zero, from 2 to 3 it is negative, from 3 to 4 it is zero again, and from 4 to the end it is positive. This means that up to the trough line $\partial^2 \alpha / \partial s^2$ is negative and that from the trough line to the next ridge line it is positive. Thus the vorticity advection is negative (anticyclonic) to the vicinity of the trough line and positive (cyclonic) from there to the ridge line.

In diagrams $B$ and $C$, the first term operates in the same way as in $A$, but $\partial \alpha / \partial n$ is not zero, so both terms must be considered. In diagram $B$, $\partial \alpha / \partial n$ is positive to the west of the trough line and negative to the east of it. From the western boundary to 1 both members of the second term are positive, so with the negative sign in front of the second term and with the first term negative in that region, the effects combine to produce advection of negative vorticity. From 1 to 2, $\partial \alpha / \partial s = 0$, so the first term rules as in $A$. From 2 to the trough line the two members of the second term are of opposite signs so this term opposes the first. From the trough line to 3 both members of the second term are negative and the second term tends to balance the first. From 3 to 4 again $\partial \alpha / \partial s = 0$ and the first term operates as in $A$. From 4 to the ridge line the two members of the second term are of opposite sign and therefore, with due regard for sign, the first and second terms work together to produce positive advection of vorticity.

In diagram $C$ the conditions with regard to $\partial\alpha/\partial s$ and $\partial^2\alpha/\partial s^2$ are the same as in $A$ and $B$ but $\partial\alpha/\partial n$ everywhere in $C$ has a sign opposite to that in $B$. Thus from 0 to 1 we have opposing effects between the two terms, from 1 to 2 the effects are as in $A$ and $B$, from 2 to the trough the two terms combine to produce anticyclonic advection, from the trough to 3 the two terms add together for cyclonic-vorticity advection, from 3 to 4 the effect is the same as in $A$ and $B$, and from 4 to the ridge line the two terms are opposing.

Returning now to the first term in Eq. (17–79), the tendency of the thickness gradient, it will be helpful to examine the factors contributing to it. From the hyposometric formula applied to the layer between two fixed isobaric surfaces $p_0$ and $p$ it is noted that

$$\frac{\partial Z}{\partial n} = \frac{R}{mg}\frac{\partial}{\partial n}\left(\bar{T}^* \int_p^{p_0} \frac{dp}{p}\right)$$
$$= \frac{R}{mg}\ln\frac{p_0}{p}\frac{\partial \bar{T}^*}{\partial n} \tag{17–85}$$

where $\bar{T}^*$ is the mean virtual temperature of the layer. Then

$$\frac{g}{f}\frac{\partial}{\partial t}\left(\frac{\partial^2 Z}{\partial n^2}\right) = \frac{R}{mf}\ln\frac{p_0}{p}\frac{\partial}{\partial t}\left(\frac{\partial^2 \bar{T}^*}{\partial n^2}\right) = \frac{R}{mf}\ln\frac{p_0}{p}\frac{\partial^2}{\partial n^2}\left(\frac{\partial \bar{T}^*}{\partial t}\right) \tag{17–86}$$

The change in the mean virtual temperature of the column will be made up of the changes taking place at all the different levels. These changes can be examined from considerations based on the first law of thermodynamics as expressed in Eq. (7–44):

$$C_p\,dT = dq + \frac{RT}{mp}\,dp$$

For an adiabatic process in a parcel

$$\frac{DT}{Dp} = \frac{RT}{mp}$$

For a nonadiabatic process in a parcel, with this last relation substituted,

$$\frac{DT}{Dt} = \frac{1}{C_p}\frac{dq}{dt} + \frac{DT}{Dp}\frac{Dp}{Dt} \tag{17–87}$$

This individual change may be expanded into

$$\frac{DT}{Dt} = \frac{\partial T}{\partial t} + c_n\frac{\partial T}{\partial n} + w_p\frac{\partial T}{\partial p} \tag{17–88}$$

where both a vertical (convection) and a horizontal (advection) transport are added to the local change. Upon substitution of this equation into the preceding one and recognizing that $Dp/Dt = w_p$, we have the local change

$$\frac{\partial T}{\partial t} = -c_n \frac{\partial T}{\partial n} + w_p \left( \frac{DT}{Dp} - \frac{\partial T}{\partial p} \right) + \frac{1}{C_p} \frac{dq}{dt} \qquad (17\text{--}89)$$

The portion of the second term on the right which is in parentheses is the difference between the adiabatic rate and the prevailing local lapse rate, both expressed in terms of pressure instead of height. This difference is an expression of the vertical stability of the air. When this part is negative, it is associated with vertical accelerations which determine $w_p$ itself. Normally this difference is positive. Since $w_p$ is positive downward (toward increasing pressure), positive stability with downward motion and negative stability with upward motion will both increase the temperature.

The terms affecting the temperature, and therefore the thickness, are according to Eq. (17–89) of three kinds: (1) the horizontal temperature advection, (2) a stability or adiabatic term, and (3) a nonadiabatic term. In practice the first term can be considered as $-c\,\partial T/\partial s$. Note that there is no distinction made in the nonadiabatic term as to whether the heat is added to a parcel or whether it is added locally. It is pointless to make this distinction; all that is required is that the heat be added in the air column under consideration. If it is added outside, it could possibly be reflected in the temperature of the advected or convected air.

Only the first term can be determined quantitatively from synoptic-aerologic charts. The other two are considered only in a qualitative sense. For example, the second term assists cyclonic development in the case of unstable, moist air and the third term will be important in the same way when cold air moves over a warm ocean surface in winter. The various effects are treated qualitatively in Petterssen's book.

In summary, it may be said that the development equation (17–79) involves the vorticity advection at the level of nondivergence, which can be evaluated without great difficulty, and a term for the change in the thickness pattern between the surface (or 1000 mb) and that level, only part of which can be determined quantitatively.

**Some Important Qualitative Methods.** A number of relations, some of which might be determined quantitatively under certain ideal conditions, can be applied qualitatively in various forecasting situations. Riehl[1] and his collaborators have compiled a summary of qualitative

---

[1] Riehl, H., et al., Forecasting in Middle Latitudes, *Meteorol. Monographs*, vol. 1, no. 5, 1952.

methods that have been tested and proved useful in forecasting, particularly in the upper-air prognosis.   Certain aspects of the jet stream were found to be of prognostic value.

By charting the speeds as they vary along the jet (isotach analysis), one can see the regions of probable horizontal convergence, where the wind decreases downstream.   At the jet-stream altitudes these zones of divergence and convergence are associated with vorticity-producing vertical circulations.   As might be expected, the maximum gradients in wind speed are around the speed maxima.   These speed maxima move along the jet, seemingly shot off from perturbations upstream.   There is often enough time lag between their appearance and the development of cyclones to make them useful predictors.

Extended forecasting, that is, the prediction of conditions for five days or more in advance, is based on a variety of qualitative applications. In this time period the flow patterns cannot be extrapolated because the decay time of the perturbation pattern is of the order of 3 to 5 days.

# CHAPTER 18

# CONDENSATION, PRECIPITATION, AND ATMOSPHERIC ELECTRICITY

As demonstrated by several experimenters toward the end of the last century, condensation of water vapor to the liquid phase occurs on certain available nuclei. Some of these nuclei can serve only if a considerable degree of supersaturation occurs. Such are the small ions and the small particles studied by physicists in cloud chambers. Others, especially if large and composed of substances having a chemical affinity to water, take on water and grow into noticeable droplets even before saturation is reached. Given a variety of particles in an atmosphere containing water vapor, one finds that, as saturation is approached, condensation will occur first on those nuclei that are large and *hygroscopic*, or at least not hydrophobic. It is an observed fact that in the atmosphere with temperatures favorable for liquid condensation appreciable supersaturation is not necessary for condensation and that not infrequently it takes place with less than 100 per cent relative humidity. This fact indicates that there is an ample supply of large and chemically favorable condensation nuclei.

The nucleation process for the passage from vapor to the crystalline phase, or crystallization, is not the same as that for condensation; at low temperatures a different set of circumstances prevails, and supersaturation with respect to ice is noted. This indicates that suitable crystallization nuclei are scarce in the atmosphere and that those suitable for condensation are not very suitable for crystallization.

Saturation, or 100 per cent relative humidity, in its ordinary sense and in the sense that it is used in this discussion refers to a plane surface of pure water and means that if the liquid water and the vapor in the space above it are at the same temperature and in equilibrium, they will have the same (saturation) vapor pressure. Or we may say that then the vapor pressure in the space is the same as the vapor tension of a pure, flat water surface at that temperature. If supersaturation is an equilibrium condition over any other kind of surface, then that surface must exert a greater vapor tension than does a plane surface of pure water at the same temperature.

As tiny fog or cloud droplets begin to form in the atmosphere, they are not at exact saturation according to this standard, because they neither are pure water nor have a plane surface. While the curvature causes the vapor pressure at their surfaces to be higher than standard saturation, at the small sizes where this effect is appreciable the impurity introduced in the form of the usual nucleus tends to counteract this effect. If the nucleus is a hygroscopic substance, such as sea salt, the appreciable concentration of salt at small-droplet sizes tends to make the equilibrium vapor pressure less than that of standard saturation.

**Size Spectrum of Atmospheric Particles.** Particles of meteorological interest in the atmosphere range in size from molecules to giant hailstones. The principal particles with which we shall be concerned are listed in Table 18–1.

TABLE 18–1. SIZES OF PARTICLES AND SUPERSATURATIONS REQUIRED FOR CONDENSATION ON THEM

| Class of particles | Approximate equivalent spherical diameter, cm | Supersaturation required, per cent | |
|---|---|---|---|
| | | Hygroscopic | Nonhygroscopic |
| Small ions | $<10^{-7}$ | . . . . . . . | 400–100 |
| Medium ions | $10^{-7}$–$5 \times 10^{-6}$ | 0.50–1.8 | 100–5 |
| Large ions | $5 \times 10^{-6}$–$2 \times 10^{-5}$ | 1.8–0.4 | 5–1.2 |
| Aitken nuclei | $5 \times 10^{-6}$–$2 \times 10^{-5}$ | 1.8–0.4 | 5–1.2 |
| Smoke, dust, haze | $10^{-5}$–$2 \times 10^{-4}$ | 0.85–<0 | 2.4–0.001 |
| Large condensation nuclei | $2 \times 10^{-5}$–$10^{-3}$ | 0.4–<0 | 1.2–0.0003 |
| Giant condensation nuclei | $10^{-3}$–$3 \times 10^{-3}$ | <0 | 0.0003–0.0001 |
| Cloud or fog droplets | $10^{-4}$–$10^{-2}$ | | |
| Drizzle drops | $10^{-2}$–$5 \times 10^{-2}$ | | |
| Raindrops | $5 \times 10^{-2}$–$4 \times 10^{-1}$ | | |

First on the list are the small ions. An ion is a particle that has one extra elementary charge so that it is not in neutral balance, or it may lack one such charge. An ion can be a molecule or a large particle, as indicated by the range of sizes in the table. The small ions are constantly being formed by the ionizing action of cosmic rays entering the atmosphere and from radioactive gases escaping from the soil and rocks over continents. Ions are also created through man-made nuclear reactions. The small ions disappear by recombination among themselves and by attaching themselves to larger particles to produce large ions. In fact, the medium and large ions are apparently only formed from capture of the small ones by the particles.

From the column listing the ranges of diameters, it appears that large ions and Aitken nuclei are the same, and other facts about them bear out this identity.   Beginning around 1880, the British physicist John Aitken developed an instrument for producing condensation in a chamber through expansion and for counting the condensed droplets.   He recognized that each droplet was forming on a nucleus.   The nuclei around which droplets condense in an Aitken counter are called Aitken nuclei. They may or may not be the nuclei around which natural clouds are formed, since the atmospheric supersaturations may be less than those created by the expansion in Aitken's chamber.   The Aitken nuclei are an abundant class of particles and, in addition to their possibilities as natural condensation nuclei, they play an important role in the ionization balance of the lower atmosphere.   Combustion products contribute greatly to the number of Aitken nuclei, hence the largest counts are found in industrial cities, running as high as millions per cubic centimeter. Over the oceans, sea salt particles may be abundant as a result of spray and foam in stormy areas, but the numbers seldom exceed a few tens of thousands per cubic centimeter.   On the average, the counts are lowest over the oceans.   The numbers decrease rapidly with height, dropping off by a factor of 10 every 2 km or so.   However, over calm ocean areas where the counts can be extremely low, an increase through the first kilometer or two may be observed, indicating upper transport from a disturbed area.

Smoke, dust, and haze are classed together in the table, since no clear distinction can be made between them.   The smaller particles in this category could be Aitken nuclei but are put in a different classification because they have been collected in a different manner.   The term "dust" is occasionally used to denote all types of dry material in the atmosphere.   Dust blown into the atmosphere in dust storms usually has a yellowish color while smoke tends to be more bluish, but this difference must be due to different particle sizes, the dust-storm particles being fairly large.   Haze is often composed of particles to which considerable quantities of water are attached.   The hygroscopic particles will take on water while the humidity is below saturation and will grow as the relative humidity increases, until near saturation they become fog or cloud droplets.   These hygroscopic nuclei may be produced in smoke or may be detached from the ocean or land by the air motion.   Many of the smoke or "dust" particles are active condensation nuclei.

Most of the atmospheric condensation appears to occur on what are classed as "large" condensation nuclei in Table 18–1.   Although less abundant than the Aitken nuclei, they occur in the atmosphere in sufficient numbers to facilitate cloud and fog formation without appreciable supersaturation.

It should be noted that there is considerable overlapping in the size ranges of smoke, haze, large condensation nuclei, and cloud or fog droplets. This circumstance is in agreement with the fact, to be discussed in more detail in this chapter, that condensation is a process of continuous growth of particles.

The giant nuclei, although relatively few in number, play an important part in condensation and precipitation, because as the relative humidity reaches 100 per cent they have attained the size of drizzle drops.

The last two columns in Table 18–1 show the supersaturations required to produce condensation on particles of the size indicated in the preceding column. It is seen that hygroscopic particles of the given size require much less supersaturation than do nonhygroscopic nuclei of the same dimensions. For dry hygroscopic nuclei of equivalent spherical diameter of about $10^{-4}$ cm ($1\ \mu$) or larger, growth to droplet size proceeds even though the relative humidity is less than 100 per cent (supersaturation $< 0$). All evidence indicates that in the natural atmosphere supersaturations greater than 0.1 per cent with respect to pure liquid water are not to be expected. Thus hygroscopic particles of a dry equivalent spherical diameter greater than $10^{-5}$ cm ($0.1\ \mu$) must be the prevailing condensation nuclei. In the lower troposphere where most of the above-freezing condensation occurs, there appears to be an ample supply of such nuclei. In the middle troposphere where summer or tropical temperatures may be high enough to permit liquid condensation, particles in the middle of the Aitken-nuclei spectrum may be utilized owing to a shortage of the larger ones. However, the same upward currents that carry water vapor through the troposphere also carry large nuclei, so that regions of shortage of nuclei are likely to be regions of subsidence and dry air.

The extreme supersaturations required in perfectly "clean" air in which exist only the ever-present small ions were first demonstrated by C. T. R. Wilson in 1897. His investigations should have dispelled the erroneous notion that small ions serve as condensation nuclei for clouds, but this idea is sometimes revived even today.

**Solution Effect.** The surface of a nucleus growing into a droplet is not flat and the water is not pure. The equilibrium vapor pressure over such a surface will be affected by the curvature effect and the solution effect. We shall consider these two effects separately and start by discussing the equilibrium over a flat surface of a solution. Later the curvature effect will be studied and the two will be combined to obtain the true equilibrium over a droplet.

Let us consider a solution consisting of $M$ moles of an electrolyte in $M_0$ moles of water. The mole fraction, that is, the ratio of the number of moles of solute to the number of moles of solution, would be $M/(M + M_0)$. If $e$ is the equilibrium vapor pressure over this surface and $e_s$ is that over a pure water surface, both flat, the relative humidity over the solution would be given by Rauolt's law as

$$\frac{e}{e_s} = 1 - \frac{iM}{iM + M_0} \qquad (18\text{--}1)$$

where $i$ is called the van't Hoff factor and is related to the degree of dissociation of the solute in water. To express the relative humidity in percentage the expression is multiplied by 100. It is seen that the equilibrium relative humidity is less than 100 per cent and that its value is determined by the strength of the solution and by the value of $i$. Table 18–2 is an abridged table of the values of the van't Hoff factor $i$ for solutions of sodium chloride. Note that it varies with the molality and with the temperature. Molality is defined as the number of moles of solute in 1000 g of solvent and therefore is closely related to the mole fraction. (The student can find the exact form of the relation.)

TABLE 18–2. VALUES OF THE VAN'T HOFF FACTOR $i$ FOR AQUEOUS
SOLUTIONS OF NaCl OF MOLALITY $M$

| $M$ | $i$ |
|------|------|
| 0.044 | 1.96 |
| 0.2 | 1.82* |
| 1.0 | 1.89 |
| 2.0 | 2.04 |
| 5.0 | 2.66 |

* Minimum.

A growing solution droplet contains $M$ moles of solute, which is a constant determined by the nucleus, but $M_0$, the number of moles of water, increases with the mass of the droplet.

$$M_0 = \frac{\text{mass of droplet}}{\text{molecular weight}} = \frac{\tfrac{4}{3}\pi r^3 \rho_l}{18}$$

where $\rho_l$ is the density of water, assumed constant, so that

$$M_0 = \text{const} \times r^3$$

It is assumed that $M_0$ is a couple of orders of magnitude greater than $M$ so that $M + M_0 \approx M_0$. For example, a nucleus may consist of $10^{-15}$ g of NaCl, molecular weight 58.5, so that $M$ is $1.7 \times 10^{-17}$ while $M_0$ may be in a droplet of 0.5 micron diameter, or $6.3 \times 10^{-14}$ g of water, so that $M_0$ is $3.5 \times 10^{-15}$. We can say that $10^{-15} + 10^{-17} \approx 10^{-15}$ and, since $i$ is between 1 and 2, we can make the simplification

$$\frac{e}{e_s} = 1 - \frac{iM}{M_0}$$

$$= 1 - i\,\frac{\text{const}}{r^3} \qquad (18\text{--}2)$$

The latter is true for a droplet around a specified nucleus. The equilibrium relative humidity is less than 100 per cent by an amount inversely proportional to the cube of the radius. If the expression is differentiated, it is found that the equilibrium relative humidity increases at a rate inversely proportional to the fourth power of the radius. Thus in a growing drop the equilibrium value increases very rapidly at first, then more slowly.

**The Curvature Effect.** The occurrence of a greater vapor tension over a curved liquid surface than over a flat one is related to the surface tension. Intermolecular forces in the liquid hold the liquid together and at the surface boundary these forces are unbalanced owing to the absence of molecules beyond the surface, so the molecules are pulled back and there is a tendency for the surface to contract. In order to increase the free surface of a liquid, work must be done. Thus to make a flat surface into a curved one requires work.

The surface tension is defined as the work per unit area done in extending the surface of the liquid at constant temperature. Since work is the product of a force and the distance through which it acts, work per unit area is in the units of force per unit length. If, as in Fig. 18–1, a line of unit length is drawn, surface $A$ on one side of the line pulls the surface $B$ on the other side with a force of $\sigma$ dynes. On a sphere, a circumference line or great circle divides the surface into the two parts, so

$$\sigma = \frac{F}{L} = \frac{F}{2\pi r} \qquad (18\text{--}3)$$

But $F = pA$, where $A$ is the area enclosed by the circumference, so

$$\sigma = \frac{pA}{2\pi r} = \frac{\pi r^2 p}{2\pi r} = \frac{rp}{2} \qquad (18\text{--}4)$$

The pressure in this case is that used in shrinking or stretching the surface of the sphere.

If a droplet is to grow, it can do so by having water vapor condense on it to form the added volume of water $dv$. By comparison with the volume occupied by the vapor, the condensed volume may be regarded as zero. To arrive at the effect of the curvature on the condensation, we equate the work of the water vapor contracting from volume $v$ to zero to the work of the droplet in expanding its outer film of water. Equilibrium will exist when the two are equal.

The work of contracting the specific volume of the vapor from $v$ to $0$, is given by

$$\int_0^v e \, dv \qquad (18\text{--}5)$$

The process is considered to be adiabatic and isothermal, so the work also is expressed by

$$\int_{e_s}^{e} v \, de = \int_{e_s}^{e} \frac{1}{\rho_w} de = \int_{e_s}^{e} \frac{RT}{m_w} \frac{de}{e} = \frac{RT}{m_w} \int_{e_s}^{e} \frac{de}{e}$$
$$= \frac{RT}{m_w} \ln \frac{e}{e_s} \tag{18-6}$$

The work in stretching the outer film of water is given by the change in volume of unit mass at constant pressure, or by

$$\int_{0}^{v} p \, dv = pv = \frac{p}{\rho_l} \tag{18-7}$$

where $\rho_l$ is the density of water. Equating these two work expressions, we have

$$\frac{RT}{m_w} \ln \frac{e}{e_s} = \frac{p}{\rho_l} \tag{18-8}$$

The $p$ is the same as in the surface-tension equation (18–4), so the substitution is made to obtain

$$\ln \frac{e}{e_s} = \frac{2\sigma m_w}{r \rho_l RT} \tag{18-9}$$

Since all terms are positive, it is clear that the equilibrium relative humidity over a droplet of pure water must be greater than 100 per cent ($e/e_s > 1$). The surface tension and the density of water vary slightly with temperature only. If the temperature is constant, the natural logarithm of the vapor-pressure ratio is inversely proportional to the radius only, so that as $r$ becomes larger $e$ decreases toward the value of $e_s$.

It can be shown that in a strong electric field the charge carried on the surface of a drop might have an effect on the equilibrium vapor pressure over the drop. It turns out that this effect is important only when the drop is very large.

**Combined Effects.** The equilibrium vapor pressure over a solution droplet is obtained by applying the two equations in succession. If the equilibrium over a flat surface of the solution is computed first, that value is used for the $e_s$ in obtaining the higher $e$ resulting from the curvature. Conversely, one can compute the value over a pure droplet, then use that as the $e_s$ in the Raoult equation.

Equilibrium values for a pure water droplet, for a bulk salt (NaCl) solution of a given initial concentration, and for a droplet of the same concentration are plotted against size in Fig. 18–2. The solution is considered to be diluted with water in the same way as a growing droplet, so the scale of droplet size, which is the abscissa in this figure, is related to the diluteness of the solution. To magnify the effects, only the portions of the curves near saturation are represented in the figure. The initial dry salt nucleus is taken as having an equivalent spherical diameter of $10^{-4}$ cm or 1 micron, thus falling in the class of large condensation nuclei such as produce most cloud condensation. If a smaller initial nucleus were taken, the curve would have a higher peak above the saturation line and if one were chosen ten times larger than is shown, there would be no point above the saturation line.

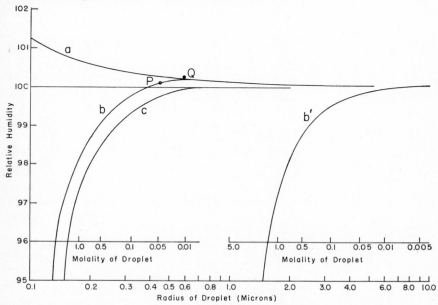

Fig. 18–2. Equilibrium relative humidity over (a) a pure droplet, (b,b') solution droplets of 0.1 μ and 1 μ initial radii, and (c) bulk solution having the same molality as (b).

If the salt nucleus b were placed in an environment having a relative humidity of 100.1 per cent it would grow to the size represented by the point P and remain in equilibrium at that size. A relative humidity at Q of 100.3 per cent would be higher than the maximum equilibrium value for this droplet. Under this condition it would never reach equilibrium and would keep right on growing. As it became larger and purer its equilibrium vapor pressure would decrease, so in this supersaturated environment it would be growing at an accelerated rate. Actually this growth does not go on indefinitely; the droplet must compete with other droplets and nuclei for the available water. From the maximum point of the curve, it is seen that the critical relative humidity for the growth of this droplet to the usual cloud droplet size of from 10 to 20 microns diameter would be 100.23 per cent.

The rates of growth will be taken up in the next section. They can be quite fast. The droplet represented in the figure probably would reach a diameter of 20 microns in less than a second. By the time this droplet has reached a diameter of about 2 microns its solution is so weak that it may be considered pure water.

**Growth and Evaporation of Drops.** As pointed out in Chap. 14 [Eq. (14–3)], the flux of water vapor in the direction $x$ by diffusion in air is given by

$$E = -D \frac{\partial \rho_w}{\partial x}$$

where $D$ is the diffusivity of water vapor in air. The flux in a radial direction outward from a drop (evaporation) would be given by

$$E = -D \frac{\partial \rho_w}{\partial r} \tag{18–10}$$

and the growth of the drop by diffusion would be given by

$$\frac{dM}{dt} = DA \frac{\partial \rho_w}{\partial r} = 4\pi r^2 D \frac{\partial \rho_w}{\partial r} \tag{18–11}$$

The area of the drop is included since flux is defined for unit area. The positive sign indicates that the mass of the drop increases when the vapor density increases radially outward from the drop.

It is reasonable to assume that the vapor gradient is symmetrical around the drop and to use ordinary instead of partial derivatives. We can then integrate the expression. At the boundary of the drop we set $r = r$ and $\rho_w = \rho_{0w}$. In the ambient space we may assume that $r = \infty$ since the distance to where the ambient vapor density $\rho_w = \rho_w$ prevails is infinitely large when compared with the radius of the drop. In the integration it is proper to assume a steady-state growth so that $dM/dt$ is constant. We multiply both sides of Eq. (18–11) by $dr/r^2$ and form the integrals

$$\frac{dM}{dt} \int_r^\infty \frac{dr}{r^2} = 4\pi D \int_{\rho_{0w}}^{\rho_w} d\rho_w \tag{18–12}$$

which results in

$$\frac{dM}{dt} = 4\pi Dr(\rho_w - \rho_{0w}) \tag{18–13}$$

The growth of the spherical drop by a shell thickness $dr$ is

$$\frac{dM}{dt} = \rho_l \, 4\pi r^2 \frac{dr}{dt} \tag{18–14}$$

Equating the last two equations, one finds

$$r \, dr = \frac{D}{\rho_l} \, (\rho_w - \rho_{0w}) \, dt \tag{18-15}$$

From $t = 0$ to $t = t$, $r$ goes from $r_0$ to $r$, so the integration is

$$\int_{r_0}^{r} r \, dr = \frac{D}{\rho_l} \, (\rho_w - \rho_{0w}) \int_{0}^{t} dt \tag{18-16}$$

resulting in

$$r^2 = r_0{}^2 + \frac{2D}{\rho_l} \, (\rho_w - \rho_{0w}) t \tag{18-17}$$

By substitution from the equation of state, the relation can be expressed in terms of vapor pressure as

$$r^2 = r_0{}^2 + \frac{2D m_w}{\rho_l R} \left( \frac{e}{T} - \frac{e_0}{T_0} \right) t \tag{18-18}$$

The $e_0$ is the saturation vapor pressure at the temperature $T_0$ of the surface of the droplet and $e$ and $T$ are the ambient vapor pressure and temperature.

The differential equation (18-15) and its integral (18-17) govern the growth or evaporation and the size of a droplet after it has reached the size where neither the solution nor the curvature effects have any importance. If the vapor pressure in the environment is greater than at the surface of the droplet, it will grow, but if the ambient vapor pressure is less, the part in parentheses is negative in conformance with the condition of evaporation. It can be seen from these expressions that the change in size for a given moisture gradient is greatest for the smaller droplets.

If the drops are so large that they have an appreciable rate of fall with respect to the air (see next section for rate-of-fall data), a ventilation effect caused by the air's moving past the drop will alter the rate of diffusion of water vapor to or from it. In the case of growth, diffusion is important only for the cloud droplets which have no appreciable fall velocity, the larger ones growing mainly by collisions and coalescence with others, as will be shown presently. In the evaporation of raindrops the ventilation effect may be important.

There is an important heat-transfer effect which cannot be neglected in any case. The condensation or evaporation involve the addition or removal of latent heat from the evironment. In a steady state the latent heat added in unit time is given to each droplet and is expressed, after the manner of Eq. (8-22) of Chap. 8, by

$$L \frac{dM}{dt} \tag{18-19}$$

Sensible heat is conducted to the droplet in the same way that water vapor is diffused to it, so we have a similar expression. In place of the diffusivity of water vapor $D$, we use the thermal diffusivity, also called thermometric conductivity $\kappa$. Heat is expressed in the usual way by the product of mass times specific heat times temperature. Like the equation (18–13) for the diffusion of matter to the droplet, the conduction of heat to the droplet is

$$\frac{dQ}{dt} = 4\pi \rho r \, \kappa \, c_p(T_0 - T) \qquad (18\text{–}20)$$

or, with the more commonly used thermal conductivity $K = \rho c_p \kappa$, we may write

$$\frac{dQ}{dt} = 4\pi r K(T_0 - T) \qquad (18\text{–}21)$$

The latent-heat exchange is balanced by the conduction of sensible heat. We substitute the value of $dM/dt$ in Eq. (18–13) into Eq. (18–19) and equate (18–19) to (18–21), obtaining

$$LD4\pi r(\rho_w - \rho_{0w}) = 4\pi r K(T_0 - T)$$
$$\frac{\rho_w - \rho_{0w}}{T_0 - T} = \frac{K}{DL} \qquad (18\text{–}22)$$

Values for the coefficients on the right can be obtained from tables such as the Smithsonian Meteorological Tables. They vary slightly with temperature and $D$ also varies with pressure.

Since the quantites on the right in Eq. (18–22) are always positive, the numerator and denominator on the left must be of the same sign. Thus when the droplet is growing ($\rho_w - \rho_{0w} > 0$), it must be warmer than the environment, and during evaporation it must be colder. This, of course, is in agreement with the known thermodynamics of the latent-heat exchange. Note that the temperature and vapor-density gradients are always opposed.

By substitution from the equation of state the expression can be written in terms of vapor pressure in the form

$$\frac{e/T - e_0/T_0}{T_0 - T} = \frac{e - e_0 T/T_0}{T(T_0 - T)} = \frac{KR}{DLm_w} \qquad (18\text{–}23)$$

or, within an error of 1 per cent,

$$\frac{e - e_0}{T(T_0 - T)} = -\frac{\Delta e}{T \, \Delta T} = \frac{KR}{DLm_w} \qquad (18\text{–}24)$$

The negative $\Delta e/\Delta T$ signifies that the gradients are opposite.

The saturation vapor pressure is a complicated function of the temperature and is derived from tables. The fitting of $\Delta T$ to the $\Delta e$ to satisfy the relation can be done by trial and error. For example, suppose that $T$ and $e$, the ambient temperature and vapor pressure, are given and it is desired to find $e_0$ and $T_0$, hence $\Delta e$, so that from Eq. (18–18) $r^2 - r_0^2$ can be determined after a brief time $t$. An $e_0$ and its corresponding $T_0$ must be found that will satisfy the relation. The resulting values are then substituted in Eq. (18–18).

**Growth by Coalescence.** Several factors inhibit the growth of droplets to very large sizes by diffusion. It is generally recognized that the growth to raindrop sizes is accomplished by other means. Equation (18–15) shows that for a given gradient of vapor, $dr/dt$ is inversely proportional to $r$ and Eq. (18–14) expresses the fact that for any sphere the ratio of $dr/dt$ to $dM/dt$ is proportional to $1/r^2$. Furthermore, the rate of transfer of latent heat to the drop depends on $dM/dt$, so that for a given increment of radius, more heat is added as the drop grows larger, thus causing a greater reduction of the vapor gradient. Finally, unless there is rapid adiabatic expansion in a cloud updraft, the excess water vapor is used up and the cloud approaches exact saturation equilibrium.

As a result of these limiting factors, most cloud and fog droplets have radii of less than about 20 $\mu$ ($2 \times 10^{-3}$ cm), with a peak frequency of droplets of somewhere between 1 and 10 $\mu$ radius. Thus the vast majority of clouds do not produce rain.

Growth to raindrops might be expected by collision and coalescence of cloud droplets. It is observed that such an effect does not occur in the usual cloud or fog conditions. In a shower bath or steam room intense condensation may occur and although water may be running down the cool walls and windows there is apparently little or no coalescence of drops in the air and there is a great uniformity in size. As more and more condensation occurs, the supersaturated vapor goes toward the formation of more droplets of the same size as those already predominant rather than causing the growth of larger droplets.

Collision and coalescence could conceivably be caused by irregular relative motions similar to Brownian movements or very small-scale turbulence. Knowledge and experience of the mid-twentieth century has indicated no appreciable effect of this kind. Another possibility is the effect of electrical attraction between droplets. It can be demonstrated in the laboratory that colliding drops have a better chance of coalescing when they are in an appreciable electric field than when there is no space charge, but the collisions themselves depend on relative motions among the droplets, which would not be found in clouds consisting of uniformly small droplets. The only important way in which collisions can occur is through the relative motions of the droplets in the gravitational field of the earth. The velocity of fall of the drops, the so-called *terminal* velocity, depends on the drop size as will now be shown.

In a medium having a certain viscosity, such as the air, motion under the acceleration of gravity reaches a fixed terminal velocity defined as that velocity attained when the inertial forces are equal to the viscous or resistance forces $F = F_r$. Under the acceleration of gravity, the inertial force is the buoyancy force, or for spherical drops,

$$F = \tfrac{4}{3}\pi\rho_l r^3 g - \tfrac{4}{3}\pi\rho r^3 g \tag{18-25}$$

where the first term is the force or weight of the sphere in a vacuum and the second term is the weight of the displaced air, or the air buoyancy. Separating the common factors, we obtain

$$F = \tfrac{4}{3}\pi(\rho_l - \rho)r^3 g \tag{18-26}$$

From fluid mechanics the resistance force on a sphere can be calculated, but the result only will be given here; it is as follows:

$$F_r = 6\pi\mu rvN \tag{18-27}$$

where $\mu$ is the molecular viscosity of the medium (air) and $v$ is the relative speed of the sphere and the medium. $N$ is a quantity involving two parameters—the *drag coefficient* $C_d$ and a nondimensional number $Re$, much used in hydrodynamics, called the *Reynolds number*—such that

$$N = \frac{C_d Re}{24} \tag{18-28}$$

Since the viscosity $\mu$ has the dimensions $g \ cm^{-1} \ sec^{-1}$, it is apparent from Eq. (18-27) that $N$ is nondimensional, and, in fact, $Re$ and $C_d$ are both nondimensional.

For droplets of radius up to 40 $\mu$, $Re = 24/C_d$ and $N = 1$, so in that size range

$$F_r = 6\pi\mu rv \tag{18-29}$$

This relation is known as Stokes' law and the size range through which it applies is known as the Stokes'-law range.

To obtain the terminal velocity $v_T$ we equate the inertial and resistance forces and obtain for the Stokes'-law range

$$\tfrac{4}{3}\pi(\rho_l - \rho)r^3 g = 6\pi\mu rv_T$$
$$v_T = \frac{2}{9}\frac{\rho_l - \rho}{\mu}gr^2 \tag{18-30}$$

Outside this range the factor $1/N$ appears on the right, but in practice it is better to use experimentally determined values for drops with radii

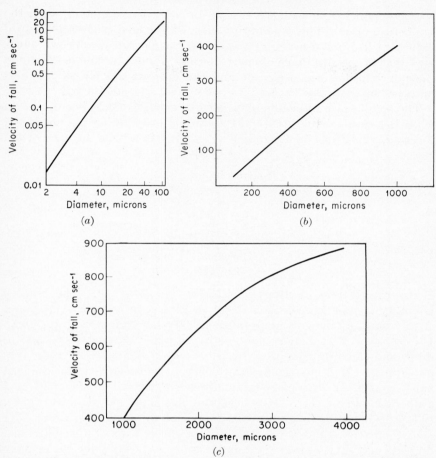

FIG. 18–3. Velocity of fall of droplets of various diameters. In (a) the droplets fall in accordance with Stokes' law. The values in (b) and (c) were determined experimentally in still air near normal temperature and pressure by Gunn and Kinzer (*see reference*). The sizes are computed from the mass to give an equivalent diameter, assuming a spherical mass. At sizes in the upper ranges of curve (c) it is known that the drops are markedly nonspherical.

greater than 40 $\mu$, such as the values obtained by Gunn and Kinzer.[1] The values are reproduced in the Smithsonian Meteorological Tables.

Terminal velocities as a function of drop diameters are plotted in Fig. 18–3. In (a) the droplets fall in accordance with Stokes' law. The values in (b) and (c) were determined by Gunn and Kinzer in still air near normal temperature and pressure. The sizes of the larger drops

[1] Gunn, R., and G. D. Kinzer, *J. Meteorol.*, vol. 6, p. 243, 1949.

were computed from the mass to give an equivalent diameter, assuming a spherical mass. The larger drops are known to be nonspherical, shaped somewhat like round loaves of bread with the flat side downward. It is seen that in the size range of cloud droplets, from 2 to 40 $\mu$ in diameter, the fall velocities are negligible and the droplets are for all practical purposes suspended in the air.

The significance of clouds as suspended small droplets is emphasized when the terminal velocities and the rates of evaporation are considered together. In Table 18–3, computed by Findeisen,[1] the distance of fall

TABLE 18–3. DISTANCE OF FALL BEFORE EVAPORATION
(Computed by Findeisen)

| Radius of drop, cm | Distance of fall before evaporation | |
|---|---|---|
| 0.0001 | $3.3 \times 10^{-4}$ cm | } Cloud particles |
| 0.001 | 3.3 cm | |
| 0.01 | 150 m | |
| 0.10 | 42 km | } Raindrops |
| 0.25 | 280 km | |

before evaporation of drops of various sizes is given. The relative humidity is assumed constant at 90 per cent, a reasonable value under cloud bases, and the pressure is taken as 900 mb with temperature of 5°C. It is apparent that there is more reason for differentiating between raindrops and cloud droplets than the mere fact of difference in size. It is also apparent that any cloud with the usual atmospheric turbulence in it must consist of droplets continually being formed in one part and evaporating in another. In a small cumulus cloud it is doubtful that a collection of water molecules can remain in the form of a droplet for more than a few minutes. In a stable atmosphere with stratus, individual droplets may exist as such for many minutes or possibly for one or more hours.

From the data on terminal velocities it is possible to obtain an impression of the spectrum of sizes that would be required in a cloud for collisions to occur. It is seen that in a cloud with droplets mainly of 10 $\mu$ diameter, a drop measuring somewhere between 40 and 100 $\mu$ in diameter would have a fair chance of colliding with some of the smaller ones if the latter were of the order of 1 cm apart. The computation of the collision-coalescence effects on drop growth will now be considered.

Let $r_i$ be the radii of cloud droplets of various small sizes. The mass of liquid water in a unit volume of air containing $n_i$ droplets is

$$\chi = \tfrac{4}{3}\pi \sum_i n_i r_i^3 \qquad (18\text{--}31)$$

[1] Findeisen, W., *Meteorol. Z.*, vol. 56, p. 453, 1939.

A larger drop of radius $r$ falling distance $dz$ through this collection of droplets sweeps out a cylindrical volume

$$dV = \pi r^2 \, dz = \pi r^2 v_T \, dt \qquad (18\text{--}32)$$

and sweeps out a mass of water $\chi \, dV$, or

$$dM' = \chi \, dV = \chi \pi r^2 v_T \, dt \qquad (18\text{--}33)$$

where $dM'$ is the mass of water contained in the droplets of radius $r_i$ occupying the volume $dV$. If all of these droplets struck the larger falling drop and coalesced with it, $dM'$ would also represent the increase in mass of the drop. However, some of the droplets in the cylindrical volume are carried around the falling drop by the air stream and others bounce off after striking. Only a fraction $E$ of the droplets is collected, so we multiply by this fraction, calling it the *collection efficiency*, to obtain the growth of the drop by accretion in the form:

$$dM = \chi E \pi r^2 v_T \, dt \qquad (18\text{--}34)$$

This produces an additional spherical shell of growth having thickness $dr$ on the drop such that

$$dM = 4\pi \rho_l r^2 \, dr \qquad (18\text{--}35)$$

This value of $dM$ is substituted on the left in Eq. (18–34) and the expression is solved for $dr/dt$, resulting in

$$\frac{dr}{dt} = \frac{E\chi v_T}{4\rho_l} \qquad (18\text{--}36)$$

This equation is deceiving in its simplicity. A major effort in cloud physics is devoted to the determination of the collection efficiency $E$. Analytical and experimental approaches have both been used but there are some conflicting data. The efficiency is greatly increased by the presence of an electric field of a strength slightly greater than that occurring in fair weather. Analytically the collection efficiency can be shown to depend on a factor involving the ratio of the square of the radius of the small droplets to the first power of the radius of the larger drop, indicating that the size of the collected droplets is more critical than the size of the falling drop. Of course, $v_T$ is dependent on the radius of the falling drop, so the growth rate is not necessarily the fastest where the collection efficiency is the greatest.

The development of rain in clouds appears to result from accretion in many cases. It is believed that the giant nuclei, which, as pointed out earlier in this chapter, can have diameters of from 50 to 100 $\mu$ at relative humidities of 99 per cent, provide enough large drops having fall velocities of about 8 to 27 cm per sec to collect the droplets until raindrop sizes are reached. The process is favored by thick clouds and sustained updrafts so that the drop can grow quite large before falling out of the bottom of the cloud.

**Growth in Mixed Clouds.** As already stated in Chap. 8, undercooled water, i.e., water in the liquid phase at temperatures well below freezing, is a common occurrence in clouds. Undercooling to $-5$ or $-10°C$ is to be expected in nearly all clouds within that temperature range. Liquid droplets at $-20$ to $-30°C$ are not uncommon, and cases of natural undercooled clouds at temperatures approaching $-40°C$ have been reported. The undercooling involves not only droplets condensed at above-freezing temperatures and carried to the colder altitudes but also new condensation in the liquid form occurring at subfreezing temperatures. It is not difficult to demonstrate in the laboratory that, although water maintains a temperature of $0°C$ while freezing, undisturbed bulk water can be cooled at least a degree or so below the nominal freezing point before forming ice. When it starts to freeze its temperature will rise to $0°C$ and will remain at that value until the freezing is completed.

A laboratory experiment on drops of water will produce much greater undercooling than is possible with bulk water. A convenient procedure is to float the drops at the interface between two liquids, one heavier and one lighter than water, e.g., carbon tetrachloride and Silicone oil. The drops are sprayed to the surface of the oil with an atomizer, then sink through the oil, coming to rest at the interface. The drops are thus at a place where the temperature can be easily measured with a thermocouple and a microscope can be focused on them. The container is cooled in dry ice and a microphotograph is taken when the temperature reaches $-5$, $-10$, $-15$, etc. From their appearance, the frozen drops are clearly distinguishable from the unfrozen ones. It is found that the largest drops freeze first and that the smaller the drop, the lower the temperature will be at which it freezes. In all cases, undercooling to a much lower temperature than is possible in bulk water is noted. Figure 18–4 shows the results of such an experiment conducted by this author's colleagues.

In both the bulk-water and water-drop cases, the freezing can be started immediately by shaking or by otherwise disturbing the water. This effect is important in the formation of ice on airplanes or on stationary objects on windy mountain tops. As the undercooled droplets strike the airplane or other object, they freeze, usually as rime, into an icy mass (see hydrometeors, Chap. 4).

Let us now examine the humidity conditions in an undercooled water cloud. If such a cloud is to maintain itself, the relative humidity must be at least 100 per cent or a fraction of a percentage higher. This relative humidity is that with respect to water. With respect to ice in this cloud there would be supersaturation, as a glance at Table 8–1 shows, for the saturation vapor pressure over water at subfreezing temperatures is greater than that over ice.   The difference is maximum at a temperature of about −11.5°C, but since the relative humidity with respect to

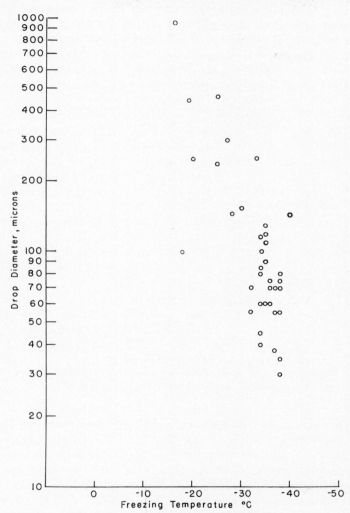

FIG. 18–4. Freezing temperatures of drops of various sizes in a typical experiment

ice would be given by $e_{sw}/e_{si}$, where the subscripts refer to saturation over water and ice, respectively, the percentage of supersaturation increases steadily with decreasing temperature.   Figure 18–5 shows curves of the vapor-pressure difference and of the relative humidity with respect to ice corresponding to 100 per cent with respect to water, plotted as a function of temperature.

It is significant that ice crystals do not usually form naturally in clouds unless the supersaturation with respect to ice is of the order of 10 per cent. This behavior is quite different from that of water condensation where supersaturations of less than 1 per cent suffice. This difference suggests that the atmosphere does not have nucleating agents as suitable for ice as for water. The subject of natural and artificial ice-nucleating substances will be treated in later paragraphs. Furthermore, a discussion of the minutiae of ice-crystal growth will be found on subsequent pages.

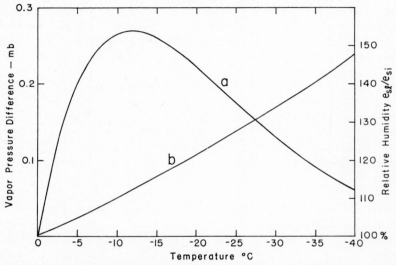

FIG. 18–5. Vapor-pressure difference for water − ice (curve a), and relative humidity at water saturation (curve b) measured with respect to ice saturation, i.e., $e_{s\ \text{liquid}}$ divided by $e_{s\ \text{ice}}$.

For the sake of the present discussion we need only say that the growth of an ice crystal is by diffusion, at a rate depending upon the gradient of vapor concentration between the ambient cloudy air and the immediate boundary layer of the crystal, in much the same manner as in the diffusion growth of a droplet. In cloudy air in a typical under-cooled condition, let us say of temperature −10 to −20°C, the first ice crystals to be formed would be in an environment with a relative humidity of 100 ± 1 per cent with respect to liquid water. At these temperatures this would mean a relative humidity with respect to ice of 110.0 to 121.5 per cent, so the crystals would be in a strongly supersaturated environment. Their rate of growth would accordingly be very fast. As vapor diffused to the crystals, the ambient vapor concentration would diminish to less than the equilibrium value for the droplets. The latter would then start evaporating and we would have a steady state for a while in which water would evaporate from the droplets, move in the vapor form to the crystals, and condense or crystallize there. As long as the crystals remained in a cloud which was predominantly water, they would grow, at least until all the water was used up. Meanwhile some would have attained a size large enough to fall out as snow or, on reaching warm levels, would melt into raindrops.

The process of the formation of snow and rain in mixed liquid and ice clouds is sometimes called the Bergeron process or Bergeron-Findeisen process after its discoverer and principal investigator, respectively.[1,2] Meteorologists accepted the theory enthusiastically and for a few years believed that this was the only way rain could form outside the tropics, but the coalescence process in warm clouds is now known to be of almost equal importance. Once the rain has started to fall, coalescence, or *accretion* as it is sometimes called, is the only important way in which the raindrops or snowflakes can grow. In the case of snowflakes the collisions can be with other snowflakes to form a clumped mass or with under-cooled droplets to form rimed snowflakes or snow pellets. In most situations the great bulk of water reaching the ground has been picked up by the falling precipitation as it passes through the lower portions of clouds or through lower cloud layers not attached to the generating layer.

**Ice Nucleation.** From the preceding discussion it is apparent that the nucleating agents for ice crystals require a considerable degree of super-saturation of vapor with respect to ice before they can become effective. This fact is borne out by laboratory experiments. Tests on undercooled clouds made by blowing steam or one's breath into a frozen-food chest were conducted extensively by Schaefer[3] who found that the temperature "threshold" for the first appearance of ice crystals in the undercooled clouds depends upon the kind of particles available in the air for nucleating. In fairly clean laboratory air it was discovered that no ice crystals would form until the temperature reached $-39$ or $-40°C$. This was subsequently called the *Schaefer point* or *temperature of spontaneous nucleation*, suggesting that at this temperature crystallization will occur regardless of nuclei. Schaefer tested some natural dusts in the cold box. Dust from a loam at Rugby, North Dakota, had its threshold of activity as a nucleating agent at $-8°C$ and became "completely" active at

[1] Bergeron, T., On the Physics of Cloud and Precipitation, *Mem. de l'Union Géodésique et Géophysique Internationale*, Lisbon, 1933.

[2] Findeisen, W., Die kolloidmeteorologischen Vorgänge der Niederschlagsbildung, *Meteorol. Z.*, vol. 55, p. 121, 1938.

[3] Schaefer, V. J., *Science*, vol. 104, p. 457, 1946.

−25°C. Certain soils, clays, and sands are slightly active at −10 to −15°C, but many have thresholds of activity below −15 or −20°C. For spores the threshold is at about −36°C.

A variety of cold boxes for measuring the ice-nucleating temperature thresholds in various parts of the natural atmosphere, at the surface and aloft, have been devised. The measurements show that there is a variation from day to day and from place to place. In one situation ice crystals will be seen glittering in the box after a cooling to only about −5°C and on other occasions the temperature may have to reach −30°C before the first crystals appear. Ordinary condensation nuclei, particularly the larger ones, appear to be active as ice nuclei after a certain amount of undercooling.

Impressed by the seeming inadequacy of ice nucleation in natural clouds, Langmuir and Schaefer[1] considered the possibility of hastening the process artificially. They recognized that this would also induce precipitation by the Bergeron process in undercooled clouds. They successfully demonstrated two ways of doing this. One way is to drop very cold particles, such as pellets of solid $CO_2$, into the clouds from an airplane. Along the path of fall of the pellets a momentary cooling to the Schaefer point or lower occurs, and narrow streaks of ice crystals are created in the cloud. The spread of ice crystals through the cloud is extremely rapid, once a few are created. When a dry-ice pellet is dropped into a fogged cold chamber of about ten cubic feet in size, crystals are found throughout the volume in about three minutes. In atmospheric clouds the process is helped by eddy diffusion. Crystals once produced act as nucleating agents themselves to infect other parts of the cloud.

The crystal-to-crystal nucleation process is well known in laboratory and industrial chemistry. In fact, the effect can be created by crystals that differ slightly from those to be nucleated. Langmuir, Schaefer, et al.,[2] recognized the similarity between water and silver iodide in the crystalline state. The two principal lattice constants of ice, in angstrom units, are 4.53 and 7.41 while the corresponding ones for silver iodide are 4.58 and 7.49. Both crystals have hexagonal symmetry. Other substances such as lead iodide, cadmium iodide, and quartz have similar crystal configurations but not resembling ice as closely as in the case of silver iodide. By test in the cold box, silver iodide was found to have a nucleating threshold temperature of −4°C and to be completely active at −10°C. This is the highest threshold temperature of any of the nucleating agents tested, except, of course, ice crystals themselves.

Since it is not practical to create and handle real ice crystals for

[1] Langmuir, I., V. J. Schaefer, et al., General Electric Research Laboratory, *Project Cirrus Progr. Repts.*, Schenectady, New York, 1947–1951.
[2] *Ibid.*

artificially stimulated nucleation, silver iodide makes a good substitute. It can be spread into the atmosphere as an aerosol made by a crude type of smoke generator.  Its advantage over the dry-ice method lies in the fact that it can be spread upward by the air currents, and under favorable conditions, clouds may be nucleated from generators located on the ground.  Commercial and public rain-stimulation ventures are usually based on this principle.  The effectiveness of these ventures in increasing the precipitation will not be discussed here.  The interested student can find literature[1] on the subject, some of it controversial.

With the emphasis on rainmaking, less attention has been attracted to another aspect of artificial nucleation, namely, the artificial dissipation of stratified cloud layers.  By dispersing dry ice or silver iodide smoke into an undercooled, stable, stratified cloud layer, the undercooled droplets can be changed to ice crystals which will settle out and leave a clear area.  Dry ice is best, because it is active at temperatures nearer freezing and because the atmosphere with stratus clouds is not favorable for the vertical transport from the ground by air currents.  An airplane flying along the top of such an undercooled cloud layer, dispensing dry-ice pellets at a rate of several pounds per mile, can make a rift in the clouds that will grow to a width of a mile or more in 20 or 30 min, remaining that way for a similar period of time.  The usefulness of this technique in clearing airport approach areas in certain winter conditions is obvious.

In warm clouds, such as warm-weather cumulus with updrafts in them, the rain mechanism can be artificially initiated by spraying water in the cloud from an airplane flying through it.  Spray drops from 50 to 100 microns in diameter coalesce with the cloud droplets to form raindrops. By the time these drops reach a diameter of 5 to 7 mm they split into several drops, all of which, in turn, coalesce with cloud droplets to multiply the process many times.  Tests by the Chicago group[2] made in tropical cumulus clouds in the Caribbean area show conclusively that light rains can be initiated in this manner.  An updraft in the clouds is necessary in order to give the water drops a long enough residence time in the cloud to acquire an appreciable amount of water by accretion.

**Growth of Ice Crystals.**   After nucleation, ice crystals grow in a supersaturated environment by diffusion of water vapor to them in essentially the same way as water droplets do.   The basic crystal shape is hexagonal and no matter how large it grows its appearance will reflect that basic

[1] For example, the pamphlet "Cloud Physics and Rainmaking" by the Department of Meteorology, University of Chicago, 1957.

[2] Braham, R. R., Jr., L. J. Battan, and H. R. Byers, Artificial Nucleation of Cumulus Clouds *in* Cloud and Weather Modification, *Am. Meteorol. Soc. Monographs*, vol. 2, 1957.

pattern, so long as no nondiffusive processes such as accretion or clumping have complicated its structure. Lacking the radial symmetry of a sphere, the crystal cannot be governed in its growth precisely by Eq. (18–17), which is for a sphere, for there is the well-known tendency for it to grow much more in one plane than in others to form the familiar flake or, on some occasions, column or needle structures.

It is not possible to measure the water-vapor distribution in minute detail around an ice crystal, but from observed crystal-growth habits and by analogy with similar situations encountered in physics, an asymmetrical distribution of water vapor around these shapes can be inferred.

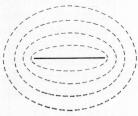

The best-known analogous situation is that of an electrical condenser in an electrical field in air. The heavy horizontal line in Fig. 18–6 represents an edge-on view of a condenser in the form of a circular disk of infinitesimal thickness. The dashed lines are lines of equal electrical potential in the air around the condenser. The surface of the condenser must be a surface of constant potential, yet at a considerable distance away from the condenser the equipotential surfaces must become spherical. The condensing plate thus distorts the field in such a manner that the equipotential surfaces are more crowded near the edges than they are over the surfaces of the condenser. In other words the potential gradient is greater at the edges.

FIG. 18–6. Equipotential lines around a disk represented in the plane perpendicular to the plane of the disk.

By analogy we can consider in place of the condenser a thin plate of ice with the vapor tension $\rho_{0w}$ on its surface. The dashed lines may then represent different values of the vapor density with the outermost one corresponding to the "ambient" value $\rho_w$. In the electrical analogy the flow of current to or from the condenser is proportional to, among other things, the capacity of the condenser, which is a function only of its geometry. For a sphere, the capacity is $r$, the radius of the sphere. The diffusion of water vapor to a snow crystal thus can be represented as in Eq. (18–13) if we substitute the capacity $C$ for $r$, in the form

$$\frac{dM}{dt} = 4\pi DC(\rho_w - \rho_{0w}) \qquad (18\text{–}37)$$

To obtain size corresponding to this increase in mass, the shape and average density must be known.

The values of $C$ have been tabulated only for the simplest of geometrical forms, but they can be assumed to apply to other actual shapes that are not too dissimilar. For example, a hexagonal plate may be assumed to have the capacity of a circular plate without large error. For

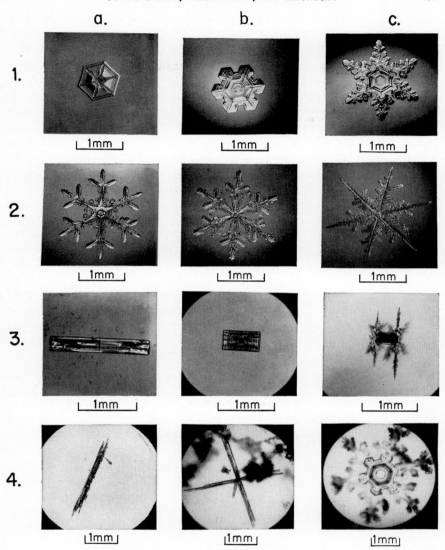

Fig. 18–7. Microphotographs of some of the elementary forms of ice crystals: 1a, b, c, hexagonal plates showing some growth at corners in b and c; 2a, b, c, dendritic forms; 3a, b, columns; 3c, capped column, shown in end view in 4c; 4a, b, needles. (*Photographs 1a through 3a by Mr. Kazuhiko Itagaki; 3b through 4c by Dr. Ukichiro Nakaya.*)

a disk the capacitance is $2r\pi^{-1}$ and for an ellipsoid of revolution it is given by

$$\frac{\epsilon L \ln (1 + \epsilon)}{1 + \epsilon}$$

where $\epsilon$ is the eccentricity and $L$ is the length of the major axis.

The hexagonal plate is the most common small snow crystal in the laboratory as well as in the atmosphere. If the equipotential surfaces are considered around a hexagon, it stands to reason that the greatest concentration of these surfaces would be in the vicinity of the six corners illustrated in Fig. 18–7. This being the case, one would expect the greatest growth to occur at these corners to produce star-shaped or dendritic (branched) forms. While these shapes are common in snow crystals, there are others which must be accounted for. Marshall and Langleben[1] suggested that because of curvature effects, as in the case of droplets, the vapor tension of the crystal is higher at edges and corners than on the flat faces, meaning that $\rho_{0w}$ is least on the faces. Our "condenser," then, is not an equipotential surface.

From this circumstance it would be expected that plates, stars, and dendrites would grow when the ambient vapor density $\rho_w$ showed the greatest supersaturation, so that minor differences in $\rho_{0w}$ would not have a critical effect on the difference $\rho_w - \rho_{0w}$. The greater vapor gradient at the corners and edges would then more than compensate for the higher vapor tension of the crystal at these locations. Work of Nakaya[2] and others points toward a predominance of these forms at the temperatures at which the difference between the saturation vapor density over water and over ice is at a maximum. In Nakaya's laboratory experiments, however, temperature seems to be more important than supersaturation in determining the growth habit, since a given type of crystal can be obtained over a wide range of supersaturation. Shaw and Mason[3] obtained results which indicate that the growth of crystal faces is not determined solely by the ambient conditions but partly by certain characteristics of the faces themselves which control the incorporation of molecules into the crystal.

Depending on the part of the crystal upon which the main growth occurs, the following general types of snow crystals are seen:

1. Uniform growth around the *perimeter*, producing hexagonal plates without noticeable extensions at the corners but in some cases with the

[1] Marshall, J. S. and M. P. Langleben, A Theory of Snow Crystal Habit and Growth, *J. Meteorol.*, vol. 11, pp. 104–120, 1954.

[2] Nakaya, U., The Formation of Ice Crystals, *Compendium of Meteorol.*, 1951, pp. 207–220.

[3] Shaw, D., and B. J. Mason, The Growth of Ice Crystals from the Vapour, *Phil. Mag.*, vol. 46, p. 249, 1955.

six sectors of the hexagon clearly marked by the peculiar orientation of the structural elements.

2. Growth predominantly at the *corners*, resulting in extensions ranging from simple growths on a hexagonal plate to complicated, lacy 6-pointed dendrites.

3. Growth mainly from the *principal faces*, producing columns, prisms, and needles.

Microphotographs of some of the principal forms are reproduced in Fig. 18–7.

Everybody living in a snowy climate has probably seen these simple snow crystals falling to the ground. In many cases, however, large, irregular snowflakes are seen. These are composed of simple snow crystals that have clumped together, sometimes melting and fusing again, or of heavily rimed snow crystals. Snow pellets or snow grains are sometimes observed. They probably represent a combination or riming and evaporation (sublimation) of extending points.

## ATMOSPHERIC ELECTRICITY

**General Geophysical Aspects.** The surface of the earth and the conducting layers of the upper atmosphere (ionosphere) may be regarded as the plates of a spherical condenser between which lies the main part of the atmosphere. The outer plate has a net positive charge, and the inner one a net negative charge. The condenser leaks because the atmosphere conducts electricity between the two plates; therefore they have to be recharged frequently or continuously. It is estimated that the leakage current is about 1800 amp and that the atmosphere has an effective resistance of 200 ohms, thus giving a potential of 360,000 volts. Measurements show that these values are not uniformly distributed throughout the atmosphere. At sea level the electrical potential gradient is of the order of 100 volts per m, decreasing with height.

The air conductivity is brought about by the presence of ions. The conductivity is proportional to the number and *mobility* of the ions, the mobility being defined as the velocity the ion would have in a field of 1 volt per cm. Only the small ions, having mobilities of the order of 1 to 2 cm per sec/volt per cm, are of importance as conductors. Large ions, generally considered to be charged Aitken nuclei or condensation nuclei, have such low mobilities ($3 \times 10^{-4}$ to $7 \times 10^{-4}$ cm per sec/volt per cm) that they are not effective conductors.

The small ions are created by cosmic rays and by radioactive gases emanating from the solid earth. At the surface of the earth between 10 and 50 ion pairs[1] are produced per cubic centimeter per second. The

[1] An ion pair is two ions, one positive and one negative.

rate of formation does not decrease with height as one leaves the source of radioactive gases, because the cosmic-ray activity increases with height; at 12 km the rate of production is usually greater than at the surface of the earth.    Man-made releases of radioactive materials increase the ionization rate, at least temporarily.

Ion formation is balanced by processes of small-ion destruction—recombination between small ions of opposite signs, combination with large ions of opposite signs, and coalescence with neutral condensation nuclei. A balance exists between the rate of ion formation $q$ and the rate of destruction, of the form

$$q = \alpha n_+ n_- + \eta_{+-} N_- n_+ + \eta_{+0} N_0 n_+ \qquad (18\text{--}38a)$$

for positive small ions and

$$q = \alpha n_+ n_- + \eta_{-+} N_+ n_- + \eta_{-0} N_0 n_- \qquad (18\text{--}38b)$$

for negative small ions.    Here $n_+$ and $n_-$ are the number of positive and negative small ions per cubic centimeter; the $N$s similarly signify the large ions, with $N_0$ meaning neutral particles of large-ion size.    The $\alpha$ is the recombination coefficient for small ions and $\eta_{+-}$, $\eta_{+0}$, $\eta_{-+}$, and $\eta_{-0}$ are the combination coefficients of small ions of the sign represented by the first part of the subscript with large ions of the character represented by the second part of the subscript.    Over most regions of the earth, at least in the lower layers, the second term—combination of small ions with large ones of opposite signs—is the most important, so that if $q$ remains the same, $n_+$ decreases as $N_-$ increases and $n_-$ goes down as $N_+$ goes up.

The electrical conductivity is given by

$$\lambda = e \Sigma k_i n_i$$

where $e$ is the charge on an electron and $n_i$ represents the various kinds of ions of mobilities $k_i$.    If an ion balance exists, $n$ does not vary appreciably, except locally with the variations in large ions produced by smoke pollution.    The atmosphere therefore readily conducts a current.    This air-to-earth or "leakage" current is estimated as being sufficient to completely discharge the earth's condenser shell to a negligible value in an hour or so.

To maintain the electrical balance, there must be some supply current. The generator of this current is considered to be the thunderstorm. Gish[1] has computed that an average of between 3000 and 6000 centers of lightning activity must be in progress somewhere over the earth at all

[1] Gish, O. H., Universal Aspects of Atmospheric Electricity, *Compendium of Meteorol.*, 1951, pp. 101–119.

times in order to account for the supply current.    Climatological data indicate 1800 thundery situations, on an average, more or less continuously over the earth.    With two or three cells assumed for each situation, Gish's requirement is easily met.

The best indication of a link between thunderstorm activity and the daily regeneration of the earth's electric field was given by Whipple,[1] whose curve of the diurnal variation of the area covered by thunderstorms on land areas of the earth, reproduced in Fig. 18–8, matches the diurnal variation of potential gradient on the oceans.    The oceans are used because land areas have a diurnal effect caused by smoke pollution.    Figure 18–8 shows the values of the potential gradient over the oceans

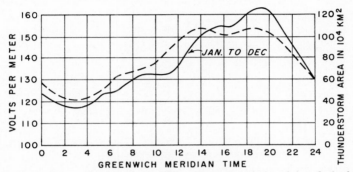

FIG. 18–8. Potential gradient and thunderstorm areas of the globe, dashed line, as functions of absolute time during the day.

plotted in terms of absolute time during the course of the day.    In each case a maximum is shown around 18 hr GMT.    It seems that at the same hours of absolute time on the average day the atmospheric condenser is recharged more vigorously than at other hours.    This is at about the time of the maximum number of thunderstorms over the land areas of the earth.    The preponderance of thunderstorms at 14 to 20 hr is due to the great effect of the afternoon and early evening thunderstorms over equatorial Africa and South America.

The majority of lightning strokes reaching the ground transfer a negative charge downward.    Thus the average lightning discharge is of the right sign to give the desired effect.    Gish and Wait[2] have measured the current flowing between the tops of thunderstorms and the higher atmosphere.    A current carrying positive ions upward from the thunder-

[1] Whipple, F. J. W., Modern Views on Atmospheric Electricity, *Quart. J. Roy. Meteorol. Soc.*, vol. 64, pp. 199–213, 1938.

[2] Wait, G. R., Aircraft Measurements of Electric Charge Carried to Ground through Thunderstorms, in Byers, H. R., (ed.), "Thunderstorm Electricity," University of Chicago Press, Chicago, 1953.

heads was found to be of the order of 0.3 to 0.6 amp for each thunderstorm cell.   This supply current from all thunderstorms over the earth must equal the leakage or air-earth current of 1800 amp, thus requiring the more or less constant presence of 3000 to 6000 thunderstorm cells over the earth.   According to the observations, this is a reasonable number of storms.

**Cloud Electricity.**   Detectable charge centers form in convective clouds in the early stages of their development and reach the spectacular magnitudes leading to lightning discharges in thunderstorms.   There are a number of plausible theories of cloud-charge generation, but rather than advocate one of them it is better to start out by noting some of the observed and measured conditions.

In the cumulus-cloud flight program of the University of Chicago and the United States Air Force, measurements of all measurable cloud parameters including certain components of the electric field have been carried out.   Included in the measurements are those of a carefully calibrated airborne radar which makes it possible to correlate the development of electric fields with the appearance and growth of radar echoes. The appearance of an echo signifies the development of rain or snow in the cloud.

The building cumulus containing no echo is typically charged negatively with respect to its surroundings, with horizontal potential gradients of up to 50 volts per cm in and near the cloud.

In warm clouds studied in the Caribbean area, not much more happens electrically even after warm rain has started.   In some cases a positive center forms around the rain echo but it does not strengthen appreciably. In the clouds of the continental United States where the first precipitation echoes are forming at or near the freezing level at a time when the cloud may be 15,000 ft tall from base to top, rapid electrical developments take place after the first echo appears.   The precipitation echo represents a center of charge that is positive both with respect to the rest of the cloud and with respect to the outside environment.   If frozen precipitation elements, such as snow pellets, are present, this positive center increases in magnitude very fast so that within 10 min the potential gradient around it increases from less than 50 to perhaps 1000 volts per cm or more.   As the rain shaft descends, it carries the positive charge downward through the cloud.   The first lightning discharge may be between this rain column and the other negatively charged portions of the cloud.   After a lightning discharge the thunderstorm can completely recharge itself in about two minutes.   The cloud-to-ground lightning flashes are between the negatively charged lower part of the cloud and the earth, which locally has an induced positive charge.   The top parts of the cloud, in the ice areas, carry a positive charge, and locally, in the heaviest downpour, all the way down to the base of the cloud, there is a core of positive charge. Some of the cloud-to-ground lightning discharges transfer this positive charge downward, but the vast majority of them carry down negative electricity. Normally the in-cloud or cloud-to-cloud discharges outnumber the cloud-to-ground lightning strokes by about two to one.

With this very general description of the electrical conditions in thunderstorms, the subject will be left at this point while in the next chapter the structure and dynamics of thunderstorms will be considered. In this way the relationship between the water circulation and the electrical aspects can be approached more meaningfully.

# CHAPTER 19

# THUNDERSTORMS AND RELATED PHENOMENA

By agreement in the World Meteorological Organization, a thunderstorm is reported if thunder is heard at the station. The thunder is the noise of the lightning discharge, and it is noticeably delayed if the lightning is at a considerable distance owing to the great difference between the speed of light and the speed of sound. Thus thunderstorms are defined in terms of their electrical manifestations. From the more general meteorological point of view, this definition may be regarded as based only on a rough measure of the size and intensity of a cumulonimbus cloud system. In studying thunderstorms we are therefore concerned with intense convection in damp air. Most theories of charge generation and separation in thunderstorms relate the electrical development to the air circulation and to hydrometeors in the clouds.

Recognizable units of cumulonimbus convective systems can range from the turrets only a mile or so in diameter, which bulge upward in a growing part of the cloud and which often contain a separate radar echo and their own electrical generating unit, to great connected masses or lines of thunderstorms extending for 50 miles or more. The synoptic analysis on the *meso*-scale of the large thunderstorm systems and squall lines has been discussed briefly in Chap. 15. A unit of convection, or "cell," having a diameter of the order of 5 miles has been identified as characteristic of thunderstorms by a number of investigations, particularly by the 1946–1947 U.S. Thunderstorm Project.[1] An isolated cell forms from several growing cumulus clouds or from active turrets in a less well-defined cloud mass. It is not often that a single-celled thunderstorm is seen very long, except possibly in arid, mountainous regions, because there is a tendency for the development and joining together of adjacent cells. Although the cells are connected by cloud structure, they can be distinguished in airplane flights by a less turbulent zone in the connect-

[1] Byers, H. R., and R. R. Braham, Jr., Thunderstorm Structure and Circulation, *J. Meteorol.*, vol. 5, pp. 71–86, 1948.

U.S. Weather Bureau, "The Thunderstorm," U.S. Government Printing Office, Washington, 1949.

ing part, and they can usually be recognized through separate patterns of radar echoes and of precipitation on the ground.

**Structure and Life Cycle of a Cell.** The life cycle of the thunderstorm cell naturally divides itself into three stages determined by the magnitude

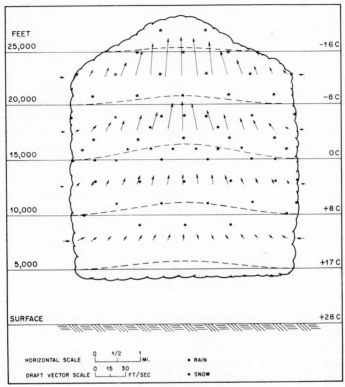

FIG. 19–1. Cumulus stage.

and direction (upward or downward) of the predominating vertical motions. These stages are:

1. The cumulus stage: a cell formed by a collection of cumulus clouds, characterized by an updraft throughout the cell.

2. The mature stage: characterized by the existence of both updrafts and downdrafts, at least in the lower half of the cell.

3. The dissipating stage: characterized by weak downdrafts throughout.

The cumulus stage is represented in a simplified vertical cross section in Fig. 19–1, showing values of updrafts, temperatures, and heights characteristic of the eastern half of the United States. The updraft is strongest at the higher altitudes and increases in magnitude toward the end of the stage. Converging air feeds the updraft not only from the surface but also from the unsaturated environment at all levels penetrated by the cell. Thus, air is entrained into the cloud system and is accommodated by the evaporation of some of the liquid water carried in the updraft. This entraining continues throughout all of the stages.

In-cloud temperatures in a strongly developing cell are higher than those of the environment at corresponding altitudes. It is noted that the hydrometeors are not represented as reaching the ground. Although pilots and observers flying through the clouds in this stage report rain or snow (flakes or pellets), particularly near the end of the stage, these condensation products may be suspended by the updraft. The first radar echo appears in this stage, often extending downward at a speed greater than the rate of fall of the precipitation particles, suggesting an almost simultaneous growth of precipitation through a considerable thickness of the cloud. In most sections of the United States in summer the first echo appears not far from the freezing level. Depending on location and the conditions characteristic of a given day, the first echo may form by the coalescence of liquid drops or around ice particles. Although concentrations of electrical space charge develop rapidly in this stage, no lightning occurs. (Isolated reports of lightning out of small clouds or "out of the blue," while authenticated, will not be considered here.)

The mature stage begins when rain first falls distinctly out of the bottom of the cloud. Except under arid conditions, the rain reaches the ground. The frictional drag exerted by the precipitation helps to change the updraft into a downdraft which, once started, can continue without this frictional drive, as will be demonstrated in the next section of this chapter. The beginning of the rain at the surface and the initial appearance of the downdraft there are nearly simultaneous. The downdraft starts at the level of rain initiation, above or below the freezing level, later growing in vertical as well as in horizontal extent (Fig. 19–2).

. The updraft also continues and often reaches the greatest strength in the early mature stage in the upper part of the cloud system. The updraft speeds may locally exceed 80 ft per sec. The downdraft is usually not as strong as the updraft and is most pronounced in the lower part of the cloud, although naturally weakening and spreading laterally near the ground. Areas of rain, downdraft, and horizontal divergence are found together at the surface.

Temperatures are low in the downdraft, compared with the environment, and contrast especially with the updraft temperatures. The greatest negative temperature anomalies are found in the lower levels. As might be expected, there is a close association between updraft and high temperatures and between downdraft and low temperatures.

In the updraft, mixing of entrained air causes evaporation of some of the liquid water, thus removing some of the heat gained from condensation.    The updraft air has its temperature reduced at an entrainment wet-adiabatic rate after the manner described in Chap. 8.    This effect does not permit the updraft air to become very much warmer than the

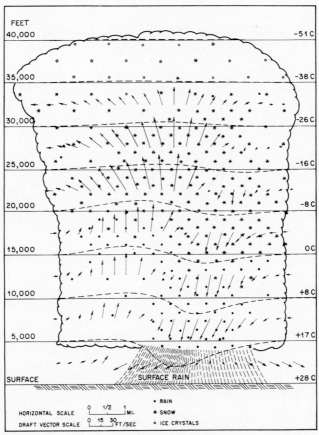

Fig. 19–2. Mature stage.

environment air.    The downdraft seems to be characterized by reversible wet-adiabatic temperature increases in which evaporation counteracts to some extent the compression effects.    Since the downdraft starts at a temperature very near that of the environment, its wet-adiabatic descent assures that it will be colder than the environment which has a lapse rate greater than the wet-adiabatic.    The cold downdraft spreads out at the surface as a cold air mass to form the pseudo-cold front advancing against the warmer surrounding surface air, a type of front often dealt with in the mesosynoptic scale.

The mature stage represents the most intense period of the thunderstorm in all of its aspects, including electrical activity.   At the ground, heavy rain and strong winds are observed while in the clouds the airplanes encounter at this stage the most severe turbulence, including in

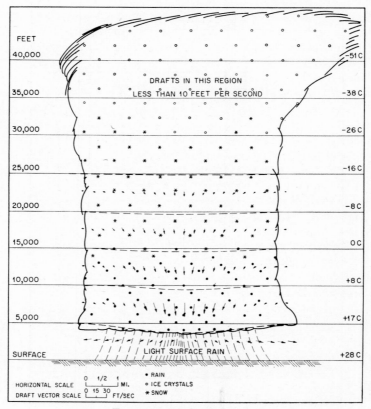

FIG. 19–3. Dissipating stage.

addition to the drafts the short, intense accelerations known in aeronautics as "gusts."   Hail, if present, is most often found in this stage. The cloud may extend to more than 60,000 ft, penetrating the tropopause, although more often the maximum height reached is from 40,000 to 45,000 ft.   With very strong updrafts it is possible for liquid water to be carried well above the freezing level.   On the Thunderstorm Project in Ohio one case of heavy rain at 26,000 ft, nearly 10,000 ft above the 0°C line of the environment, was reported.

When the updraft disappears and when the downdraft has spread over the entire area of the cell, the dissipating stage begins (Fig. 19–3). Dissipation results from the fact that there is now no longer the updraft source of condensing water. As the updraft is cut off, the mass of water available to accelerate the descending air diminishes, so the downdraft also weakens. The entire cell is colder than the environment as long as the downdraft and the rain persist. As the downdrafts give out, the temperature within the cell is restored to a value approximately equal to that of the surroundings. Then complete dissipation occurs or only stratified clouds remain. All surface signs of the thunderstorm and the downdraft ultimately disappear.

**Thermodynamics of Entrainment and of the Downdraft.** Computed and observed inflow rates in American thunderstorms show that the cell of cumulus clouds that develops into a thunderstorm entrains environment air at a rate of approximately 100 per cent per 500 mb of ascent; i.e., it doubles its mass as it rises through a pressure decrease of

500 mb. This is a lower rate of entrainment than that for individual small cumulus clouds that may be less than 15,000 ft in depth. With very much higher rates of entrainment the updraft could not be maintained, since it would then become colder than the environment or would evaporate all its liquid water to dissipate the cloud. For different air-mass conditions different critical rates of entrainment, i.e., rates which would either use up all the water or deprive the updraft of its buoyancy, can be calculated. In summer-tropical

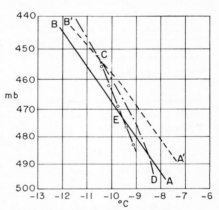

FIG. 19–4. Thermodynamics of entrainment in thunderstorm cell.

air in the Eastern United States the critical rate would be 100 per cent in 250 or 300 mb. In Europe the entrainment rates permissible for sustained convection would have to be less.

The updraft appears to follow the required thermodynamic pattern of entrainment. The downdraft is a special case, however. In Fig. 19–4 the updraft-entrainment wet-adiabatic rate in a typical, well-developed growing cumulus cell is represented by line $A'B'$ and a typical environment lapse rate for American tropical air is given by line $AB$. A saturated parcel displaced downward from $C$ would follow the wet-adiabatic $CD$, if no environment air were entrained into it. With entrainment it would warm at some other, less rapid, rate such as $CE$. If the parcel is dragged downward beyond $D$ or $E$ it will become colder than the environment and sink. The frictional drag of the mass of liquid water provides the means whereby a parcel in a thunderstorm can thus be forced below point $D$ or $E$, whence it continues as the thunderstorm downdraft. With a large quantity of liquid water available for evaporation, saturation can be maintained in spite of the increasing temperatures during descent and the parcels will reach the ground, arriving there with a temperature several degrees lower than the surface-environment wet-bulb temperature.

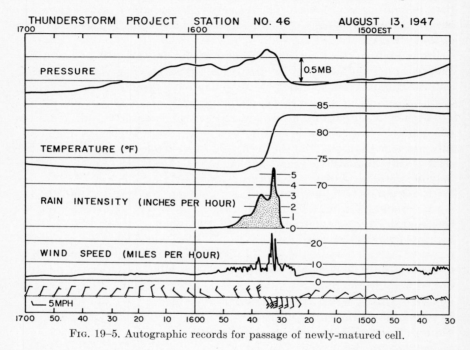

FIG. 19–5. Autographic records for passage of newly-matured cell.

**Thunderstorm Weather near the Surface.** Figure 19–5 shows the course of events as a cell passes a station just after reaching the mature stage. The data are from recording instruments of the U.S. Thunderstorm Project in Ohio. Not very many thunderstorm occurrences are of this extreme nature; if the cell has been in the mature stage for some time, the pseudo-cold front has usually spread ahead of the rain and has weakened. The complicating factors will become more obvious as we take up the details of the different weather elements.

*Rainfall.* The rainfall pattern follows closely the arrangement of the cells and reflects to a considerable extent their stages of development. Along with the downdraft and the area of horizontal divergence, the rain from a newly developed cell first covers a very small area and then gradually spreads. However, the cold air of the downdraft is able to spread laterally from the cell while the rain falls directly to the ground, so that an expanding outer area of cold air without rain develops. In the dissipating stage this cold-air area continues to expand while the rain area contracts.

If the rainfall is considered with respect to the moving cell, it is found that the duration of moderate to heavy rain from a single cell may vary from a few minutes in the case of a weak, short-lived cell to almost an hour in a large, active one. At a fixed point on the ground the duration of the rain depends upon such factors as the number, size, and longevity of the cells passing over the point, the position of each point with respect to each passing cell, and the rate of translation of the cells. In the Eastern and Southern United States the average duration of thunderstorm rain at a given station is about 25 min, although it is highly variable from case to case.

The most intense rain occurs under the core of the cell within 2 or 3 min after the first measurable rain from that cell reaches the ground, and the rain usually remains heavy for a period of from 5 to 15 min. The rainfall rate then decreases, but much more slowly than it first increased. Around the edges of the cell, lesser rainfall rates occur.

*Wind Field.* Early in the cumulus stage there is a gentle inward turning of the surface wind, forming an area of weak lateral convergence under the updraft. As the cell grows and a downdraft develops, the surface winds become strong and gusty as they flow outward from the downdraft region. The outward-flowing cold air underruns the warmer air which it displaces and a discontinuity in the wind and temperature fields is established (the pseudo-cold front). The discontinuity moves outward, pushed by the downdraft, resulting in strong horizontal divergence. Divergence values of almost $10^{-2}$ per sec over an area of 50 sq miles have been measured.

The outflow is radial in the slowest-moving storms but in most cases the wind field is asymmetrical with considerably more movement on the downwind side. The prevailing air movement of the lower layers nullifies the radial flow on the upwind side. With respect to the moving cell the outflow may still be radial in character, although not with respect to the ground. Thus the wind discontinuity in most cases is easily detected only in the forward portions of the storm, where it appears as the pseudo-cold front.

The cold dome of outflowing downdraft air has a form illustrated in Fig. 19–6. In this sketch the cell is considered to be in the mature stage and is moving from left to right. The cold air is represented as having spread out considerably farther on the downwind side of the cell than on the upwind side, as would be expected in a moving system.

In from 15 to 20 min after the outflowing starts, the discontinuity zone has traveled about five or six miles from the cell center. The surface winds near the discontinuity are still strong and gusty, but well within the cold-air dome, wind speeds have decreased so that the strongest winds are no longer underneath the cell itself. A continued settling of the outflow air, transporting momentum downward, causes the wind speed to increase as one approaches the discontinuity zone from within the cold air. Pushed by the air somewhat above the ground, the discontinuity often travels at a speed greater than any sustained speed observed at the ground.

With the discontinuity, the wind shows clockwise shifts in most cases. This is especially true in American tropical-air currents in middle latitudes

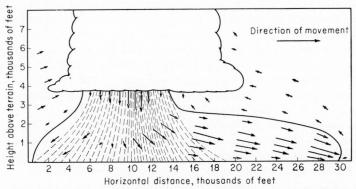

Fig. 19–6. Vertical cross section through cold dome of outflowing downdraft air.

where the winds are usually from southwest or south and shift to west or northwest at the discontinuity.

*Temperature.* The "first gust" and the "temperature break," i.e., the point on the thermograph where the temperature suddenly starts its drop, are two of the most pronounced features observed at the surface, and they occur essentially together. At the time of the formation of summer afternoon thunderstorms in the United States the temperature is usually above 85°F, often in the 90s. As a result of the rain and the downdraft, the temperature may reach a value as low as 65°F without change in air mass in the usual sense. As the thunderstorm activity dies down after sunset, the temperature has usually recovered to an intermediate value representing a mixture of strongly cooled or uncooled portions of the air mass.

The area affected by the cooling is many times greater than that over which rain falls, but the temperature change is, of course, most marked in the rain core (downdraft center). Cooling may be detected from as much as 15 to 20 miles downstream. Near the center of a mature cell the temperature reaches a minimum 10 to 15 min after the temperature break; farther from the cell the temperature drop is much slower. The amount of the temperature decrease observed in any given storm varies inversely with the distance of the observation point from a cell core. Since the downdraft is only a few miles in diameter, the area over which the first and most rapid temperature fall occurs is relatively small. As a result, strong horizontal temperature gradients are created after the downdraft reaches the ground. Gradients exceeding 20°F per mile have been observed. As the storm ages, the cold air spreads out and the magnitude of the gradient decreases. Regardless of the spread of the cold air, the area of minimum temperature remains in the general location where the cold downdraft made its first appearance at the surface, except in cases where a new cell with its own downdraft and rain core develops over another part of the cold dome.

*Pressure.* Early in the cumulus stage a fall in surface pressure almost invariably occurs. This fall is observed before the radar echo forms, and is recorded over an area several times the maximum horizontal extent of the echo. When the radar echo appears, the pressure trace levels off in the region directly underneath it, but continues to fall, frequently at a more rapid rate, in the surrounding areas. The pressure drops in the cumulus stage are usually small in magnitude—less than 0.7 mb below the diurnal change of the particular time of day—and take place over a period of 5 to 15 min. Following the fall, the pressure trace remains steady for as long as 30 min.

The pressure falls appear to be caused by the combined effects of vertically-accelerated air motions, the expansion of the air due to the release of the latent heat of condensation, and the failure of the convergence near the surface to compensate fully for the expansion or divergence aloft. Wind patterns in the vicinity of these cells show velocity convergence below 20,000 ft and divergence above, both of considerable magnitude, so if the pressure changes at the surface are due to a divergence imbalance, we are dealing with, as usual, a small difference between two large quantities.

In the mature stage, two features of the pressure trace—the "dome" and the "nose"—are recognized. The dome is registered at all stations to which the cold-air outflow penetrates. The pressure nose, the abrupt, sensational rise that some meteorologists regard as typical of the thunderstorm, really occurs only at stations that happen to be passed by the main rain and downdraft just after they have first reached the earth in the beginning of the mature stage. It is superimposed upon or may mark the start of the pressure dome.

The displacement of the warmer air by the cold outflowing air from the downdraft results in the pressure rise, initiating the pressure dome. A study of 206 thunderstorm-pressure records from the U.S. Thunderstorm Project surface micronetwork showed that in 182 of the traces there was a pressure rise associated with the arrival of the cold outflowing air. Since the rate and total amount of pressure rise depend on the slope of the cold-air mass, the temperature difference between the cold air and the displaced warm air, the depth of the cold air itself, and the speed with which the system travels, the most marked pressure changes are found near the cell core and they decrease with distance from it. The areal extent of the pressure dome is similar to that covered by the cold air. Therefore the pressure remains high for a period of from one-half hour to several hours, depending on the amount of cold air (number of cells) involved.

The distinction between the pressure nose and the pressure dome can be made only with difficulty on the conventional week-long barograph traces in most weather stations; a twelve-hour recording drum is necessary to show the effect.

After the brief pressure nose, the pressure remains at the value of the pressure dome which prevails for the particular thunderstorm. The dome persists through the dissipating stage of the cells, after which the pressure returns to the trend prevailing before the passage of the storm. In the case of a thunderstorm associated with a cold front or a fast-moving squall line, the pressure remains high or even continues to rise as a result of cold-air advection or the passage of a wave in the pressure and wind fields.

**Dry Thunderstorms.** In cases where the rain does not reach the ground, as is often the case in arid regions, the downdraft and outflow may still be felt. The pseudo-cold front with the usual manifestations of first gust, temperature break, and pressure nose or dome can be quite well developed even if the rain does not reach the ground. Dust storms are frequently stirred up by the first-gust line. Cloud-to-ground lightning strokes from such thunderstorms are treacherous as producers of forest fires because of the absence of rain to quench the flames.

**Night Thunderstorms.** In large areas of the middle western United States thunderstorms occur predominantly at night. These are not to be confused with evening thunderstorms left over from the daytime convection; in fact they show a peak of occurrence between midnight and 4 A.M. Studies have shown that they are caused by a diurnal variation in the large-scale wind system over the continent which is favorable for producing convergence in the low levels in the regions concerned at night.

The night thunderstorms usually fail to exhibit the same phenomena at the surface as those described on the preceding pages. The downdraft has difficulty penetrating to the surface because of the nocturnal temperature inversion there, so the wind and temperature features usually noted at the surface are either missing or very restricted in extent. The pressure and precipitation patterns are very nearly the same as those of daytime thunderstorms.

**Development of New Cells.**   From a study of numerous cases of new cell development, the outflowing air appears unmistakably to be important in contributing to the new growth.   When two cells in the mature stage are within a few miles of each other, the cold outflows collide and ascent of the displaced warm air triggers the building of new cells.   The greatest frequency of new development is in the area between two existing

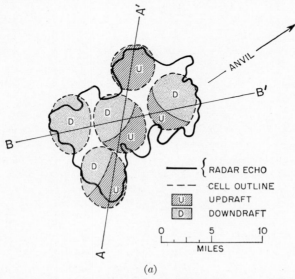

(*a*)

Fig. 19–7. Three-dimensional structure of a thunderstorm containing several cells. In *a* the thunderstorm and its cells are represented in map plan.   In *b* (next page) a vertical cross section along the line *A A'* of *a* is represented, while *c* shows a vertical cross section along the line *BB'*.   *U* stands for updraft, *D* for downdraft.   Other symbols are the conventional one sused in meteorology, such as rain, snow, and ice symbols.

cells whose edges are three or less than three miles apart.   A three-mile band downwind is next in importance, then the lateral edges, and least frequently the upwind or rear side.

In many cases the time interval between the beginning of the outflow and the appearance of the new cell on the radarscope is too short to permit explanation of the new one as a result of the underrunning cold air or a similar time-consuming process.   There are cases, as indicated by the radar echoes, in which one new cell or a cluster comes into existence almost simultaneously with the initial or parent cell; this suggests that a preferred region of convergence and ascent favors the development of several cells.

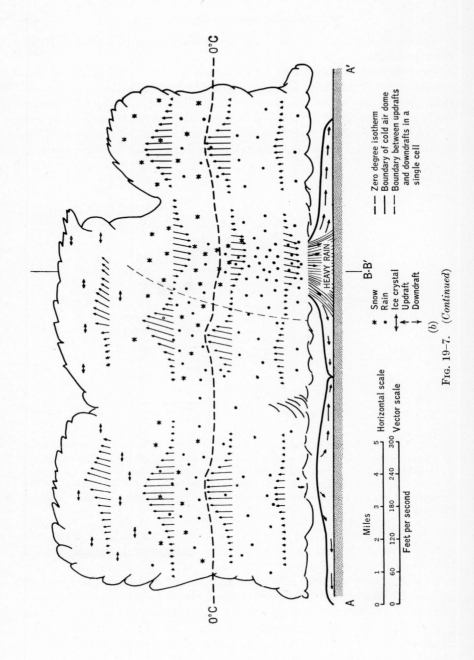

FIG. 19-7. (Continued)

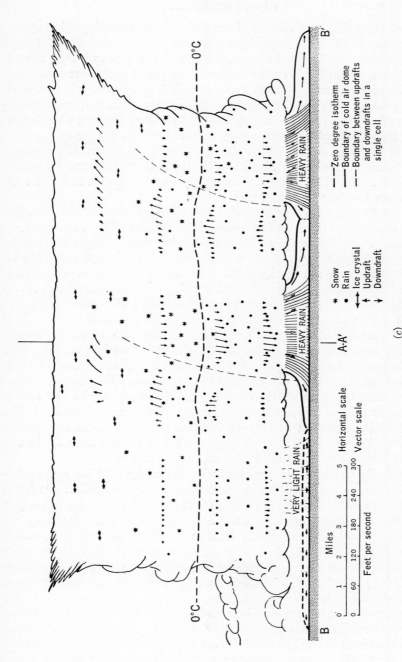

Snow ✳
Rain •
Ice crystal ⁞
Updraft ↔
Downdraft →

Horizontal scale
Vector scale

A·A′

Zero degree isotherm
Boundary of cold air dome
Boundary between updrafts
and downdrafts in a
single cell

Miles
0    1    2    3    4    5
0   60  120  180  240  300
Feet per second

Fig. 19-7. (Continued)

471

Most thunderstorms consist of several cells representing all stages of development. The cells may have been separated at one time but have come together. The cloud mass connecting the cells one with the other is usually inactive as far as vertical motions and precipitation are concerned, but generally contains enough liquid in raindrop form to return a weak radar echo. A typical thunderstorm is represented in map plan and in two vertical cross sections in Fig. 19-7. In *a* the collection of cells that make up the storm are seen as they would appear in outline on the PPI-scope of a radar. From flight measurements of gusts and vertical motions the cell boundaries and the areas of updraft and downdraft are delineated. The lines $AA'$ and $BB'$ along which the two cross sections in *b* and *c* are constructed are shown in the map in *a*.

Figure 19-7 is a slightly simplified and idealized version of a thunderstorm studied by radar and flight measurements of the U.S. Thunderstorm Project. It should be noted that while the two lines of flight penetration corresponding to the cross sections were through the center of the storm, the traverses were not ideally suited to obtaining complete representation of the features of each cell. Obviously a single penetration cannot reveal the distribution of the cells and their various stages of development.

**Hail.** Two problems enter into a study of hail formation—the cloud physics problem of the growth of hail *stones* and the synoptic-thermodynamic investigation of the conditions that produce hail *storms*. Few thunderstorms have hail reaching the ground and not many of them have it even in the most suitable parts of the clouds. Furthermore, there is an unusual geographic distribution of hail frequency; in the United States, for example, it is from four to eight times more frequent in the Great Plains and adjacent Rocky Mountain areas than in the Middle West, South, and East, even though the latter regions have up to two or three times as many thunderstorms as the former.

Physically, a hail stone appears to be formed by collision and coalescence of undercooled water drops with some kind of ice pellet. It is not difficult to understand how a coating of ice can accumulate around such a globule if it remains for some time in an undercooled cloud; we see the same thing happening on other objects such as airplanes and on mountain peaks. It is reasonable that the cloud updraft could keep the stones at levels of subfreezing temperatures for a considerable period of time. How the initial pellet forms and becomes a sizable stone is not entirely clear, however. Snow pellets (see definition, page 120) are commonly observed inside cumulus congestus clouds in the precipitation-initiation and later stages at or somewhat above the freezing level. In most cases they fall below the freezing level and melt before they have grown appreciably.

To form hail stones the pellets apparently must either originate at a much greater height than commonly observed or be supported at the subfreezing levels by unusually strong updrafts. Both of these circumstances would ensure a long sojourn in undercooled portions of the cloud to permit a substantial accumulation of ice. It is probable that mammoth hail stones such as shown in Fig. 19–8 represent severe updraft conditions at the subfreezing heights, underlain by a downdraft which lets the stones fall rapidly to earth before appreciable melting. From flight experience there is reason to believe that the updrafts in most hail storms are no more severe than in the more intense thunderstorms that do not

Fɪɢ. 19–8. Hailstones compared with teacup and baseball, Joplin, Missouri, Aug. 24, 1939. (*U.S. Weather Bureau photograph by Paul J. Sargeant.*)

produce hail. One is then led to believe that the height above the freezing level of the place of origin of the core pellet is an important factor.

There is evidence to indicate that in those regions where hail is most frequent the precipitation-initiation level is characteristically higher than in the more humid regions. This difference is shown by the results of radar detection of the first echoes formed in the growing cumulus clouds. A schematic representation of the geographical differences is shown in Fig. 19–9, based on radar "cloud census" data obtained on University of Chicago–Air Force cloud-physics flights[1] and data revealed by ground radar sets at the New Mexico Institute of Mining and Technology[2] and at the University of Arizona. Note that in the Puerto Rican region the echoes form in parts of the cloud that are warmer than freezing. In the Middle West (Mississippi Valley) they are initiated, on the average, just

[1] University of Chicago, Department of Meteorology, "Cloud Physics and Rainmaking," Chicago, 1957.

[2] Braham, R. R., Jr., S. E. Reynolds, and J. H. Harrell, Jr., *J. Meteorol.*, vol. 8, pp. 416–418, 1951.

above the freezing level and in New Mexico and Arizona the initial echoes are colder. Such geographical differences in temperatures of precipitation initiation are likely to be associated with geographical differences in hail frequency.

A characteristic often observed in hail stones, when one collects and dissects them, is a system of layers or successive shells of ice, suggesting that the stones have gone through a series of icing periods, possibly interspersed with melting. Oscillations of the stones up and down through the

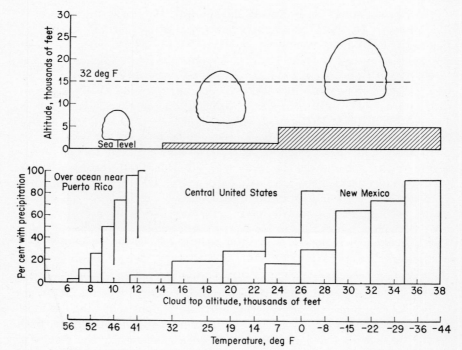

Fig. 19-9. Cumulus clouds in relation to height of base, top, and freezing level in summer in three different geographical regions.

freezing level have been surmised. It is possible that the laminations represent the difference in texture between relatively clear ice from large, runny drops and the less-dense rime ice from the smaller cloud droplets, all encountered above the freezing level.

Fragments of apparently spherical stones are sometimes observed. Occasionally these are almost perfectly shaped angular sectors of spheres of uniform size. One explanation of this condition is that the ice formed on the outside of the stone while there was still some liquid water at the core. When the core freezes, it expands and causes the sphere to explode or fracture from inside pressure.

The terminal velocities of spheres of the size and density of hail stones are of interest in thinking about the processes of their growth. The growth rate would be proportional to the relative velocity, i.e., the difference between the terminal velocity and the updraft velocity, and to the liquid water content of the cloud and the collection efficiency, just as in the case of drop coalescence. The formula can be applied only at subfreezing temperatures, of course. A further complication arises from the possibility that the undercooled liquid drops also have an appreciable terminal velocity.

Some progress has been made in the synoptic-thermodynamic study of hail storms. In the areas of high frequency of hail storms, a relation between the lapse rate, including water-vapor distribution in the air mass, and hail probability has been found. A combination of high condensation level, yet with the air not too dry, and strong instability appears to favor hail. A spring and early summer maximum, at the time when these conditions are most likely to occur, appears in the climatological records. Forecasting attempts have met with partial success based on the known correlations. There is a justifiable tendency on the part of forecasters to mention hail in most severe thunderstorm warnings. If the predicted severe storms materialize, the chances of observing hail in some parts of their violent overturnings are fairly high.

**Tornadoes.** Tornadoes are the most violent disturbances of the atmosphere, yet they are so small in their horizontal extent (usually 1 mile or less) that they never appear on the synoptic chart. Because of their highly localized nature and random distribution it is impossible to forecast the spot where they will strike. The best the meteorologist can do is to forecast the conditions under which tornadoes are likely or possible in a certain large region. Once a tornado has been spotted and the meteorologist has been informed of it by telephone, he can follow the thunderstorm echo associated with it on his radarscope and get police and local radio and television stations to warn of its approach and set in motion organized disaster plans.

Out of a great mass of literature on tornadoes, only general theories and data have come to explain their cause or describe their mode of formation. Meteorologists are practically unanimous in agreeing that they are a result of excessive instability and therefore steep lapse rates in the atmosphere. It is known that heavy thunderstorms are associated with them.

A tornado is easily recognizable in the visual range as a pendant funnel cloud reaching downward from the clouds, as shown in Fig. 19–10. After it strikes the ground the funnel sucks up dust and debris, but the main part of the funnel is considered to consist of condensed water as in a cloud. The tornado often comes with the first gust of the squall before appreciable rain has fallen, but instances of occurrence in virtually all parts of a major thunderstorm area have been reported.

Fig. 19–10. Four stages in the development of a tornado, Gothenberg, Nebraska, June 24, 1930. (*U.S. Weather Bureau.*)

Barograph, wind, and radar data show that the tornado is inside what is known as the *tornado cyclone*, a low-pressure area perhaps 10 miles in diameter with winds of 50 knots, more or less.   The tornado seems to be between the center and right-hand side of this cyclone, that is, to the right of the all-over upper wind and therefore to the right of the direction of displacement of the system.   As might be expected, the horizontal wind speeds are greatest on that side.   The tornado itself has exceptionally low pressure at its center, although no barograph has survived to record it.   The pressure is so low that much of the damage to buildings comes from explosion resulting from the sudden drop in pressure outside as the tornado hits.   Winds up to 500 mph are indicated by the patterns of damage.

Of the nearly 200 tornadoes per year occurring on the average in the United States, about 90 per cent of them are ahead of cold fronts, the average distance ahead being something like 150 miles.   This is the same distribution as that observed for squall lines, particularly in the central part of the country.   Tornadoes have also occurred in advance of warm

fronts and behind cold fronts, breaking down through the lower layer of cold air from their origin in the unstable tropical air above. Their paths range from a few miles to some hundred or so.   However, in the case of long paths there are indications of dissipation, re-forming, and skipping, with new funnels replacing the old.

In some instances a radar with antenna sweeping the horizon receives echo patterns by means of which it is possible to recognize the circulation of the tornado cyclone in which the tornado is imbedded. At first a hook-shaped extension from the thunderstorm echo is observed, then as the circulation carries the echo-producing cloud

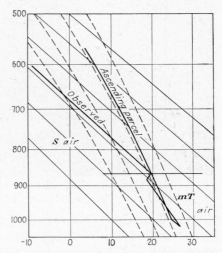

Fig. 19–11. Hypothetical conditions for formation of tornadoes in unstable $S$ air overrunning $mT$.

elements in a cyclonically curved path the hook closes into a pattern looking like a 6, and finally like a doughnut.

A synoptic situation that is known to have occurred in tornado conditions in the United States is one in which strong cold-air advection is found aloft.   Under certain conditions, cold air masses, usually of Pacific origin, become heated up so much in the low levels over the western plateaus that they ride up over the maritime-tropical air of the Mississippi Valley. The aridity and clear skies of the high-level heat sources of the West result in unusually high surface temperatures in air that was originally quite cold. This air preserves its low temperature at greater heights, and thus a steep lapse rate is developed. Apparently, as the air moves aloft over the maritime-tropical air, nothing much happens at first, because of the slight temperature inversion or stable layer separating it from the air below. Presently, however, some cloud formation in the maritime-tropical air may release enough heat through condensation so

Fig. 19–12. Waterspout on the South Atlantic, Jan. 29, 1927. This waterspout has developed out of low-hanging clouds. (*U.S. Weather Bureau.*)

that it will be able to penetrate into the upper layer. Here the lapse rate is so steep that an ascending parcel or cloud mass would be greatly accelerated upward, resulting in the almost explosive type of convection necessary for the development of severe local storms. The process is illustrated in Fig. 19–11 on the pseudoadiabatic diagram. Apparently it is not until the overrunning air has reached almost to the Mississippi River that in many cases the moisture content of the lower air is high enough to release the heat of condensation (to follow a pseudoadiabatic line of sufficiently high value) necessary to overcome the stability at the air-mass boundary.

This type of air-mass interaction is like an occlusion—a warm-front occlusion with a cold front aloft. However, the occluded front does not usually appear at the surface at this stage, because it is practically horizontal and does not intersect the ground at an angle sufficient to make it appear on the surface maps. In many cases the tornado-producing situation follows a series of previous charts on which an occluded front is shown. Usually there is a cold front of continental air following this former occlusion and it is this latter front with which the locations of the tornadoes are compared in the statistical averages. An indication that there is a cold front aloft comes from the statistics which reveal that the distance of tornadoes ahead of the surface cold front becomes greater toward the eastern part of the tornado belt; the upper cold air has moved faster than the surface cold front.

The Mississippi Valley is the greatest tornado region of the world. The presence of a high-level heat source to the west and an excellent source of tropical air to the south results in the production of the synoptic situation just cited in the usual type of vertical wind shear (southerly winds in the low levels, westerlies above). The spring maximum agrees with the springtime combination of cold Pacific air, early spring heating over the southern divide, and an increase in the frequency of northward incursions of tropical air from the Gulf of Mexico in the low levels. Air from the Pacific comes from a region of maximum seasonal temperature lag and passes over the southern plateau which has the minimum lag. At the same time, the air dries out, favoring further the steepening of the lapse rate. As might be expected, this is also the season of maximum frequency of dust storms in the Southern Rocky Mountain and Great Plains States.

**Waterspouts.** Waterspouts are of two kinds—those that build downward from heavy clouds and are simply tornadoes over the water and those that build upward from the surface of the water and are not directly related to the clouds. They are both called waterspouts because they draw water spray upward as tornadoes stir up dust. The noncloud type of waterspout is more of the nature of dust "devils" commonly seen over strongly heated deserts and is therefore much less violent than the tornado-cloud variety.

# CHAPTER 20

# FOG

It is unwise to attempt an exact definition of fog. It is really a stratus-cloud cover that forms at the ground or so close to it as to affect seriously the surface visibility. On mountain tops, however, almost any cloud may exist at the surface and therefore be seen as fog. In urban regions it is difficult to distinguish between fog and smoke, and indeed it is universally impossible to determine a sharp demarcation between heavy haze and fog. Local differences in designation are not uncommon, e.g., the stratus-cloud cover prevalent on the California coast is called *high fog* because the hilly nature of the region presents stratus fog on the higher ground and stratus cloud over the valleys and lowlands. For flight operations, the principal concern is with critical values of "ceiling," visibility, and slant visibility as they affect approach and landing systems rather than with what is generally regarded as fog. As the systems change, so do the practical critical values of the meteorological elements.

Stratus clouds are characteristic of the lower part of the atmosphere when a well-developed temperature inversion or nearly-isothermal layer exists there. If the air below is sufficiently moist, a stratus layer will form, its top at the base of the inversion. For the formation to take place as fog, the base of the inversion must, then, be at the ground or very close to it. Of course a temperature inversion at or near the ground is merely an expression of cooling from below and is therefore character-istic of air masses that were originally warmer than the surface over which they are passing or resting. The problem of investigating fog formation then reduces itself to the determination of the circumstances under which cooling of air masses at the surface, in the presence of high moisture content, can take place. An exception is found in certain fogs that form on cold days over warm water, especially in the arctic; these are nothing but actual steam. Also many fogs owe their immediate origin to the increase of the water-vapor content without appreciable cooling, such as in a warm-front rain. However, the air must first be rendered stable by cooling. Over continents in winter this stability due to cooling is nearly always present, and the formation of stratus or fog simply awaits the addition of sufficient moisture by rain from an overrunning warm air mass.

**Classification of Fogs.** To simplify the discussion of fogs and to clarify our understanding of the causes of their formation it is useful to have a fog classification. Such a classification should be of such a nature that it is helpful both in explaining the fog-forming processes and in providing a basis for fog forecasting. Such a classification, based on synoptic as well as physical considerations, was introduced by Willett[1] in 1928 and will be used here, with modifications. From the physical viewpoint, it recognizes that fog may form either by cooling to the dew-point temperature or by addition of water vapor until the dew-point temperature equals the actual temperature. The classification places the fogs in two main groups, depending on which of these two effects is predominant in bringing the temperature and the dew point together. These two groups are (I) air-mass fogs which form by lowering of the temperature (except steam) and (II) frontal fogs which, forming in the presence of precipitation, often have the increase of dew-point temperature as the more important factor.

A classification of fogs, modified from Willett, follows:

*A.* Air-mass fogs
    1. Advection types
        *a.* Types due to the transport of warm air over a cold surface
            (1) Land- and sea-breeze fog
            (2) Sea fog
            (3) Tropical-air fog
        *b.* Types due to the transport of cold air over a warm surface
            (1) Steam fogs (arctic "sea smoke")
    2. Radiation types
        *a.* Ground fog
        *b.* High-inversion fog
    3. Advection-radiation fog (radiation over land in damp sea air)
    4. Upslope fog (adiabatic-expansion fog)
*B.* Frontal fogs
    1. Prefrontal (warm-front) fog
    2. Postfrontal (cold-front) fog
    3. Front-passage fog

*Land- and Sea-breeze Fog.* Advection-type fogs depend on the transport of air between regions of contrasting surface temperatures. Sea-coasts fulfill these conditions at nearly all seasons. In winter, the advection of air from the relatively warm sea to the cold continent

[1] Willett, H. C., Fog and Haze, *Monthly Weather Rev.*, vol. 56, pp. 435–467, 1928.

causes fogs over the land; these fogs, however, are more closely related to radiation phenomena than to horizontal transport of air; hence they are not placed in the category of advection fogs. In summer, in localities where conditions are favorable for the transport of warm moist air from the land out over the water, an ideal type of advection fog forms—land- and sea-breeze fog.

In most cases of land- and sea-breeze fog, fluctuations in the wind direction, usually of a diurnal nature, are part of the mechanism. The air from the summer-heated land is cooled as it passes over the cooler surface afforded by the ocean. If the winds are of moderate to strong velocity, turbulence may preserve a steep lapse rate in the lowest layers, and stratus clouds will form under a turbulence inversion. If, however, the winds are light, a dense surface fog may develop over the sea. This fog may be brought over the land by a sea breeze that comes up in the middle of the afternoon, receding again at night as the land breeze again becomes dominant. In some cases, a light movement of air from the sea will prevail for a period of one or two days, giving a prolonged fog.

The land- and sea-breeze fog is of frequent occurrence in summer along the eastern New England coast. Its formation comes with light westerly winds and with widely spaced isobars. The westerly current is not only warm but also contains a high specific humidity. The cooling over the sea quickly produces condensation which, in the slight movement prevailing, must take place at the surface. Under these weak pressure gradients, afternoon sea breezes are likely, and the fog is brought inland.

A classical theory of land- and sea-breeze circulation is often invoked to explain the fog. While such a circulation is theoretically possible, observations seem to indicate that it is not present in such fogs. In this pattern, sea air is brought inland and becomes heated over the land. After heating, it then rises to join a return current (usually westerly with a shallow easterly sea breeze underneath) and is carried out to sea. There, over the cold water, the air is supposed to settle down to the surface again to complete the cycle. This is the simplest possible type of circulation and was mentioned in Chap. 10. Such a theory does not recognize the fact that sinking air heats up and dries out and that a shielding layer at the surface would prevent actual contact.

Land- and sea-breeze fogs are by their very nature coastal phenomena. They occur only on those coasts having light land breezes in warm moist air, therefore only on eastern coasts of continents. The western coasts do not have land breezes or sufficient warm moist air. These fogs also occur in summer only, particularly in early summer when the oceans are still cold. They can also occur over large inland bodies of water, such as the Great Lakes, and indeed the greater number of fogs of the Great Lakes are of this type. In any event, these fogs can never extend very far inland. At Boston and Milwaukee, where these fogs are common in spring and early summer, it is unusual to find them more than 2 or 3 miles inland.

*Sea Fog.* Fundamentally there is little difference between land- and sea-breeze fog and sea fog. While the former is developed by the cooling of land air over the ocean, the latter arises from the cooling of sea air over a cold ocean current. Sea fog, then, is not a purely coastal type but can occur anywhere over the ocean where contrasting water temperatures are found. However, many of the cold ocean waters are found in coastal currents, and sea fog often has its best development near land, e.g., on the California coast, where sea air passing over the cold California current produces persistent summer fogs.

The most extensive study of sea fogs is that made by G. I. Taylor[1] as a result of a 6-month voyage to the Grand Banks on the British whaling ship *Scotia*. Equipped with kites and balloons for making upper-air soundings from shipboard, Taylor obtained valuable meteorological records. He was able to show that the fogs of the Grand Banks are caused by the passage of air from a region of warm water to the cold currents in the vicinity of the Banks. In each case where a kite sounding was made through the fog, the intense surface cooling was shown by the existence of a pronounced temperature inversion. In one case of dense fog, the temperature at 1150 m was 21.5°C while the air at the surface had a temperature of 4°C. The effect of the turbulence accompanying strong winds was shown clearly in the 141 observations made in fog. When the wind velocities were high, mechanical turbulence carried heat downward from above and tended to diminish the inversion or perhaps actually to cause the temperature to decrease with altitude. In such cases, the formation would be a stratus cloud instead of fog at the surface. Air that was undergoing very sudden cooling from below, however, could support fog in higher winds than air that was nearer equilibrium with respect to the surface. Those fogs that were able to persist in spite of strong winds and turbulence were found, in general, only when the difference of the air temperature minus the water temperature was large.

This connection between wind force and the difference between air temperature and water temperature during fogs is shown in Table 20–1, which is taken from Taylor's report.

There is reason to believe that similar results would be obtained for sea fogs forming in other localities. In fact, the wind force and tem-

[1] Taylor, G. I., The Formation of Fog and Mist, *Quart. J. Roy. Meteorol. Soc.*, vol. 43, pp. 241–268, 1917.

TABLE 20–1. FREQUENCY OF FOG OCCURRENCE AT VARIOUS WIND FORCES AND
CORRESPONDING MEAN DIFFERENCES BETWEEN AIR AND SEA TEMPERATURES

| Wind force, Beaufort scale | Number of cases | Mean values of air temperature minus water temperature |
|---|---|---|
| 0 | 3 | −0.5 |
| 1 | 20 | 0.3 |
| 2 | 30 | 1.0 |
| 3 | 46 | 1.0 |
| 4 | 26 | 1.1 |
| 5 | 12 | 1.8 |
| 6 | 3 | 2.6 |
| 7 | 1 | 4.1 |

perature-difference relationship should hold for any type of advection fog.

*Tropical-air Fog.* This type differs from sea fog in that it depends not on the cooling by passage over a cold current but simply on the gradual cooling of the air as it moves from low latitudes poleward over the ocean. Also, it can occur in winter over the land in advancing tropical air. It is probable that many of the fogs observed on the Grand Banks by Taylor were originally tropical-air fogs already in existence before reaching the cold waters near Newfoundland. It is perhaps the most common type of fog over the open sea and in the United States forms some of the most widespread fogs that are observed on land.

Over continents in winter, the latitudinal temperature gradient is much greater than over the oceans; hence the poleward-moving tropical air is cooled more rapidly and forms fog more readily. However, turbulence over the land is greater than over the ocean on account of the roughness of the surface, and it is therefore more difficult for the condensation to take place directly as surface fog except in relatively light winds. At sea, it has generally been found that fog can maintain itself at the surface in stronger winds than those over land. The result is that tropical-air fog as such is more common over the ocean. However, over the land, very low stratus are formed, so as to constitute a hazard to aviation almost as great as that presented by the surface fogs of the oceans.

Maritime-tropical air in moving over land in winter is immediately subject to the strong radiation-cooling processes present there, and these may become more important than the cooling by latitudinal advection. Under these circumstances it is difficult to classify the fog definitely as to whether it is tropical-air fog or a radiation type.

Its name might imply that this fog can form only in distinctly tropical air. However, moist return currents of polar air may also be cooled sufficiently again to cause fog to form, and this would be classified as tropical-air fog regardless of the real "source" of the air.

Over the oceans, tropical-air fogs are common near the semipermanent cyclones, especially in their southeastern parts (in the Northern Hemisphere), which are occupied by air directly from southerly latitudes. Fogs in the Gulf of Alaska and the Aleutian Islands are frequently of this nature. Tropical-air fogs have their best development over the eastern North Atlantic and western Europe. Each tropical-air influx in this region is characterized by stability in the lowest layers and the formation of fog or stratus. In winter, the additional cooling over the land results in an increase in the cloudiness, producing dark days with stratus and fog extending through France, the British Isles, and into central Europe. In summer, the cold waters of the north, such as those of the Baltic Sea, produce fog in the tropical air.

*Steam Fogs.* Steam fog forms when cold air having a low vapor pressure passes over warm water. It is a situation that can be reproduced easily by placing a pan of water outside in very cold air. If the water is very warm, the air does not have to be very cold for the steaming to occur. It is a simple problem in vapor-pressure differences. For example, if the water has a temperature of 4°C, its vapor tension is 8.13 mb; and, if the air above has a temperature of $-10°C$, the pressure of its water vapor will be 2.86, even if at saturation. Thus there is a large vapor-pressure gradient directed out of the water, and, as one might expect, steaming of the water into the cold air takes place.

In general, steam fog is quite shallow, extending into the air 50 to 100 ft or less, but deep enough to interfere with safe shipping and over-water flying. It occurs over rivers, often when the air has been cooled by radiation, and tends to form radiation fog near the river as well as steam on the river. Such occurrences are especially common in autumn when the water is still warm but when the air is getting cold. Over the Great Lakes the principal occurrence of steam fog is in midwinter when the cold continental air passes over the lake waters, which have a temperature slightly above freezing. In the arctic, over localities where both ice and open water are present, the steam fogs are quite common and have been given the name "arctic sea smoke" by explorers.

*Ground Fog.* Nearly all fogs occurring over the land are caused wholly or in part by radiation cooling of the lower moist air. The simplest example of a radiation type is afforded by ground fog. Ordinarily this is defined as a shallow but usually fairly dense fog through which blue sky or, at night, stars are visible directly overhead. For the purposes of this discussion, ground fog will be considered as that forming from a temperature inversion at the ground caused by the radiation cooling occurring during a single night, the inversion disappearing during the day. This process, if sufficiently intense, may produce fogs deep enough to blot out the vertical visibility, but according to our genetical definition they would still be called ground fogs. Many advection fogs, particularly over the sea, form only to shallow depth, but to classify them as ground fogs would not be in accord with our system, which classifies fogs according to mode of formation rather than appearance.

Taylor,[1] in a study of radiation fog, found that the cooling in most cases is insufficient to form fog except on nights of very light winds. While the radiation intensity depends only on the universal law of the fourth power of the absolute temperature, the effect of the heat loss by radiation from the surface in cooling the lower air depends largely on other factors, and wind velocity is one of them. The greater the wind movement the less will be the chance for a sharp reduction in temperature in the lowest layers, because turbulence accompanying the wind will carry heat downward and will prevent the development of a surface-temperature inversion. Another important factor is the presence or lack of cloud cover. If clouds prevail, they will absorb part of the radiation emitted by the earth and radiate it back downward where it will be absorbed again, thus making the net loss at the surface relatively slight. Clear skies, especially if only small quantities of water vapor are present aloft, allow practically all the radiation emitted from the surface to escape to space. Thus, calm clear nights present the most nearly ideal conditions for cooling of the air near the surface.

To illustrate how wind velocities affect the formation of radiation fogs, Taylor tabulated the frequencies of winds of various strengths on 70 occasions when night fog was reported at Kew Observatory, near London, during the years 1900–1905. Taking the winds for 2000 GCT, which in most cases was before the fog had started to form, only two instances were noted of velocities in excess of 5.5 mph; and in 50 cases, or 71 per cent of the total number, the velocities were less than 3.3 mph. Taylor did not differentiate between ground fog and longer-period radiation fogs, so it is not unlikely that even lighter velocities would be found if the study were confined to fogs formed by the cooling of a single night.

If the air were perfectly calm, the cooling effect of the ground would be extended to the air above entirely by heat conduction. Taylor has computed the magnitude of the conduction in perfectly calm air and has found that a fog only 4 ft in depth could form from this process alone. He concluded, then, that slight turbulence currents were necessary in order for a deeper fog to form. It is then logical to suppose that a slight

[1] *Op. cit.*

air movement is required for the fog development; otherwise, the condensation takes place largely in the form of dew or waist-high fog. An exception to this rule is found in radiation ground fogs that form in bottom lands, narrow canyons, and gullies into which cold air has drained. In these places, the air is usually calm, but in order to drain into them it must have had some movement, although an accumulation into a land depression of successive 4-ft layers of radiation-conduction fog could build up to a considerable depth regardless of the wind motion.

George[1] has indicated that radiation fogs can occur only if the air during the day preceding the formation has been under a cloud cover. The effect of the cloud cover is to prevent the air from reaching a high temperature during the day so that at sunset, when the radiation starts, the temperature is already low.

In summer, ground fogs are the only pure radiation types that can form, because at that season daytime temperatures are so high that steep lapse rates normally prevail, and the radiation-cooling process cannot exceed that of a single night. Polar air over damp ground in summer is responsible for many ground fogs. The low moisture content aloft in this type of air mass makes it almost transparent to the terrestrial radiation, and the heat loss of the earth by that process can be very rapid. On the other hand, the damp ground supplies plenty of moisture for the condensation of fog in the lowest layers, below the top of the inversion.

*High-inversion Fog.* This type of fog is essentially a winter phenomenon and, like all radiation fogs, occurs only over the land. It is formed not as the result of a single night of radiation cooling, as in the case of ground fog, but from the long-continued net loss of heat by radiation which is characteristic of the continents outside the tropics in winter. Superimposed on this long-period cooling, of course, are the radiation effects of each night which in some cases can produce only shallow fog such as ground fog, especially in air that is inherently not very stable.

The term "high inversion" as applied to these fogs not only means that the inversion extends through a deeper layer than that of ground fogs, but also the definition includes types in which the vertical temperature curve may be isothermal, or the temperature may even decrease slightly with height, with a real temperature inversion at an altitude of 100 to 600 m above the ground. The latter type may become "high fog" or low stratus cloud during the day, changing to a dense surface fog again at night.

[1] George, J. J., Fog, Its Causes and Forecasting with Special Reference to Eastern and Southern United States, *Bull. Am. Meteorol. Soc.*, vol. 21, pp. 135–148, 261–269, and 285–291, 1940. See also various mimeographed papers on selected airports published by Eastern Air Lines, Inc., Atlanta, Georgia.

The best example of high-inversion fog is afforded by the winter fogs of the low valleys of the Far West. Here the effects of subsiding air above the cold foggy mass accentuate the temperature inversion, with the result that persistent fogs with marked inversions above them are observed. The San Joaquin Valley of California, which has more winter fog than any other region of the United States, has ideal conditions for this development. Maritime-polar air becomes trapped in the valley, and, as radiation goes on, the moisture quickly condenses to fog; then, if the air mass stagnates in the Great Basin anticyclone, subsidence over the cold moist air makes its isolation complete. The result is a fog of several days' duration, which ends only with the breaking down of the high-pressure area over the Great Basin and Plateau region.

*Advection-radiation Fog.* This name is given to fog that forms by nighttime radiational cooling in air that has come inland from the sea during the day. In general, it is like other types of radiation fog except that it is derived from special circumstances. The importance of this fog and the nature of its formation processes have been brought out in a series of papers on the fogs of the Southeastern United States by J. J. George.[1] Air of high humidity coming from a warm-water surface is cooled by radiation during the night. For example, air from the Gulf of Mexico having a temperature of 76°F and a dew-point temperature of 66°F will come inland to a station where the nighttime temperature will go down, let us say, to 62°F owing to radiation. The advection of the sea air with its high dew-point temperature makes it possible for fog to form with the normal nocturnal cooling. Beyond the easy reach of this air, fog-free conditions may prevail even though the temperature has gone lower.

In addition to providing a high water-vapor content for the air, the sea surface, at least in the warmer half of the year, prevents the air from reaching a high temperature during the day. Thus, at sunset, the cooling starts with a temperature value that is already fairly low. The effect of this retardation of the daytime heating by a cloud cover has already been mentioned in the discussion of ground fogs. A maritime trajectory has the same effect as a trajectory under clouds in inhibiting daytime heating.

This fog occurs mainly in the late summer and autumn when the water is rather warm and is therefore capable of producing a high dew-point temperature in the overlying air and when the nights are long enough for considerable cooling.

*Upslope Fog.* In regions where the land slopes gradually upward, such as on the Great Plains of the United States and Canada, fogs sometimes form as a result of the cooling of the air by adiabatic expansion as it moves to the higher elevations.

[1] *Op. cit.*

This is one of the few kinds of fog that can be maintained in relatively high wind velocities. The reason for this fact is that the more rapidly the air moves up the slope the faster will be the cooling process, and the downward transport of heat by turbulence will be counteracted to some extent. As a general rule, however, stratus clouds form in winds of really strong force.

The fogs are often formed by the combined effects of ascent and radiation and in some instances by moisture increases due to falling rain.

*Prefrontal (Warm-front) Fog.* Rain falling into stable air can raise the dew-point temperature until fog is formed even without cooling of the lower air. These conditions are best fulfilled in the cold air ahead of warm fronts. If the air in the cold wedge does not have the required stable lapse rate, the added moisture is carried upward by turbulence or convection and condensed into stratus, stratocumulus or, in some cases, cumulus clouds. Continental-polar air of winter is the type that is most often stable; and when it is overrun by precipitating warmer air masses, fogs or very low stratus commonly form. True maritime-polar air that has not undergone an appreciable amount of cooling is usually not stable enough for this type of fog to form.

As in all other fog types, wind velocities also are a factor. Since warm fronts are associated with cyclones in which the wind movement is usually above normal, warm-front stratus clouds are more common than warm-front fog. There are, however, numerous circumstances under which precipitating warm fronts can exist for a considerable period of time with only very light winds in advance of them. A condition especially favorable for low prefrontal velocities is to be found in the area of weak pressure gradient existing between a low-pressure center and a nearby secondary low. In the middle and northern Atlantic Coast states where secondary disturbances in winter are of frequent occurrence, these fogs are not unusual. Their existence is also noted in the valleys of the Appalachian and related mountain chains. Here the protection from strong winds afforded by the hills plus a certain amount of cold-air drainage into the valleys are added factors.

*Postfrontal (Cold-front) Fog.* Genetically there is little difference between warm- and cold-front fog, as each is formed from the moisture of falling precipitation. However, since the precipitation band associated with a cold front is much more restricted in area than that of a warm front, the post-cold-front fogs are less widespread. In fact, it is only a cold front that has become quasi-stationary, usually lying in an east-to-west direction and therefore closely resembling warm-front conditions, that has associated with it an extensive fog area. As in the case of the warm-front fog, these circumstances cause fog only if the cold air is stable. Unstable cold air masses, such as maritime-polar, have cumuliform clouds associated with them.

In the stable continental-polar air masses of the Middle Western part of the United States, stratus or fog forms for some distance behind nearly all cold fronts that have produced general precipitation. The moisture is not taken from the rain directly but is supplied by the damp ground. In most cases, low stratus cloud forms in these situations rather than surface fog.

*Front-passage Fog.* There are a variety of ways in which fog may form temporarily during the passage of a front. The mixing of the warm and cold air masses in the frontal zone can produce fog if the winds are very light and both air masses were near saturation before mixing. The sudden cooling of the air over moist ground with the passage of a well-marked precipitating cold front may cause a temporary fog to form along the front. In summer, especially in low latitudes, cooling of the surface by evaporation of rain water that fell during a front-passage shower may cause both cooling and moisture addition sufficient to create a fog. Over the oceans, the front may be accompanied by clouds reaching as a stratus or nimbus form to the surface of the sea; and even over land, heavy clouds of cold-front showers may reach practically to the ground.

**The Fogs of the United States.** Probably there is no type of fog that is not well represented in some region of the United States or its adjacent waters. It is well to devote some attention to the various fog regimes of this area not only for practical reasons but also to furnish illustrations of the various types that we have classified. In doing so, each of the principal regions where fogs are observed will be discussed in the order of most frequent fog occurrence. We have, then, the following regions: (1) California coast, (2) New England outer coast, (3) northern Pacific Coast line, (4) Appalachian valleys, (5) Pacific Coast valleys, (6) middle Atlantic Coast, (7) Great Lakes, (8) southern Atlantic and Gulf coastal waters, (9) Gulf and Atlantic coastal plain and piedmont, (10) Great Plains, (11) Ohio, Missouri, and Upper Mississippi valleys. The delineation of the various regions is based to a large extent on the data presented by Stone[1] which consider the former Weather Bureau definition of fog as including only those cases where the visibility is less than 1000 ft. Sections of the country not included in the list have, in general, less than 5 days a year with visibility of less than 1000 ft due to fog.

The map in Fig. 20-1 shows in a rough way the various regions. Also, where possible, the predominating fog type is indicated by index letters, and, where well defined, the months of fog maxima are shown.

1. *California Coast.* The fogs of the outer California coast are sea fogs associated with a cold ocean current. The coldness of the water is caused by the action of the wind. In summer, the prevailing north-

[1] Stone, R. G., Fog in the United States, *Geograph. Rev.*, vol. 26, pp. 111–134, 1936.

west wind exerts a stress on the water directed toward the southeast.
The water moving under this stress has its own coriolis force, which is
directed to the right.    This component of its motion carries surface water
away from the coast toward the southwest, and this water has to be
replaced near the coast by the colder water from below the surface.    The
California current is cold, owing to this "upwelling" of cold water.[1]
Since the northwest wind favorable for this effect is present only in the

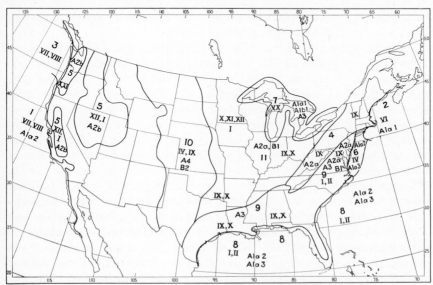

Fig. 20–1. The fog regions of the United States.    Large Arabic numbers correspond
to the numbering of the regions as given in this section (e.g., 10 represents Great
Plains).    The letters and numbers such as A1a2 correspond to the lettering and
numbering of the different kinds of fog in the classification appearing at the beginning
of the chapter.    The Roman numerals give the month of maximum fog occurrence
(I for Jan., II for Feb., etc.).

summer half of the year, the cold current and the fogs are essentially
summer phenomena.

If the definition of fog is restricted to the condition in which the
visibility over a flat unelevated surface is reduced to 1000 ft or less, then
the California coast is second in importance to certain parts of the outer
coast of New England.    Stone has constructed a map showing the
number of days per year in which fog of this density is observed at various
places in the United States, and it shows a maximum near Nantucket
Island, Massachusetts.    The station at Point Reyes, California, which

[1] For a more complete discussion of this process, see H. U. Sverdrup, "Oceanography for Meteorologists," Prentice-Hall, Inc., Englewood Cliffs, New Jersey, 1942.

has 60 per cent more days with dense fog than Nantucket, is not used for comparison purposes, because it is on a rock about 500 ft above the ocean. Because no comparably exposed stations exist on the New England coast, it is not possible to determine whether fogs at 400 to 500 ft altitude are more prevalent at one place or the other.    However, fog at this height along the California coast has a greater practical significance because of the hilly or mountainous character of the coast which causes such a fog to be in contact with the ground except at one or two places such as the Golden Gate.    Even so, about half the fogs that are dense at Point Reyes are also dense on the surface of the sea.

The reason for the prevalence of the fog at some height above the surface is to be found in the high wind velocities along the coast.    At Point Reyes, the average hourly wind movement for the 3 months June, July, and August is 23.1 miles, which is by far the highest of any Weather Bureau station except mountain-peak exposures.    Even in the extreme ocean-temperature contrasts of the Grand Banks, fogs at the surface with winds of force greater than 4 Beaufort were rare in Taylor's observations; therefore it is logical to expect that turbulence in the California coastal winds would by the same token keep the fog from forming at the surface. Although the Point Reyes station is at an elevation of 500 ft, other observations indicate that the winds near the ocean surface are about 5 mph less.    The two factors, mechanical turbulence and cooling from below, working together produce a temperature inversion which on the average begins at about 1700 ft, and it is at this height that the lowest temperature occurs, altitudes above 10,000 ft excepted.    From the surface up to this inversion the temperature steadily decreases.    The vertical distribution of temperature is shown in the typical curves of Fig. 20–2, which represent airplane ascents at Sunnyvale, near San Francisco Bay, and at North Island, San Diego Bay.    The ascents are selected in each case for a day on which low stratus clouds were observed.    The Sunnyvale data cannot be taken as wholly representative of conditions over the sea, because the station is located in a coastal valley with land elevations of more than 2000 ft to the west separating it from the sea but slightly exposed to the ocean by a low place in the hills just south of San Francisco, some 30 miles to the northwest.    The San Diego data probably give a true representation of the conditions existing over the ocean off Southern California.

In addition to the effects of cooling from below and mechanical turbulence, three other processes—subsidence, cooling by radiation, and thermal convection—enter into the vertical temperature structure at various stages in its development.    It is well known that the air in the oceanic high-pressure cells is subsiding, and data from various parts of the earth indicate that this effect is especially marked in their eastern part.    The

California coast is in this zone of most active subsidence of the Pacific anticyclone, and considerable evidence points to the fact that the warm dry air observed above the cold west and northwest winds of summer has settled from higher altitudes, thus serving to sharpen the inversion.   The cloudy air below this inversion sends out from its upper surface long-wave radiation, which is transmitted upward into the warm dry air above. When this upper air is very dry and not too warm it will absorb and send back less radiant energy than it receives, in spite of its higher temperature, because of the low water-vapor content.   The cloud base absorbs

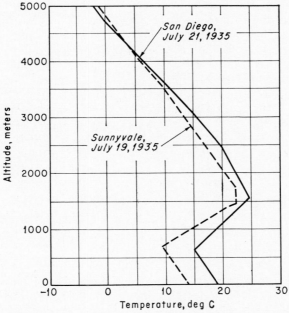

Fig. 20–2. Vertical distribution of temperature during occurrence of stratus cloud on the California coast.

the radiation coming upward from the earth and, since it is at a lower temperature than the surface, radiates less than it receives.   This gain of heat by radiation at the bottom and loss from the top may serve to steepen the lapse rate in the clouds.

The coldest ocean water lies along the coast north of San Francisco. As the air moves toward the Southern California coast it passes over water that is becoming gradually warmer.   Convection then becomes important.   However, the purely mechanical turbulence becomes less on account of a diminution in wind speed, and the subsidence continues. Thus, in spite of surface heating of about 8°C, the stratus remains, even in Lower California (Mexico), and the height of the inversion shows no appreciable change.    This is illustrated in Fig. 20–2, in which the San Diego sounding shows no change in the conditions except for the increased temperature below and above the inversion.

The role of surface heating is especially prominent as the air moves over the land during the day.    This results in steepening the lapse rate and produces convection currents that in some cases change the clouds from stratus to stratocumulus.    Ordinarily, however, the inversion is so low and the air above so dry that convection, in breaking down the inversion, simply introduces warm clear air.    The dry clear weather characteristic of the valleys in summer is caused by the breakdown of the inversion due to intense surface heating.    The maritime air, owing to its original low temperature, does not contain enough moisture for clouds at the higher temperature and the downward mixing of the upper air accentuates the dryness.

In coastal valleys that are partly protected from the ocean, nighttime radiation cooling of the surface layers is often pronounced if the skies are clear in the early part of the night.    Normally these valleys have been filled with the moist sea air during the afternoon, and the nighttime radiation reduces the temperature to the dew point.    The absence of an appreciable wind movement in these protected valleys is a factor favorable to the formation of a surface fog.    The San Fernando Valley, on the northern city limits of Los Angeles, has this type of fog occasionally in summer.    During September of 1932, there were 12 days when dense fog of this type was observed at the Weather Bureau airport station at Burbank, located in this valley.    This probably should be classed as advection-radiation fog.

2. *New England Outer Coast.*    During the summer months there are long periods when the temperature and humidity of the air over the Eastern part of the United States are equivalent to those of real tropical regions.    Air of this type, which usually comes with winds from a direction between south and west, is transported over the cool ocean waters that lie between the Gulf Stream and the shore northward from Cape Hatteras, and the moisture condenses into fog.

From Cape Cod and Nantucket Island northward, this type, which according to our classification we call land- and sea-breeze fog, is predominant; but southward from there, other forms are relatively more important.    Since the winds are mostly from the land, the fog is generally found only offshore and is brought a short distance inland only under certain conditions, e.g., when an afternoon sea breeze springs up or when a low-pressure area to the south is accompanied by easterly winds of longer period.    It is well known that, outside the tropics, east-coast stations have essentially continental characteristics in nearly all the meteorological elements, and it is only at the outer fringe of the coast that the oceanic effects are noticeable. Nantucket Island, located 40 to 60 miles from the mainland, is thoroughly representative of this type. The fog distribution through the year shows the pronounced effect of this essentially summer land-breeze condition. According to the data given by Stone showing the average number of days per month with dense fog, there appears a distinct maximum of 14 days per month in mid-summer with a minimum in the middle of winter of from 2 to 5 days per month. Stone's data for stations along the coast in harbors and bays show an annual fog distribution combining the land and sea breeze and continental radiation-fog types.

All over New England, whether influenced by fogs from the sea or not, the warmer half of the year is the time of the greater amount of fog, because it is at that time of year that humid air is present. However, fogs are not uncommon in winter, either as formations in tropical-air masses which occasionally make their way up the coast or as prefrontal warm-front fogs. As a matter of fact, warm-front fogs are perhaps better developed in the Northeastern part of the United States than in any other region of the world, owing to the combined circumstances of uncommonly stable polar-air masses and a nearby source of maritime-tropical air which can overrun the polar masses to produce warm-front precipitation. Almost any extensive outbreak of tropical air over the continent in winter, whether at the surface or overrunning aloft, is attended by widespread fog areas. The warm-front situations may properly be regarded as the most serious weather hazard to aviation in this country. Frequently when flying under precipitating altostratus, pilots find themselves suddenly cut off from landing fields by a wide-spread, rapidly forming blanket of fog or dangerously low stratus layer formed by the recondensation of the precipitated water. It is not uncommon to encounter raindrops or wet clouds at subfreezing temperatures, adding ice formation to the dangers.

3. *Northern Pacific Coast Line.* The fogs of the coast of northern Oregon and Washington represent another summer-maximum type. Although it is difficult to separate the southern part of this area from the prevalent California coast regime, it seems evident that a different set of circumstances is operating. No exceptionally cold ocean current is involved such as is found farther south; the summer sea-surface temperatures off northern Washington are higher than along the northern California coast. However, the ocean near the coast is colder than it is farther at sea.

A combination of tropical-air fog and sea fog seems to be characteristic of this region. Tatoosh Island, located on the Washington side of the entrance to the Strait of Juan de Fuca, might be considered typical for this locality. It shows a sharp maximum of fog occurrence in August, when 12 days of visibility of 1000 ft or less is normal. This is at the time of year when the greatest amount of tropical air would be expected at a station of its latitude. At this season the polar air masses and the subpolar cyclones are displaced well to the north, and the subtropical anticyclones dominate the circulation over the ocean. Tatoosh Island is near a region where the summer winds from the Pacific anticyclone are spreading out, one branch going southeastward toward the semipermanent thermal cyclone of the deserts, the other going northward toward the center of the Aleutian low. During most of the summer months, the vicinity of Tatoosh Island has lighter winds in this tropical current than other parts of the Pacific Coast, a factor that induces the formation of a surface rather than high fog.

During the month of August, when the maximum fogginess occurs at Tatoosh Island, there probably is added to the tropical-air fog a certain amount of sea fog caused by the passage of the air over a cold current which in most years is found near the outer coast of Vancouver Island. This cold current is apparently caused by upwelling of cold water from the depths just as in the case of the California current. The movement of the wind parallel to the coast of Vancouver Island in August favors this upwelling.

Unlike east-coast locations, Tatoosh Island has very little fog in winter. This is largely because the warm-front fogs are lacking as a result of the strong winds and the absence of pronounced stability in the prefrontal polar air. No exceptionally cold inshore waters such as exist on the Atlantic Coast in winter are found at this season at Tatoosh Island.

4. *Appalachian Valleys.* In this region are included all the mountainous or hilly regions of the Eastern United States, not counting stations located on or near summits of peaks and ridges. It is a region in which fog forms by radiation cooling and air drainage in valleys, swamps, and lowlands that are surrounded by hills and thus protected from strong winds.

Radiation fogs naturally have their maximum occurrence at the time of year when there is a considerable amount of water vapor and cooling by nocturnal radiation. In the Eastern part of the United States, the water-vapor content is highest during July, August, and early September with June also fairly moist. The shortest nights of the year are in the latter half of June and early part of July, but in August and September the nights are becoming noticeably longer; and since the high specific humidities of summer prevail at that time, then comes the most favorable combination for fog formation.

The mountain valleys of West Virginia have the greatest number of days per year with dense fog of this type, according to Stone's data. This is probably to be explained by the lower moisture farther north and less favorable cooling conditions to the south. Elkins, West Virginia, is the most representative station for this type. It has 62 days of dense fog in the average year with a maximum in the four months July to October, inclusive, and the greatest number in September.

The mountain-valley stations show the same general characteristics with regard to prefrontal warm-front fogs as do other stations in the Eastern section of the country. Since these occur in winter as well as at other seasons, there is not a month in the year when the stations in this region do not have, on the average, 1 or 2 days with dense fog.

5. *Pacific Coast Valleys.* The high-inversion type of radiation fog is represented in the United States by the winter fogs of the Pacific Coast valleys. Although confined almost entirely to the cold season, these fogs are the most persistent and tenacious to be found anywhere over the land. While many of the radiation fogs of other parts of the country are of the ground-fog type and therefore tend to disappear shortly after sunrise, those of the Pacific Coast valleys are of the type that can continue without interruption for several days at a time. Therefore, in comparing the data of such a station as Fresno, California, with Elkins, West Virginia, the fact that the latter has more days with dense fog in the course of a year than the former is misleading. It is probable that, if the actual number of hours of fog were tabulated, the comparison would be a very different one.

The winter fogs of the Far West have been the subject of several scientific contributions. Of fundamental importance is the discussion by Lockhart[1] of these fogs in the San Joaquin Valley of California. This study demonstrates that the following processes are at work in forming the fog:

1. The inflow of moist maritime-polar air into the San Joaquin Valley.

2. The stagnation of an anticyclone over the Great Basin and Columbia Plateau accompanied by pronounced subsidence.

3. The spread of this subsiding air downward over the maritime air of the San Joaquin Valley to produce a sharp inversion in temperature and to trap the air in the valley so that it cannot escape through the mountains.

4. Cooling of the air in the shielding layer below the subsidence inversion by radiation from the surface of the earth and from the upper surface of the shielding layer.

The last factor is favored by the presence of very dry, clear air aloft in the subsiding mass, which is practically transparent to the outgoing radiation. In the case studied by Lockhart (Dec. 20 to 24, 1928),

---

[1] Byers, H. R. (with W. M. Lockhart), Characteristic Weather Phenomena of California, *Mass. Inst. Technol. Meteorol. Papers*, vol. 1, no. 2, 1931.

the specific humidity at Mount Hamilton, elevation 4200 ft, was less than 0.5 g per kg, while saturation existed at Fresno with a vapor content of 4 g per kg. The temperature at Mount Hamilton was often some 20° warmer than at Fresno during this period, the greatest differences usually occurring in the early morning when the mountain station could not have had temperatures higher than those of the free air at the same altitude. The highest temperature of the inversion probably was at about 2000 ft, and so it is probable that the use of the Mount Hamilton data has minimized the magnitude of the inversion.

The fog at such stations as Fresno occurs almost entirely in the early part of winter, with a maximum amount in December. At Portland, the maximum comes in November, as is also the case at Spokane. At Seattle and in the Willamette Valley, according to Stone, the maximum comes earlier because there is a more open maritime exposure in many places. It is also probable that these places have shallow ground fogs under influences similar to those in the Appalachian valleys.

6. *Middle Atlantic Coast.* The waters of the continental shelf from Cape Cod to Cape Hatteras are coldest during the latter part of the winter. This is generally true of sea surfaces elsewhere in these latitudes; but in this region, the February and March minimum is emphasized not only by the loss of heat to the cold continental atmosphere but also by the fact that several large rivers, such as the Connecticut, Hudson, Delaware, Susquehanna, and Potomac, discharge water that at this season is near freezing, thereby giving to the surface an almost-arctic chill. The contrast in temperature between this and the Gulf Stream water provides an ideal situation for the formation of advection-type fogs. It is a condition typical of coast locations where cold inshore waters are associated with high surface temperatures farther at sea.

The fogs at coast stations from Cape Hatteras to Cape Cod have their greatest frequency during late winter and early spring when the water temperatures are lowest. This type of seasonal distribution is confined entirely to the coast, however, as is shown in comparing such a station as Sandy Hook, New Jersey, located on the outer coast, with Hadley Field, New Jersey, inland about 30 miles. The latter shows the typical eastern radiation-fog maximum of the late summer and early autumn, while the former is a typical middle Atlantic Coast station.

The cooling of sea air over the coastal waters produces what would be classified as sea fogs or perhaps, in some cases, tropical-air fogs. During summer, however, land- and sea-breeze fogs of the same type as observed on the New England coast would be expected, but they are generally outweighed as to frequency by the spring sea- or tropical-air fogs. Most of the stations north of Cape Cod show a secondary maximum in the spring but this is not so pronounced as farther south, because the temperature contrasts are not so sharp as along the middle Atlantic Coast at this season.

Typical stations of the middle Atlantic Coast regime, according to Stone's data, are New London, Connecticut; Cape May, Sandy Hook and Atlantic City, New Jersey; and to some extent New York City.

Sometimes the coastal stations apparently are enveloped in radiation fogs that have formed inland and drifted to the shore. Also, as is the case with all eastern localities, prefrontal warm-front fogs are not uncommon.

7. *Great Lakes.* The seasonal lag in temperature of large bodies of water in relation to the surrounding atmosphere is aptly demonstrated by the Great Lakes. In the spring and early summer when the atmosphere is rapidly becoming warmer, the lake waters retain much of their winter chill; and in the fall when the first cold-air outbreaks come down from the North, the lakes still have the warmth of summer.

The spring and early-summer conditions are conducive to the formation of land- and sea- (lake-) breeze fogs; and in the fall, advection-radiation fogs on the nearby land are the rule. Practically all Great Lakes stations show the effects of these two spearate fog-frequency maxima. In addition, during autumn and winter, steam fogs are observed over the lakes themselves.

The land breeze cooled over the lakes produces fogs only when the cooling is of considerable magnitude, which means, of course, that only the warmer air masses are of importance. Therefore the fog forms most often in weak gradient winds from the south or southwest. The development of a lake breeze on the western shores of the lakes occurs in the same manner as in the case of the sea breeze on the New England coast. A very weak pressure gradient carrying air from the southwest is the typical situation with the lake breeze developing as a thermal circulation when the land areas become heated during the afternoon. Duluth, Minnesota, Marquette, Michigan, and to some extent, Oswego, New York, show, according to Stone's data, the spring and early-summer maximum indicating prevalence of this kind of fog.

The second fog maximum in the Great Lakes region is that in the autumn due to the prevalence of advection-radiation fog. This is especially pronounced at stations located some distance from the lake itself so that radiation effects are important and the spring lake-breeze fogs are not prominent. Stations showing a higher frequency maximum in autumn than in spring are Toronto, Ontario, and Houghton and Port Huron, Michigan. Some of the monthly frequency values for Great Lakes fogs are shown in Fig. 20–3.

In addition to the fogs at shore stations, steam fog on the Great Lakes is of considerable practical importance. It may start in the fall and occur at various times throughout the colder part of the year. It dissipates quickly near the coast, particularly where the ice is plentiful.

8. *Southern Atlantic and Gulf Coastal Waters.* In many respects, the southern Atlantic and Gulf coasts of the United States have conditions similar to those prevailing along the middle Atlantic Coast. In the late winter and spring, the river discharge produces cold inshore waters that

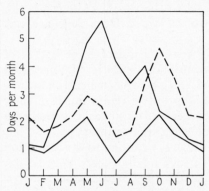

FIG. 20–3. Monthly fog frequencies at Great Lakes stations, according to Stone. Upper solid curve, Port Arthur, Ontario; lower solid curve, Alpena, Michigan; broken curve, Toronto, Ontario.

affect the air from the warm Gulf Stream or the Gulf of Mexico itself sufficiently enough to produce fog. The contrasts in temperature of the surface are not so great as along the middle Atlantic Coast, and therefore the frequency of fogs is less in the southern region. On the Florida peninsula, where the river discharge is negligible and the real oceanic water lies close to shore, fogs are rare.

In general, the time of maximum fog frequency in this region comes somewhat earlier than along the middle Atlantic Coast, the fogs usually disappearing entirely in April or May; December and January

have a fairly high frequency. At Galveston, Texas, which is representative of this region, we find from Stone's tabulation that normally December has less than 3 days with dense fogs; January, February, and March have from 5 to 6 each; and April has less than 2.

9. *Gulf and Atlantic Coastal Plain and Piedmont.* Fogs due to various causes occur in this region, but they are predominantly radiation types— either direct-radiation ground fogs or advection-radiation fogs. Prefrontal warm-front fogs also are important.

Numerous studies of fogs in this large and important area have been made, particularly by J. J. George.[1] At Hadley Airport, New Jersey, about 30 miles southwest of New York (near New Brunswick), Willett[2] found that 116 out of 193 cases of fog occurring in a period of 27½ months were radiation fogs, and, with two or three possible exceptions, these were all ground fogs. These no doubt included advection-radiation fogs, which Willett did not distinguish from the others. Second in frequency of occurrence were the same fogs as those observed on the New Jersey outer

---

[1] *Op. cit.*

[2] Willett, H. C., Synoptic Studies in Fog, *Mass. Inst. Technol. Meteorol. Papers,* vol. 1, no. 1, 1930.

coast—sea fogs or tropical-air fogs (Willett's "monsoon" fog). These
have a maximum in spring and early summer. Prefrontal fogs, with a
maximum in winter, were third in frequency. Willett points out that,
although the number of cases of radiation types is overwhelmingly large
and really accounts for the late summer and fall maximum, these fogs

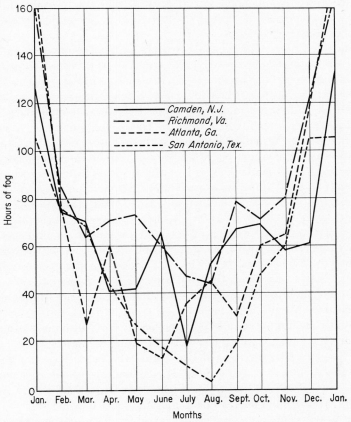

FIG. 20–4. Hours of fog in each month at selected stations in Eastern and Southern
United States, according to George.

usually dissipate shortly after sunrise and may not be so troublesome as
the less frequent but more persistent winter fogs.

Studies of fog at Camden, New Jersey; Richmond, Virginia; Atlanta,
Georgia; Jacksonville, Florida; Houston and San Antonio, Texas; and
various other airports in this region also show the preponderance of pure
radiation and advection-radiation types. George's definitions of fog are
not comparable with Stone's or Willett's and include cases of stratus.
Some of his curves of monthly frequency are shown in Fig. 20–4.

In the more southerly parts of this region the moisture content of the air is high in the autumn, partly because of the fact that the coastal waters are still warm. Since the nights are long and therefore favorable for radiation cooling, it should be expected that fogs, particularly advection-radiation fogs, would be most frequent then. Also, many of the fogs occur during cyclonic activity, such as during the passage of a weak cyclone when sea air is brought inland by the cyclonic circulation; or prefrontal fogs may develop.

In the Piedmont region, the true fall maximum appears again, and conditions become more nearly like those of the Appalachian valleys. Upslope movement of the air causes it to cool adiabatically and thus to help the process of fog formation. Since this upward motion is steady and gradual, it does not materially affect the previous stability of the air, so that a temperature inversion can be preserved.

10. *The Great Plains.* The fogs of the western Great Plains, called by Stone the "Cheyenne type," represent one of the few ideal cases of upslope fog. The gradual ascent of the prairies from near sea level to some 5000 to 6000 ft presents an almost perfect upglide surface for air from an easterly direction. A wind of this type usually occurs behind a quasi-stationary cold front over the Middle West, the air has usually had moisture added to it by precipitation along the front, and some of the fogs may be classed as postfrontal cold-front types. Moisture evaporated from the Great Lakes and from the Gulf of Mexico sometimes enters into the fog process. Air from this direction in the central states is in most cases of continental-polar origin, forming an air mass with a stable temperature lapse rate.

Adiabatic cooling of the ascending air, combined with a certain amount of radiation cooling, is the main cause of the fog. In the vicinity of the Platte River, westward toward Cheyenne, the land slopes upward at a rate of about 3000 ft in 180 miles. If air should move up this slope with an east wind of 10 mph, it would be cooled adiabatically 11°F in 12 hr. Similarly, the upslope effect of air moving toward Amarillo, Texas, can produce about the same amount of cooling. Along the valley of the Canadian River the land rises upward to the west at a rate of about 2000 ft in 130 miles. An upslope wind of 10 mph in this case would account for an adiabatic decrease in temperature of 10°F in 12 hr. When a certain amount of cooling by nocturnal radiation is added, it is no wonder that dense fogs can result.

The surprising feature of these fogs is that they can develop and maintain themselves in strong winds. Normally, fogs over the continents are not found at the surface when the winds are in excess of about 10 mph; however, it is not uncommon for dense surface fogs to exist at stations such as Cheyenne and Amarillo when the winds are blowing from 20 to 30

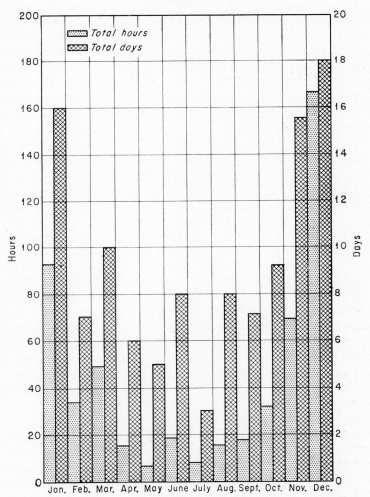

Fig. 20-5. Graph by G. T. Stephens for Omaha, Nebraska, showing total number of days on which "closed" conditions occurred at the airport owing to radiation fog and stratus, by months; also total number of hours' duration.

mph, and a few memorable cases of dense fogs with even greater velocities are on record.

In a study of fogs at Cheyenne, Clapp[1] has shown that precipitation is an important factor in the formation of the fogs, and he finds that the monthly fog frequency follows quite closely the monthly precipitation amounts. Also the frequency of fogs with various wind directions

[1] Clapp, P. F., The Causes and Forecasting of Fogs at Cheyenne, Wyoming, *Bull. Am. Meteorol. Soc.*, vol. 19, pp. 66–72, 1938.

agreed with the average yearly precipitation with these wind directions. Saturation from precipitation occurring prior to the fog formation was most important. The importance of cold-front passages and post-cold-front fog conditions was also stressed.

11. *Ohio, Missouri, and Upper Mississippi Valleys.* This region is one of spectacular differences in fog distribution depending on the effects

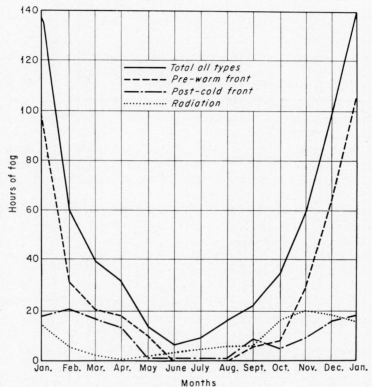

FIG. 20–6. Hours of fog (ceiling 600 ft, visibility 1 mile) in each month at Louisville, Kentucky, according to George.

of air drainage, proximity of rivers and other water bodies, city smoke, etc. The contrast between the amount of fogginess in bottom lands of the rivers and the higher surroundings is especially striking. For example, during 1932 there were 20 days of dense fog at the Abbe Observatory in Cincinnati, elevation 670 ft, while at the old Cincinnati airport at 500-ft elevation there were 38 days. Similar differences between the city and airport weather bureaus are noticed at such places as Omaha and Kansas City, where airports are in bottom lands.

These highly localized fogs are of course radiation ground fogs that normally disappear during the day. Fogs of longer duration in this locality are usually frontal types. It is in this area that the only really significant postfrontal cold-front types occur. After nearly every cold-front passage that has been accompanied by general rains, low stratus spread over the central states, and in many instances they reach to the surface and therefore can be classed as fogs. Prefrontal warm-front fogs and stratus are of great importance.

Studies of fog and stratus in this region, including an investigation of fogs at Omaha by Stephens[1] and at Louisville by George,[2] have shown interesting relations between fog formation and meteorological and physical factors. Fog-frequency data from these studies are shown in Figs. 20–5 and 20–6.

**Foggy Regions of the Earth.** Over the earth as a whole, by far the greater number of fogs are those occurring over the oceans, which are therefore advective in character. These ocean fogs occur wherever air moves from a warmer region over a cold ocean current. Therefore a study of fog involves a study of ocean currents and ocean temperatures. In monsoon areas or elsewhere where continental air goes over the ocean the land temperatures must be compared.

Just as there is a symmetry in the general circulation and pressure distribution over the earth, so there is a symmetry in ocean currents and fog areas. For example, the California current with its attendant fog phenomenon has its counterparts in both hemispheres where the eastern sides of the oceanic high-pressure cells produce circulations favorable for upwelling along the west coasts of continents in the horse latitudes. Thus along the coast of Peru and Chile the cold Humboldt or Peru current produces one of the foggiest regions of the world. The other counterparts of this situation are the west coast of South Africa (Benguela current), the northwestern African coast (Canaries current), and the Australian west coast (West Australian current). It is note-worthy that, largely because of the stability of the air and despite the prevailing winds from the sea, great coastal deserts exist in the low-latitude portions of these areas. Thus we have the great coastal deserts of northern Chile and Peru, Lower California, the western Sahara, the Kalahari Desert of South Africa, and the western desert of Australia.

The prevalence of summer fogs in the Newfoundland area of the North Atlantic has already been mentioned. A counterpart of this fog region is found northeast of Japan where the warm Japan current, or Kuroshio, meets the cold current from the Bering Sea and the Sea of

[1] Stephens, G. T., A Study in the Forecasting of Fog and Radiation Stratus at Omaha, *Univ. of Chicago Inst. Meteorol., Misc. Repts.*, no. 11, 1943.

[2] George, J. J., Mimeographed Report, Eastern Air Lines, Inc., Atlanta, Georgia.

Okhotsk. This region has even more fog than the Grand Banks of New-foundland. Neither of these regions has as much fog in winter as in summer, because of the prevalence of cold land air in winter which is being heated rather than cooled over the water. Somewhat analogous situations are found off the southeastern coast of South America where the warm Brazil current meets the colder west-wind drift, also southeast of South Africa, and between Tasmania and New Zealand.

Tropical-air fogs are also common over the oceans. In the North Atlantic, praticularly near the European side, the occurrence of fogs and stratus clouds in tropical-air warm sectors serves as an important means of identifying tropical air masses. Over the North Pacific, particularly near the Aleutian Islands and in the Gulf of Alaska, tropical-air fogs are likely to occur in advance of the cold fronts.

*Fogs in Europe.* In winter, the tropical-air fogs that are formed over the eastern Atlantic are also present over Western Europe. The cold continent adds to the cooling effect in this air, and in all warm marine air masses stratus or fog is to be expected in winter. Unlike the mountainous western coast of the United States, Western Europe is comparatively flat and permits the marine air to flow freely inland, producing maritime conditions even in Central Europe.

The maritime-polar air masses also produce fogs in Europe during winter. These are similar to the high-inversion fogs formed in the interior of the Pacific Coast states. In some of the industrial valleys, such as the Ruhr Valley and Saar Basin, the marine air is to some extent trapped, and the smoke pollution adds to the creation of fog.

Advection-radiation types are important for many sections of Europe. The famous fogs of London are, to a large extent, of this type and, in fact, the British Isles, surrounded by warm seas, have ideal conditions for advection-radiation fog. At all land stations, fogs appear to be most frequent in the winter months.

The Baltic Sea has abundant spring and summer fogs, since it is very slow to warm up after the cold of winter and remains through spring and summer as the cold spot of Europe. Similarly, although to a much lesser extent, the Mediterranean and Black Sea produce fogs. Fogs in the Mediterranean are most common in June.

*Fogs of the Orient.* Very little has been written or reported on the fogs of the Far East. Data from ship reports show that in summer the cold seas from the Bering Sea southwestward along the coast through the Okhotsk, Japan, Yellow, and East China Seas have a considerable amount of fog. In winter, the predominant flow of air is outward from the land in the great Asiatic winter monsoon, and thus no fog, except possibly steam fog, can be formed. However, in summer the monsoon winds are reversed and air comes from the warm Japan current over the cold seas.

Advection-radiation fogs must also be prominent in locations near the coast, especially in late summer and fall in a situation similar to that of the Southeastern United States. Fogs of this type are numerous in Japan, particularly on the east coast, and on the west coast the fogs of the Japan Sea often extend some distance inland.

*Fogs of South America.* The coast of Chile and Peru is one of the foggiest regions of the world, although the formation is often stratus rather than fog. The cold Peru current is present at all seasons of the year, although most pronounced in the warm season. The situation is analogous to the California coastal fog. In the protected coastal valleys or on the broader coastal plain, advection-radiation fogs are important. The sea breeze fills the valleys and plains in the afternoon with cool damp air, and the nighttime cooling under clear skies and light winds produces a dense surface fog.

In the vicinity of Argentina, near the Atlantic Coast, important but less frequent fogs occur. These seem to be predominantly of the advection-radiation type similar to those of the Gulf and Atlantic coastal plains in the Southeastern United States. A light easterly wind with calm conditions at night seems to be favorable for this fog. Also, what appears to be a combination prefrontal warm-front and tropical-air fog occurs in this area with northerly winds coming from tropical Brazil. Farther south, near the coast of Patagonia, Tierra del Fuego, and the Falkland Islands, sea fogs form because of the proximity of the warm Brazil current from the north and because of the cold west-wind drift current.

**Smog.** The contraction "smog," designating a combination of smoke and fog, was first applied many years ago to the London fogs in which a pall of black smoke mixes with a dense fog. Near the turn of the century, measurements by Aitken and others showed that the condensation nuclei were of such a nature as to cause highly restricted visibilities at relative humidities of 90 per cent or lower. In the 1940s, as the typical Southern California haze combined with city air and pollution became a serious annoyance, Los Angeles newspapers began to apply the term "smog" to this condition. Popular usage has resulted in the application of the word to any situation of poor visibility in polluted air.

The Los Angeles haze is associated with the inversion typical of the California ocean areas in summer. In the southern part of the region the condition continues to some extent into other seasons because of the persistence of the Pacific anticyclone. As the coast line curves eastward south of Points Arguello and Concepcion, a lee eddy of light westerly or southwesterly winds is found near shore, with the stronger winds from the northwest farther at sea. The orientation of the Los Angeles Basin and the San Fernando Valley and the absence of low-level gaps to the east and north contribute further to the stagnation of air. When the winds are light and of sea origin, the haze reduces the visibility to about 3 miles even on clear days over the ocean. In city smoke, the visibility may be a mile or less even in the middle of a warm summer or fall afternoon.

Except for heavy traffic of motor vehicles, the pollution of the Los Angeles air is less than that of other cities its size. The problem is severe because of the peculiar meteorological conditions, in part determined by the relief features of the area. The ozone content of the lower tropospheric air is greater in the Pacific anticyclone than elsewhere, producing a strong oxidizing effect on atmospheric pollutants. Some of the hydrocarbons in motor fuels have caused unpleasant eye irritation in the Los Angeles atmosphere.

Lethal fogs resulting in numerous deaths of aged persons and persons with respiratory troubles have occurred in the modern industrial age. Notable examples are those of Liège, Belgium, in 1930; Donora, Pennsylvania, in 1948; and London, England, in 1952. In these cases a dense fog under a stagnant anticyclone with subsidence inversion continued for several days, with industrial and domestic smoke and other pollutants entering the foggy air. In the absence of normal atmospheric diffusion, the concentration of gases and aerosols increased to toxic levels.

**Ice Fog.** At low temperatures, $-30°C$ or colder, fogs consisting mainly of ice crystals are observed. Undercooled-water fogs may occur at higher subfreezing temperatures, but the presence of snow on the surface reduces the possibility of undercooled droplets in the lowest levels. The familiar difference in vapor tension of ice and water at the subfreezing temperatures accounts for this effect. The condensation must occur on the snow surface rather than in the air if the usual diffusion processes are operating. Nevertheless there can be cases of water fog near the snow if warm, moist air is continually brought in at heights of tens of meters above the surface and is mixed by turbulence with the cold air below. When very low stratus is included in the definition of fog, undercooled droplets are to be expected. Data on fog frequencies at some high-latitude stations show a minimum at temperatures around $-15°C$ with a maximum at $-40$ to $-50°C$. The latter are ice fogs. Such statistics lend support to the idea that undercooled droplets are not favored over a snow surface.

In the arctic and subarctic regions ice fog occurs most frequently near settlements, resulting in the exasperating situation for pilots of flying for hundreds of miles over fog-free wastes to find the air terminals fog-bound. Air bases themselves are among the most frequently foggy places at ice-fog temperatures. The explanation is to be found in the large amount of water vapor released in combustion. Airplanes running up their engines will cover an airport with ice fog at temperatures of

−40 to −50°C.   Chimneys at the air base or in the town will produce a
similar effect.   In the case of the airplanes, the fog is similar to that
seen in the form of condensation trails from high-flying airplanes in other
latitudes.   Cases have also been reported of herds of caribou setting up
their own ice fog from their exhalations.

Steam fogs, or arctic sea smoke, apparently always consist of supercooled droplets.   The droplets only exist in the atmosphere for a few
seconds, coming off the water and evaporating within a hundred feet or so.

**Fog Forecasting.**   With increasing air traffic, especially of jet airplanes,
and with the development of electronic approach and landing systems,

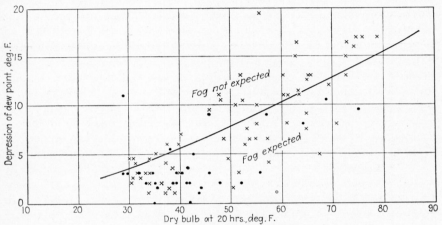

FIG. 20–7. Taylor's simplified fog-forecasting chart for Kew Observatory, 1917.

there has been an increasing demand for accurate forecasts of fog formation and dissipation at air terminals.   To this end empirical or "engineering" forecast methods based on fog statistics for a given location have
been developed and used with considerable success.

Perhaps the earliest attempt at a simplified yet systematic method of
fog forecasting was that proposed by G. I. Taylor[1] in 1917.   Taylor took
every case at the Kew Observatory, London, in which the wind and cloud
conditions at 20 hr GCT were suitable for the formation of radiation fog,
i.e., every case in which the wind was less than 5.5 mph and the sky was
not covered by clouds, and found the depression of the dew point.   He
then marked each of these on a diagram representing the state of the air
by points plotted against the temperature as abscissa and the depression
of the dew point as ordinate.   The diagram, shown in Fig. 20–7, contains
a round dot for every night that fog occurred and a small cross for every
night that it did not.   The line that Taylor drew diagonally across the

[1] *Op. cit.*

diagram had some prognostic value, for only three of the fog situations occurred following a 2000 GCT observation with the conditions represented above the line.   Below the line, however, there seemed to be about a fifty-fifty chance of fog occurring or not.   Taylor then concluded that, if this diagram had been used on all occasions when the wind and sky contions were favorable for fog, absence of fog owing to an insufficiency of moisture would have been predicted on 34 occasions, and only three mistakes would have been made.   The user of this chart would have predicted fog for conditions below the line and would have achieved complete verification in only half the cases.

Twenty years after Taylor's original suggestion, the use of similar empirical graphical methods for fog forecasting came into prominence again, especially through the work of J. J. George[1] who applied the method to fog from data of various air terminals in the southern and eastern parts of the United States.   The applications are still being enlarged upon by his associates and some of the U.S. Weather Bureau forecasters.   A number of factors in addition to the depression of the dew point at sunset have been worked into the diagrams.   For example, the number of hours of sunshine during the day determines the beginning point of nighttime cooling in terms of temperature and obscure heat-exchange factors. Wind speed may enter into the calculation or, especially in the case of coastal stations, the wind direction may be important.   The rate at which the dew point may be increasing or decreasing is taken into consideration. In some cases a series of dependent graphs form a sort of check list to determine whether fog is likely to develop or not.   Graphical methods have also been worked out for predicting the dissipation of fog or stratus from daytime heating.

Other aids to forecasting include future trajectories to determine the likelihood of the air passing over water surfaces of different temperatures or through rain areas and under cloud covers, whether upslope or downslope.   Also, the delineation of areas of convergence and divergence may be pertinent to the problem, since fog is more likely to occur in areas of divergent flow than elsewhere.

---

[1] See for example J. J. George, Fog, *Compendium of Meteorol.*, p. 1179, 1951.

# CHAPTER 21

# TURBULENCE

An examination of anemograph records shows that the wind, in both speed and direction, generally exhibits rapid, irregular fluctuations. The average value within these variations is taken as the mean wind velocity which is given in ordinary weather reports. These fluctuations indicate that the air flow is of a turbulent, eddying character, at least near the surface. The exact structure of the eddies is difficult to determine, but they are highly irregular, involving axes with both vertical and horizontal components. The occurrence of wide variations in speed is always accompanied by marked fluctuations in direction. Wind changes of lesser frequency, often aperiodic and associated with larger eddies, perhaps of the size of a cumulus cloud, comprise what are generally recognized as gusts when experienced at the ground. Aeronautical engineers, measuring turbulent eddies from the point of view of acceleration loads on aircraft in flight, refer to all natural eddies affecting aircraft as "gusts."

The degree of turbulence has been found to depend on the speed of the wind, the roughness of the surface, the vertical temperature lapse rate, and certain lesser factors. As thermal instability is approached, convection currents become part of the turbulent structure. Indeed, the temperature lapse rate is the most striking controlling parameter for a given terrain, causing pronounced diurnal and, to some extent, seasonal variations. In convective clouds, especially in thunderstorms, energy is released at cloud heights to set off updrafts and downdrafts, representing very large eddy-type motions, which give rise to a wide spectrum of smaller turbulent eddies.

**The Search for an Eddy Coefficient.** In Chap. 14 it is shown that the conduction of heat and the diffusion of a property such as water vapor through the atmosphere by eddies can be expressed by substituting eddy conductivity and exchange coefficients in the usual conduction and diffusion equations. These coefficients are

$$K = -\rho \, \frac{H}{\partial T/\partial z} \tag{21-1}$$

$$D' = -\frac{E}{\partial q/\partial z} \tag{21-2}$$

where $H$ and $E$ are the upward fluxes of heat and water vapor ($q$), respectively. It is seen that the coefficients are given by the ratios of the fluxes to the gradients. This relation is simple enough, but unfortunately only one of the variables, the gradient, can be measured directly. Furthermore, all quantities vary over a wide range and within a relatively short time. For example, one might think of obtaining $E$ for water vapor at the ground by measuring evaporation through successive weighings of a large slice of soil, including vegetative cover, maintained on a subsurface weighing platform in its natural environment. One would find that during the time required for measurable evaporation to take place, $D'$ and $\partial q/\partial z$ would have changed within the diurnal cycle and only crude mean values could be obtained. In the natural atmosphere the coefficients $K$ and $D'$ may vary through three orders of magnitude or more as the lapse rate, wind speed, and ground roughness vary.

The flux equations with general eddy coefficients are useful for defining the process and establishing the theoretical background but cannot be applied to the specific solution of real problems in the atmosphere. The coefficients are too variable and elusive.

**Eddy Viscosity, Shear, and Momentum Transport.** The subject of turbulence also includes the problem of eddy viscosity and the horizontal *shearing stress*. The latter is defined as the force exerted by a moving sheet of fluid upon a parallel sheet a unit distance from it. The ordinary or molecular coefficient of viscosity is given by the ratio of the shearing stress to the rate of shear, and the eddy viscosity is similarly defined as the ratio of the horizontal component of the eddy stress to the vertical rate of shear, or

$$\eta' = \frac{\tau}{\partial u/\partial z} \qquad (21\text{--}3)$$

where $u$ is taken in the direction of flow. This coefficient, like the others, also varies by three orders of magnitude or more. The vertical shear of the wind is the only one of the three variables that can be measured directly, but even this measurement is complicated by the fact that the wind changes direction with height and is seldom steady. The Ekman spiral, described in Chap. 9, derived from these concepts, gives a theoretical change of wind with height based on certain assumptions.

From the law of conservation of momentum it follows that parcels of air carried upward or downward will preserve their momentum. Thus the vertical flux of momentum can be expressed in an equation similar to that for the flux of other conservative properties. For unit volume, the momentum is $\rho u$ and the upward flux is

$$F_m = -\eta' \frac{\partial(\rho u)}{\partial z} \qquad (21\text{--}4)$$

Since the wind almost invariably increases with height in the lowest kilometer thousands to a million times faster than the density of the air decreases, momentum is normally transported downward.

The diurnal and annual variations of the momentum flux were shown in a classical study by Åkerblom[1] made in the early part of the century from observations on the Eiffel Tower in Paris. Figure 21–1 shows vectors of the ratios of wind at the ground to those on the tower at various hours of the day. It is seen that the winds in the park are nearest to those on the tower in the afternoon at the time of the greatest lapse rate of temperature and that the vertical shear is greatest in the early morning when the air

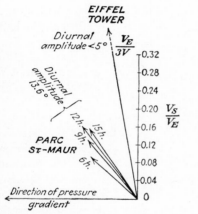

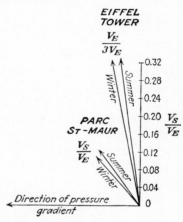

FIG. 21–1. Diurnal variation of the wind in Parc St-Maur in Paris compared with wind on the Eiffel Tower. The lengths of the wind vectors for the park are given by the ratio of the wind there to the wind on the tower ($V_S/V_E$).

FIG. 21–2. Annual variation of the wind in Parc St-Maur in Paris compared with the wind on the Eiffel Tower.

is most stable. A similar difference between winter and summer is shown in Fig. 21–2. The explanation is found in the suppression of vertical eddies in a stable atmosphere. With reduced eddy action, the coupling between upper and lower layers, or the eddy viscosity, is smaller and momentum is not appreciably transported downward. A strong vertical shear of the wind is maintained. In the afternoon the momentum is more uniformly distributed, so the wind at the ground reaches its greatest diurnal value while on the tower it is at its daily minimum. In the early morning the winds on the tower reach a maximum and those on the ground a minimum. In the annual cycle the vertical shear is seen to be greatest in winter, least in summer.

[1] Åkerblom, F., Recherches sur les courants les plus bas de l'atmosphère au-dessus de Paris, *Nova Acta Regiae Soc. Sci. Upsaliensis*, ser. 4, vol. 2, no. 2, 1908.

**Wind in the Surface Boundary Layer.** The surface boundary layer, comprising the lowest 10 m or so, is the part of the atmosphere in which standard anemometers are usually placed. In this layer the wind may be considered as not turning with height and the stress $\tau$ may be regarded as constant with height both in magnitude and direction. Under such conditions it is possible to determine $\tau$ and $\eta'$ as functions of a "roughness" parameter and the temperature lapse rate.

In the case of an adiabatic-equilibrium lapse rate, $\eta'$ is found to vary linearly with height according to

$$\eta' = 0.4\sqrt{\tau\rho}\,(z - z_0) \tag{21-5}$$

where $\tau$ and $\rho$ may be considered as constant. $z_0$ is the so-called "roughness length." Over rough ground there is no well-defined $z = 0$, so a certain amount of turbulent mixing occurs at the chosen $z = 0$. The rougher the surface is, the greater will be the amount of this mixing and the greater will be $z_0$. It has a value between $\frac{1}{10}$ and $\frac{1}{30}$ of the height of the prevailing roughness elements. With a park-like distribution of trees, $z_0$ is about 100 cm, but over a large, flat area of mowed grass it can be less than 1 cm. It can be determined for each wind direction at a given location by the application of relations to be discussed next.

If this expression for $\eta'$ is substituted in Eq. (21-3), then

$$\tau = 0.4\sqrt{\tau\rho}\,(z - z_0)\frac{\partial u}{\partial z} \tag{21-6}$$

If $\tau$ is constant with height, this expression can be integrated to obtain $u$ at height $z$, with the result

$$u = \frac{1}{0.4}\sqrt{\frac{\tau}{\rho}}\ln\frac{z + z_0}{z_0} \tag{21-7}$$

and

$$\sqrt{\frac{\tau}{\rho}} = \frac{0.4u}{\ln(z + z_0/z_0)} \tag{21-8}$$

$$\tau = \frac{0.16\rho u^2}{(\ln z + z_0/z_0)^2} \tag{21-9}$$

$$\sqrt{\tau\rho} = \frac{0.4\rho u}{\ln(z + z_0)/z_0} \tag{21-10}$$

and, by substitution,

$$\eta' = 0.16\rho u\,\frac{z + z_0}{\ln(z + z_0)/z_0} \tag{21-11}$$

Thus $\tau$ and $\eta'$ can be determined from the readings of an anemometer at height $z$ in this adiabatic case if the roughness length is known. It is also interesting to note that the stress is proportional to the square of the wind speed at a given level and that increasing roughness means increasing stress. It is seen that, if $\sqrt{\tau/\rho}$ is constant, $z_0$ can be obtained from two anemometers at heights $z_1$ and $z_2$, giving readings $u_1$ and $u_2$, so that

$$\frac{u_1}{u_2} = \frac{\ln (z_1 + z_0)/z_0}{\ln (z_2 + z_0)/z_0} \tag{21-12}$$

H. Panofsky[1] suggests a formula of E. L. Deacon applicable to various lapse rates and roughness lengths. It is:

$$u = \frac{(\tau/\rho)^{\frac{1}{2}}}{0.4(1 - \beta)} \left[ \left( \frac{z + z_0}{z_0} \right)^{1-\beta} - 1 \right] \tag{21-13}$$

where $\beta$ is a lapse-rate parameter. For neutral stability $\beta \to 1$ and it can be shown that this equation reduces to Eq. (21–7). For large lapse rates $\beta > 1$; for stable conditions $\beta < 1$. A typical diurnal variation under clear skies given by Panofsky is from $\beta = 0.8$ at night to $\beta = 1.25$ in the daytime.

It is evident that in the surface boundary layer where $\tau$ may be considered constant with height, the turbulent parameters can be obtained with reasonable approximation from anemometers placed at more than one level. Thus the first step in studying turbulence is to build a tower with several anemometer levels. For obvious reasons, it is convenient to space them logarithmically. Equation (21–7) shows that in the boundary layer under adiabatic-equilibrium conditions the vertical wind profile is logarithmic.

Another useful set of relationships can be obtained by writing Eq. (21–6) in the form

$$\frac{du}{dz} = \frac{1}{0.4(z + z_0)} \sqrt{\frac{\tau}{\rho}} \tag{21-14}$$

and, integrating between two levels, we obtain

$$u_2 - u_1 = \frac{1}{0.4} \sqrt{\frac{\tau}{\rho}} \int_{z_1}^{z_2} \frac{dz}{z + z_0} = \frac{1}{0.4} \sqrt{\frac{\tau}{\rho}} \ln \frac{z_2 + z_0}{z_1 + z_0} \tag{21-15}$$

If the heights are of the order of a meter or more above the ground, $z_0$ does not have an appreciable effect on the values obtained from this expression, since it is nearly always less than 10 cm. So we may write

$$u_2 - u_1 = \frac{1}{0.4} \sqrt{\frac{\tau}{\rho}} \ln \frac{z_2}{z_1} \tag{21-16}$$

$$\sqrt{\frac{\tau}{\rho}} = 0.4 \frac{u_2 - u_1}{\ln z_2/z_1} \tag{21-17}$$

[1] Panofsky, H., "Introduction to Dynamic Meteorology," p. 194, Pennsylvania State University Press, University Park, Pennsylvania, 1956.

Eqs. (21–5) and (21–17) may be combined to show that

$$\eta' = 0.4\rho(z + z_0)\sqrt{\frac{\tau}{\rho}}$$

$$= \frac{0.16\rho(z + z_0)(u_2 - u_1)}{\ln z_2/z_1} \tag{21–18}$$

Summarizing this section, it may be stated that a method has been found for getting at the troublesome coefficients of turbulence, at least in the surface boundary layer. The theory is based on an empirically determined variation of $\eta'$ with height in an adiabatic boundary layer, Eq. (21–5). In that expression the term $\sqrt{\tau\rho}$ was obtained by working from a relation of the form of Eqs. (21–6) and (21–9), based on the relation of $\tau$ to the square of the velocity. The value of 0.4 in Eq. (21–5) is a constant introduced by von Kármán, based on wind-tunnel measurements of the shearing stress. The student will note that it is nondimensional. With the roughness length, this constant has given meteorologists a starting point for a practical approach to the problem of turbulence in the surface boundary layer.

**Evaporation.** The evaporation of water from a land or water surface is a problem of the flux of a property (water vapor) through the surface boundary layer. Hence it can be approached from the boundary-layer methods described in the previous section. The vertical flux is represented in crude form by the familiar relation

$$E = -D'\frac{\partial q}{\partial z} \tag{21–19}$$

Some success has been obtained by considering that in this layer $D'$ and $\eta'$ are equivalent; i.e., the coefficient relating the stress to the shear is equivalent to that represented by the ratio of the flux of property to the gradient of that property. This is not a valid assumption, but reasonable values of evaporation can be obtained from it, although some workers apply a correction depending on temperature lapse rate and possibly other factors. If there is a reasonable equivalence between the two coefficients, we may substitute from Eq. (21–18) to obtain

$$E = -\frac{0.16\rho(z + z_0)(u_2 - u_1)}{\ln z_2/z_1}\frac{dq}{dz} \tag{21–20}$$

We neglect $z_0$ and note that $z/dz$ is the inverse logarithmic differential. With finite differences,

$$z\frac{\Delta q}{\Delta z} = \frac{q_2 - q_1}{\ln z_2/z_1} = -\frac{q_1 - q_2}{\ln z_2/z_1} \tag{21–21}$$

and a much-used expression for evaporation measurements from wind and humidity records at two different levels is obtained as follows:

$$E = \frac{0.16\rho(u_2 - u_1)(q_1 - q_2)}{(\ln z_2/z_1)} \tag{21-22}$$

The air density is obtained from the ordinary pressure and temperautre records at the station.

Equation (21–22) was derived by the assumption of an adiabatic boundary layer. Holzman[1] introduced a modification, based on physical reasoning, which takes into account other lapse-rate conditions. The expression is

$$E = \frac{0.16(u_2 - u_1)(q_1 - q_2)}{\ln z_2/z_1 \ln [z_2(1 - sz_1)/z_1(1 - sz_2)]} \tag{21-23}$$

where $s$ is an experimentally determined stability parameter. In an adiabatic lapse rate, $s = 0$ and Eq. (21–23) reduces to Eq. (21–22). $s$ is a small fraction, positive for superadiabatic conditions and negative when the layer is stable.

Other theoretical and practical approaches to the evaporation or property-flux problem have been made. One will be suggested in a later section. Another is that based on the heat balance in the surface layers, as described in Chap. 14, and involving the Bowen ratio. It is especially valuable in studying the evaporation over the oceans in a climatological sense, but systems have been devised for its application on land.

**Reynolds Stresses and Fluxes.** Another method which avoids troublesome coefficients is based on concepts developed by Osborne Reynolds in 1883. Turbulent motion is defined as the difference between the actual motion and the mean motion. The components of the turbulent motion are, then,

$$u' = u - \bar{u} \qquad v' = v - \bar{v} \qquad w' = w - \bar{w} \tag{21-24}$$

These motions are eddy motions, highly variable, but with a mean value of zero. Each eddy carries to a new location a property such as $q'$ which is different from the actual or mean value $q$ or $\bar{q}$ at that location. If $q'$ is the specific humidity, the mass of water vapor per unit volume in the eddy is $\rho q'$. The volume of air carried vertically by an eddy through 1 cm² is $w' \times 1$ cm³ sec$^{-1}$. The average vertical flux of water vapor from the eddies is $\rho \overline{w'q'}$ g cm² sec$^{-1}$, where the bar indicates an average. The horizontal fluxes, if there are any, are given by $\rho \overline{u'q'}$ and $\rho \overline{v'q'}$. The evaporation can be represented by

$$E = \rho \overline{w'q'} \tag{21-25}$$

[1] Holzman, B., *Ann. N.Y. Acad. Sci.*, vol. 44, p. 13, 1943.

Similarly, the upward flux of heat by turbulence may be given as

$$H = \overline{c_p \rho \theta' w'} \tag{21-26}$$

where $\theta'$ is the potential temperature of a turbulent element. The density variations are neglected, since this quantity varies by a few per cent, while the wind variations may be as high as 75 per cent in a short interval of time.

Sensitive instrument systems for averaging this flux over various periods of time have been developed. They consist of sensors and recorders of vertical velocity and of the property transported. Descriptions of instruments in use at mid-century are described in a book edited by Lettau and Davidson.[1]

Since vertical turbulent elements also transport horizontal momentum downward, we have the quantities $-\rho\overline{u'w'}$, etc., which are called the *Reynolds stresses*. (The analogy between flux and stress has already been made apparent in this chapter.) We can write

$$\tau_{xz} = -\rho\overline{u'w'} \tag{21-27a}$$
$$\tau_{yz} = -\rho\overline{v'w'} \tag{21-27b}$$

For motion under stress the two component velocities must be correlated in such a way that their product does not vanish. This may be illustrated by considering the air motion along the surface and along the $x$ axis in a positive direction. Sudden increases in the wind are represented by positive values of $u'$ and lulls are denoted by negative $u'$. For the product $-\overline{u'w'}$ not to vanish, the two components must be either negatively or positively correlated; i.e., there must be a preponderance of either equal or opposite signs between them so that the product will not become zero. In the normal situation, sudden increases of the wind are supported by downward thrusts of momentum by negative $w'$ and upward motions are accompanied by lulls. Therefore, in the case chosen, $u'$ and $w'$ would be of opposite signs and, since the negative sign appears in Eq. (21-27a), the horizontal stress would be in the positive $x$ direction. If the motion is in the negative $x$ direction, increasing with height in the friction layer, $u'$ is negative in accelerations, with negative $w'$, so the stress is in the negative direction.

**Diffusion from Small Sources.** The vertical diffusion by eddies of properties such as water vapor is essentially from an infinite source. Another problem is that of the diffusion of smoke, gases, or radioactive particles from a point source or a small-area source. A branch of practical meteorology with a strong theoretical background is concerned with smoke

[1] Lettau, H., and B. Davidson, eds., "Exploring the Atmosphere's First Mile," Pergamon Press, New York, 1957.

pollution, diffusion of products of atomic or thermonuclear explosions, military uses of smokes and gases, and problems of waste disposal in the atmosphere.

The diffusion of concentrated plumes of material has only a partial dependence on the gradient of the concentration. The diffusion is, of course, three-dimensional. As in the case of other forms of eddy flux, the thermal stability of the air has a powerful control on the eddy motions. Wind speed and roughness of the ground are also important parameters. The photography of smoke plumes themselves provides an interesting study of the nature of atmospheric eddies. In a stable atmosphere the plume is straight and horizontal with only slight widening downwind. In unstable conditions the plume assumes pronounced gyrations, cut-off portions, and rapid loss of perceptible concentration.

Statistical approaches, based on a form of logic similar to that of the statistical mechanics used in the study of molecular motions, are used in describing eddy motions related to diffusion. For a discussion of the methods the student is referred to a more specialized text, such as Sutton.[1]

[1] Sutton, O. G., "Micrometeorology," McGraw-Hill Book Company, Inc., New York, 1953.

# INDEX